✳ **HAESE & HARRIS PUBL**

Specialists in mathematics p

Mathematics

for the international student
Pre-Diploma SL and HL (MYP 5 Plus)
second edition
Presumed Knowledge for SL and HL courses

Pamela Vollmar

Edward Kemp

Michael Haese

Robert Haese

Sandra Haese

Mark Humphries

Chris Sangwin

for use with
IB Middle Years
Programme

MATHEMATICS FOR THE INTERNATIONAL STUDENT
Pre-Diploma SL and HL (MYP 5 Plus) second edition
Presumed Knowledge for SL and HL courses

Pamela Vollmar	B.Sc.(Hons.), PGCE.
Edward Kemp	B.Sc., M.A.
Michael Haese	B.Sc.(Hons.), Ph.D.
Robert Haese	B.Sc.
Sandra Haese	B.Sc.
Mark Humphries	B.Sc.(Hons.)
Chris Sangwin	M.A., M.Sc., Ph.D.

Haese Mathematics
3 Frank Collopy Court, Adelaide Airport, SA 5950, AUSTRALIA
Telephone: +61 8 8355 9444, Fax: + 61 8 8355 9471
Email: info@haesemathematics.com.au
Web: www.haesemathematics.com.au

National Library of Australia Card Number & ISBN 978-1-876543-89-1

© Haese & Harris Publications 2008

Published by Raksar Nominees Pty Ltd
3 Frank Collopy Court, Adelaide Airport, SA 5950, AUSTRALIA

First Edition	2006		
Second Edition	2008	*Reprinted*	2008, 2010, 2011, 2012

Cartoon artwork by John Martin. Artwork by Piotr Poturaj and David Purton.
Cover design by Piotr Poturaj.
Computer software by David Purton, Thomas Jansson and Troy Cruickshank.

Typeset in Australia by Susan Haese (Raksar Nominees). Typeset in Times Roman $10\frac{1}{2}/11\frac{1}{2}$

The textbook and its accompanying CD have been developed independently of the International Baccalaureate Organization (IBO). The textbook and CD are in no way connected with, or endorsed by, the IBO.

Acknowledgements: The publishers acknowledge the cooperation of Oxford University Press, Australia, for the reproduction of material originally published in textbooks produced in association with Haese & Harris Publications.

While every attempt has been made to trace and acknowledge copyright, the authors and publishers apologise for any accidental infringement where copyright has proved untraceable. They would be pleased to come to a suitable agreement with the rightful owner.

Disclaimer: All the internet addresses (URLs) given in this book were valid at the time of printing. While the authors and publisher regret any inconvenience that changes of address may cause readers, no responsibility for any such changes can be accepted by either the authors or the publisher.

FOREWORD

Pre-Diploma SL and HL (MYP 5 Plus) second edition is an attempt to cover, in one volume, the Presumed Knowledge required for the IB Diploma courses 'Mathematics SL' and 'Mathematics HL'. This book may also be used as a general textbook at about 10th Grade level in classes where students complete a rigorous course in preparation for the study of mathematics at a high level in their final two years of high school.

Feedback from teachers using the first edition suggested that while it provided satisfactory preparation for prospective Mathematics SL students, several sections needed to be more rigorous to prepare students thoroughly for Mathematics HL. The first edition has been revised throughout and the highlighted topics in the table of contents show at a glance the main areas that have been substantially revised and extended.

In terms of the IB Middle Years Programme (MYP), this book does not pretend to be a definitive course. In response to requests from teachers who use 'Mathematics for the International Student' at IB Diploma level, we have endeavoured to interpret their requirements, as expressed to us, for a book that will prepare students for Mathematics SL and Mathematics HL. We have developed this book independently of the International Baccalaureate Organization (IBO) in consultation with experienced teachers of IB Mathematics. The text is not endorsed by the IBO.

It is not our intention that each chapter be worked through in full. Teachers must select carefully, according to the abilities and prior knowledge of their students, to make the most efficient use of time and give as thorough coverage of content as possible.

Three additional chapters appear on the CD as printable pages:

Chapter 23: Counting and probability
Chapter 24: Locus
Chapter 25: Networks

These chapters were selected because the content could be regarded as extension beyond what might be seen as an essential prerequisite for IB Diploma mathematics.

We understand the emphasis that the IB MYP places on the five Areas of Interaction and in response there are links on the CD to printable pages which offer ideas for projects and investigations to help busy teachers (see p. 5).

Frequent use of the interactive features on the CD should nurture a much deeper understanding and appreciation of mathematical concepts. The inclusion of our new **Self Tutor** software (see p. 4) is intended to help students who have been absent from classes or who experience difficulty understanding the material.

The book contains many problems to cater for a range of student abilities and interests, and efforts have been made to contextualise problems so that students can see the practical applications of the mathematics they are studying.

We welcome your feedback.   Email: info@haesemathematics.com.au

Web: www.haesemathematics.com.au

PV, EK, PMH, RCH, SHH, MH, CS

Acknowledgements

The authors and publishers would like to thank all those teachers who have read proofs and offered advice and encouragement.

Among those who submitted courses of study for Middle Years Mathematics and who offered to read and comment on the proofs of the textbook are: Margie Karbassioun, Kerstin Mockrish, Todd Sharpe, Tamara Jannink, Yang Zhaohui, Cameron Hall, Brendan Watson, Daniel Fosbenner, Rob DeAbreu, Philip E. Hedemann, Alessandra Pecoraro, Jeanne-Mari Neefs, Ray Wiens, John Bush, Jane Forrest, Dr Andrzej Cichy, William Larson, Wendy Farden, Chris Wieland, Kenneth Capp, Sara Locke, Rae Deeley, Val Frost, Mal Coad, Pia Jeppesen, Wissam Malaeb, Eduardo Betti, Robb Kitcher, Catherine Krylova, Julie Tan, Rosheen Gray, Jan-Mark Seewald, Nicola Cardwell, Tony Halsey, Ros McCabe, Alison Ryan, Mark Bethune, Keith Black, Vivienne Verschuren, Mark Willis, Curtis Wood, Ufuk Genc, Fran O'Connor. Special thanks to Heather Farish. To anyone we may have missed, we offer our apologies.

The publishers wish to make it clear that acknowledging these individuals does not imply any endorsement of this book by any of them, and all responsibility for the content rests with the authors and publishers.

USING THE INTERACTIVE CD

The interactive CD is ideal for independent study.

Students can revisit concepts taught in class and undertake their own revision and practice. The CD also has the text of the book, allowing students to leave the textbook at school and keep the CD at home.

By clicking on the relevant icon, a range of new interactive features can be accessed:

♦ Self Tutor
♦ Areas of Interaction links to printable pages
♦ Printable Chapters
♦ Interactive Links – to spreadsheets, video clips, graphing and geometry software, computer demonstrations and simulations

INTERACTIVE LINK

SELF TUTOR is a new exciting feature of this book.

The ◀) **Self Tutor** icon on each worked example denotes an active link on the CD.

NEW!

Simply 'click' on the ◀) **Self Tutor** (or anywhere in the example box) to access the worked example, with a teacher's voice explaining each step necessary to reach the answer.

Play any line as often as you like. See how the basic processes come alive using movement and colour on the screen.

Ideal for students who have missed lessons or need extra help.

Example 7　　　　　　　　　　　　　　　　　◀) **Self Tutor**

Sketch each of the following functions on the same set of axes as $y = x^2$. In each case state the coordinates of the vertex.

a $y = (x - 2)^2 + 3$ 　　　　　　　　**b** $y = (x + 2)^2 - 5$

a We draw $y = x^2$ and translate it by $\begin{pmatrix} 2 \\ 3 \end{pmatrix}$.

b We draw $y = x^2$ and translate it by $\begin{pmatrix} -2 \\ -5 \end{pmatrix}$.

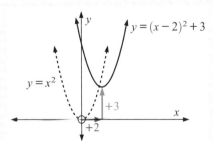

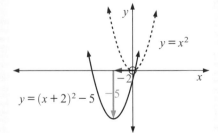

The vertex is at $(2, 3)$.　　　　　　　　The vertex is at $(-2, -5)$.

See **Chapter 17, Quadratic functions**, p. 421

AREAS OF INTERACTION

The International Baccalaureate Middle Years Programme focuses teaching and learning through five Areas of Interaction:

- Approaches to learning
- Community and service
- Human ingenuity
- Environments
- Health and social education

The Areas of Interaction are intended as a focus for developing connections between different subject areas in the curriculum and to promote an understanding of the interrelatedness of different branches of knowledge and the coherence of knowledge as a whole.

Click on the heading to access a printable 'pop-up' version of the link.

In an effort to assist busy teachers, we offer the following printable pages of ideas for projects and investigations:

LINKS
click here

SATISFYING PAPER PROPORTIONS

Areas of interaction:
Approaches to learning/Environments/Human ingenuity

Links to printable pages of ideas for projects and investigations

TABLE OF CONTENTS

Content has been revised throughout and the highlighted areas show the topics that have been substantially revised and extended in this second edition.

Graphics calculator instructions

Contents:

In this course it is assumed that you have a **graphics calculator**. If you learn how to operate your calculator successfully, you should experience little difficulty with future arithmetic calculations.

There are many different brands (and types) of calculators. Different calculators do not have exactly the same keys. It is therefore important that you have an instruction booklet for your calculator, and use it whenever you need to.

However, to help get you started, we have included here some basic instructions for the **Texas Instruments TI-83** and the **Casio fx-9860G** calculators. Note that instructions given may need to be modified slightly for other models.

GETTING STARTED

Texas Instruments TI-83

The screen which appears when the calculator is turned on is the **home screen**. This is where most basic calculations are performed.

You can return to this screen from any menu by pressing 2nd MODE .

When you are on this screen you can type in an expression and evaluate it using the ENTER key.

Casio fx-9860g

Press MENU to access the Main Menu, and select **RUN·MAT**.

This is where most of the basic calculations are performed.

When you are on this screen you can type in an expression and evaluate it using the EXE key.

A   BASIC CALCULATIONS

Most modern calculators have the rules for **Order of Operations** built into them. This order is sometimes referred to as BEDMAS.

This section explains how to enter different types of numbers such as negative numbers and fractions, and how to perform calculations using grouping symbols (brackets), powers, and square roots. It also explains how to round off using your calculator.

NEGATIVE NUMBERS

To enter negative numbers we use the **sign change** key. On both the **TI-83** and **Casio** this looks like .

Simply press the sign change key and then type in the number.

For example, to enter -7, press (−) 7.

FRACTIONS

On most scientific calculators and also the **Casio** graphics calculator there is a special key for entering fractions. No such key exists for the **TI-83**, so we use a different method.

Texas Instruments TI-83

To enter common fractions, we enter the fraction as a division.

For example, we enter $\frac{3}{4}$ by typing   3 $\boxed{÷}$ 4.   If the fraction is part of a larger calculation, it is generally wise to place this division in brackets, i.e., $\boxed{(}$ 3 $\boxed{÷}$ 4 $\boxed{)}$.

To enter mixed numbers, either convert the mixed number to an improper fraction and enter as a common fraction *or* enter the fraction as a sum.

For example, we can enter $2\frac{3}{4}$ as $\boxed{(}$ 11 $\boxed{÷}$ 4 $\boxed{)}$ *or* $\boxed{(}$ 2 $\boxed{+}$ 3 $\boxed{÷}$ 4 $\boxed{)}$.

Casio fx-9860g

To enter fractions we use the **fraction** key $\boxed{a\,b/c}$.

For example, we enter $\frac{3}{4}$ by typing   3 $\boxed{a\,b/c}$ 4   and $2\frac{3}{4}$ by typing   2 $\boxed{a\,b/c}$ 3 $\boxed{a\,b/c}$ 4. Press $\boxed{SHIFT}$ $\boxed{a\,b/c}$ $(a\frac{b}{c} \leftrightarrow \frac{d}{c})$ to convert between mixed numbers and improper fractions.

SIMPLIFYING FRACTIONS & RATIOS

Graphics calculators can *sometimes* be used to express fractions and ratios in simplest form.

Texas Instruments TI-83

To express the fraction $\frac{35}{56}$ in simplest form, press   35 $\boxed{÷}$ 56 $\boxed{MATH}$ 1 $\boxed{ENTER}$.   The result is $\frac{5}{8}$.

To express the ratio $\frac{2}{3} : 1\frac{1}{4}$ in simplest form, press $\boxed{(}$ 2 $\boxed{÷}$ 3 $\boxed{)}$ $\boxed{÷}$ $\boxed{(}$ 1 $\boxed{+}$ 1 $\boxed{÷}$ 4 $\boxed{)}$ $\boxed{MATH}$ 1 $\boxed{ENTER}$.

The ratio is   8 : 15.

```
35/56►Frac
            5/8
(2/3)/(1+1/4)►Fr
ac
            8/15
```

Casio fx-9860g

To express the fraction $\frac{35}{56}$ in simplest form, press   35 $\boxed{a\,b/c}$ 56 $\boxed{EXE}$.   The result is $\frac{5}{8}$.

To express the ratio $\frac{2}{3} : 1\frac{1}{4}$ in simplest form, press   2 $\boxed{a\,b/c}$ 3 $\boxed{÷}$ 1 $\boxed{a\,b/c}$ 1 $\boxed{a\,b/c}$ 4 $\boxed{EXE}$.   The ratio is 8 : 15.

```
35⌐56
            5⌐8
2⌐3÷1⌐1⌐4
            8⌐15

►MAT
```

ENTERING TIMES

In questions involving time, it is often necessary to be able to express time in terms of hours, minutes and seconds.

Texas Instruments TI-83

To enter 2 hours 27 minutes, press   2 [2nd] [MATRX] (ANGLE)
1:^{o} 27 [2nd] [MATRX] **2:'**.   This is equivalent to 2.45 hours.

To express 8.17 hours in terms of hours, minutes and seconds,
press   8.17 [2nd] [MATRX] **4:▶DMS** [ENTER] .
This is equivalent to 8 hours, 10 minutes and 12 seconds.

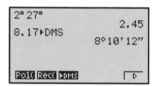

Casio fx-9860g

To enter 2 hours 27 minutes, press 2 [OPTN] [F6] [F5] (ANGL)
[F4] ($^{o\prime\prime\prime}$) 27 [F4] ($^{o\prime\prime\prime}$) [EXE] .   This is equivalent to 2.45 hours.

To express 8.17 hours in terms of hours, minutes and seconds,
press   8.17 [OPTN] [F6] [F5] (ANGL) [F6] [F3] (▶DMS) [EXE] .
This is equivalent to 8 hours, 10 minutes and 12 seconds.

B | BASIC FUNCTIONS

GROUPING SYMBOLS (BRACKETS)

Both the **TI-83** and **Casio** have bracket keys that look like [(] and [)] .

Brackets are regularly used in mathematics to indicate an expression which needs to be evaluated before other operations are carried out.

For example, to enter $2 \times (4 + 1)$ we type   2 [×] [(] 4 [+] 1 [)] .

We also use brackets to make sure the calculator understands the expression we are typing in.

For example, to enter $\frac{2}{4+1}$ we type   2 [÷] [(] 4 [+] 1 [)] .   If we typed   2 [÷] 4 [+] 1 the calculator would think we meant $\frac{2}{4} + 1$.

In general, it is a good idea to place brackets around any complicated expressions which need to be evaluated separately.

POWER KEYS

Both the **TI-83** and **Casio** also have power keys that look like [∧] . We type the base first, press the power key, then enter the index or exponent.

For example, to enter 25^3 we type   25 [∧] 3.

Note that there are special keys which allow us to quickly evaluate squares.

Numbers can be squared on both **TI-83** and **Casio** using the special key [x^2] .

For example, to enter 25^2 we type   25 [x^2] .

SQUARE ROOTS

To enter square roots on either calculator we need to use a secondary function (see the **Secondary Function and Alpha Keys**).

Texas Instruments TI-83

The **TI-83** uses a secondary function key 2nd .

To enter $\sqrt{36}$ we press 2nd x^2 36) .

The end bracket is used to tell the calculator we have finished entering terms under the square root sign.

Casio fx-9860g

The Casio uses a shift key SHIFT to get to its second functions.

To enter $\sqrt{36}$ we press SHIFT x^2 36.

If there is a more complicated expression under the square root sign you should enter it in brackets.

For example, to enter $\sqrt{18 \div 2}$ we press SHIFT x^2 (18 ÷ 2) .

ROUNDING OFF

You can use your calculator to round off answers to a fixed number of decimal places.

Texas Instruments TI-83

To round to 2 decimal places, press MODE then ▼ to scroll down to Float.

Use the ▶ button to move the cursor over the 2 and press ENTER . Press 2nd MODE to return to the home screen.

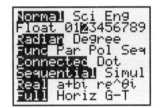

If you want to unfix the number of decimal places, press MODE ▼ ENTER to highlight Float.

Casio fx-9860g

To round to 2 decimal places, select **RUN·MAT** from the Main Menu, and press SHIFT MENU to enter the setup screen. Scroll down to Display, and press F1 (**Fix**). Press 2 EXE to select the number of decimal places. Press EXIT to return to the home screen.

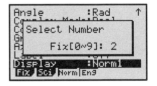

To unfix the number of decimal places, press SHIFT MENU to return to the setup screen, scroll down to Display, and press F3 (**Norm**).

INVERSE TRIGONOMETRIC FUNCTIONS

To enter inverse trigonometric functions, you will need to use a secondary function (see the **Secondary Function and Alpha Keys**).

Texas Instruments TI-83

The inverse trigonometric functions $\sin^{-1}$, $\cos^{-1}$ and $\tan^{-1}$ are the secondary functions of SIN , COS and TAN respectively. They are accessed by using the secondary function key 2nd .

For example, if $\cos x = \frac{3}{5}$, then $x = \cos^{-1}\left(\frac{3}{5}\right)$.

To calculate this, press 2nd COS 3 ÷ 5) ENTER .

Casio fx-9860g

The inverse trigonometric functions $\sin^{-1}$, $\cos^{-1}$ and $\tan^{-1}$ are the secondary functions of sin , cos and tan respectively. They are accessed by using the secondary function key SHIFT .

For example, if $\cos x = \frac{3}{5}$, then $x = \cos^{-1}\left(\frac{3}{5}\right)$.

To calculate this, press SHIFT cos (3 ÷ 5) EXE .

SCIENTIFIC NOTATION

If a number is too large or too small to be displayed neatly on the screen, it will be expressed in scientific notation, that is, in the form $a \times 10^n$ where $1 \leqslant a < 10$ and n is an integer.

Texas Instruments TI-83

To evaluate 2300^3, press 2300 ^ 3 ENTER . The answer displayed is 1.2167E10, which means 1.2167×10^{10}.

To evaluate $\frac{3}{20\,000}$, press 3 ÷ 20 000 ENTER . The answer displayed is 1.5E−4, which means 1.5×10^{-4}.

You can enter values in scientific notation using the EE function, which is accessed by pressing 2nd , .

For example, to evaluate $\frac{2.6 \times 10^{14}}{13}$, press 2.6 2nd , 14 ÷ 13 ENTER . The answer is 2×10^{13}.

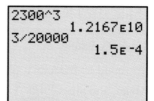

Casio fx-9860g

To evaluate 2300^3, press 2300 $\boxed{\wedge}$ 3 $\boxed{\text{EXE}}$. The answer displayed is 1.2167E+10, which means 1.2167×10^{10}.

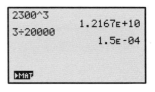

To evaluate $\frac{3}{20\,000}$, press 3 $\boxed{\div}$ 20 000 $\boxed{\text{EXE}}$. The answer displayed is 1.5E−04, which means 1.5×10^{-4}.

You can enter values in scientific notation using the $\boxed{\text{EXP}}$ key. For example, to evaluate $\frac{2.6 \times 10^{14}}{13}$, press 2.6 $\boxed{\text{EXP}}$ 14 $\boxed{\div}$ 13 $\boxed{\text{EXE}}$. The answer is 2×10^{13}.

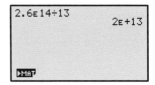

SECONDARY FUNCTION AND ALPHA KEYS

Texas Instruments TI-83

The **secondary function** of each key is displayed in yellow above the key. It is accessed by pressing the $\boxed{\text{2nd}}$ key, followed by the key corresponding to the desired secondary function. For example, to calculate $\sqrt{36}$, press $\boxed{\text{2nd}}$ $\boxed{x^2}$ 36 $\boxed{)}$ $\boxed{\text{ENTER}}$.

The **alpha function** of each key is displayed in green above the key. It is accessed by pressing the $\boxed{\text{ALPHA}}$ key followed by the key corresponding to the desired letter. The main purpose of the alpha keys is to store values into memory which can be recalled later. Refer to the **Memory** section.

Casio fx-9860g

The **shift function** of each key is displayed in yellow above the key. It is accessed by pressing the $\boxed{\text{SHIFT}}$ key followed by the key corresponding to the desired shift function.

For example, to calculate $\sqrt{36}$, press $\boxed{\text{SHIFT}}$ $\boxed{x^2}$ 36 $\boxed{\text{EXE}}$.

The **alpha function** of each key is displayed in red above the key. It is accessed by pressing the $\boxed{\text{ALPHA}}$ key followed by the key corresponding to the desired letter. The main purpose of the alpha keys is to store values which can be recalled later.

MEMORY

Utilising the memory features of your calculator allows you to recall calculations you have performed previously. This not only saves time, but also enables you to maintain accuracy in your calculations.

SPECIFIC STORAGE TO MEMORY

Values can be stored into the variable letters A, B, ..., Z using either calculator. Storing a value in memory is useful if you need that value multiple times.

Texas Instruments TI-83

Suppose we wish to store the number 15.4829 for use in a number of calculations. Type in the number then press $\boxed{\text{STO}\blacktriangleright}$ $\boxed{\text{ALPHA}}$ $\boxed{\text{MATH}}$ (A) $\boxed{\text{ENTER}}$.

We can now add 10 to this value by pressing $\boxed{\text{ALPHA}}$ $\boxed{\text{MATH}}$ $\boxed{+}$ 10 $\boxed{\text{ENTER}}$, or cube this value by pressing $\boxed{\text{ALPHA}}$ $\boxed{\text{MATH}}$ $\boxed{\wedge}$ 3 $\boxed{\text{ENTER}}$.

```
15.4829→A
              15.4829
A+10
              25.4829
A^3
          3711.563767
```

Casio fx-9860g

Suppose we wish to store the number 15.4829 for use in a number of calculations. Type in the number then press $\boxed{\rightarrow}$ $\boxed{\text{ALPHA}}$ $\boxed{\text{X},\theta,\text{T}}$ (A) $\boxed{\text{EXE}}$.

We can now add 10 to this value by pressing $\boxed{\text{ALPHA}}$ $\boxed{\text{X},\theta,\text{T}}$ $\boxed{+}$ 10 $\boxed{\text{EXE}}$, or cube this value by pressing $\boxed{\text{ALPHA}}$ $\boxed{\text{X},\theta,\text{T}}$ $\boxed{\wedge}$ 3 $\boxed{\text{EXE}}$.

```
15.4829→A
              15.4829
A+10
              25.4829
A^3
          3711.563767
▶MAT
```

ANS VARIABLE

Texas Instruments TI-83

The variable **Ans** holds the most recent evaluated expression, and can be used in calculations by pressing $\boxed{\text{2nd}}$ $\boxed{(-)}$.

For example, suppose you evaluate 3×4, and then wish to subtract this from 17. This can be done by pressing 17 $\boxed{-}$ $\boxed{\text{2nd}}$ $\boxed{(-)}$ $\boxed{\text{ENTER}}$.

```
3*4
               12
17-Ans
                5
```

If you start an expression with an operator such as $\boxed{+}$, $\boxed{-}$, etc, the previous answer **Ans** is automatically inserted ahead of the operator. For example, the previous answer can be halved simply by pressing $\boxed{\div}$ 2 $\boxed{\text{ENTER}}$.

If you wish to view the answer in fractional form, press $\boxed{\text{MATH}}$ **1** $\boxed{\text{ENTER}}$.

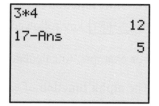

```
               12
17-Ans
                5
Ans/2
              2.5
Ans▶Frac
              5/2
```

Casio fx-9860g

The variable **Ans** holds the most recent evaluated expression, and can be used in calculations by pressing [SHIFT] [(−)]. For example, suppose you evaluate 3×4, and then wish to subtract this from 17. This can be done by pressing 17 [−] [SHIFT] [(−)] [EXE] .

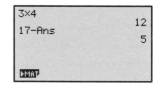

If you start an expression with an operator such as [+] , [−] , etc, the previous answer Ans is automatically inserted ahead of the operator. For example, the previous answer can be halved simply by pressing [÷] 2 [EXE] .

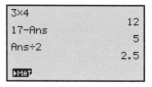

If you wish to view the answer in fractional form, press [F↔D] .

RECALLING PREVIOUS EXPRESSIONS

Texas Instruments TI-83

The **ENTRY** function recalls previously evaluated expressions, and is used by pressing [2nd] [ENTER] .

This function is useful if you wish to repeat a calculation with a minor change, or if you have made an error in typing.

Suppose you have evaluated $100 + \sqrt{132}$. If you now want to evaluate $100 + \sqrt{142}$, instead of retyping the command, it can be recalled by pressing [2nd] [ENTER] .

The change can then be made by moving the cursor over the 3 and changing it to a 4, then pressing [ENTER] .

If you have made an error in your original calculation, and intended to calculate $1500 + \sqrt{132}$, again you can recall the previous command by pressing [2nd] [ENTER] .

Move the cursor to the first 0.

You can insert the digit 5, rather than overwriting the 0, by pressing [2nd] [DEL] 5 [ENTER] .

Casio fx-9860g

Pressing the left cursor key allows you to edit the most recently evaluated expression, and is useful if you wish to repeat a calculation with a minor change, or if you have made an error in typing.

Suppose you have evaluated $100 + \sqrt{132}$.

If you now want to evaluate $100 + \sqrt{142}$, instead of retyping the command, it can be recalled by pressing the left cursor key.

Move the cursor between the 3 and the 2, then press [DEL] 4 to remove the 3 and change it to a 4. Press [EXE] to re-evaluate the expression.

LISTS

Lists are used for a number of purposes on the calculator. They enable us to enter sets of numbers, and we use them to generate number sequences using algebraic rules.

CREATING A LIST

Texas Instruments TI-83

Press [STAT] 1 to take you to the **list editor** screen.

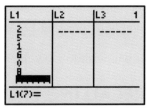

To enter the data {2, 5, 1, 6, 0, 8} into **List1**, start by moving the cursor to the first entry of **L1**. Press 2 [ENTER] 5 [ENTER] ...... and so on until all the data is entered.

Casio fx-9860g

Selecting **STAT** from the Main Menu takes you to the **list editor** screen.

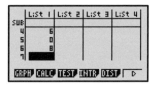

To enter the data {2, 5, 1, 6, 0, 8} into **List 1**, start by moving the cursor to the first entry of **List 1**. Press 2 [EXE] 5 [EXE] ...... and so on until all the data is entered.

DELETING LIST DATA

Texas Instruments TI-83

Pressing [STAT] **1** takes you to the **list editor** screen.

Move the cursor to the heading of the list you want to delete then press [CLEAR] [ENTER] .

Casio fx-9860g

Selecting **STAT** from the Main Menu takes you to the **list editor** screen.

Move the cursor to anywhere on the list you wish to delete, then press [F6] (▷) [F4] (**DEL-A**) [F1] (**Yes**).

REFERENCING LISTS

Texas Instruments TI-83

Lists can be referenced by using the secondary functions of the keypad numbers 1–6.

For example, suppose you want to add 2 to each element of **List1** and display the results in **List2**. To do this, move the cursor to the heading of **L2** and press [2nd] 1 [+] 2 [ENTER] .

Casio fx-9860g

Lists can be referenced using the List function, which is accessed by pressing [SHIFT] **1**.

For example, if you want to add 2 to each element of **List 1** and display the results in **List 2**, move the cursor to the heading of **List 2** and press [SHIFT] 1 **(List)** 1 [+] 2 [EXE] .

Casio models without the List function can do this by pressing [OPTN] [F1] **(LIST)** [F1] **(List)** 1 [+] 2 [EXE] .

NUMBER SEQUENCES

Texas Instruments TI-83

You can create a sequence of numbers defined by a certain rule using the *seq* command.

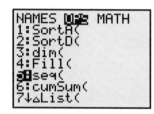

This command is accessed by pressing [2nd] [STAT] [▶] to enter the **OPS** section of the List menu, then selecting **5:seq**.

For example, to store the sequence of even numbers from 2 to 8 in **List3**, move the cursor to the heading of **L3**, then press [2nd] [STAT] [▶] 5 to enter the *seq* command, followed by 2 [X,T,θ,n] [,] [X,T,θ,n] [,] 1 [,] 4 [)] [ENTER] .

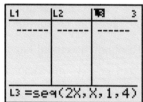

This evaluates $2x$ for every value of x from 1 to 4.

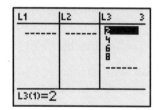

Casio fx-9860g

You can create a sequence of numbers defined by a certain rule using the *seq* command.

This command is accessed by pressing [OPTN] [F1] **(LIST)** [F5] **(Seq)**.

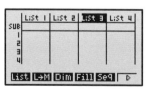

For example, to store the sequence of even numbers from 2 to 8 in **List 3**, move the cursor to the heading of **List 3**, then press [OPTN] [F1] [F5] to enter a sequence, followed by 2 [X,θ,T] [,] [X,θ,T] [,] 1 [,] 4 [,] 1 [)] [EXE] .

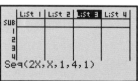

This evaluates $2x$ for every value of x from 1 to 4 with an increment of 1.

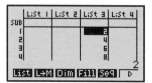

F STATISTICAL GRAPHS

STATISTICS

Your graphics calculator is a useful tool for analysing data and creating statistical graphs.

In this section we will produce descriptive statistics and graphs for the data set   5 2 3 3 6
4 5 3 7 5 7 1 8 9 5.

Texas Instruments TI-83

Enter the data set into **List1** using the instructions on page **18**. To obtain descriptive statistics of the data set, press   STAT ► **1:1-Var Stats**
2nd **1 (L₁)** ENTER .

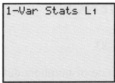 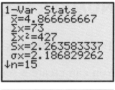

To obtain a boxplot of the data, press 2nd
Y= (STAT PLOT) **1** and set up **Statplot1** as shown. Press ZOOM **9:ZoomStat** to graph the boxplot with an appropriate window.

 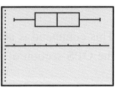

To obtain a vertical bar chart of the data, press 2nd Y= **1**, and change the type of graph to a vertical bar chart as shown. Press ZOOM **9:ZoomStat** to draw the bar chart. Press WINDOW and set the **Xscl** to 1, then GRAPH to redraw the bar chart.

We will now enter a second set of data, and compare it to the first.

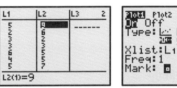

Enter the data set 9 6 2 3 5 5 7 5 6 7 6
3 4 4 5 8 4 into **List2**, press 2nd Y= **1**, and change the type of graph back to a boxplot as shown. Move the cursor to the top of the screen and select **Plot2**. Set up **Statplot2** in the same manner, except set the **XList** to L₂. Press ZOOM **9:ZoomStat** to draw the side-by-side boxplots.

 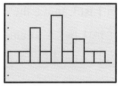

Casio fx-9860g

Enter the data into **List 1** using the instructions on page **18**. To obtain the descriptive statistics, press F6 (▷) until the **GRPH** icon is in the bottom left corner of the screen, then press F2 (**CALC**) F1 (**1VAR**).

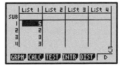 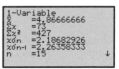

To obtain a boxplot of the data, press EXIT EXIT F1 (GRPH) F6 (SET), and set up StatGraph 1 as shown. Press EXIT F1 (GPH1) to draw the boxplot.

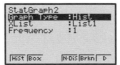

To obtain a vertical bar chart of the data, press EXIT F6 (SET) F2 (GPH 2), and set up StatGraph 2 as shown. Press EXIT F2 (GPH 2) to draw the bar chart (set Start to 0, and Width to 1).

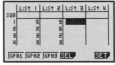
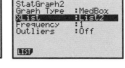

We will now enter a second set of data, and compare it to the first.

Enter the data set 9 6 2 3 5 5 7 5 6 7 6 3 4 4 5 8 4 into **List 2**, then press F6 (SET) F2 (GPH2) and set up **StatGraph 2** to draw a boxplot of this data set as shown. Press EXIT F4 (SEL), and turn on both **StatGraph 1** and **StatGraph 2**. Press F6 (DRAW) to draw the side-by-side boxplots.

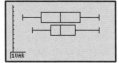

G   WORKING WITH FUNCTIONS

GRAPHING FUNCTIONS

Texas Instruments TI-83

Pressing Y= selects the **Y=** editor, where you can store functions to graph. Delete any unwanted functions by scrolling down to the function and pressing CLEAR .

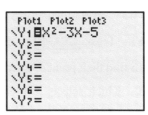

To graph the function $y = x^2 - 3x - 5$, move the cursor to **Y**₁, and press X,T,θ,n x^2 − 3 X,T,θ,n − 5 ENTER . This stores the function into **Y**₁. Press GRAPH to draw a graph of the function.

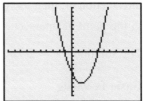

To view a table of values for the function, press 2nd GRAPH (**TABLE**). The starting point and interval of the table values can be adjusted by pressing 2nd WINDOW (**TBLSET**).

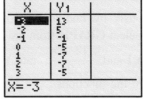

Casio fx-9860g

Selecting **GRAPH** from the Main Menu takes you to the Graph Function screen, where you can store functions to graph. Delete any unwanted functions by scrolling down to the function and pressing DEL F1 **(Yes)**.

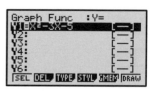

To graph the function $y = x^2 - 3x - 5$, move the cursor to **Y1** and press X,θ,T x^2 − 3 X,θ,T − 5 EXE . This stores the function into **Y1**. Press F6 **(DRAW)** to draw a graph of the function.

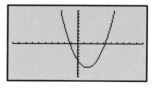

To view a table of values for the function, press MENU and select **TABLE**. The function is stored in **Y1**, but not selected. Press F1 **(SEL)** to select the function, and F6 **(TABL)** to view the table. You can adjust the table settings by pressing EXIT and then F5 **(SET)** from the Table Function screen.

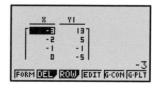

FINDING POINTS OF INTERSECTION

It is often useful to find the points of intersection of two graphs, for instance, when you are trying to solve simultaneous equations.

Texas Instruments TI-83

We can solve $y = 11 - 3x$ and $y = \dfrac{12 - x}{2}$ simultaneously by finding the point of intersection of these two lines. Press Y= , then store $11 - 3x$ into **Y1** and $\dfrac{12 - x}{2}$ into **Y2**. Press GRAPH to draw a graph of the functions.

To find their point of intersection, press 2nd TRACE **(CALC)** **5**, which selects **5:intersect**. Press ENTER twice to specify the functions **Y1** and **Y2** as the functions you want to find the intersection of, then use the arrow keys to move the cursor close to the point of intersection and press ENTER once more.

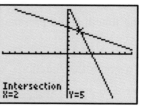

The solution $x = 2$, $y = 5$ is given.

Casio fx-9860g

We can solve $y = 11 - 3x$ and $y = \dfrac{12 - x}{2}$ simultaneously by finding the point of intersection of these two lines. Select **GRAPH** from the Main Menu, then store $11 - 3x$ into **Y1** and $\dfrac{12 - x}{2}$ into **Y2**. Press F6 **(DRAW)** to draw a graph of the functions.

To find their point of intersection, press $\boxed{F5}$ **(G-Solv)** $\boxed{F5}$ **(ISCT)**. The solution $x = 2$, $y = 5$ is given.

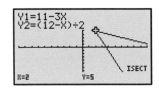

Note: If there is more than one point of intersection, the remaining points of intersection can be found by pressing $\boxed{\blacktriangleright}$.

SOLVING $f(x) = 0$

In the special case when you wish to solve an equation of the form $f(x) = 0$, this can be done by graphing $y = f(x)$ and then finding when this graph cuts the x-axis.

Texas Instruments TI-83

To solve $x^3 - 3x^2 + x + 1 = 0$, press $\boxed{Y=}$ and store $x^3 - 3x^2 + x + 1$ into **Y₁**. Press $\boxed{GRAPH}$ to draw the graph.

To find where this function first cuts the x-axis, press $\boxed{2nd}$ $\boxed{TRACE}$ **(CALC) 2**, which selects **2:zero**. Move the cursor to the left of the first zero and press $\boxed{ENTER}$, then move the cursor to the right of the first zero and press $\boxed{ENTER}$. Finally, move the cursor close to the first zero and press $\boxed{ENTER}$ once more. The solution $x \approx -0.414$ is given.

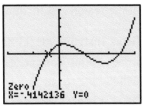

Repeat this process to find the remaining solutions $x = 1$ and $x \approx 2.41$.

Casio fx-9860g

To solve $x^3 - 3x^2 + x + 1 = 0$, select **GRAPH** from the Main Menu and store $x^3 - 3x^2 + x + 1$ into **Y1**. Press $\boxed{F6}$ **(DRAW)** to draw the graph.

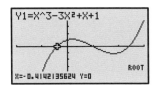

To find where this function cuts the x-axis, press $\boxed{F5}$ **(G-Solv)** $\boxed{F1}$ **(ROOT)**. The first solution $x \approx -0.414$ is given.

Press $\boxed{\blacktriangleright}$ to find the remaining solutions $x = 1$ and $x \approx 2.41$.

TURNING POINTS

Texas Instruments TI-83

To find the turning point (vertex) of $y = -x^2 + 2x + 3$, press $\boxed{Y=}$ and store $-x^2 + 2x + 3$ into **Y₁**. Press $\boxed{GRAPH}$ to draw the graph.

From the graph, it is clear that the vertex is a maximum, so press $\boxed{2nd}$ $\boxed{TRACE}$ **(CALC) 4** to select **4:maximum**.

Move the cursor to the left of the vertex and press ENTER , then move the cursor to the right of the vertex and press ENTER . Finally, move the cursor close to the vertex and press ENTER once more. The vertex is $(1, 4)$.

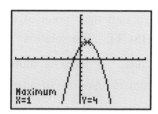

Casio fx-9860g

To find the turning point (vertex) of $y = -x^2 + 2x + 3$, select **GRAPH** from the Main Menu and store $-x^2 + 2x + 3$ into **Y1**. Press F6 **(DRAW)** to draw the graph.

From the graph, it is clear that the vertex is a maximum, so to find the vertex press F5 **(G-Solv)** F2 **(MAX)**.

The vertex is $(1, 4)$.

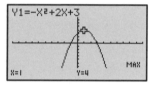

ADJUSTING THE VIEWING WINDOW

When graphing functions it is important that you are able to view all the important features of the graph. As a general rule it is best to start with a large viewing window to make sure all the features of the graph are visible. You can then make the window smaller if necessary.

Texas Instruments TI-83

Some useful commands for adjusting the viewing window include:

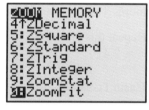

ZOOM **0:ZoomFit** :   This command scales the y-axis to fit the minimum and maximum values of the displayed graph within the current x-axis range.

ZOOM **6:ZStandard** :   This command returns the viewing window to the default setting of $-10 \leqslant x \leqslant 10$, $-10 \leqslant y \leqslant 10$.

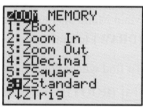

If neither of these commands are helpful, the viewing window can be adjusted manually by pressing WINDOW and setting the minimum and maximum values for the x and y axes.

Casio fx-9860g

The viewing window can be adjusted by pressing SHIFT F3 **(V-Window)**. You can manually set the minimum and maximum values of the x and y axes, or press F3 **(STD)** to obtain the standard viewing window $-10 \leqslant x \leqslant 10$, $-10 \leqslant y \leqslant 10$.

SUMMARY OF CIRCLE PROPERTIES

Click on the appropriate icon to revisit these well known theorems.

Theorem	Statement	Diagram
Angle in a semi-circle	The angle in a semi-circle is a right angle.	$\hat{ABC} = 90^o$ GEOMETRY PACKAGE
Chords of a circle	The perpendicular from the centre of a circle to a chord bisects the chord.	$AM = BM$ GEOMETRY PACKAGE
Radius-tangent	The tangent to a circle is perpendicular to the radius at the point of contact.	$\hat{OAT} = 90^o$ GEOMETRY PACKAGE
Tangents from an external point	Tangents from an external point are equal in length.	$AP = BP$ GEOMETRY PACKAGE
Angle at the centre	The angle at the centre of a circle is twice the angle on the circle subtended by the same arc.	$\hat{AOB} = 2 \times \hat{ACB}$ GEOMETRY PACKAGE
Angles subtended by the same arc	Angles subtended by an arc on the circle are equal in size.	$\hat{ADB} = \hat{ACB}$ GEOMETRY PACKAGE
Angle between a tangent and a chord	The angle between a tangent and a chord at the point of contact is equal to the angle subtended by the chord in the alternate segment.	$\hat{BAS} = \hat{BCA}$ GEOMETRY PACKAGE

SUMMARY OF MEASUREMENT FACTS

PERIMETER FORMULAE

The distance around a closed figure is its **perimeter**.

The length of an arc is a fraction of the circumference of a circle.

For some shapes we can derive a formula for perimeter. The formulae for the most common shapes are given below:

square	rectangle	triangle	circle	arc
$P = 4l$	$P = 2(l+w)$	$P = a+b+c$	$C = 2\pi r$ or $C = \pi d$	$l = \left(\frac{\theta}{360}\right)2\pi r$

AREA FORMULAE

Shape	Figure	Formula
Rectangle		$\text{Area} = \text{length} \times \text{width}$
Triangle		$\text{Area} = \frac{1}{2}\text{base} \times \text{height}$
Parallelogram		$\text{Area} = \text{base} \times \text{height}$
Trapezium or **Trapezoid**		$\text{Area} = \left(\dfrac{a+b}{2}\right) \times h$
Circle		$\text{Area} = \pi r^2$
Sector		$\text{Area} = \left(\dfrac{\theta}{360}\right) \times \pi r^2$

SURFACE AREA FORMULAE

RECTANGULAR PRISM

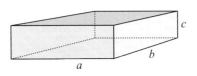

$$A = 2(ab + bc + ac)$$

SPHERE

Area,
$$A = 4\pi r^2$$

CYLINDER

Hollow cylinder

$A = 2\pi rh$
(no ends)

Open can

$A = 2\pi rh + \pi r^2$
(one end)

Solid cylinder

$A = 2\pi rh + 2\pi r^2$
(two ends)

CONE

Open cone

$A = \pi rs$
(no base)

Solid cone

$A = \pi rs + \pi r^2$
(solid)

VOLUME FORMULAE

Solids of uniform cross-section

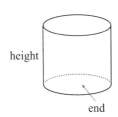

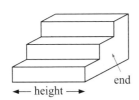

Volume of uniform solid = area of end × length

Pyramids and cones

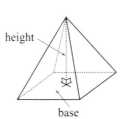

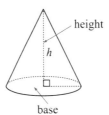

Volume of a pyramid or cone $= \frac{1}{3}$(area of base × height)

Spheres

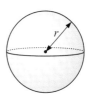

Volume of a sphere $= \frac{4}{3}\pi r^3$

CHALLENGE SETS

Click on the icon to access printable Challenge Sets.

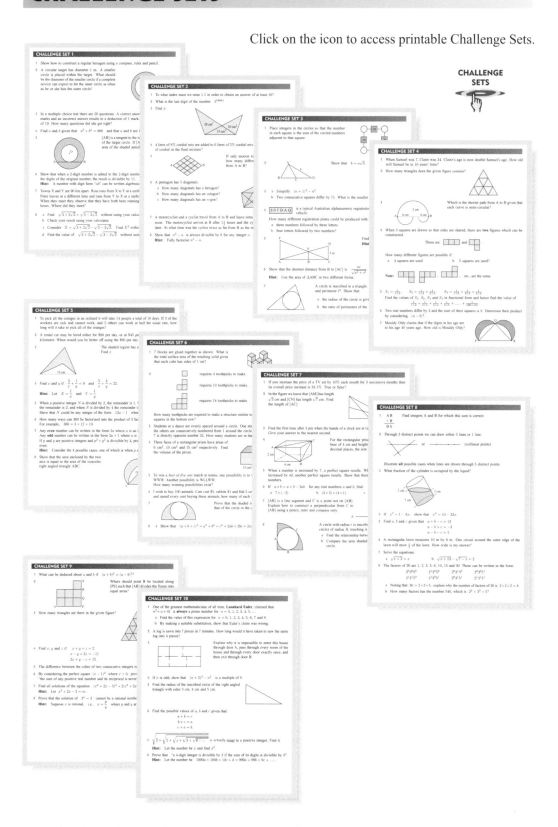

CHALLENGE SETS

Chapter 1

Sets and Venn diagrams

Contents:

OPENING PROBLEM

A city has two newspapers, The Sun and The Advertiser. 56% of the people read The Sun and 71% of the people read The Advertiser. 18% read neither of these newspapers.

What percentage of the people read:

- both of the newspapers
- at least one of the newspapers
- The Sun, but not The Advertiser
- exactly one of the two newspapers?

A   NUMBER SETS

A **set** is a collection of objects or things.

For example: $V = \{\text{vowels}\} = \{a, e, i, o, u\}$
$E = \{\text{even numbers}\} = \{2, 4, 6, 8, 10, 12, \dots\}$ are both sets.

The number of elements in set S is represented by $n(S)$.

Using this notation, $n(V) = 5$ and $n(E)$ is infinite.

V is a **finite set** as it has a finite number of elements.

E is an **infinite set** as it has infinitely many elements.

We use $\in$ to mean 'is a member of' or 'is in'. So, $a \in V$ and $28 \in E$.

We use $\notin$ to mean 'is not a member of' or 'is not in'. So, $w \notin V$ and $117 \notin E$.

SPECIAL NUMBER SETS

We use:

- $\mathbb{N}$ to represent the set of all **natural numbers** $\{0, 1, 2, 3, 4, 5, 6 \dots\}$

- $\mathbb{Z}$ to represent the set of all **integers** $\{0, \pm1, \pm2, \pm3, \pm4, \pm5, \pm6 \dots\}$

- $\mathbb{Z}^+$ to represent the set of all **positive integers** $\{1, 2, 3, 4, 5, 6 \dots\}$

- $\mathbb{Q}$ to represent the set of all **rational numbers**

Rational numbers have the form $\dfrac{p}{q}$ where p and q are integers, and $q \neq 0$.

For example: $\frac{15}{4}$, $10 \left(= \frac{10}{1}\right)$, $0.5 \left(= \frac{1}{2}\right)$, $-\frac{3}{8}$ are all rational numbers.

Numbers which cannot be written in rational form are called **irrational numbers**.

For example: Radicals or surds such as $\sqrt{2}$ and $\sqrt{7}$ are irrational.

π which is $3.14159265.......$ is an irrational number.

Non-recurring decimal numbers and numbers such as $0.12233344445.......$ are irrationals.

- $\mathbb{R}$ to represent the set of all **real numbers**

Real numbers include all numbers which can be placed on the number line.

For example, $\frac{1}{8} = 0.125$, $\sqrt{2} = 1.41421356....$, $\pi = 3.14159265....$
are all real numbers.

$\frac{2}{0}$ and $\sqrt{-2}$ are not real numbers because we cannot write them in decimal form.

Example 1　　　　　　　　　　　　　　　　　　　　🔊 **Self Tutor**

Show that $0.\overline{36}$, which is $0.36363636....$, is a rational number.

Let $x = 0.\overline{36} = 0.36363636....$

$\therefore \quad 100x = 36.363636.... = 36 + x$

$\therefore \quad 99x = 36 \quad$ and so $\quad x = \frac{36}{99} = \frac{4}{11}$

So, $0.\overline{36}$ is actually the rational number $\frac{4}{11}$.

EXERCISE 1A

1 True or false?

  a $3 \in \mathbb{Z}^+$ **b** $6 \in \mathbb{Z}$ **c** $\frac{3}{4} \in \mathbb{Q}$ **d** $\sqrt{2} \notin \mathbb{Q}$

  e $-\frac{1}{4} \notin \mathbb{Q}$ **f** $2\frac{1}{3} \in \mathbb{Z}$ **g** $0.3684 \in \mathbb{R}$ **h** $\dfrac{1}{0.1} \in \mathbb{Z}$

2 Which of these are rational?

  a 8 **b** -8 **c** $2\frac{1}{3}$ **d** $-3\frac{1}{4}$

  e $\sqrt{3}$ **f** $\sqrt{400}$ **g** 9.176 **h** $\pi - \pi$

3 List the members of set S which contains the:

  a factors of 6   **b** multiples of 6   **c** factors of 17   **d** multiples of 17

  e prime numbers less than 20   **f** composite numbers between 10 and 30

4 Find $n(S)$ for each set in **3**.

5 Show that these numbers are rational: **a** $0.\overline{7}$ **b** $0.\overline{41}$ **c** $0.\overline{324}$

6 **a** Why is 0.527 a rational number?

  b $0.\overline{9}$ is a rational number. In fact, $0.\overline{9} \in \mathbb{Z}$. Give evidence to support this statement.

7 Explain why these statements are false:

  a The sum of two irrationals is irrational.

  b The product of two irrationals is irrational.

B   INTERVAL NOTATION

Interval or **set notation** allows us to quickly describe sets of numbers using mathematical symbols only.

For example: $\{x \mid -3 < x \leqslant 2, \ x \in \mathbb{R}\}$

  reads "the set of all real x such that x lies between minus 3 and 2, including 2".

  Unless stated otherwise, we assume we are dealing with *real* numbers. Thus, the set can also be written as $\{x \mid -3 < x \leqslant 2\}$.

  We can represent the set on a number line as

Sometimes we want to restrict a set to include only integers or rationals.

For example: $\{x \mid -5 < x < 5, \ x \in \mathbb{Z}\}$

  reads "the set of all integers x such that x lies between minus 5 and 5".

  We can represent the set on a number line as

Example 2	◀) Self Tutor

Write in set notation:

a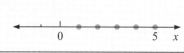

b

  a $\{x \mid 1 \leqslant x \leqslant 5, x \in \mathbb{N}\}$ **b** $\{x \mid -3 \leqslant x < 6\}$
  or $\{x \mid 1 \leqslant x \leqslant 5, x \in \mathbb{Z}\}$

EXERCISE 1B

1 Write verbal statements for the meaning of:

  a $\{x \mid x > 4\}$ **b** $\{x \mid x \leqslant 5\}$ **c** $\{y \mid 0 < y < 8\}$

  d $\{x \mid 1 \leqslant x \leqslant 4\}$ **e** $\{t \mid 2 < t < 7\}$ **f** $\{n \mid n \leqslant 3 \ \text{or} \ n > 6\}$

2 Write in set notation:

a

b
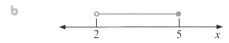

c

d

e

f

3 Sketch the following number sets:

   a $\{x \mid 4 \leqslant x < 8, \, x \in \mathbb{N}\}$ **b** $\{x \mid -5 < x \leqslant 4, \, x \in \mathbb{Z}\}$

   c $\{x \mid -3 < x \leqslant 5, \, x \in \mathbb{R}\}$ **d** $\{x \mid x > -5, \, x \in \mathbb{Z}\}$

   e $\{x \mid x \leqslant 6\}$ **f** $\{x \mid -5 \leqslant x \leqslant 0\}$

C   VENN DIAGRAMS

The **universal set** is the set of all elements under consideration.

A **Venn diagram** consists of a universal set U represented by a rectangle, and sets within it that are generally represented by circles.

THE COMPLEMENT OF A SET

S', the **complement** of S, consists of all the members of U which are not in S.

$$S' = \{x \mid x \in U, \; x \notin S\}.$$

SUBSETS

Consider two sets A and B.

A is a **subset** of B, written $A \subseteq B$,   if every element of A is also in B.

For example,   for $A = \{2, 3, 5\}$, $B = \{1, 2, 3, 4, 5, 6, 7\}$ and $C = \{3, 5, 8\}$

we see that $A \subseteq B$ as every element of A is also in B,   but
C is not a subset of B as C contains 8 which is not in B.

THE EMPTY SET

An **empty set** has no elements. It is represented by $\varnothing$ or $\{\ \}$.

Example 3   ◀ŵ) **Self Tutor**

Draw a Venn diagram to show the set $S = \{2, 4, 6, 7\}$ within the universal set $U = \{x \mid x \leqslant 10,\ x \in \mathbb{Z}^+\}$.

Hence list the elements of the complement set S'.

$U = \{1, 2, 3, 4, 5, 6, 7, 8, 9, 10\}$

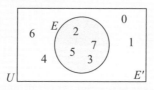

$S' = \{1, 3, 5, 8, 9, 10\}$

Example 4   ◀ŵ) **Self Tutor**

If $U = \{0, 1, 2, 3, 4, 5, 6, 7\}$ and $E = \{2, 3, 5, 7\}$, list the set E' and illustrate E and E' on a Venn diagram. Hence find:

   a $n(E)$ **b** $n(E')$ **c** $n(U)$

$E' = \{0, 1, 4, 6\}$

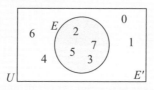

  a E contains 4 elements, so $n(E) = 4$

  b $n(E') = 4$ **c** $n(U) = 8$

This Venn diagram displays real numbers, rational numbers, integers and natural numbers.

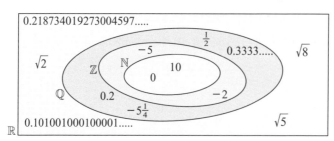

Example 5   ◀ŵ) **Self Tutor**

Illustrate the following numbers on a Venn diagram:

$\sqrt{3},\ 8\tfrac{1}{2},\ -2,\ 7.1,\ 16,\ 0.115$

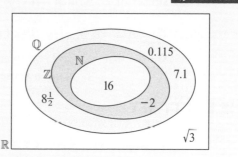

Example 6

◀» **Self Tutor**

If $U = \{x \mid 0 \leqslant x \leqslant 12, \ x \in \mathbb{Z}\}, \quad A = \{2, 3, 5, 7, 11\}$

and $B = \{1, 3, 6, 7, 8\}, \quad$ show A and B on a Venn diagram.

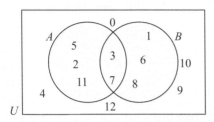

We notice that 3 and 7 are in both A and B so the circles representing A and B must overlap.

We place 3 and 7 in the overlap, then fill in the rest of A, then fill in the rest of B.

The remaining elements of U go outside the two circles.

EXERCISE 1C

1 Suppose $U = \{x \mid x \leqslant 8, \ x \in \mathbb{Z}^+\}$ and $A = \{\text{prime numbers} \leqslant 8\}$.

   a Show set A on a Venn diagram.
         b List the set A'.

2 Suppose $U = \{\text{letters of the English alphabet}\}$ and
         $V = \{\text{letters of the English alphabet which are vowels}\}$.

   a Show these two sets on a Venn diagram.
         b List the set V'.

3

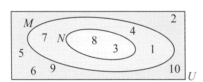

   a List the elements of:
        i U ii N iii M
   b What are $n(N)$ and $n(M)$?
   c Is $M \subseteq N$?

4 Show A and B on a Venn diagram if:

   a $U = \{1, 2, 3, 4, 5, 6\}, \quad A = \{1, 2, 3, 4\}, \quad B = \{3, 4, 5, 6\}$

   b $U = \{4, 5, 6, 7, 8, 9, 10\}, \quad A = \{6, 7, 9, 10\}, \quad B = \{5, 6, 8, 9\}$

   c $U = \{3, 4, 5, 6, 7, 8, 9\}, \quad A = \{3, 5, 7, 9\}, \quad B = \{4, 6, 8\}$

5 Suppose the universal set is $U = \mathbb{R}$, the set of all real numbers.

   $\mathbb{Q}, \ \mathbb{Z},$ and $\mathbb{N}$ are all subsets of $\mathbb{R}$.

   a Copy the given Venn diagram and label the sets $U, \mathbb{Q}, \mathbb{Z},$ and $\mathbb{N}$ on it.

   b Place these numbers on the Venn diagram:
      $\frac{1}{2}, \ \sqrt{2}, \ 0.\overline{3}, \ -5, \ -5\frac{1}{4}, \ 0, \ 10,$ and
      $0.2137005618.....$ which does not terminate or recur.

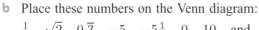

   c True or false?   i $\mathbb{N} \subseteq \mathbb{Z}$ ii $\mathbb{Z} \subseteq \mathbb{Q}$ iii $\mathbb{N} \subseteq \mathbb{Q}$

   d Shade the region representing the set of irrationals $\mathbb{Q}'$.

6 Show the following information on a Venn diagram:

   a $U = \{\text{triangles}\}, \quad E = \{\text{equilateral triangles}\}, \quad I = \{\text{isosceles triangles}\}$

   b $U = \{\text{quadrilaterals}\}, \quad P = \{\text{parallelograms}\}, \quad R = \{\text{rectangles}\}$

7 Suppose $U = \{x \mid x \leqslant 30,\ x \in \mathbb{Z}^+\}$,
$A = \{\text{prime numbers} \leqslant 30\}$,
$B = \{\text{multiples of } 5 \leqslant 30\}$
and $C = \{\text{odd numbers} \leqslant 30\}$.

Use the Venn diagram shown to display the elements of the sets.

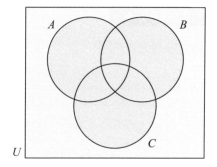

  UNION AND INTERSECTION

THE UNION OF TWO SETS

$A \cup B$ denotes the **union** of sets A and B. This set contains all elements belonging to **A or B or both** A and B.

$A \cup B = \{x \mid x \in A \quad \textbf{or} \quad x \in B\}$

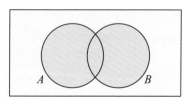

$A \cup B$ is shaded green.

THE INTERSECTION OF TWO SETS

$A \cap B$ denotes the **intersection** of sets A and B.   This is the set of all elements common to both sets.

$A \cap B = \{x \mid x \in A \quad \textbf{and} \quad x \in B\}$

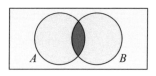

$A \cap B$ is shaded red.

In the Venn diagram alongside,

$A = \{2,\ 3,\ 4,\ 7\}$ and $B = \{1,\ 3,\ 7,\ 8,\ 10\}$.

We can see that $A \cap B = \{3,\ 7\}$
and $A \cup B = \{1,\ 2,\ 3,\ 4,\ 7,\ 8,\ 10\}$

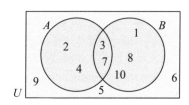

DISJOINT SETS

Two sets A and B are said to be **disjoint** if they have no elements in common, i.e., if $A \cap B = \varnothing$.

If A and B have elements in common then they are **non-disjoint**.

Example 7   ◀) **Self Tutor**

If $U = \{$postive integers $\leqslant 12\}$, $A = \{$primes $\leqslant 12\}$ and $B = \{$factors of 12$\}$:

a   List the elements of the sets A and B.

b   Show the sets A, B and U on a Venn diagram.

c   List the elements in: i A' ii $A \cap B$ iii $A \cup B$

d   Find: i $n(A \cap B)$ ii $n(A \cup B)$ iii $n(B')$

---

a $A = \{2, 3, 5, 7, 11\}$ and $B = \{1, 2, 3, 4, 6, 12\}$

b

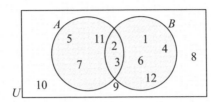

c   i $A' = \{1, 4, 6, 8, 9, 10, 12\}$ ii $A \cap B = \{2, 3\}$

   iii $A \cup B = \{1, 2, 3, 4, 5, 6, 7, 11, 12\}$

d   i $n(A \cap B) = 2$ ii $n(A \cup B) = 9$

   iii $B' = \{5, 7, 8, 9, 10, 11\}$,   so $n(B') = 6$

EXERCISE 1D.1

1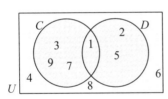

a   List:
   i   set C ii   set D iii   set U
   iv   set $C \cap D$ v   set $C \cup D$

b   Find:
   i $n(C)$ ii $n(D)$ iii $n(U)$
   iv $n(C \cap D)$ v $n(C \cup D)$

2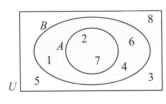

a   List:
   i   set A ii   set B iii   set U
   iv   set $A \cap B$ v   set $A \cup B$

b   Find:
   i $n(A)$ ii $n(B)$ iii $n(U)$
   iv $n(A \cap B)$ v $n(A \cup B)$

3   Consider $U = \{x \mid x \leqslant 12, \ x \in \mathbb{Z}^+\}$,

   $A = \{2, 7, 9, 10, 11\}$ and $B = \{1, 2, 9, 11, 12\}$.

a   Show these sets on a Venn diagram.

b   List the elements of: i $A \cap B$ ii $A \cup B$ iii B'

c   Find: i $n(A)$ ii $n(B')$ iii $n(A \cap B)$ iv $n(A \cup B)$

4   If A is the set of all factors of 36 and B is the set of all factors of 63, find:

a $A \cap B$ b $A \cup B$

5 If $X = \{A, B, D, M, N, P, R, T, Z\}$ and $Y = \{B, C, M, T, W, Z\}$, find:

   a $X \cap Y$ **b** $X \cup Y$

6 If $U = \{x \mid x \leqslant 30, \; x \in \mathbb{Z}^+\}$,

      $A = \{\text{factors of } 30\}$ and $B = \{\text{prime numbers} \leqslant 30\}$:

   a Find: **i** $n(A)$ **ii** $n(B)$ **iii** $n(A \cap B)$ **iv** $n(A \cup B)$

   b Use **a** to verify that $n(A \cup B) = n(A) + n(B) - n(A \cap B)$

7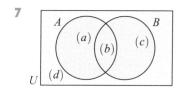

   a Use the Venn diagram given to show that:

      $n(A \cup B) = n(A) + n(B) - n(A \cap B)$.

      Note: (a) means that there are a elements in this region, so $n(A) = a + b$.

   b Suppose A and B are disjoint events. Explain why $n(A \cup B) = n(A) + n(B)$.

8 Simplify:

   a $X \cap Y$ for $X = \{1, 3, 5, 7\}$ and $Y = \{2, 4, 6, 8\}$

   b $A \cup A'$ for any set $A \in U$.

   c $A \cap A'$ for any set $A \in U$.

USING VENN DIAGRAMS TO ILLUSTRATE REGIONS

We can use a Venn diagram to help illustrate the union or intersection of regions.

Shaded regions of a Venn diagram can be used to verify **set identities**. These are equations involving sets which are true for *all* sets.

Examples of set identities include:

$$A \cup A' = U \qquad\qquad A \cap A' = \varnothing$$
$$(A \cup B)' = A' \cap B' \qquad (A \cap B)' = A' \cup B'$$

Example 8   **◀》 Self Tutor**

On separate Venn diagrams, shade the region representing:

   a in A or in B but not in both   **b** $A' \cap B$

a

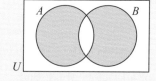

b We look for where the outside of A intersects (overlaps) with B.

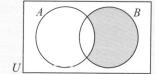

Example 9   ◀)) **Self Tutor**

Verify that $(A \cup B)' = A' \cap B'$.

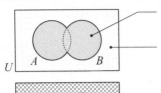

— this shaded region is $(A \cup B)$

∴ this shaded region is $(A \cup B)'$

represents A'

represents B'

represents $A' \cap B'$

Thus $(A \cup B)'$ and $A' \cap B'$ are represented by the same regions, verifying that $(A \cup B)' = A' \cap B'$.

EXERCISE 1D.2

1 On separate Venn diagrams like the one given, shade the region representing:

   a not in A **b** in both A and B

   c $A \cap B'$ **d** in either A or B

   e $A \cup B'$ **f** $(A \cup B)'$

   g $(A \cap B)'$ **h** in exactly one of A or B

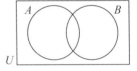

2 Describe in words, the shaded region of:

   a 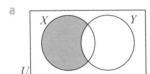   **b** 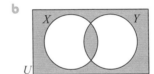   **c**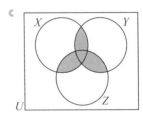

3 If A and B are two non-disjoint sets, shade the region of a Venn diagram representing:

   a A' **b** $A' \cap B$ **c** $A \cup B'$ **d** $A' \cap B'$

4 The diagram alongside is the most general case for three events in the same sample space U.

On separate Venn diagrams shade:

   a A **b** B' **c** $B \cap C$ **d** $A \cup C$

   e $A \cap B \cap C$ **f** $(A \cup B) \cap C$

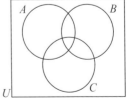

5 Verify that:

   a $(A \cap B)' = A' \cup B'$

   b $A \cup (B \cap C) = (A \cup B) \cap (A \cup C)$

   c $A \cap (B \cup C) = (A \cap B) \cup (A \cap C)$

COMPUTER DEMO

E | PROBLEM SOLVING WITH VENN DIAGRAMS

Example 10   ◀) **Self Tutor**

The Venn diagram alongside illustrates the number of people in a sporting club who play tennis (T) and hockey (H). Determine the number of people:

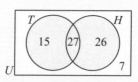

 a   in the club

 b   who play hockey

 c   who play both sports

 d   who play neither sport

 e   who play at least one sport.

---

 a   Number in the club
     $= 15 + 27 + 26 + 7 = 75$

 b   Number who play hockey
     $= 27 + 26 = 53$

 c   Number who play both sports $= 27$

 d   Number who play neither sport $= 7$

 e   Number who play at least one sport
     $= 15 + 27 + 26 = 68$

EXERCISE 1E

1   The Venn diagram alongside illustrates the number of students in a particular class who study French (F) and Spanish (S). Determine the number of students:

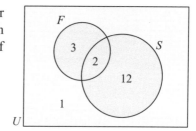

 a   in the class

 b   who study both subjects

 c   who study at least one of the subjects

 d   who only study Spanish.

2   In a survey at a resort, people were asked whether they went sailing (S) or fishing (F) during their stay. Use the Venn diagram to determine the number of people:

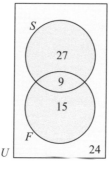

 a   in the survey

 b   who did both activities

 c   who did neither activity

 d   who did exactly one of the activities.

3 In a class of 30 students, 19 study Physics, 17 study Chemistry and 15 study both of these subjects. Display this information on a Venn diagram and hence determine the number of students who study:

    a both subjects   b at least one of the subjects

    c Physics, but not Chemistry   d exactly one of the subjects

    e neither subject.

4 In a class of 40 students, 19 play tennis, 20 play netball and 8 play neither of these sports. Determine the number of students in the class who:

    a play tennis   b do not play netball

    c play at least one of the sports   d play one and only one of the sports

    e play netball, but not tennis.

5 In a class of 25 students, 15 play hockey and 16 play basketball. If there are 4 students who play neither sport, determine the number of students who play both hockey and basketball.

6 In a class of 40 students, 34 like bananas, 22 like pineapples and 2 dislike both fruits. Find the number of students who:

    a like both fruits   b like at least one fruit.

7 In a group of 50 students, 40 study Mathematics and 32 study Physics. Each student studies at least one of these subjects. From a Venn diagram, find how many students:

    a study both subjects   b study Mathematics but not Physics.

8 In a class of 40 students, 23 have dark hair, 18 have brown eyes, and 26 have dark hair, brown eyes or both. How many students have:

    a dark hair and brown eyes   b neither dark hair nor brown eyes

    c dark hair but not brown eyes?

9 400 families were surveyed. It was found that 90% had a TV set and 60% had a computer. Every family had at least one of these items. How many of the families had both a TV set and a computer?

10 In a certain town, three newspapers are published. 20% of the population read A, 16% read B, 14% read C, 8% read A and B, 5% read A and C, 4% read B and C and 2% read all 3 newspapers. What percentage of the population read:

    a none of the papers   b at least one of the papers

    c exactly one of the papers   d either A or B e A only?

11 In a circle of music lovers, 14 people play the piano or violin, 8 people are piano players, and 5 people play both instruments. Find the number of violin players.

12 Our team scored well in the interschool athletics carnival. Eight of us gained places in running events, 5 gained places in both running and jumping events, and 14 of us collected exactly one place in running or jumping. How many places were gained by our team?

13 64% of students at a school study a language, 79% study Mathematics, and each student studies at least one of these subjects. What percentage of students study both a language and Mathematics?

14 A survey is made of the investments of the members of a club. All of the 133 members own at least one type of share; 96 own mining shares, 70 own oil shares, and 66 members own industrial shares. Of those who own mining shares, 40 also own oil shares and 45 also own industrial shares. The number who own both oil shares and industrial shares is 28. How many members of the club own all three types of share?

15 At a certain school there are 90 students studying for their matriculation certificate. They are required to study at least one of the subjects: Physics, French or History. Of these students, 50 are studying Physics, 60 are studying French, and 55 are studying History. Thirty students are studying both Physics and French, while 10 students are studying both French and History but not Physics. Twenty students are studying all three subjects. Construct and explain a Venn diagram which represents this situation.

Use this diagram to determine:

   a how many students are studying both Physics and History, but not French

   b how many students are studying at least two of these three subjects.

16 In a school of 405 pupils, a survey on sporting activities shows that 251 pupils play tennis, 157 play hockey, and 111 play softball. There are 45 pupils who play both tennis and hockey, 60 who play hockey and softball, and 39 who play tennis and softball. What conclusion may be drawn about the number of students who participate in all three sports?

F   THE ALGEBRA OF SETS (EXTENSION)

For the set of real numbers $\mathbb{R}$, we can write laws for the operations $+$ and $\times$. For real numbers a, b and c, we know the following laws:

- **commutative** $a + b = b + a$ and $ab = ba$
- **identity** Identity elements 0 and 1 exist such that
  $a + 0 = 0 + a = a$ and $a \times 1 = 1 \times a = a$.
- **associativity** $(a + b) + c = a + (b + c)$ and $(ab)c = a(bc)$
- **distributive** $a(b + c) = ab + ac$

In **Exercise 1D.2** we used a Venn diagram to verify that $A \cup (B \cap C) = (A \cup B) \cap (A \cup C)$.

This result looks very much like the *distributive* law for real numbers, but with real numbers replaced by sets, $\times$ replaced by $\cup$, and $+$ replaced by $\cap$.

The following are the **laws for the algebra of sets** under the operations $\cup$ and $\cap$:

- **commutative** $A \cap B = B \cap A$ and $A \cup B = B \cup A$
- **associativity** $A \cap (B \cap C) = (A \cap B) \cap C$ and $A \cup (B \cup C) = (A \cup B) \cup C$
- **idempotent** $A \cap A = A$ and $A \cup A = A$
- **distributive** $A \cup (B \cap C) = (A \cup B) \cap (A \cup C)$ and
  $A \cap (B \cup C) = (A \cap B) \cup (A \cap C)$
- **DeMorgan's** $A \cap \varnothing = \varnothing$, $A \cup U = U$, $(A \cap B)' = A' \cup B'$, $(A \cup B)' = A' \cap B'$
- **complement** $(A')' = A$

EXERCISE 1F

1 With the aid of Venn diagrams, explain why the following laws are valid:

    a the *commutative* laws $A \cap B = B \cap A$ and $A \cup B = B \cup A$

    b the *idempotent* laws $A \cap A = A$ and $A \cup A = A$

    c the *associative* laws $A \cap (B \cap C) = (A \cap B) \cap C$ and $A \cup (B \cup C) = (A \cup B) \cup C$

    d the *complement* law $(A')' = A$.

2 Use the laws for the algebra of sets to show that:

    a $A \cup (B \cup A') = U$ for all B

    b $A \cap (B \cap A') = \varnothing$ for all B

    c $A \cup (B \cap A') = A \cup B$

    d $(A' \cup B')' = A \cap B$

    e $(A \cup B) \cap (A' \cap B') = \varnothing$

    f $(A \cup B) \cap (C \cup D) = (A \cap C) \cup (A \cap D) \cup (B \cap C) \cup (B \cap D)$.

REVIEW SET 1A

1   **a** Explain why 1.3 is a rational number.

    b True or false: $\sqrt{4000} \in \mathbb{Q}$?

    c List the set of all prime numbers between 20 and 40.

    d Write a statement describing the meaning of $\{t \mid -1 \leqslant t < 3\}$.

    e Write in set notation:

    f Sketch the number set $\{x \mid -2 \leqslant x \leqslant 3,\ x \in \mathbb{Z}\}$.

2 Suppose $U = \{x \mid x \leqslant 12,\ x \in \mathbb{Z}^+\}$ and $A = \{\text{multiples of } 3 \leqslant 12\}$.

    a Show A on a Venn diagram.

    b List the set A'.

    c Find $n(A')$.

    d True or false: If $C = \{1, 2, 4\}$,   then $C \subseteq A$?

3 True or false: **a** $\mathbb{N} \subseteq \mathbb{Z}^+$ **b** $\mathbb{Q} \subseteq \mathbb{Z}$?

4

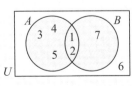

    a List:

      i set A **ii** set B **iii** set U

      iv set $A \cup B$ **v** set $A \cap B$

    b Find:

      i $n(A)$ **ii** $n(B)$ **iii** $n(A \cup B)$

5 Consider $U = \{x \mid x \leqslant 10,\ x \in \mathbb{Z}^+\}$, $P = \{2, 3, 5, 7\}$ and $Q = \{2, 4, 6, 8\}$.

    a Show these sets on a Venn diagram.

    b List the elements of: **i** $P \cap Q$ **ii** $P \cup Q$ **iii** Q'

    c Find: **i** $n(P')$ **ii** $n(P \cap Q)$ **iii** $n(P \cup Q)$

    d True or false: $P \cap Q \subseteq P$?

6 Describe in words the shaded region of:

a

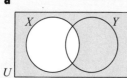

b

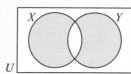

c

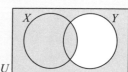

REVIEW SET 1B

1 **a** True or false: $-2 \in \mathbb{Z}^+$?

  b True or false: $\frac{1}{\sqrt{7}} \in \mathbb{Q}$?

  c Show that $0.\overline{51}$ is a rational number.

  d Write in set notation:

  e Sketch the number set $\{x \mid x \leqslant 3 \text{ or } x > 7, \, x \in \mathbb{R}\}$.

2 Illustrate these numbers on a Venn diagram like the one shown:

$-1, \sqrt{2}, 2, 3.1, \pi, 4.\overline{2}$

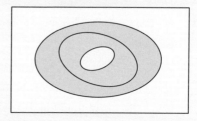

3 Show this information on a Venn diagram:

  a $U = \{10, 11, 12, 13, 14, 15\}, \quad A = \{10, 12, 14\}, \quad B = \{11, 12, 13\}$

  b $U = \{\text{quadrilaterals}\}, \quad S = \{\text{squares}\}, \quad R = \{\text{rectangles}\}$

4 If A is the set of all factors of 24 and B is the set of all factors of 18, find:

  a $A \cap B$ **b** $A \cup B$

5 On separate Venn diagrams like the one shown, shade the region representing:

  a B' **b** in A and in B **c** $(A \cup B)'$

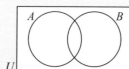

6

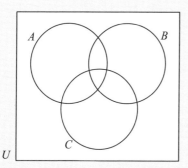

Using separate Venn diagrams like the one shown, shade regions to verify that $(A \cap B) \cup C = (A \cup C) \cap (B \cup C)$.

Chapter 2

Algebraic expansion and factorisation

Contents:

The study of **algebra** is vital for many areas of mathematics. We need it to manipulate equations, solve problems for unknown variables, and also to develop higher level mathematical theories.

In this chapter we consider the **expansion** of expressions which involve brackets, and the reverse process which is called **factorisation**.

REVISION OF EXPANSION LAWS

In this section we revise the laws for expanding algebraic expressions.

DISTRIBUTIVE LAW

$$a(b + c) = ab + ac$$

Example 1	◀) Self Tutor

Expand the following:

   a $2(3x - 1)$ b $-3x(x + 2)$

  a $2(3x - 1)$
        $= 2 \times 3x + 2 \times (-1)$
        $= 6x - 2$

  b $-3x(x + 2)$
        $= -3x \times x + -3x \times 2$
        $= -3x^2 - 6x$

THE PRODUCT $(a + b)(c + d)$

$$(a + b)(c + d) = ac + ad + bc + bd$$

Example 2	◀) Self Tutor

Expand and simplify:

   a $(x + 4)(x - 3)$ b $(2x - 5)(-x + 3)$

  a $(x + 4)(x - 3)$
        $= x \times x + x \times (-3) + 4 \times x + 4 \times (-3)$
        $= x^2 - 3x + 4x - 12$
        $= x^2 + x - 12$

  b $(2x - 5)(-x + 3)$
        $= 2x \times (-x) + 2x \times 3 - 5 \times (-x) - 5 \times 3$
        $= -2x^2 + 6x + 5x - 15$
        $= -2x^2 + 11x - 15$

DIFFERENCE OF TWO SQUARES

$$(a + b)(a - b) = a^2 - b^2$$

Example 3   ◀) **Self Tutor**

Expand and simplify:

  a $(x + 4)(x - 4)$ **b** $(3x - 2)(3x + 2)$

---

  a $(x + 4)(x - 4)$ **b** $(3x - 2)(3x + 2)$

      $= x^2 - 4^2$ $= (3x)^2 - 2^2$

      $= x^2 - 16$ $= 9x^2 - 4$

PERFECT SQUARES EXPANSION

$$(a + b)^2 = a^2 + 2ab + b^2$$

Example 4   ◀) **Self Tutor**

Expand and simplify:

  a $(2x + 1)^2$ **b** $(3 - 4y)^2$

---

  a $(2x + 1)^2$ **b** $(3 - 4y)^2$

      $= (2x)^2 + 2 \times 2x \times 1 + 1^2$ $= 3^2 + 2 \times 3 \times (-4y) + (-4y)^2$

      $= 4x^2 + 4x + 1$ $= 9 - 24y + 16y^2$

EXERCISE 2A

1 Expand and simplify:

  a $3(2x + 5)$ **b** $4x(x - 3)$ **c** $-2(3 + x)$ **d** $-3x(x + y)$

  e $2x(x^2 - 1)$ **f** $-x(1 - x^2)$ **g** $-ab(b - a)$ **h** $x^2(x - 3)$

2 Expand and simplify:

  a $2(x + 3) + 5(x - 4)$ **b** $2(3 - x) - 3(4 + x)$ **c** $x(x + 2) + 2x(1 - x)$

  d $x(x^2 + 2x) - x^2(2 - x)$ **e** $a(a + b) - b(a - b)$ **f** $x^3(x^2 - 3x + 2)$

3 Expand and simplify:

  a $(x + 2)(x + 5)$ **b** $(x - 3)(x + 4)$ **c** $(x + 5)(x - 3)$

  d $(x - 2)(x - 10)$ **e** $(2x + 1)(x - 3)$ **f** $(3x - 4)(2x - 5)$

  g $(2x + y)(x - y)$ **h** $(x + 3)(-2x - 1)$ **i** $(x + 2y)(-x - 1)$

4 Expand and simplify:

  a $(x + 7)(x - 7)$ **b** $(3 + a)(3 - a)$ **c** $(5 - x)(5 + x)$

  d $(2x + 1)(2x - 1)$ **e** $(4 - 3y)(4 + 3y)$ **f** $(3x - 4z)(4z + 3x)$

5 Expand and simplify:

    a $(x + 5)^2$ **b** $(2x + 3)^2$ **c** $(x + y)^2$

    d $(3x + 4)^2$ **e** $(5 + x^2)^2$ **f** $(3x + 2z)^2$

6 Expand and simplify:

    a $(x - 3)^2$ **b** $(2 - x)^2$ **c** $(3x - 1)^2$

    d $(x - y)^2$ **e** $(2x - 5y)^2$ **f** $(ab - 2)^2$

B   REVISION OF FACTORISATION

Factorisation is the process of writing an expression as a **product** of its **factors**.

In this section we revise factorisation by using the expansion laws in reverse.

FACTORISING WITH COMMON FACTORS

If every term in an expression has the same common factor then we can place this factor in front of a set of brackets. This is the reverse of the distributive law for expansion.

Example 5   ◀) **Self Tutor**

Fully factorise:

  a $6x^2 + 4x$ **b** $-4(a + 1) + (a + 2)(a + 1)$

  a $6x^2 + 4x$ **b** $-4(a + 1) + (a + 2)(a + 1)$

     $= 2 \times 3 \times x \times x + 2 \times 2 \times x$ $= (a + 1)[-4 + (a + 2)]$

     $= 2x(3x + 2)$ $= (a + 1)(a - 2)$

DIFFERENCE OF TWO SQUARES FACTORISATION

$$a^2 - b^2 = (a + b)(a - b)$$

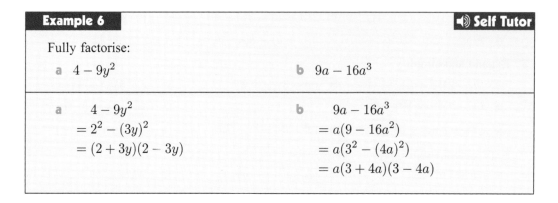

Example 6   ◀) **Self Tutor**

Fully factorise:

  a $4 - 9y^2$ **b** $9a - 16a^3$

  a $4 - 9y^2$ **b** $9a - 16a^3$

     $= 2^2 - (3y)^2$ $= a(9 - 16a^2)$

     $= (2 + 3y)(2 - 3y)$ $= a(3^2 - (4a)^2)$

                                $= a(3 + 4a)(3 - 4a)$

PERFECT SQUARES FACTORISATION

$$a^2 + 2ab + b^2 = (a+b)^2 \quad \text{and} \quad a^2 - 2ab + b^2 = (a-b)^2$$

Example 7	◀) **Self Tutor**

Factorise:

a $4x^2 + 4x + 1$

b $8x^2 - 24x + 18$

a
$$\begin{aligned} &4x^2 + 4x + 1 \\ &= (2x)^2 + 2 \times 2x \times 1 + 1^2 \\ &= (2x+1)^2 \end{aligned}$$

b
$$\begin{aligned} &8x^2 - 24x + 18 \\ &= 2(4x^2 - 12x + 9) \\ &= 2((2x)^2 - 2 \times 2x \times 3 + 3^2) \\ &= 2(2x - 3)^2 \end{aligned}$$

EXERCISE 2B

1   Fully factorise:

   a $3x - 9$
   b $2x^2 + 6x$
   c $4x - 2xy$

   d $3ab - 6b$
   e $2x^2 + 8x^3$
   f $-6x^2 + 12x$

   g $x^3 + 2x$
   h $x^3 + x^2$
   i $2x^2 - 4x^3$

2   Fully factorise:

   a $3(x+5) + x(x+5)$
   b $a(b+3) - 5(b+3)$

   c $x(x+4) + x + 4$
   d $x(x+2) + (x+2)(x+5)$

   e $a(c-d) + b(c-d)$
   f $y(2+y) - y - 2$

   g $ab(x-1) + c(x-1)$
   h $a(x+2) - x - 2$

3   Fully factorise:

   a $x^2 - 16$
   b $64 - x^2$
   c $9x^2 - 1$

   d $49 - 4x^2$
   e $y^2 - 4x^2$
   f $4a^2 - 25b^2$

   g $81x^2 - 16y^2$
   h $4x^4 - y^2$
   i $9a^2b^2 - 16$

4   Fully factorise:

   a $2x^2 - 8$
   b $3y^2 - 27$
   c $2 - 18x^2$

   d $4x - 9x^3$
   e $a^3b - ab^3$
   f $25 - x^2y^2$

   g $9b^3 - 4b$
   h $4x^2y^2 - 1$
   i $x^4 - y^4$

5   Factorise:

   a $x^2 + 4x + 4$
   b $x^2 - 10x + 25$
   c $9x^2 + 30x + 25$

   d $x^2 - 8x + 16$
   e $4x^2 + 28x + 49$
   f $x^2 - 20x + 100$

6   Factorise:

   a $-9x^2 + 6x - 1$
   b $3x^2 + 18x + 27$
   c $-18x^2 + 12x - 2$

   d $2x^2 - 50$
   e $2x^2 - 16x + 32$
   f $-3x^2 - 18x - 27$

FURTHER EXPANSION

In this section we expand more complicated expressions by repeated use of the expansion laws.

Consider the expansion of $(a+b)(c+d+e)$.

Now $(a+b)(c+d+e)$ Compare: $\Box(c+d+e)$
$= (a+b)c + (a+b)d + (a+b)e$ $= \Box c + \Box d + \Box e$
$= ac + bc + ad + bd + ae + be$

Notice that there are 6 terms in this expansion and that each term within the first bracket is multiplied by each term in the second.

2 terms in first bracket $\times$ 3 terms in second bracket $\longrightarrow$ 6 terms in expansion.

Example 8   ◀)) **Self Tutor**

Expand and simplify: $(x+3)(x^2+2x+4)$

$(x+3)(x^2+2x+4)$
$= x^3 + 2x^2 + 4x$ {all terms of 2nd bracket $\times$ x}
$\quad + 3x^2 + 6x + 12$ {all terms of 2nd bracket $\times$ 3}
$= x^3 + 5x^2 + 10x + 12$ {collecting like terms}

Example 9   ◀)) **Self Tutor**

Expand and simplify:

  a $x(x+1)(x+3)$ **b** $(x+1)(x-3)(x+2)$

  a $x(x+1)(x+3)$
            $= (x^2+x)(x+3)$ {all terms in first bracket $\times$ x}
            $= x^3 + 3x^2 + x^2 + 3x$ {expand remaining factors}
            $= x^3 + 4x^2 + 3x$ {collect like terms}

  b $(x+1)(x-3)(x+2)$
            $= (x^2 - 3x + x - 3)(x+2)$ {expand first two factors}
            $= (x^2 - 2x - 3)(x+2)$ {collect like terms}
            $= x^3 - 2x^2 - 3x + 2x^2 - 4x - 6$ {expand remaining factors}
            $= x^3 - 7x - 6$ {collect like terms}

EXERCISE 2C

1 Expand and simplify:

a $(x+2)(x^2+x+4)$

b $(x+3)(x^2+2x-3)$

c $(x+3)(x^2+2x+1)$

d $(x+1)(2x^2-x-5)$

e $(2x+3)(x^2+2x+1)$

f $(2x-5)(x^2-2x-3)$

g $(x+5)(3x^2-x+4)$

h $(4x-1)(2x^2-3x+1)$

Each term of the first bracket is multiplied by each term of the second bracket.

2 Expand and simplify:

a $x(x+2)(x+4)$

b $x(x-3)(x+2)$

c $x(x-4)(x-5)$

d $2x(x+2)(x+5)$

e $3x(x-2)(3-x)$

f $-x(2+x)(6-x)$

g $-3x(3x-1)(x+4)$

h $x(1-5x)(2x+3)$

i $(x-2)(x+2)(x-3)$

3 Expand and simplify:

a $(x+4)(x+3)(x+2)$

b $(x-3)(x-2)(x+4)$

c $(x-3)(x-2)(x-5)$

d $(2x-3)(x+3)(x-1)$

e $(3x+5)(x+1)(x+2)$

f $(4x+1)(3x-1)(x+1)$

g $(2-x)(3x+1)(x-7)$

h $(x-2)(4-x)(3x+2)$

4 State how many terms you would obtain by expanding the following:

a $(a+b)(c+d)$

b $(a+b+c)(d+e)$

c $(a+b)(c+d+e)$

d $(a+b+c)(d+e+f)$

e $(a+b+c+d)(e+f)$

f $(a+b+c+d)(e+f+g)$

g $(a+b)(c+d)(e+f)$

h $(a+b+c)(d+e)(f+g)$

D · THE BINOMIAL EXPANSION

Consider $(a+b)^n$.   We note that:

- $a+b$ is called a **binomial** as it contains two terms
- any expression of the form $(a+b)^n$ is called a **power of a binomial**
- the **binomial expansion** of $(a+b)^n$ is obtained by writing the expression without brackets.

INVESTIGATION 1   THE BINOMIAL EXPANSION OF $(a+b)^3$

The purpose of this investigation is to discover the binomial expansion for $(a+b)^3$.

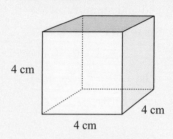

What to do:

1 Find a large potato and cut it to obtain a 4 cm by 4 cm by 4 cm cube.

2 By making 3 cuts parallel to the cube's surfaces, divide the cube into 8 rectangular prisms as shown.

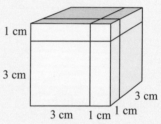

3 How many prisms would be:

    a 3 by 3 by 3   **b** 3 by 3 by 1

    c 3 by 1 by 1   **d** 1 by 1 by 1?

4 Now instead of using $4 \text{ cm} = 3 \text{ cm} + 1 \text{ cm}$, suppose the original cube has dimensions $(a+b)$ cm. Suppose you made cuts so each edge was divided into a cm and b cm. How many prisms would be:

    a a by a by a **b** a by a by b

    c a by b by b **d** b by b by b?

5 Explain why the volume of the cube in **4** is given by $(a+b)^3$.

By adding the volumes of the 8 rectangular prisms, find an expression for the total volume. Hence write down the binomial expansion of $(a+b)^3$.

Another method of finding the binomial expansion of $(a+b)^3$ is to expand the brackets.

$$\begin{aligned}(a+b)^3 &= (a+b)^2(a+b) \\ &= (a^2+2ab+b^2)(a+b) \\ &= a^3 + 2a^2b + ab^2 + a^2b + 2ab^2 + b^3 \\ &= a^3 + 3a^2b + 3ab^2 + b^3\end{aligned}$$

So, $$(a+b)^3 = a^3 + 3a^2b + 3ab^2 + b^3.$$

The binomial expansion of $(a+b)^3$ can be used to expand other perfect cubes.

For example:

Notice the use of brackets in these expansions.

- to expand $(2x+3)^3$ we substitute $a=(2x)$ and $b=3$,

    $\therefore$ $(2x+3)^3 = (2x)^3 + 3 \times (2x)^2 \times 3 + 3 \times (2x) \times 3^2 + 3^3$

- to expand $(3x-4)^3$ we substitute $a=(3x)$ and $b=(-4)$,

    $\therefore$ $(3x-4)^3 = (3x)^3 + 3 \times (3x)^2 \times (-4) + 3 \times (3x) \times (-4)^2 + (-4)^3$

Example 10   ◄》 **Self Tutor**

Expand and simplify using the rule $(a+b)^3 = a^3 + 3a^2b + 3ab^2 + b^3$:

a $(x+2)^3$ **b** $(x-5)^3$

a We substitute $a = x$ and $b = 2$

$\therefore \quad (x+2)^3 = x^3 + 3 \times x^2 \times 2 + 3 \times x \times 2^2 + 2^3$
$= x^3 + 6x^2 + 12x + 8$

b We substitute $a = x$ and $b = (-5)$

$\therefore \quad (x-5)^3 = x^3 + 3 \times x^2 \times (-5) + 3 \times x \times (-5)^2 + (-5)^3$
$= x^3 - 15x^2 + 75x - 125$

EXERCISE 2D

1 Use the binomial expansion for $(a+b)^3$ to expand and simplify:

a $(x+1)^3$ **b** $(x+3)^3$ **c** $(x+4)^3$ **d** $(x+y)^3$

e $(x-1)^3$ **f** $(x-5)^3$ **g** $(x-4)^3$ **h** $(x-y)^3$

i $(2+y)^3$ **j** $(2x+1)^3$ **k** $(3x+1)^3$ **l** $(2y+3x)^3$

m $(2-y)^3$ **n** $(2x-1)^3$ **o** $(3x-1)^3$ **p** $(2y-3x)^3$

2 Copy and complete the argument $(a+b)^4 = (a+b)(a+b)^3$
$= (a+b)(a^3 + 3a^2b + 3ab^2 + b^3)$
$\vdots$ etc.

3 Use the binomial expansion $(a+b)^4 = a^4 + 4a^3b + 6a^2b^2 + 4ab^3 + b^4$ to expand and simplify:

a $(x+y)^4$ **b** $(x+1)^4$ **c** $(x+2)^4$ **d** $(x+3)^4$

e $(x-y)^4$ **f** $(x-1)^4$ **g** $(x-2)^4$ **h** $(2x-1)^4$

4 Consider:

$$(a+b)^1 = \qquad\qquad\qquad\quad a \;\; + \;\; b$$
$$(a+b)^2 = \qquad\qquad\quad a^2 \;\; + \;\; 2ab \;\; + \;\; b^2$$
$$(a+b)^3 = \qquad\quad a^3 \;\; + \;\; 3a^2b \;\; + \;\; 3ab^2 \;\; + \;\; b^3$$
$$(a+b)^4 = \quad a^4 \;\; + \;\; 4a^3b \;\; + \;\; 6a^2b^2 \;\; + \;\; 4ab^3 \;\; + \;\; b^4$$

The expressions on the right hand side
of each identity contain coefficients

$$
\begin{array}{ccccccccc}
 & & & & 1 & & 1 & & \\
 & & & 1 & & 2 & & 1 & \\
 & & 1 & & 3 & & 3 & & 1 \\
 & 1 & & 4 & & 6 & & 4 & & 1
\end{array}
$$

This triangle of numbers is called **Pascal's triangle**.

a Predict the next two rows of Pascal's triangle and explain how you found them.

b Hence, write down the binomial expansion for:

i $(a+b)^5$ **ii** $(a-b)^5$ **iii** $(a+b)^6$ **iv** $(a-b)^6$

E   FACTORISING EXPRESSIONS WITH FOUR TERMS

Some expressions with four terms do not have an overall common factor, but can be factorised by pairing the four terms.

For example, $ab + ac + bd + cd$

$= a(b + c) + d(b + c)$ {factorising each pair separately}

$= (b + c)(a + d)$ {removing common factor $(b + c)$}

Note:

- Many expressions with four terms cannot be factorised using this method.
- Sometimes it is necessary to reorder the terms first.

Example 11   ◄⑴ **Self Tutor**

Factorise: **a** $3ab + d + 3ad + b$ **b** $x^2 + 2x + 5x + 10$

a $3ab + d + 3ad + b$

$= 3ab + b + 3ad + d$

$= b(3a + 1) + d(3a + 1)$

$= (3a + 1)(b + d)$

b $x^2 + 2x + 5x + 10$

$= x(x + 2) + 5(x + 2)$

$= (x + 2)(x + 5)$

Example 12   ◄⑴ **Self Tutor**

Factorise: **a** $x^2 + 3x - 4x - 12$ **b** $x^2 + 3x - x - 3$

a $x^2 + 3x - 4x - 12$

$= x(x + 3) - 4(x + 3)$

$= (x + 3)(x - 4)$

b $x^2 + 3x - x - 3$

$= x(x + 3) - (x + 3)$

$= x(x + 3) - 1(x + 3)$

$= (x + 3)(x - 1)$

EXERCISE 2E

1 Factorise:

a $2a + 2 + ab + b$

b $4d + ac + ad + 4c$

c $ab + 6 + 2b + 3a$

d $mn + 3p + np + 3m$

e $x^2 + 3x + 7x + 21$

f $x^2 + 5x + 4x + 20$

g $2x^2 + x + 6x + 3$

h $3x^2 + 2x + 12x + 8$

i $20x^2 + 12x + 5x + 3$

2 Factorise:

a $x^2 - 4x + 5x - 20$

b $x^2 - 7x + 2x - 14$

c $x^2 - 3x - 2x + 6$

d $x^2 - 5x - 3x + 15$

e $x^2 + 7x - 8x - 56$

f $2x^2 + x - 6x - 3$

g $3x^2 + 2x - 12x - 8$

h $4x^2 - 3x - 8x + 6$

i $9x^2 + 2x - 9x - 2$

F FACTORISING QUADRATIC TRINOMIALS

A **quadratic trinomial** is an algebraic expression of the form $ax^2 + bx + c$ where x is a variable and a, b, c are constants, $a \neq 0$.

Consider the expansion of the product $(x + 2)(x + 5)$:

$$\begin{aligned}
(x + 2)(x + 5) &= x^2 + 5x + 2x + 2 \times 5 \qquad \{\text{using FOIL}\} \\
&= x^2 + [5 + 2]x + [2 \times 5] \\
&= x^2 + [\textbf{sum of 2 and 5}]x + [\textbf{product of 2 and 5}] \\
&= x^2 + 7x + 10
\end{aligned}$$

So, if we want to factorise the quadratic trinomial $x^2 + 7x + 10$ into $(x + ...)(x + ...)$ we must find two numbers to fill the vacant places which have a *sum* of 7 and a *product* of 10.

In general, $\qquad x^2 \; + \; (\alpha + \beta)\,x \; + \; \alpha\beta \; = \; (x + \alpha)\,(x + \beta)$

the coefficient of x is the **sum** of α and β the constant term is the **product** of α and β

Example 13 | ◄) Self Tutor

Factorise: $x^2 + 11x + 24$

We need to find two numbers which have sum $= 11$, product $= 24$.

Pairs of factors of 24:

Factor product	1×24	2×12	3×8	4×6
Factor sum	25	14	11	10

The numbers we want are 3 and 8.

$\therefore \; x^2 + 11x + 24 = (x + 3)(x + 8)$

> Most of the time we can find the two numbers mentally.

Note: With practice, you should be able to perform factorisations like this in your head.

Example 14 | ◄) Self Tutor

Factorise: $x^2 - 7x + 12$

sum $= -7$ and product $= 12$

$\therefore$ the numbers are -3 and -4

$\therefore \; x^2 - 7x + 12 = (x - 3)(x - 4)$

> The sum is negative but the product is positive, so both numbers must be negative.

Example 15   ◀ Self Tutor

Factorise: **a** $x^2 - 2x - 15$ **b** $x^2 + x - 6$

a   sum $= -2$ and   product $= -15$

∴   the numbers are -5 and $+3$

∴ $x^2 - 2x - 15 = (x - 5)(x + 3)$

b   sum $= 1$ and   product $= -6$

∴   the numbers are $+3$ and -2

∴ $x^2 + x - 6 = (x + 3)(x - 2)$

> As the product is negative, the numbers are opposite in sign.

Example 16   ◀ Self Tutor

Fully factorise by first removing a common factor: $3x^2 + 6x - 72$

$3x^2 + 6x - 72$ {first look for a **common factor**}

$= 3(x^2 + 2x - 24)$ {sum $= 2$,   product $= -24$

$= 3(x + 6)(x - 4)$ ∴   the numbers are 6 and -4}

Example 17   ◀ Self Tutor

Fully factorise by first removing a common factor: $77 + 4x - x^2$

$77 + 4x - x^2$

$= -x^2 + 4x + 77$ {rewrite in descending powers of x}

$= -1(x^2 - 4x - 77)$ {remove -1 as a common factor}

$= -(x - 11)(x + 7)$ {sum $= -4$, product $= -77$

∴   the numbers are -11 and 7}

EXERCISE 2F

1 Find two numbers which have:

    a product 12 and sum 7   **b** product 15 and sum 8

    c product 16 and sum 10   **d** product 18 and sum 11

    e product -21 and sum 4   **f** product -21 and sum -4

    g product -12 and sum -4 **h** product -30 and sum 13

2 Factorise:

    a $x^2 + 4x + 3$ **b** $x^2 + 11x + 24$ **c** $x^2 + 10x + 21$

    d $x^2 + 15x + 54$ **e** $x^2 + 9x + 20$ **f** $x^2 + 8x + 15$

    g $x^2 + 10x + 24$ **h** $x^2 + 9x + 14$ **i** $x^2 + 6x + 8$

3 Factorise:

   a $x^2 - 3x + 2$ **b** $x^2 - 4x + 3$ **c** $x^2 - 5x + 6$

   d $x^2 - 14x + 33$ **e** $x^2 - 16x + 39$ **f** $x^2 - 19x + 48$

   g $x^2 - 11x + 28$ **h** $x^2 - 14x + 24$ **i** $x^2 - 20x + 36$

4 Factorise:

   a $x^2 - 7x - 8$ **b** $x^2 + 4x - 21$ **c** $x^2 - x - 2$

   d $x^2 - 2x - 8$ **e** $x^2 + 5x - 24$ **f** $x^2 - 3x - 10$

   g $x^2 + 3x - 54$ **h** $x^2 + x - 72$ **i** $x^2 - 4x - 21$

   j $x^2 - x - 6$ **k** $x^2 - 7x - 60$ **l** $x^2 + 7x - 60$

   m $x^2 + 3x - 18$ **n** $x^2 - 7x - 18$ **o** $x^2 - 12x + 35$

5 Fully factorise by first removing a common factor:

   a $2x^2 + 10x + 8$ **b** $3x^2 - 21x + 18$ **c** $2x^2 + 14x + 24$

   d $2x^2 - 44x + 240$ **e** $4x^2 - 8x - 12$ **f** $3x^2 - 42x + 99$

   g $2x^2 - 2x - 180$ **h** $3x^2 - 6x - 24$ **i** $2x^2 + 18x + 40$

   j $x^3 - 7x^2 - 8x$ **k** $4x^2 - 24x + 36$ **l** $14x^2 + 7x - 7$

   m $5x^2 - 30x - 80$ **n** $x^3 - 3x^2 - 28x$ **o** $x^4 + 2x^3 + x^2$

6 Fully factorise:

   a $-x^2 - 3x + 54$ **b** $-x^2 - 7x - 10$ **c** $-x^2 - 10x - 21$

   d $4x - x^2 - 3$ **e** $-4 + 4x - x^2$ **f** $3 - x^2 - 2x$

   g $-x^2 + 2x + 48$ **h** $6x - x^2 - 9$ **i** $10x - x^2 - 21$

   j $-2x^2 + 4x + 126$ **k** $20x - 2x^2 - 50$ **l** $-x^3 + x^2 + 2x$

G   FACTORISATION BY SPLITTING

INVESTIGATION 2   FACTORISATION BY SPLITTING THE MIDDLE TERM

Consider

$$(2x + 3)(4x + 5)$$
$$= 8x^2 + 10x + 12x + 15 \quad \{\text{using FOIL}\}$$
$$= 8x^2 + 22x + 15$$

In reverse,

$$8x^2 + 22x + 15$$
$$= \underline{8x^2 + 10x} + \underline{12x + 15}$$
$$= 2x(4x + 5) + 3(4x + 5)$$
$$= (4x + 5)(2x + 3)$$

So, we can factorise $8x^2 + 22x + 15$ into $(2x + 3)(4x + 5)$ by splitting the $+22x$ into a suitable sum, in this case $+10x + 12x$.

In general, if we start with a quadratic trinomial we will need a method to work out how to do the splitting.

Consider the expansion in greater detail:

$$(2x + 3)(4x + 5) = 2 \times 4 \times x^2 + [2 \times 5 + 3 \times 4]x + 3 \times 5 = 8x^2 + 22x + 15$$

The four numbers 2, 3, 4 and 5 are present in the *middle term*, and also in the *first* and *last* terms combined.

As 2×5 and 3×4 are factors of $2 \times 3 \times 4 \times 5 = 120$, this gives us the method for performing the splitting.

Step 1:   Multiply the coefficient of x^2 and the constant term.

In our case, $8 \times 15 = 120$.

Step 2:   Look for the factors of this number which add to give the coefficient of the middle term.

What factors of 120 add to give us 22? The answer is   10 and 12.

Step 3:   These numbers are the coefficients of the split terms.

So, the split is $10x + 12x$.

Consider another example, $6x^2 + 17x + 12$.

The product of the coefficient of x^2 and the constant term is $6 \times 12 = 72$.

We now need two factors of 72 whose *sum* is 17.   These numbers are   8 and 9.

So, $6x^2 + 17x + 12$

$= \underbrace{6x^2 + 8x} + \underbrace{9x + 12}$ $\{17x$ has been split into $8x$ and $9x\}$

$= 2x(3x + 4) + 3(3x + 4)$

$= (3x + 4)(2x + 3)$

or $6x^2 + 17x + 12$

$= \underbrace{6x^2 + 9x} + \underbrace{8x + 12}$

$= 3x(2x + 3) + 4(2x + 3)$

$= (2x + 3)(3x + 4)$

> When splitting the middle term it does not matter the order in which you list the two new terms.

What to do:

1 For the following quadratics, copy and complete the table below:

	quadratic	product	sum	'split'
e.g.	$10x^2 + 29x + 21$	210	29	$14x + 15x$
a	$2x^2 + 11x + 12$			
b	$3x^2 + 14x + 8$			
c	$4x^2 + 16x + 15$			
d	$6x^2 - 5x - 6$			
e	$4x^2 - 13x + 3$			
f	$6x^2 - 17x + 5$			

2 Use your tabled results to factorise each of the quadratics **a** to **f**.

From the investigation you should have learnt the process for factorising a quadratic trinomial by splitting the middle term.

Example 18   🔊 **Self Tutor**

Factorise $3x^2 + 17x + 10$.

For $3x^2 + 17x + 10$, $3 \times 10 = 30$

We need to find two factors of 30 which have a sum of 17.

These are 2 and 15.

$$\therefore \quad 3x^2 + 17x + 10 = 3x^2 + 2x + 15x + 10$$
$$= x(3x + 2) + 5(3x + 2)$$
$$= (3x + 2)(x + 5)$$

Example 19   🔊 **Self Tutor**

Factorise $6x^2 - 11x - 10$.

For $6x^2 - 11x - 10$, $6 \times -10 = -60$

We need to find two factors of -60 which have a sum of -11.

These are -15 and 4.

$$\therefore \quad 6x^2 - 11x - 10 = 6x^2 - 15x + 4x - 10$$
$$= 3x(2x - 5) + 2(2x - 5)$$
$$= (2x - 5)(3x + 2)$$

As the product is -60, the two numbers must be opposite in sign with the larger one being negative.

EXERCISE 2G

1 Fully factorise:

a $2x^2 + 5x + 3$	**b** $2x^2 + 7x + 5$	**c** $7x^2 + 9x + 2$
d $3x^2 + 7x + 4$	**e** $3x^2 + 13x + 4$	**f** $3x^2 + 8x + 4$
g $8x^2 + 14x + 3$	**h** $21x^2 + 17x + 2$	**i** $6x^2 + 5x + 1$
j $6x^2 + 19x + 3$	**k** $10x^2 + 17x + 3$	**l** $14x^2 + 37x + 5$

2 Fully factorise:

a $2x^2 - 9x - 5$	**b** $3x^2 + 5x - 2$	**c** $3x^2 - 5x - 2$
d $2x^2 + 3x - 2$	**e** $2x^2 + 3x - 5$	**f** $5x^2 - 14x - 3$
g $5x^2 - 8x + 3$	**h** $11x^2 - 9x - 2$	**i** $3x^2 - 7x - 6$
j $2x^2 - 3x - 9$	**k** $3x^2 - 17x + 10$	**l** $5x^2 - 13x - 6$
m $3x^2 + 10x - 8$	**n** $2x^2 + 17x - 9$	**o** $2x^2 + 9x - 18$
p $2x^2 + 11x - 21$	**q** $15x^2 + x - 2$	**r** $21x^2 - 62x - 3$

3 Fully factorise:

a $15x^2 + 19x + 6$ b $15x^2 + x - 6$ c $15x^2 - x - 6$

d $30x^2 - 38x + 12$ e $18x^2 - 12x + 2$ f $48x^2 + 72x + 27$

g $16x^2 + 12x + 2$ h $16x^2 + 4x - 2$ i $40x^2 - 10x - 5$

j $32x^2 - 24x + 4$ k $25x^2 + 25x + 6$ l $25x^2 - 25x + 6$

m $25x^2 - 10x - 8$ n $25x^2 - 149x - 6$ o $36x^2 + 24x - 5$

p $36x^2 + 11x - 5$ q $36x^2 + 9x - 10$ r $36x^2 + 52x - 3$

H MISCELLANEOUS FACTORISATION

The following flowchart may prove useful:

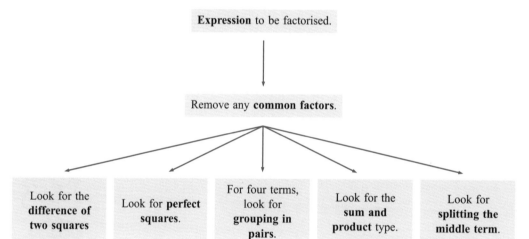

EXERCISE 2H

1 Fully factorise:

a $3x^2 + 2x$ b $x^2 - 81$ c $2p^2 + 8$

d $3b^2 - 75$ e $2x^2 - 32$ f $n^4 - 4n^2$

g $x^2 - 8x - 9$ h $d^2 + 6d - 7$ i $x^2 + 8x - 9$

j $4t + 8t^2$ k $3x^2 - 108$ l $2g^2 - 12g - 110$

m $4a^2 - 9d^2$ n $5a^2 - 5a - 10$ o $2c^2 - 8c + 6$

p $x^4 - x^2$ q $d^4 + 2d^3 - 3d^2$ r $x^3 + 4x^2 + 4x$

2 Find the pattern in the following expressions and hence factorise:

a $x^2 - 6x + 9$ b $x^2 - 121$ c $x^2 - 2x + 1$

d $y^2 + 10y + 25$ e $x^2 + 22x + 121$ f $x^2 - 2xy + y^2$

g $1 - x^2$ h $25y^2 - 1$ i $49y^2 - 36z^2$

j $4d^2 + 28d + 49$ k $4ab^2 - ac^2$ l $2\pi R^2 - 2\pi r^2$

3 Fully factorise:

    a $ab + ac - 2a$ **b** $a^2b^2 - 2ab$ **c** $18x - 2x^3$

    d $x^2 + 14x + 49$ **e** $4a^3 - 4ab^2$ **f** $x^3y - 4xy$

    g $4x^4 - 4x^2$ **h** $(x-2)y - (x-2)z$ **i** $(x+1)a + (x+1)b$

    j $(x-y)a + (x-y)$ **k** $x(x+2) + 3(x+2)$ **l** $x^3 + x^2 + x + 1$

4 Factorise completely:

    a $7x - 35y$ **b** $2g^2 - 8$ **c** $-5x^2 - 10x$

    d $m^2 + 3mp$ **e** $a^2 + 8a + 15$ **f** $m^2 - 6m + 9$

    g $5x^2 + 5xy - 5x^2y$ **h** $xy + 2x + 2y + 4$ **i** $y^2 + 5y - 9y - 45$

    j $2x^2 + 10x + x + 5$ **k** $3y^2 - 147$ **l** $3p^2 - 3q^2$

    m $4c^2 - 1$ **n** $3x^2 + 3x - 36$ **o** $2bx - 6b + 10x - 30$

5 Fully factorise:

    a $12 - 11x - x^2$ **b** $-2x^2 - 6 + 8x$ **c** $14 - x^2 - 5x$

    d $4x^2 - 2x^3 - 2x$ **e** $(a+b)^2 - 9$ **f** $(x+2)^2 - 4$

6 Fully factorise:

    a $2x^2 + 17x + 21$ **b** $2x^2 + 11x + 15$ **c** $4x^2 + 12x + 5$

    d $12x^2 + 13x + 3$ **e** $6x^2 - 29x - 5$ **f** $16x^2 + 8x + 1$

    g $25x^2 - 16$ **h** $12x^2 - 71x - 6$ **i** $12x^2 - 38x + 6$

    j $9x^2 + 3x - 12$ **k** $12x^2 - 29x + 15$ **l** $36x^2 + 3x - 14$

REVIEW SET 2A

1 Expand and simplify:

    a $3x(x-2)$ **b** $-3x(x-5)$ **c** $(x+3)(x-8)$

    d $(x+3)^2$ **e** $-(x-2)^2$ **f** $(4x+1)(4x-1)$

    g $(4x+1)(3x-2)$ **h** $(x+3)(x-1) - (3-x)(x+4)$

2 Fully factorise:

    a $3x^2 - 12x$ **b** $15x - 6x^2$ **c** $2x^2 - 98$

    d $x^2 - 6x + 9$ **e** $a^2 + 2ab + b^2$ **f** $(x+2)^2 - 3(x+2)$

3 Fully factorise:

    a $5x - 5 + xy - y$ **b** $3x + 7 + 6bx + 14b$

4 Fully factorise:

    a $x^2 + 10x + 21$ **b** $x^2 + 4x - 21$ **c** $x^2 - 4x - 21$

    d $6 - 5x + x^2$ **e** $4x^2 - 8x - 12$ **f** $-x^2 - 13x - 36$

5 Fully factorise:

    a $8x^2 + 22x + 15$ **b** $12x^2 - 20x + 3$ **c** $12x^2 - 7x - 10$

6 **a** Write down the first three rows of Pascal's Triangle.

b Write down the binomial expansion of:

    i $(a+b)^3$ **ii** $(2x+5)^3$ **iii** $\left(x+\dfrac{1}{x}\right)^3$

7 **a** Show that $\left(n+\frac{1}{2}\right)^2 = n(n+1) + \frac{1}{4}$.

b Use **a** to find: **i** $\left(3\frac{1}{2}\right)^2$ **ii** $\left(10\frac{1}{2}\right)^2$.

c Write a short paragraph which explains how to square numbers like those in **bi** and **ii** mentally.

REVIEW SET 2B

1 Expand and simplify:

  a $(3x-y)^2$ **b** $-2a(b-a)$ **c** $(4x+1)(1-3x)$

  d $(2x+7)^2$ **e** $-(5-x)^2$ **f** $(1-7x)(1+7x)$

  g $(4x+1)(5x-4)$ **h** $2(x+3)(x+2) - 3(x+2)(x-1)$

2 Fully factorise:

  a $5ab + 10b^2$ **b** $3x^2 - 12$ **c** $x^2 + 8x + 16$

  d $2a^2 - 4ab + 2b^2$ **e** $3x^3 + 6x^2 - 9x$ **f** $(x-3)^2 - 3x + 9$

3 Fully factorise: $2xy - z - 2xz + y$

4 Fully factorise:

  a $x^2 + 12x + 35$ **b** $x^2 + 2x - 35$ **c** $x^2 - 12x + 35$

  d $2x^2 - 4x - 70$ **e** $30 - 11x + x^2$ **f** $-x^2 + 12x - 20$

5 Fully factorise:

  a $12x^2 + 5x - 2$ **b** $12x^2 + x - 6$ **c** $24x^2 + 28x - 12$

6 Use the binomial expansion $(a+b)^4 = a^4 + 4a^3b + 6a^2b^2 + 4ab^3 + b^4$ to expand and simplify:

  a $(2x+1)^4$ **b** $(x-3)^4$ **c** $\left(x-\dfrac{1}{x}\right)^4$

7 Show that the difference between an integer and its cube is always the product of three consecutive integers.

For example: $3^3 - 3 = 24 = 2 \times 3 \times 4$

              $4^3 - 4 = 60 = 3 \times 4 \times 5.$

Chapter 3

Radicals and surds

Contents:

In this chapter we consider **radicals**, which are numbers that are written using the **radical sign** $\sqrt{}$. Radicals are often referred to as **surds**, though this is not strictly correct because a surd is actually a radical that is *irrational*.

Radicals and surds occur frequently in mathematics, often as solutions to equations involving squared terms. We will see a typical example of this in **Chapter 4** when we study Pythagoras' theorem.

SQUARE ROOTS

The **square root of** a, written $\sqrt{a}$, is the *positive* solution of the equation $x^2 = a$.

$\sqrt{a}$ is the *positive* number which obeys the rule $\sqrt{a} \times \sqrt{a} = a$.

For example, $\sqrt{2} \times \sqrt{2} = 2$, $\sqrt{3} \times \sqrt{3} = 3$, $\sqrt{4} \times \sqrt{4} = 4$, and so on.

We know that the square of any real number is non-negative. This means that, in the context of real numbers,

$$\sqrt{a} \text{ has meaning for } a \geqslant 0 \text{ only.}$$

HIGHER ROOTS

In this course we will concentrate mainly on square roots, but it is important to understand that other radicals exist. For example:

The **cube root of** a, written $\sqrt[3]{a}$, satisfies the rule $\left(\sqrt[3]{a}\right)^3 = a$.

If $a > 0$ then $\sqrt[3]{a} > 0$.

If $a < 0$ then $\sqrt[3]{a} < 0$.

We can also define higher roots in a similar way.

RATIONAL AND IRRATIONAL RADICALS

Some radicals are rational, but most are irrational and referred to as **surds**. Remember that:

An **irrational number** is a number which cannot be written in the form $\dfrac{p}{q}$, where p and q are integers with $q \neq 0$.

Examples of rational radicals include: $\quad \sqrt{1} = \sqrt{1^2} = 1 \quad$ or $\quad \frac{1}{1}$

$$\sqrt{4} = \sqrt{2^2} = 2 \quad \text{or} \quad \tfrac{2}{1}$$

$$\sqrt{\tfrac{1}{4}} = \sqrt{\left(\tfrac{1}{2}\right)^2} = \tfrac{1}{2}$$

Two examples of surds are $\quad \sqrt{2} \approx 1.414\,214$

and $\quad \sqrt{3} \approx 1.732\,051$.

HISTORICAL NOTE

The name **surd** and the **radical** sign $\sqrt{}$ both had a rather absurd past. Many centuries after Pythagoras, when the Golden Age of the Greeks was past, the writings of the Greeks were preserved, translated, and extended by Arab mathematicians.

The Arabs thought of a square number as growing out of its roots. The roots had to be extracted. The Latin word for "root" is **radix**, from which we get the words **radical** and radish! The printed symbol for radix was first **R**, then **r**, which was copied by hand as $\sqrt{}$.

The word **surd** actually came about because of an error of translation by the Arab mathematician Al-Khwarizmi in the 9th century AD. The Greek word **a-logos** means "irrational" but also means "deaf". So, the Greek **a-logos** was interpreted as "deaf" which in Latin is **surdus**. Hence to this day, **irrational radicals** like $\sqrt{2}$ are called **surds**.

A   BASIC OPERATIONS WITH RADICALS

In the following sections we discuss some properties of radicals. These properties are of course also properties of surds since surds are just irrational radicals.

Example 1   ◀)) **Self Tutor**

Simplify: **a** $(\sqrt{5})^2$

   b $\left(\dfrac{1}{\sqrt{5}}\right)^2$

a $(\sqrt{5})^2$
$= \sqrt{5} \times \sqrt{5}$
$= 5$

b $\left(\dfrac{1}{\sqrt{5}}\right)^2$
$= \dfrac{1}{\sqrt{5}} \times \dfrac{1}{\sqrt{5}}$
$= \frac{1}{5}$

Example 2   ◀)) **Self Tutor**

Simplify:

   a $(2\sqrt{5})^3$ **b** $-2\sqrt{5} \times 3\sqrt{5}$

a $(2\sqrt{5})^3$
$= 2\sqrt{5} \times 2\sqrt{5} \times 2\sqrt{5}$
$= 2 \times 2 \times 2 \times \sqrt{5} \times \sqrt{5} \times \sqrt{5}$
$= 8 \times 5 \times \sqrt{5}$
$= 40\sqrt{5}$

b $-2\sqrt{5} \times 3\sqrt{5}$
$= -2 \times 3 \times \sqrt{5} \times \sqrt{5}$
$= -6 \times 5$
$= -30$

EXERCISE 3A.1

1 Simplify:

a $(\sqrt{7})^2$ b $(\sqrt{13})^2$ c $(\sqrt{15})^2$ d $(\sqrt{24})^2$

e $\left(\dfrac{1}{\sqrt{3}}\right)^2$ f $\left(\dfrac{1}{\sqrt{11}}\right)^2$ g $\left(\dfrac{1}{\sqrt{17}}\right)^2$ h $\left(\dfrac{1}{\sqrt{23}}\right)^2$

2 Simplify:

a $(\sqrt[3]{2})^3$ b $(\sqrt[3]{-5})^3$ c $\left(\dfrac{1}{\sqrt[3]{5}}\right)^3$

3 Simplify:

a $3\sqrt{2} \times 4\sqrt{2}$ b $-2\sqrt{3} \times 5\sqrt{3}$ c $3\sqrt{5} \times (-2\sqrt{5})$

d $-2\sqrt{2} \times (-3\sqrt{2})$ e $(3\sqrt{2})^2$ f $(3\sqrt{2})^3$

g $(2\sqrt{3})^2$ h $(2\sqrt{3})^3$ i $(2\sqrt{2})^4$

ADDING AND SUBTRACTING RADICALS

'Like radicals' can be added and subtracted in the same way as 'like terms' in algebra.

Consider $2\sqrt{3} + 4\sqrt{3}$, which has the same form as $2x + 4x$.

If we interpret this as 2 'lots' of $\sqrt{3}$ plus 4 'lots' of $\sqrt{3}$, we have 6 'lots' of $\sqrt{3}$.

So, $2\sqrt{3} + 4\sqrt{3} = 6\sqrt{3}$, and we can compare this with $2x + 4x = 6x$.

Example 3	◀) **Self Tutor**

Simplify:

a $3\sqrt{2} + 4\sqrt{2}$ b $5\sqrt{3} - 6\sqrt{3}$

a $3\sqrt{2} + 4\sqrt{2}$
 $= 7\sqrt{2}$

b $5\sqrt{3} - 6\sqrt{3}$
 $= -1\sqrt{3}$
 $= -\sqrt{3}$

{Compare: $3x + 4x = 7x$}   {Compare: $5x - 6x = -x$}

EXERCISE 3A.2

1 Simplify:

a $\sqrt{2} + \sqrt{2}$ b $\sqrt{2} - \sqrt{2}$ c $3\sqrt{2} - 2\sqrt{2}$

d $2\sqrt{3} - \sqrt{3}$ e $5\sqrt{7} + 2\sqrt{7}$ f $3\sqrt{5} - 6\sqrt{5}$

g $3\sqrt{2} + 4\sqrt{2} - \sqrt{2}$ h $6\sqrt{2} - 9\sqrt{2}$ i $\sqrt{5} + 7\sqrt{5}$

j $3\sqrt{2} - 5\sqrt{2} - \sqrt{2}$ k $3\sqrt{3} - \sqrt{3} + 2\sqrt{3}$ l $3\sqrt{5} + 7\sqrt{5} - 10$

2 Simplify:

a $3\sqrt{2} + 2\sqrt{3} - \sqrt{2} + 5\sqrt{3}$

b $7\sqrt{2} - 4\sqrt{3} - 2\sqrt{2} + 3\sqrt{3}$

c $-6\sqrt{2} - 2\sqrt{3} - \sqrt{2} + 6\sqrt{3}$

d $2\sqrt{5} + 4\sqrt{2} + 9\sqrt{5} - 9\sqrt{2}$

e $3\sqrt{2} - 5\sqrt{7} - \sqrt{2} - 5\sqrt{7}$

f $3\sqrt{2} + 4\sqrt{11} + 6 - \sqrt{2} - \sqrt{11} - 3$

g $6\sqrt{6} - 2\sqrt{2} - \sqrt{2} - 5\sqrt{6} + 4$

h $5\sqrt{3} - 6\sqrt{7} - 5 + 4\sqrt{3} + \sqrt{7} - 8$

B   PROPERTIES OF RADICALS

INVESTIGATION 1   PROPERTIES OF RADICALS

Notice that $\sqrt{4 \times 9} = \sqrt{36} = 6$ and $\sqrt{4} \times \sqrt{9} = 2 \times 3 = 6$
which suggests that $\sqrt{4} \times \sqrt{9} = \sqrt{4 \times 9}$.

Also, $\sqrt{\dfrac{36}{4}} = \sqrt{9} = 3$ and $\dfrac{\sqrt{36}}{\sqrt{4}} = \dfrac{6}{2} = 3$

which suggests that $\dfrac{\sqrt{36}}{\sqrt{4}} = \sqrt{\dfrac{36}{4}}$.

What to do:

Test the following possible properties or rules for radicals by substituting different values of a and b. Use your calculator to evaluate the results.

1 $\sqrt{a} \times \sqrt{b} = \sqrt{ab}$ for all $a \geqslant 0$ and $b \geqslant 0$.

2 $\sqrt{\dfrac{a}{b}} = \dfrac{\sqrt{a}}{\sqrt{b}}$ for all $a \geqslant 0$ and $b > 0$.

3 $\sqrt{a + b} = \sqrt{a} + \sqrt{b}$ for all $a \geqslant 0$ and $b \geqslant 0$.

4 $\sqrt{a - b} = \sqrt{a} - \sqrt{b}$ for all $a \geqslant 0$ and $b \geqslant 0$.

From the investigation, you should have discovered the following properties of radicals:

- $\sqrt{a} \times \sqrt{b} = \sqrt{a \times b}$ for $a \geqslant 0$, $b \geqslant 0$

- $\dfrac{\sqrt{a}}{\sqrt{b}} = \sqrt{\dfrac{a}{b}}$ for $a \geqslant 0$, $b > 0$

Example 4	◀) Self Tutor

Write in simplest form:

a $\sqrt{3} \times \sqrt{2}$ b $2\sqrt{5} \times 3\sqrt{2}$

$$\begin{aligned}
\textbf{a} \quad & \sqrt{3} \times \sqrt{2} \\
= & \sqrt{3 \times 2} \\
= & \sqrt{6}
\end{aligned}$$

$$\begin{aligned}
\textbf{b} \quad & 2\sqrt{5} \times 3\sqrt{2} \\
= & 2 \times 3 \times \sqrt{5} \times \sqrt{2} \\
= & 6 \times \sqrt{5 \times 2} \\
= & 6\sqrt{10}
\end{aligned}$$

Example 5　　　　　　　　　　　　　　　　　　🔊 **Self Tutor**

Simplify:　　**a** $\dfrac{\sqrt{32}}{\sqrt{2}}$ 　　 **b** $\dfrac{\sqrt{12}}{2\sqrt{3}}$

$$\begin{aligned}
\textbf{a} \quad & \frac{\sqrt{32}}{\sqrt{2}} \\
= & \sqrt{\frac{32}{2}} \\
= & \sqrt{16} \\
= & 4
\end{aligned}$$

$$\begin{aligned}
\textbf{b} \quad & \frac{\sqrt{12}}{2\sqrt{3}} \\
= & \tfrac{1}{2}\sqrt{\frac{12}{3}} \quad \{\text{using } \frac{\sqrt{a}}{\sqrt{b}} = \sqrt{\frac{a}{b}}\} \\
= & \tfrac{1}{2}\sqrt{4} \\
= & \tfrac{1}{2} \times 2 \\
= & 1
\end{aligned}$$

Example 6　　　　　　　　　　　　🔊 **Self Tutor**

Write $\sqrt{32}$ in the form $k\sqrt{2}$.

$$\begin{aligned}
& \sqrt{32} \\
= & \sqrt{16 \times 2} \\
= & \sqrt{16} \times \sqrt{2} \quad \{\text{using } \sqrt{ab} = \sqrt{a} \times \sqrt{b}\} \\
= & 4\sqrt{2}
\end{aligned}$$

EXERCISE 3B.1

1 Simplify:

  a $\sqrt{2} \times \sqrt{5}$ 　　　　　 **b** $\sqrt{3} \times \sqrt{7}$ 　　　　　 **c** $\sqrt{3} \times \sqrt{11}$

  d $\sqrt{7} \times \sqrt{7}$ 　　　　　 **e** $\sqrt{3} \times 2\sqrt{3}$ 　　　　　 **f** $2\sqrt{2} \times \sqrt{5}$

  g $3\sqrt{3} \times 2\sqrt{2}$ 　　　　 **h** $2\sqrt{3} \times 3\sqrt{5}$ 　　　　 **i** $\sqrt{2} \times \sqrt{3} \times \sqrt{5}$

  j $\sqrt{3} \times \sqrt{2} \times 2\sqrt{2}$ 　　**k** $-3\sqrt{2} \times (\sqrt{2})^3$ 　　　 **l** $(3\sqrt{2})^3 \times (\sqrt{3})^3$

2 Simplify:

  a $\dfrac{\sqrt{8}}{\sqrt{2}}$ 　　　　 **b** $\dfrac{\sqrt{2}}{\sqrt{8}}$ 　　　　 **c** $\dfrac{\sqrt{18}}{\sqrt{2}}$ 　　　　 **d** $\dfrac{\sqrt{2}}{\sqrt{18}}$

  e $\dfrac{\sqrt{20}}{\sqrt{5}}$ 　　　 **f** $\dfrac{\sqrt{5}}{\sqrt{20}}$ 　　　 **g** $\dfrac{\sqrt{27}}{\sqrt{3}}$ 　　　 **h** $\dfrac{\sqrt{18}}{\sqrt{3}}$

  i $\dfrac{\sqrt{3}}{\sqrt{30}}$ 　　　 **j** $\dfrac{\sqrt{50}}{\sqrt{2}}$ 　　　 **k** $\dfrac{2\sqrt{6}}{\sqrt{24}}$ 　　　 **l** $\dfrac{5\sqrt{75}}{\sqrt{3}}$

3 Write the following in the form $k\sqrt{2}$:

   a $\sqrt{8}$ **b** $\sqrt{18}$ **c** $\sqrt{50}$ **d** $\sqrt{98}$

   e $\sqrt{200}$ **f** $\sqrt{288}$ **g** $\sqrt{20\,000}$ **h** $\sqrt{\frac{1}{2}}$

4 Write the following in the form $k\sqrt{3}$:

   a $\sqrt{12}$ **b** $\sqrt{27}$ **c** $\sqrt{75}$ **d** $\sqrt{\frac{1}{3}}$

5 Write the following in the form $k\sqrt{5}$:

   a $\sqrt{20}$ **b** $\sqrt{45}$ **c** $\sqrt{125}$ **d** $\sqrt{\frac{1}{5}}$

6 **a** Find:

      i $\sqrt{16}+\sqrt{9}$ **ii** $\sqrt{16+9}$ **iii** $\sqrt{25}-\sqrt{9}$ **iv** $\sqrt{25-9}$

   b **i** Does $\sqrt{16+9}=\sqrt{16}+\sqrt{9}$?   **ii** Does $\sqrt{25-9}=\sqrt{25}-\sqrt{9}$?

   c Copy and complete: In general $\sqrt{a+b}\neq$ ......   and $\sqrt{a-b}\neq$ ......

SIMPLEST RADICAL FORM

A radical is in **simplest form** when the number under the radical sign is the smallest integer possible.

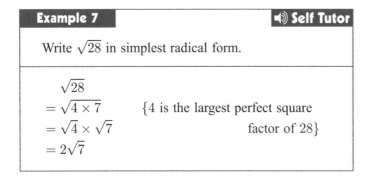

Example 7 ◀ Self Tutor

Write $\sqrt{28}$ in simplest radical form.

$\sqrt{28}$
$=\sqrt{4\times7}$ {4 is the largest perfect square
$=\sqrt{4}\times\sqrt{7}$ factor of 28}
$=2\sqrt{7}$

Look for the largest perfect square factor.

EXERCISE 3B.2

1 Write the following in simplest radical form:

   a $\sqrt{24}$ **b** $\sqrt{50}$ **c** $\sqrt{54}$ **d** $\sqrt{40}$

   e $\sqrt{56}$ **f** $\sqrt{63}$ **g** $\sqrt{52}$ **h** $\sqrt{44}$

   i $\sqrt{60}$ **j** $\sqrt{90}$ **k** $\sqrt{96}$ **l** $\sqrt{68}$

   m $\sqrt{175}$ **n** $\sqrt{162}$ **o** $\sqrt{128}$ **p** $\sqrt{700}$

2 Write the following in simplest radical form:

   a $\sqrt{\frac{5}{9}}$ **b** $\sqrt{\frac{18}{4}}$ **c** $\sqrt{\frac{12}{16}}$ **d** $\sqrt{\frac{75}{36}}$

C   MULTIPLICATION OF RADICALS

The rules for expanding brackets involving radicals are identical to those for ordinary algebra.

We can thus use:

$$a(b+c) = ab + ac$$
$$(a+b)(c+d) = ac + ad + bc + bd$$
$$(a+b)^2 = a^2 + 2ab + b^2$$
$$(a-b)^2 = a^2 - 2ab + b^2$$
$$(a+b)(a-b) = a^2 - b^2$$

Example 8   ◀ᴾ) Self Tutor

Expand and simplify:

a $\sqrt{2}(\sqrt{2} + \sqrt{3})$

b $\sqrt{3}(6 - 2\sqrt{3})$

a $\sqrt{2}(\sqrt{2} + \sqrt{3})$
$= \sqrt{2} \times \sqrt{2} + \sqrt{2} \times \sqrt{3}$
$= 2 + \sqrt{6}$

b $\sqrt{3}(6 - 2\sqrt{3})$
$= (\sqrt{3})(6 + -2\sqrt{3})$
$= (\sqrt{3})(6) + (\sqrt{3})(-2\sqrt{3})$
$= 6\sqrt{3} + -6$
$= 6\sqrt{3} - 6$

Example 9   ◀ᴾ) Self Tutor

Expand and simplify:

a $-\sqrt{2}(\sqrt{2} + 3)$

b $-\sqrt{3}(7 - 2\sqrt{3})$

a $-\sqrt{2}(\sqrt{2} + 3)$
$= -\sqrt{2} \times \sqrt{2} + -\sqrt{2} \times 3$
$= -2 - 3\sqrt{2}$

b $-\sqrt{3}(7 - 2\sqrt{3})$
$= (-\sqrt{3})(7 - 2\sqrt{3})$
$= (-\sqrt{3})(7) + (-\sqrt{3})(-2\sqrt{3})$
$= -7\sqrt{3} + 6$

Example 10   ◀ᴾ) Self Tutor

Expand and simplify: $(3 - \sqrt{2})(4 + 2\sqrt{2})$

$(3 - \sqrt{2})(4 + 2\sqrt{2})$
$= (3 - \sqrt{2})(4) + (3 - \sqrt{2})(2\sqrt{2})$
$= 12 - 4\sqrt{2} + 6\sqrt{2} - 4$
$= 8 + 2\sqrt{2}$

Example 11   ◀⅃) **Self Tutor**

Expand and simplify:

   a $(\sqrt{3}+2)^2$ b $(\sqrt{3}-\sqrt{7})^2$

  a $(\sqrt{3}+2)^2$ b $(\sqrt{3}-\sqrt{7})^2$

      $= (\sqrt{3})^2 \; + \; 2 \times \sqrt{3} \times 2 \; + \; 2^2$ $= (\sqrt{3})^2 \; - \; 2 \times \sqrt{3} \times \sqrt{7} \; + \; (\sqrt{7})^2$

      $= 3 + 4\sqrt{3} + 4$ $= 3 - 2\sqrt{21} + 7$

      $= 7 + 4\sqrt{3}$ $= 10 - 2\sqrt{21}$

Example 12   ◀⅃) **Self Tutor**

Expand and simplify:

  a $(3+\sqrt{2})(3-\sqrt{2})$ b $(2\sqrt{3}-5)(2\sqrt{3}+5)$

  a $(3+\sqrt{2})(3-\sqrt{2})$ b $(2\sqrt{3}-5)(2\sqrt{3}+5)$

      $= 3^2 - (\sqrt{2})^2$ $= (2\sqrt{3})^2 - 5^2$

      $= 9 - 2$ $= (4 \times 3) - 25$

      $= 7$ $= 12 - 25$

                               $= -13$

Did you notice that these answers are **integers**?

EXERCISE 3C

1 Expand and simplify:

    a $\sqrt{2}(\sqrt{5}+\sqrt{2})$ b $\sqrt{2}(3-\sqrt{2})$ c $\sqrt{3}(\sqrt{3}+1)$

    d $\sqrt{3}(1-\sqrt{3})$ e $\sqrt{7}(7-\sqrt{7})$ f $\sqrt{5}(2-\sqrt{5})$

    g $\sqrt{11}(2\sqrt{11}-1)$ h $\sqrt{6}(1-2\sqrt{6})$ i $\sqrt{3}(\sqrt{3}+\sqrt{2}-1)$

    j $2\sqrt{3}(\sqrt{3}-\sqrt{5})$ k $2\sqrt{5}(3-\sqrt{5})$ l $3\sqrt{5}(2\sqrt{5}+\sqrt{2})$

2 Expand and simplify:

    a $-\sqrt{2}(3-\sqrt{2})$ b $-\sqrt{2}(\sqrt{2}+\sqrt{3})$ c $-\sqrt{2}(4-\sqrt{2})$

    d $-\sqrt{3}(1+\sqrt{3})$ e $-\sqrt{3}(\sqrt{3}+2)$ f $-\sqrt{5}(2+\sqrt{5})$

    g $-(\sqrt{2}+3)$ h $-\sqrt{5}(\sqrt{5}-4)$ i $-(3-\sqrt{7})$

    j $-\sqrt{11}(2-\sqrt{11})$ k $-(\sqrt{3}-\sqrt{7})$ l $-2\sqrt{2}(1-\sqrt{2})$

    m $-3\sqrt{3}(5-\sqrt{3})$ n $-7\sqrt{2}(\sqrt{2}+\sqrt{6})$ o $(-\sqrt{2})^3(3-\sqrt{2})$

3 Expand and simplify:

    a $(1+\sqrt{2})(2+\sqrt{2})$ b $(2+\sqrt{3})(2+\sqrt{3})$

    c $(\sqrt{3}+2)(\sqrt{3}-1)$ d $(4-\sqrt{2})(3+\sqrt{2})$

    e $(1+\sqrt{3})(1-\sqrt{3})$ f $(5+\sqrt{7})(2-\sqrt{7})$

    g $(\sqrt{5}+2)(\sqrt{5}-3)$ **h** $(\sqrt{7}-\sqrt{3})(\sqrt{7}+\sqrt{3})$

    i $(2\sqrt{2}+\sqrt{3})(2\sqrt{2}-\sqrt{3})$ **j** $(4-\sqrt{2})(3-\sqrt{2})$

4 Expand and simplify:

    a $(1+\sqrt{2})^2$ **b** $(2-\sqrt{3})^2$ **c** $(\sqrt{3}+2)^2$

    d $(1+\sqrt{5})^2$ **e** $(\sqrt{2}-\sqrt{3})^2$ **f** $(5-\sqrt{2})^2$

    g $(\sqrt{2}+\sqrt{7})^2$ **h** $(4-\sqrt{6})^2$ **i** $(\sqrt{6}-\sqrt{2})^2$

    j $(\sqrt{5}+2\sqrt{2})^2$ **k** $(\sqrt{5}-2\sqrt{2})^2$ **l** $(6+\sqrt{8})^2$

    m $(5\sqrt{2}-1)^2$ **n** $(3-2\sqrt{2})^2$ **o** $(1+3\sqrt{2})^2$

5 Expand and simplify:

    a $(4+\sqrt{3})(4-\sqrt{3})$ **b** $(5-\sqrt{2})(5+\sqrt{2})$ **c** $(\sqrt{5}-2)(\sqrt{5}+2)$

    d $(\sqrt{7}+4)(\sqrt{7}-4)$ **e** $(3\sqrt{2}+2)(3\sqrt{2}-2)$ **f** $(2\sqrt{5}-1)(2\sqrt{5}+1)$

    g $(5-3\sqrt{3})(5+3\sqrt{3})$ **h** $(2-4\sqrt{2})(2+4\sqrt{2})$ **i** $(1+5\sqrt{7})(1-5\sqrt{7})$

6 Expand and simplify:

    a $(\sqrt{3}+\sqrt{2})(\sqrt{3}-\sqrt{2})$ **b** $(\sqrt{7}+\sqrt{11})(\sqrt{7}-\sqrt{11})$ **c** $(\sqrt{x}-\sqrt{y})(\sqrt{y}+\sqrt{x})$

D   DIVISION BY RADICALS

When an expression involves division by a radical, we can write the expression with an **integer denominator** which does **not** contain radicals.

If the denominator contains a simple radical such as $\sqrt{a}$ then we use the rule $\sqrt{a} \times \sqrt{a} = a$.

For example: $\dfrac{6}{\sqrt{3}}$ can be written as $\dfrac{6}{\sqrt{3}} \times \dfrac{\sqrt{3}}{\sqrt{3}}$ since we are really just multiplying the original fraction by 1.

$\dfrac{6}{\sqrt{3}} \times \dfrac{\sqrt{3}}{\sqrt{3}}$ then simplifies to $\dfrac{6\sqrt{3}}{3}$ or $2\sqrt{3}$.

Example 13   🔊 **Self Tutor**

Express with integer denominator: **a** $\dfrac{7}{\sqrt{3}}$ **b** $\dfrac{10}{\sqrt{5}}$ **c** $\dfrac{10}{2\sqrt{2}}$

a $\dfrac{7}{\sqrt{3}}$

    $= \dfrac{7}{\sqrt{3}} \times \dfrac{\sqrt{3}}{\sqrt{3}}$

    $= \dfrac{7\sqrt{3}}{3}$

b $\dfrac{10}{\sqrt{5}}$

    $= \dfrac{10}{\sqrt{5}} \times \dfrac{\sqrt{5}}{\sqrt{5}}$

    $= \tfrac{10}{5}\sqrt{5}$

    $= 2\sqrt{5}$

c $\dfrac{10}{2\sqrt{2}}$

    $= \dfrac{10}{2\sqrt{2}} \times \dfrac{\sqrt{2}}{\sqrt{2}}$

    $= \dfrac{10\sqrt{2}}{4}$

    $= \dfrac{5\sqrt{2}}{2}$

If the denominator contains a radical like $a + \sqrt{b}$ then we can remove it by multiplying both the numerator and the denominator by its **radical conjugate** $a - \sqrt{b}$.

> We are really multiplying by one, which does not change the value of the original expression.

Example 14 · Self Tutor

Express $\dfrac{1}{3 + \sqrt{2}}$ with integer denominator.

$$\frac{1}{3 + \sqrt{2}} = \left(\frac{1}{3 + \sqrt{2}}\right)\left(\frac{3 - \sqrt{2}}{3 - \sqrt{2}}\right)$$

$$= \frac{3 - \sqrt{2}}{3^2 - (\sqrt{2})^2} \quad \{\text{using} \ \ (a+b)(a-b) = a^2 - b^2\}$$

$$= \frac{3 - \sqrt{2}}{7}$$

Example 15 · Self Tutor

Write $\dfrac{\sqrt{3}}{1 - \sqrt{3}} - \dfrac{1 - 2\sqrt{3}}{1 + \sqrt{3}}$ in simplest form.

$$\frac{\sqrt{3}}{1 - \sqrt{3}} - \frac{1 - 2\sqrt{3}}{1 + \sqrt{3}} = \left(\frac{\sqrt{3}}{1 - \sqrt{3}}\right)\left(\frac{1 + \sqrt{3}}{1 + \sqrt{3}}\right) - \left(\frac{1 - 2\sqrt{3}}{1 + \sqrt{3}}\right)\left(\frac{1 - \sqrt{3}}{1 - \sqrt{3}}\right)$$

$$= \frac{\sqrt{3} + 3}{1 - 3} - \frac{1 - \sqrt{3} - 2\sqrt{3} + 6}{1 - 3}$$

$$= \frac{\sqrt{3} + 3}{-2} - \frac{7 - 3\sqrt{3}}{-2}$$

$$= \frac{\sqrt{3} + 3 - 7 + 3\sqrt{3}}{-2}$$

$$= \frac{-4 + 4\sqrt{3}}{-2}$$

$$= \frac{-4}{-2} + \frac{4\sqrt{3}}{-2}$$

$$= 2 - 2\sqrt{3}$$

EXERCISE 3D

1 Express with integer denominator:

a $\dfrac{1}{\sqrt{2}}$ b $\dfrac{2}{\sqrt{2}}$ c $\dfrac{4}{\sqrt{2}}$ d $\dfrac{10}{\sqrt{2}}$ e $\dfrac{\sqrt{7}}{\sqrt{2}}$

f $\dfrac{1}{\sqrt{3}}$ g $\dfrac{3}{\sqrt{3}}$ h $\dfrac{4}{\sqrt{3}}$ i $\dfrac{18}{\sqrt{3}}$ j $\dfrac{\sqrt{11}}{\sqrt{3}}$

k $\dfrac{1}{\sqrt{5}}$ l $\dfrac{3}{\sqrt{5}}$ m $\dfrac{\sqrt{3}}{\sqrt{5}}$ n $\dfrac{15}{\sqrt{5}}$ o $\dfrac{125}{\sqrt{5}}$

p $\dfrac{\sqrt{10}}{\sqrt{2}}$ q $\dfrac{1}{2\sqrt{3}}$ r $\dfrac{2\sqrt{2}}{\sqrt{3}}$ s $\dfrac{15}{2\sqrt{5}}$ t $\dfrac{1}{(\sqrt{2})^3}$

2 Express with integer denominator:

a $\dfrac{1}{3-\sqrt{5}}$ b $\dfrac{1}{2+\sqrt{3}}$ c $\dfrac{1}{4-\sqrt{11}}$ d $\dfrac{\sqrt{2}}{5+\sqrt{2}}$

e $\dfrac{\sqrt{3}}{3+\sqrt{3}}$ f $\dfrac{5}{2-3\sqrt{2}}$ g $\dfrac{-\sqrt{5}}{3+2\sqrt{5}}$ h $\dfrac{3-\sqrt{7}}{2+\sqrt{7}}$

3 Write in the form $a+b\sqrt{2}$ where $a,b \in \mathbb{Q}$:

a $\dfrac{4}{2-\sqrt{2}}$ b $\dfrac{-5}{1+\sqrt{2}}$ c $\dfrac{1-\sqrt{2}}{1+\sqrt{2}}$ d $\dfrac{\sqrt{2}-2}{3-\sqrt{2}}$

e $\dfrac{\frac{1}{\sqrt{2}}}{1-\frac{1}{\sqrt{2}}}$ f $\dfrac{1+\frac{1}{\sqrt{2}}}{1-\frac{1}{\sqrt{2}}}$ g $\dfrac{1}{1-\frac{\sqrt{2}}{3}}$ h $\dfrac{\frac{\sqrt{2}}{2}+1}{1-\frac{\sqrt{2}}{4}}$

4 Write in simplest form:

a $\dfrac{1+\sqrt{2}}{1-\sqrt{2}}+\dfrac{1-\sqrt{2}}{1+\sqrt{2}}$ b $\dfrac{2+\sqrt{5}}{2-\sqrt{5}}-\dfrac{\sqrt{5}}{2+\sqrt{5}}$ c $\dfrac{4-\sqrt{3}}{3-2\sqrt{2}}-\dfrac{2\sqrt{3}}{3+2\sqrt{2}}$

5 Find $\sqrt{\dfrac{3+2\sqrt{2}}{3-2\sqrt{2}}}$ giving your answer in the form $a+b\sqrt{2}$ where $a,b \in \mathbb{Q}$.

6 If $\dfrac{1}{\sqrt{3}}-\dfrac{1}{\sqrt{2}}=p,$ find $\sqrt{6}$ in terms of p.

7 If $x=\sqrt{5}-\sqrt{3},$ find x^2 and hence show that $x^4-16x^2+4=0$.
You have just shown that one solution of $x^4-16x^2+4=0$ is $x=\sqrt{5}-\sqrt{3}$.

8 If $u_n=\dfrac{1}{\sqrt{5}}\left[\left(\dfrac{1+\sqrt{5}}{2}\right)^n-\left(\dfrac{1-\sqrt{5}}{2}\right)^n\right],$ evaluate u_n for $n=1,2,3$ and 4.

E   **EQUALITY OF SURDS**

We have discussed how irrational radicals such as $\sqrt{2}$, $\sqrt{3}$, $\sqrt{5}$, and $\sqrt{6}$ are also known as **surds**. In this section we develop a theorem for the equality of surds which does not hold for rational radicals.

Remember that:

> **Irrational numbers** are numbers which cannot be written in the form $\dfrac{p}{q}$
>
> where p and q are integers, $q \neq 0$.

Following is the traditional proof that $\sqrt{2}$ is an irrational number. It is an example of a proof by contradiction.

Proof: Suppose that $\sqrt{2}$ is rational.

$\therefore$ $\sqrt{2} = \dfrac{p}{q}$ where p and q are integers with $q \neq 0$ and where all common factors

of p and q have been cancelled.

Now $2 = \dfrac{p^2}{q^2}$ {squaring both sides}

$\therefore$ $p^2 = 2q^2$

$\therefore$ p^2 is even   {as it has a factor of 2 and q^2 is an integer}

$\therefore$ p is even.   .....(1)

Hence we can write $p = 2k$ where k is some integer

$\therefore$ $(2k)^2 = 2q^2$

$\therefore$ $2q^2 = 4k^2$

$\therefore$ $q^2 = 2k^2$ where k^2 is an integer.

$\therefore$ q^2 is even and so q is even .....(2)

From (1) and (2) we have a contradiction to our supposition, since if both p and q are even then they share a common factor of 2.

$\therefore$ the supposition is false and hence $\sqrt{2}$ must be irrational.

An immediate consequence of $\sqrt{2}$ being irrational is:

If a, b, c and d are rational and $a + b\sqrt{2} = c + d\sqrt{2},$ then $a = c$ and $b = d$.

Proof: Suppose a, b, c and d are rational and assume that $b \neq d$.

So, $a + b\sqrt{2} = c + d\sqrt{2}$ gives

$a - c = (d - b)\sqrt{2}$ ......(1)

$\therefore$ $\dfrac{a - c}{d - b} = \sqrt{2}$ where the LHS exists as $b \neq d$.

However, this last result is impossible as the LHS is rational and the RHS is irrational.

Thus the assumption is false, and so $b = d$.

$\therefore$ in (1), $a - c = 0$ and so $a = c$.

THEOREM FOR EQUALITY OF SURDS

Suppose $\sqrt{k}$ is irrational and a, b, c and d are rational.

If $a + b\sqrt{k} = c + d\sqrt{k}$ then $a = c$ and $b = d$.

We can easily show by counter-example that this theorem does not hold for rational radicals.

For example, $1 + 4\sqrt{4} = 3 + 3\sqrt{4}$ but $1 \neq 3$ and $4 \neq 3$.

Example 16

Solve for x and y given that they are rational:

a $x + y\sqrt{2} = 5 - 6\sqrt{2}$

b $(x + y\sqrt{2})(3 - \sqrt{2}) = -2\sqrt{2}$

a $x + y\sqrt{2} = 5 - 6\sqrt{2}$

$\therefore \quad x = 5$

and $y = -6$

b $(x + y\sqrt{2})(3 - \sqrt{2}) = -2\sqrt{2}$

$\therefore \quad x + y\sqrt{2} = \dfrac{-2\sqrt{2}}{3 - \sqrt{2}}$

$= \left(\dfrac{-2\sqrt{2}}{3 - \sqrt{2}}\right)\left(\dfrac{3 + \sqrt{2}}{3 + \sqrt{2}}\right)$

$= \dfrac{-6\sqrt{2} - 4}{9 - 2} = \dfrac{-4 - 6\sqrt{2}}{7}$

$= -\tfrac{4}{7} - \tfrac{6}{7}\sqrt{2}$

$\therefore \quad x = -\tfrac{4}{7} \quad \text{and} \quad y = -\tfrac{6}{7}$

Example 17

Find rationals a and b such that $(a + 2\sqrt{2})(3 - \sqrt{2}) = 5 + b\sqrt{2}$.

$(a + 2\sqrt{2})(3 - \sqrt{2}) = 5 + b\sqrt{2}$

$\therefore \quad 3a - a\sqrt{2} + 6\sqrt{2} - 4 = 5 + b\sqrt{2}$

$\therefore \quad [3a - 4] + [6 - a]\sqrt{2} = 5 + b\sqrt{2}$

$\therefore \quad 3a - 4 = 5 \quad \text{and} \quad 6 - a = b$

$\therefore \quad 3a = 9$

$\therefore \quad a = 3 \quad \text{and hence} \quad b = 6 - 3 = 3$

EXERCISE 3E

1   Solve for x and y given that they are rational:

a $x + y\sqrt{2} = 3 + 2\sqrt{2}$

b $15 - 4\sqrt{2} = x + y\sqrt{2}$

c $-x + y\sqrt{2} = 11 - 3\sqrt{2}$

d $x + y\sqrt{2} = 6$

e $x + y\sqrt{2} = -3\sqrt{2}$

f $x + y\sqrt{2} = 0$

2   Solve for x and y given that they are rational:

a $(x + y\sqrt{2})(2 - \sqrt{2}) = 1 + \sqrt{2}$

b $(x + y\sqrt{2})(3 + \sqrt{2}) = 1$

c $(2 - 3\sqrt{2})(x + y\sqrt{2}) = \sqrt{2}$

d $(x + y\sqrt{2})(3 - \sqrt{2}) = -4\sqrt{2}$

3   Find rationals a and b such that:

a $(a + \sqrt{2})(2 - \sqrt{2}) = 4 - b\sqrt{2}$

b $(a + 3\sqrt{2})(3 - \sqrt{2}) = 6 + b\sqrt{2}$

c $(a + b\sqrt{2})^2 = 33 + 20\sqrt{2}$

d $(a + b\sqrt{2})^2 = 41 - 24\sqrt{2}$

4 Use the binomial expansion for $(a + b)^3$ to write the following in simplest radical form:

    a $(3 + \sqrt{7})^3$ **b** $(\sqrt{3} - \sqrt{2})^3$

5 Find $\sqrt{11 - 6\sqrt{2}}$.   (Reminder: $\sqrt{2}$ is never negative.)

6 **a** Find the exact value of $\sqrt{11 + 4\sqrt{6}}$ in the form $a\sqrt{2} + b\sqrt{3}$, $a, b \in \mathbb{Q}$.

    b Can $\sqrt{11 + 4\sqrt{6}}$ be written in the form $a + b\sqrt{6}$ where a and $b \in \mathbb{Q}$?

INVESTIGATION 2   CONTINUED SQUARE ROOTS

$$X = \sqrt{2 + \sqrt{2 + \sqrt{2 + \sqrt{2 + \sqrt{2 + \dots}}}}}$$ is an example of a **continued square root**.

Some continued square roots have actual values which are integers.

What to do:

1 Use your calculator to show that

$$\sqrt{2} \approx 1.41421$$

$$\sqrt{2 + \sqrt{2}} \approx 1.84776$$

$$\sqrt{2 + \sqrt{2 + \sqrt{2}}} \approx 1.96157.$$

2 Find the values, correct to 6 decimal places, of:

    a $\sqrt{2 + \sqrt{2 + \sqrt{2 + \sqrt{2}}}}$ **b** $\sqrt{2 + \sqrt{2 + \sqrt{2 + \sqrt{2 + \sqrt{2}}}}}$

3 Continue the process and hence predict the actual value of X.

4 Use algebra to find the exact value of X.
    Hint: Find X^2 in terms of X.

5 Work your algebraic solution in **4** backwards to find a continued square root whose actual value is 3.

SATISFYING PAPER PROPORTIONS

LINKS
click here

Areas of interaction:
Approaches to learning/Environments/Human ingenuity

REVIEW SET 3A

1 **a** Simplify $(3\sqrt{2})^2$.   **b** Simplify $-2\sqrt{3} \times 4\sqrt{3}$.

    c Simplify $3\sqrt{2} - \sqrt{8}$.   **d** Write $\sqrt{48}$ in simplest radical form.

2 Expand and simplify:

   a $2\sqrt{3}(4 - \sqrt{3})$ **b** $(3 - \sqrt{7})^2$ **c** $(2 - \sqrt{3})(2 + \sqrt{3})$

   d $(3 + 2\sqrt{5})(2 - \sqrt{5})$ **e** $(4 - \sqrt{2})(3 + 2\sqrt{2})$

3 Express with integer denominator:

   a $\dfrac{8}{\sqrt{2}}$ **b** $\dfrac{15}{\sqrt{3}}$ **c** $\dfrac{\sqrt{3}}{\sqrt{2}}$ **d** $\dfrac{5}{6 - \sqrt{3}}$

4 Write $\sqrt{\dfrac{1}{7}}$ in the form $k\sqrt{7}$.

5 Write in the form $a + b\sqrt{3}$ where $a, b \in \mathbb{Q}$:

   a $\dfrac{\frac{\sqrt{3}}{2} + 1}{1 - \frac{\sqrt{3}}{2}}$ **b** $\dfrac{2 + \sqrt{3}}{2 - \sqrt{3}} - \dfrac{2\sqrt{3}}{2 + \sqrt{3}}$

6 Find $x, y \in \mathbb{Q}$ such that $(3 + x\sqrt{5})(\sqrt{5} - y) = -13 + 5\sqrt{5}$.

7 Use the binomial expansion for $(a + b)^3$ to write $(5 + \sqrt{2})^3$ in the form $a + b\sqrt{2}$ where $a, b \in \mathbb{Z}$.

REVIEW SET 3B

1 Simplify:

   a $2\sqrt{3} \times 3\sqrt{5}$ **b** $(2\sqrt{5})^2$ **c** $5\sqrt{2} - 7\sqrt{2}$

   d $-\sqrt{2}(2 - \sqrt{2})$ **e** $(\sqrt{3})^4$ **f** $\sqrt{3} \times \sqrt{5} \times \sqrt{15}$

2 Write $\sqrt{75}$ in simplest radical form.

3 Expand and simplify:

   a $(5 - \sqrt{3})(5 + \sqrt{3})$ **b** $-(2 - \sqrt{5})^2$

   c $2\sqrt{3}(\sqrt{3} - 1) - 2\sqrt{3}$ **d** $(2\sqrt{2} - 5)(1 - \sqrt{2})$

4 Express with integer denominator:

   a $\dfrac{14}{\sqrt{2}}$ **b** $\dfrac{\sqrt{2}}{\sqrt{3}}$ **c** $\dfrac{\sqrt{2}}{3 + \sqrt{2}}$ **d** $\dfrac{-5}{4 - \sqrt{3}}$

5 Write in the form $a + b\sqrt{5}$ where $a, b \in \mathbb{Q}$:

   a $\dfrac{1 - \frac{1}{\sqrt{5}}}{2\sqrt{5} + \frac{1}{\sqrt{5}}}$ **b** $\dfrac{3 - \sqrt{5}}{3 + \sqrt{5}} - \dfrac{4}{3 - \sqrt{5}}$ **c** $\sqrt{\dfrac{3 - \sqrt{5}}{3 + \sqrt{5}}}$

6 Find $p, q \in \mathbb{Q}$ such that $(p + 3\sqrt{7})(5 + q\sqrt{7}) = 9\sqrt{7} - 53$.

7 Use the binomial expansion $(a + b)^4 = a^4 + 4a^3b + 6a^2b^2 + 4ab^3 + b^4$ to write $(\sqrt{2} + \sqrt{3})^4$ in simplest radical form.

Chapter 4

Pythagoras' theorem

Contents:

Right angles (90° angles) are used when constructing buildings and dividing areas of land into rectangular regions.

The ancient **Egyptians** used a rope with 12 equally spaced knots to form a triangle with sides in the ratio 3 : 4 : 5.

This triangle has a right angle between the sides of length 3 and 4 units.

In fact, this is the simplest right angled triangle with sides of integer length.

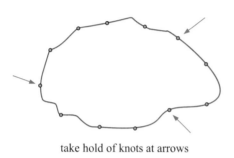

take hold of knots at arrows

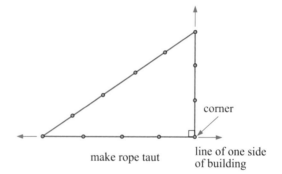

make rope taut

corner

line of one side of building

OPENING PROBLEM

Karrie is playing golf in the US Open. She hits a wayward tee shot on the opening hole. Her caddy paces out some distances and finds that Karrie has hit the ball 250 m, but 70 m from the centre of the fairway. A marker which is 150 m from the hole is further up the fairway as shown.

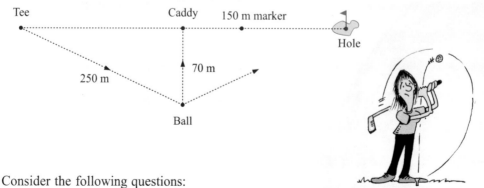

Consider the following questions:

a From where he stands on the fairway, how far is the caddy from the tee?

b If he knows the hole is 430 m long, how far is the caddy from the 150 m marker?

c How far does Karrie need to hit her ball with her second shot to reach the hole?

A   PYTHAGORAS' THEOREM

A **right angled triangle** is a triangle which has a right angle as one of its angles.

The side **opposite** the **right angle** is called the **hypotenuse** and is the **longest** side of the triangle.

The other two sides are called the **legs** of the triangle.

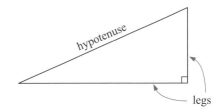

Around 500 BC, the Greek mathematician **Pythagoras** discovered a rule which connects the lengths of the sides of all right angled triangles. It is thought that he discovered the rule while studying tessellations of tiles on bathroom floors. Such patterns, like the one illustrated, were common on the walls and floors of bathrooms in ancient **Greece**.

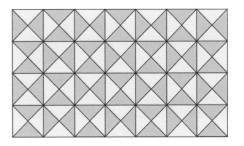

PYTHAGORAS' THEOREM

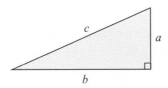

In a right angled triangle with hypotenuse c and legs a and b, $c^2 = a^2 + b^2$.

In geometric form, **Pythagoras' theorem** is:

In any right angled triangle, the area of the square on the hypotenuse is equal to the sum of the areas of the squares on the other two sides.

By looking at the tile pattern above, can you see how Pythagoras may have discovered the rule?

Hy-pot-en-use

GEOMETRY PACKAGE

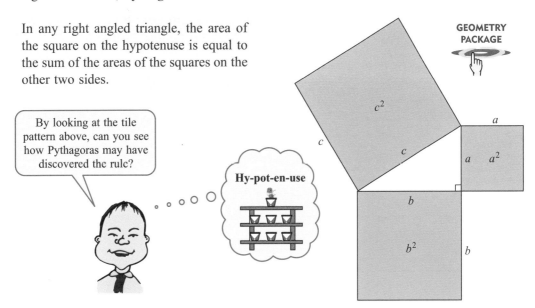

There are over 400 different proofs of Pythagoras' theorem. Here is one of them:

Proof:

On a square we draw 4 identical (congruent) right angled triangles, as illustrated. A smaller square is formed in the centre.

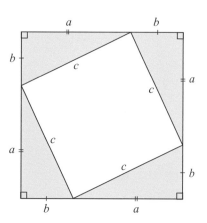

Suppose the legs are of length a and b and the hypotenuse has length c.

The total area of the large square
$= 4 \times$ area of one triangle $+$ area of smaller square,

$$\therefore \quad (a+b)^2 = 4(\tfrac{1}{2}ab) + c^2$$
$$\therefore \quad a^2 + 2ab + b^2 = 2ab + c^2$$
$$\therefore \quad a^2 + b^2 = c^2$$

Example 1   ◀ **Self Tutor**

Find the length of the hypotenuse in:

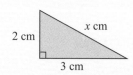

The hypotenuse is opposite the right angle and has length x cm.

$$\therefore \quad x^2 = 3^2 + 2^2$$
$$\therefore \quad x^2 = 9 + 4$$
$$\therefore \quad x^2 = 13$$
$$\therefore \quad x = \sqrt{13} \quad \{\text{as } x > 0\}$$

$\therefore$ the hypotenuse is $\sqrt{13}$ cm.

> If $x^2 = k$, then $x = \pm\sqrt{k}$, but we reject $-\sqrt{k}$ as lengths must be positive!

Example 2   ◀ **Self Tutor**

Find the length of the third side of:

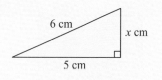

The hypotenuse has length 6 cm.

$$\therefore \quad x^2 + 5^2 = 6^2 \qquad \{\text{Pythagoras}\}$$
$$\therefore \quad x^2 + 25 = 36$$
$$\therefore \quad x^2 = 11$$
$$\therefore \quad x = \sqrt{11} \qquad \{\text{as } x > 0\}$$

$\therefore$ the third side is $\sqrt{11}$ cm long.

Example 3   🔊 **Self Tutor**

Find x in the following:

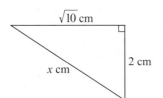

The hypotenuse has length x cm.

$\therefore \quad x^2 = 2^2 + (\sqrt{10})^2 \qquad$ {Pythagoras}

$\therefore \quad x^2 = 4 + 10$

$\therefore \quad x^2 = 14$

$\therefore \quad x = \sqrt{14} \qquad\qquad$ {as $x > 0$}

Example 4   🔊 **Self Tutor**

Find the value of x:

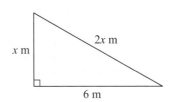

$(2x)^2 = x^2 + 6^2 \qquad$ {Pythagoras}

$\therefore \quad 4x^2 = x^2 + 36$

$\therefore \quad 3x^2 = 36$

$\therefore \quad x^2 = 12$

$\therefore \quad x = \sqrt{12} \qquad$ {as $x > 0$}

$\therefore \quad x = 2\sqrt{3}$

Example 5   🔊 **Self Tutor**

Find the value of any unknowns:

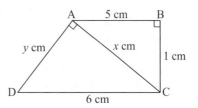

In triangle ABC, the hypotenuse is x cm.

$\therefore \quad x^2 = 5^2 + 1^2 \qquad$ {Pythagoras}

$\therefore \quad x^2 = 26$

$\therefore \quad x = \pm\sqrt{26}$

$\therefore \quad x = \sqrt{26} \qquad$ {as $x > 0$}

In triangle ACD, the hypotenuse is 6 cm.

$\therefore \quad y^2 + (\sqrt{26})^2 = 6^2 \qquad$ {Pythagoras}

$\therefore \quad y^2 + 26 = 36$

$\therefore \quad y^2 = 10$

$\therefore \quad y = \pm\sqrt{10}$

$\therefore \quad y = \sqrt{10} \qquad$ {as $y > 0$}

EXERCISE 4A

1   Find the length of the hypotenuse in the following triangles, leaving your answer in radical form where appropriate:

a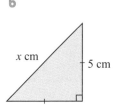

b

c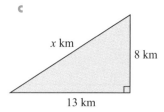

2   Find the length of the third side of the following right angled triangles.
    Where appropriate, leave your answer in radical form.

a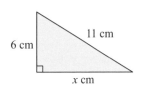

b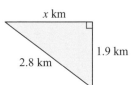

c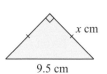

3   Find x in the following:

a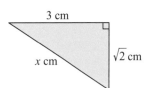

b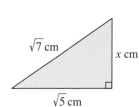

c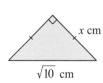

4   Solve for x:

a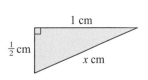

b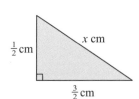

c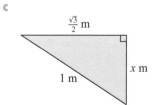

5   Find the value of x:

a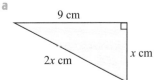

b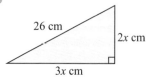

c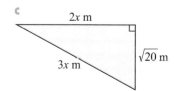

6 Find the value of any unknowns:

a

b

c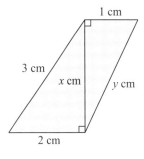

7 Find x:

a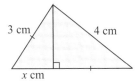

b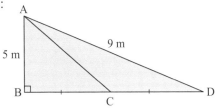

8 Find the length of [AC] in:

9 Find the distance AB in the following figures.

a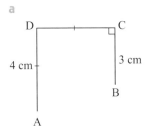

b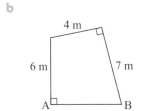

c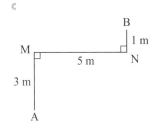

B   THE CONVERSE OF PYTHAGORAS' THEOREM

If we have a triangle whose three sides have known lengths, we can use the **converse** of **Pythagoras' theorem** to test whether it is right angled.

THE CONVERSE OF PYTHAGORAS' THEOREM

GEOMETRY PACKAGE

If a triangle has sides of length a, b and c units and $a^2 + b^2 = c^2$,

then the triangle is right angled.

Example 6

🔊 **Self Tutor**

Is the triangle with sides 6 cm, 8 cm and 5 cm right angled?

The two shorter sides have lengths 5 cm and 6 cm.

Now $5^2 + 6^2 = 25 + 36 = 61$,   but $8^2 = 64$.

$\therefore$ $5^2 + 6^2 \neq 8^2$ and hence the triangle is not right angled.

EXERCISE 4B.1

1 The following figures are not drawn to scale. Which of the triangles are right angled?

a
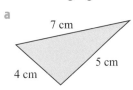

b
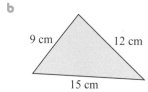

c
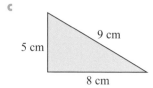

d
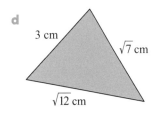

e
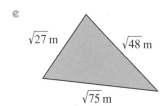

f
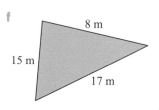

2 The following triangles are not drawn to scale. If any of them is right angled, find the right angle.

a
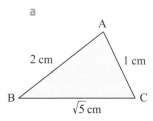

b
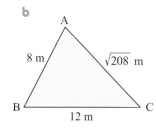

c
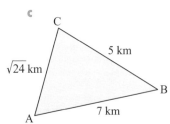

PYTHAGOREAN TRIPLES

The simplest right angled triangle with sides of **integer** length is the **3-4-5 triangle**.

The numbers 3, 4, and 5 satisfy the rule $3^2 + 4^2 = 5^2$.

> The set of positive integers $\{a,\ b,\ c\}$ is a **Pythagorean triple** if it obeys the rule $a^2 + b^2 = c^2$.

Other examples are: $\{5,\ 12,\ 13\}$, $\{7,\ 24,\ 25\}$, $\{8,\ 15,\ 17\}$.

Example 7   ◀) **Self Tutor**

Show that $\{5, 12, 13\}$ is a Pythagorean triple.

We find the square of the **largest** number first.

$$13^2 = 169$$
$$\text{and} \quad 5^2 + 12^2 = 25 + 144 = 169$$
$$\therefore \quad 5^2 + 12^2 = 13^2$$

i.e., $\{5, 12, 13\}$ is a Pythagorean triple.

Example 8   ◀) **Self Tutor**

Find k if $\{9, k, 15\}$ is a Pythagorean triple.

Let $9^2 + k^2 = 15^2$ {Pythagoras}
$$\therefore \quad 81 + k^2 = 225$$
$$\therefore \quad k^2 = 144$$
$$\therefore \quad k = \pm\sqrt{144}$$
$$\therefore \quad k = 12 \quad \{\text{as } k > 0\}$$

EXERCISE 4B.2

1 Determine if the following are Pythagorean triples:

    a $\{8, 15, 17\}$ **b** $\{6, 8, 10\}$ **c** $\{5, 6, 7\}$

    d $\{14, 48, 50\}$ **e** $\{1, 2, 3\}$ **f** $\{20, 48, 52\}$

2 Find k if the following are Pythagorean triples:

    a $\{8, 15, k\}$ **b** $\{k, 24, 26\}$ **c** $\{14, k, 50\}$

    d $\{15, 20, k\}$ **e** $\{k, 45, 51\}$ **f** $\{11, k, 61\}$

3 For what values of n does $\{n, n+1, n+2\}$ form a Pythagorean triple?

4 Show that $\{n, n+1, n+3\}$ cannot form a Pythagorean triple.

INVESTIGATION   **PYTHAGOREAN TRIPLES SPREADSHEET**

  Well known Pythagorean triples include $\{3, 4, 5\}$,
$\{5, 12, 13\}$, $\{7, 24, 25\}$ and $\{8, 15, 17\}$.

SPREADSHEET

Formulae can be used to generate Pythagorean triples.

An example is $2n+1$, $2n^2 + 2n$, $2n^2 + 2n + 1$ where n is a positive integer.

A spreadsheet can quickly generate sets of Pythagorean triples using such formulae.

What to do:

1 Open a new spreadsheet and enter the following:

a in column A, the values of n for $n = 1, 2, 3, 4, 5, \ldots$

b in column B, the values of $2n + 1$

c in column C, the values of $2n^2 + 2n$

d in column D, the values of $2n^2 + 2n + 1$.

	A	B	C	D
1	n	a	b	c
2	1	=2*A2+1	=2*A2^2+2*A2	=C2+1
3	=A2+1	↓	↓	↓
4			fill down	
5	↓			

2 Highlight the appropriate formulae and **fill down** to Row 11 to generate the first 10 sets of triples.

	A	B	C	D
1	n	a	b	c
2	1	3	4	5
3	2	5	12	13
4	3	7	24	25
5	4	9	40	41

3 Check that each set of numbers is indeed a triple by adding columns to find $a^2 + b^2$ and c^2.

4 Your final task is to prove that the formulae $\{2n + 1, \quad 2n^2 + 2n, \quad 2n^2 + 2n + 1\}$ will produce sets of Pythagorean triples for all positive integer values of n.

Hint: Let $a = 2n + 1$, $b = 2n^2 + 2n$ and $c = 2n^2 + 2n + 1$, then simplify $c^2 - b^2 = (2n^2 + 2n + 1)^2 - (2n^2 + 2n)^2$ using the *difference of two squares* factorisation.

PROBLEM SOLVING USING PYTHAGORAS' THEOREM

Many practical problems involve triangles. We can apply Pythagoras' theorem to any triangle that is right angled, or use the converse of the theorem to test whether a right angle exists.

SPECIAL GEOMETRICAL FIGURES

The following special figures contain right angled triangles:

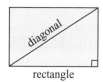

rectangle

In a **rectangle**, right angles exist between adjacent sides.

Construct a **diagonal** to form a right angled triangle.

square

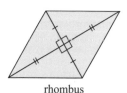

rhombus

In a **square** and a **rhombus**, the diagonals bisect each other at right angles.

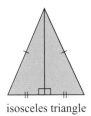
isosceles triangle

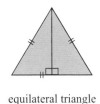
equilateral triangle

In an **isosceles triangle** and an **equilateral triangle**, the altitude bisects the base at right angles.

THINGS TO REMEMBER

- Draw a neat, clear diagram of the situation.
- Mark on known lengths and right angles.
- Use a symbol such as x to represent the unknown length.
- Write down Pythagoras' Theorem for the given information.
- Solve the equation.
- Where necessary, write your answer in sentence form.

Example 9
◀) **Self Tutor**

A rectangular gate is 3 m wide and has a 3.5 m diagonal. How high is the gate?

Let x m be the height of the gate.

Now $(3.5)^2 = x^2 + 3^2$ {Pythagoras}

$\therefore \quad 12.25 = x^2 + 9$

$\therefore \quad 3.25 = x^2$

$\therefore \quad x = \sqrt{3.25}$ {as $x > 0$}

$\therefore \quad x \approx 1.80$

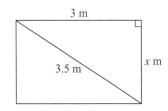

Thus the gate is approximately 1.80 m high.

Example 10
◀) **Self Tutor**

A rhombus has diagonals of length 6 cm and 8 cm.

Find the length of its sides.

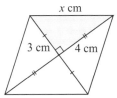

The diagonals of a rhombus bisect at right angles.

Let each side of the rhombus have length x cm.

$\therefore \quad x^2 = 3^2 + 4^2$ {Pythagoras}

$\therefore \quad x^2 = 25$

$\therefore \quad x = \pm\sqrt{25}$

$\therefore \quad x = 5$ {as $x > 0$}

Thus the sides are 5 cm in length.

Example 11   ◀)) **Self Tutor**

A man rides his bicycle due east at 16 km h^{-1}. His son rides his bicycle due south at 20 km h^{-1}. If they both leave point A at the same time, how far apart are they after 4 hours?

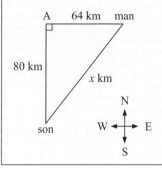

After 4 hours the man has travelled $4 \times 16 = 64$ km. His son has travelled $4 \times 20 = 80$ km.

Thus $x^2 = 64^2 + 80^2$ {Pythagoras}

∴ $x^2 = 10\,496$

∴ $x = \sqrt{10\,496}$ {as $x > 0$}

∴ $x \approx 102$

∴   they are 102 km apart after 4 hours.

Example 12   ◀)) **Self Tutor**

An equilateral triangle has sides of length 6 cm. Find its area.

The altitude bisects the base at right angles.

∴ $a^2 + 3^2 = 6^2$ {Pythagoras}

∴ $a^2 + 9 = 36$

∴ $a^2 = 27$

∴ $a = \sqrt{27}$ {as $a > 0$}

Now,   area $= \frac{1}{2} \times$ base $\times$ height

$= \frac{1}{2} \times 6 \times \sqrt{27}$

$= 3\sqrt{27}$ cm^2

≈ 15.6 cm^2

So, the area is about 15.6 cm^2.

EXERCISE 4C.1

1   A rectangle has sides of length 8 cm and 3 cm. Find the length of its diagonals.

2   The longer side of a rectangle is three times the length of the shorter side. If the length of the diagonal is 10 cm, find the dimensions of the rectangle.

3   A rectangle with diagonals of length 20 cm has sides in the ratio 2 : 1. Find the:

    a   perimeter   b   area of the rectangle.

4   A rhombus has sides of length 6 cm. One of its diagonals is 10 cm long. Find the length of the other diagonal.

5   A square has diagonals of length 10 cm. Find the length of its sides.

6   A rhombus has diagonals of length 8 cm and 10 cm. Find its perimeter.

7 A yacht sails 5 km due west and then 8 km due south. How far is it from its starting point?

8 Pirate Captain William Hawk left his hat on Treasure Island. He sailed 18 km northeast through the Forbidden Strait, then 11 km southeast to his home before realising it was missing. If he sent his parrot to fetch the hat, how far did the bird need to fly?

9 Town A is 50 km south of town B. Town C is 120 km east of town B. Is it quicker to travel directly from A to C by car at 90 km h^{-1} or from A to C via B in a train travelling at 120 km h^{-1}?

10 Two runners set off from town A at the same time. One runs due east to town B and the other runs due south to town C at twice the speed of the first. They arrive at B and C two hours later. If B and C are 50 km apart, find the average speeds at which each runner travelled.

11 Find any unknowns in the following:

a

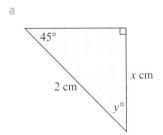

b

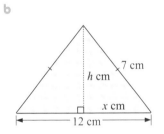

c

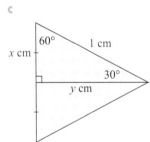

12 An equilateral triangle has sides of length 12 cm. Find the length of one of its altitudes.

13 An isosceles triangle has equal sides of length 8 cm and a base of length 6 cm. Find the area of the triangle.

14 An extension ladder rests 4 m up a wall. If the ladder is extended a further 0.8 m without moving the foot of the ladder, then it will now rest 1 m further up the wall. How long is the extended ladder?

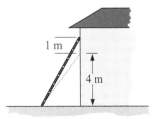

15 An equilateral triangle has area $16\sqrt{3}$ cm^2. Find the length of its sides.

16 Revisit the **Opening Problem** on page **80** and answer the questions posed.

TRUE BEARINGS

We can measure a direction by comparing it with the **true north direction**. We call this a **true bearing**. Measurements are always taken in the **clockwise** direction.

Imagine you are standing at point A, facing north. You turn **clockwise** through an angle until you face B. The **bearing of B from A** is the angle through which you have turned.

So, the bearing of B from A is the clockwise measure of the angle between [AB] and the 'north' line through A.

In the diagram alongside, the bearing of B from A is 72° from true north. We write this as 72^oT or 072°.

To find the true **bearing of A from B**, we place ourselves at point B and face north. We then measure the clockwise angle through which we have to turn so that we face A. The true bearing of A from B is 252°.

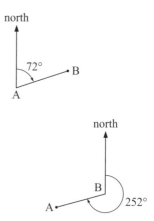

Note: • A true bearing is always written using three digits. For example, we write 072° rather than 72°.

• The bearings of A from B and B from A always differ by 180°. You should be able to explain this using angle pair properties for parallel lines.

Example 13   ◀) **Self Tutor**

A helicopter travels from base station S on a true bearing of 074° for 112 km to outpost A. It then travels 134 km on a true bearing of 164° to outpost B. How far is outpost B from base station S?

> In bearings problems we use the properties of parallel lines to find angles.

Let SB be x km.

From the diagram alongside, we see in triangle SAB that $\hat{SAB} = 90^o$.

$$x^2 = 112^2 + 134^2 \quad \{\text{Pythagoras}\}$$
$$\therefore \quad x^2 = 30\,500$$
$$\therefore \quad x = \sqrt{30\,500} \qquad \{\text{as } x > 0\}$$
$$\therefore \quad x \approx 175$$

So, outpost B is 175 km from base station S.

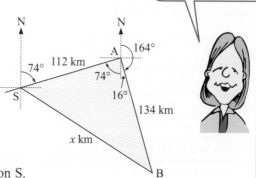

EXERCISE 4C.2

1   Two bushwalkers set off from base camp at the same time. One walks on a true bearing of 049° at an average speed of 5 km h^{-1}, while the other walks on a true bearing of 319° at an average speed of 4 km h^{-1}. Find their distance apart after 3 hours.

2 James is about to tackle an orienteering course. He has been given these instructions:

- the course is triangular and starts and finishes at S
- the first checkpoint A is in the direction 056° from S
- the second checkpoint B is in the direction 146° from A
- the distance from A to B is twice the distance from S to A
- the distance from B to S is 2.6 km.

Find the length of the orienteering course.

3 A fighter plane and a helicopter set off from airbase A at the same time. The helicopter travels on a bearing of 152° and the fighter plane travels on a bearing of 242° at three times the speed. They arrive at bases B and C respectively, 2 hours later. If B and C are 1200 km apart, find the average speed of the helicopter.

D   CIRCLE PROBLEMS

There are certain properties of circles which involve right angles. In these situations we can apply Pythagoras' theorem. The properties will be examined in more detail in **Chapter 21**.

ANGLE IN A SEMI-CIRCLE

The angle in a semi-circle is a right angle.

No matter where C is placed on the arc AB, $A\widehat{C}B$ is always a right angle.

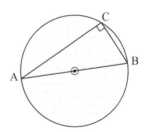

Example 14	🔊 **Self Tutor**

A circle has diameter [XY] of length 13 cm. Z is a point on the circle such that XZ is 5 cm. Find the length YZ.

From the angle in a semi-circle theorem, we know $X\widehat{Z}Y$ is a right angle.
Let the length YZ be x cm.

$\therefore \quad 5^2 + x^2 = 13^2$ {Pythagoras}

$\therefore \quad x^2 = 169 - 25 = 144$

$\therefore \quad x = \sqrt{144}$ {as $x > 0$}

$\therefore \quad x = 12$

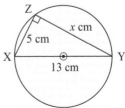

So, YZ has length 12 cm.

A CHORD OF A CIRCLE

The line drawn from the centre of a circle at right angles to a chord bisects the chord.

This follows from the **isosceles triangle theorem**. The construction of radii from the centre of the circle to the end points of the chord produces two right angled triangles.

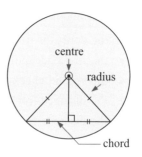

Example 15   ◀) **Self Tutor**

A circle has a chord of length 10 cm. If the radius of the circle is 8 cm, find the shortest distance from the centre of the circle to the chord.

The shortest distance is the 'perpendicular distance'. The line drawn from the centre of a circle, perpendicular to a chord, bisects the chord, so

$$AB = BC = 5 \text{ cm.}$$

In $\triangle AOB, \quad 5^2 + x^2 = 8^2$ {Pythagoras}

$$\therefore \quad x^2 = 64 - 25 = 39$$

$$\therefore \quad x = \sqrt{39} \qquad \{\text{as } x > 0\}$$

$$\therefore \quad x \approx 6.24$$

So, the shortest distance is about 6.24 cm.

TANGENT-RADIUS PROPERTY

A tangent to a circle and a radius at the point of contact meet at right angles.

Notice that we can now form a right angled triangle.

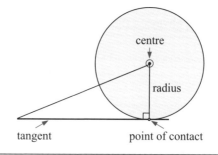

Example 16   ◀) **Self Tutor**

A tangent of length 10 cm is drawn to a circle with radius 7 cm. How far is the centre of the circle from the end point of the tangent?

Let the distance be d cm.

$$\therefore \quad d^2 = 7^2 + 10^2 \qquad \{\text{Pythagoras}\}$$

$$\therefore \quad d^2 = 149$$

$$\therefore \quad d = \sqrt{149} \qquad \{\text{as } d > 0\}$$

$$\therefore \quad d \approx 12.2$$

So, the centre is 12.2 cm from the end point of the tangent.

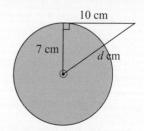

Example 17

Two circles have a common tangent with points of contact at A and B. The radii are 4 cm and 2 cm respectively. Find the distance between the centres given that AB is 7 cm.

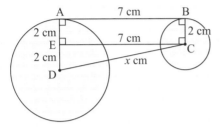

For centres C and D, we draw [BC], [AD], [CD] and [CE] ∥ [AB].

∴   ABCE is a rectangle

∴   CE = 7 cm   {as CE = AB}

and   DE = 4 − 2 = 2 cm

Now $x^2 = 2^2 + 7^2$ {Pythagoras in $\triangle$DEC}

∴ $x^2 = 53$

∴ $x = \sqrt{53}$ {as $x > 0$}

∴ $x \approx 7.3$

∴   the distance between the centres is about 7.3 cm.

EXERCISE 4D

1   A circle has diameter [AB] of length 10 cm. C is a point on the circle such that AC is 8 cm. Find the length BC.

2   A rectangle with side lengths 11 cm and 6 cm is inscribed in a circle. Find the radius of the circle.

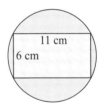

3   An engineer needs to measure the diameter of a large circular fountain. Unfortunately his tape measure is not long enough to go all the way across. So, he chooses a point on the side and measures 7 m to another point on the side. He then uses a set square to measure a right angle, and his tape to measure in this direction to another point on the side. He finds this distance is 7.24 m. Explain how the engineer can find the diameter of the fountain. What is this diameter to the nearest centimetre?

4   A chord of a circle has length 3 cm. If the circle has radius 4 cm, find the shortest distance from the centre of the circle to the chord.

5   A chord of length 6 cm is 3 cm from the centre of a circle. Find the length of the circle's radius.

6   A chord is 5 cm from the centre of a circle of radius 8 cm. Find the length of the chord.

7   A circle has radius 3 cm. A tangent is drawn to the circle from point P which is 9 cm from O, the circle's centre. How long is the tangent?

8 Find the radius of a circle if a tangent of length 12 cm has its end point 16 cm from the circle's centre.

9 If the Earth has a radius of 6400 km and you are in a rocket 40 km directly above the Earth's surface, determine the distance to the horizon.

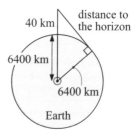

10 A circular table of diameter 2 m is placed in the corner of a room so that its edges touch two adjacent walls. Find the shortest distance from the corner of the room to the edge of the table.

11 A and B are the centres of two circles with radii 4 m and 3 m respectively. The illustrated common tangent has length 10 m. Find the distance between the centres.

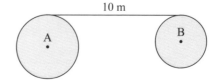

12 The illustration shows two circles of radii 4 cm and 2 cm respectively. The distance between the two centres is 8 cm. Find the length of the common tangent [AB].

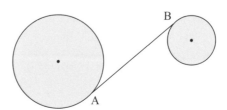

13 In the given figure, AB = 1 cm and AC = 3 cm.   Find the radius of the circle.

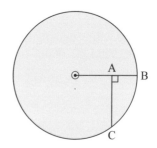

E   # THREE-DIMENSIONAL PROBLEMS

Pythagoras' theorem is often used to find lengths in **three-dimensional** problems. In these problems we sometimes need to apply it *twice*.

Example 18	◀) **Self Tutor**

A 50 m rope is attached inside an empty cylindrical wheat silo of diameter 12 m as shown. How high is the wheat silo?

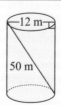

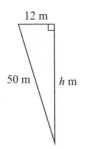

Let the height be h m.

$\therefore \quad h^2 + 12^2 = 50^2$ {Pythagoras}

$\therefore \quad h^2 + 144 = 2500$

$\therefore \qquad h^2 = 2356$

$\therefore \qquad h = \sqrt{2356}$ {as $h > 0$}

$\therefore \qquad h \approx 48.5$

So, the wheat silo is about 48.5 m high.

Example 19   ◀ᵇ) **Self Tutor**

The floor of a room is 6 m by 4 m, and its height is 3 m. Find the distance from a corner point on the floor to the opposite corner point on the ceiling.

The required distance is AD. We join [BD].

In $\triangle$BCD, $x^2 = 4^2 + 6^2$ {Pythagoras}

In $\triangle$ABD, $y^2 = x^2 + 3^2$ {Pythagoras}

$\therefore \quad y^2 = 4^2 + 6^2 + 3^2$

$\therefore \quad y^2 = 61$

$\therefore \quad y = \sqrt{61}$ {as $y > 0$}

$\therefore \quad y \approx 7.81$

$\therefore$ the distance is about 7.81 m.

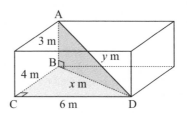

EXERCISE 4E

1   A cone has a slant height of 17 cm and a base radius of 8 cm. How high is the cone?

2   Find the length of the longest nail that could fit entirely within a cylindrical can of radius 3 cm and height 8 cm.

3   A 20 cm nail just fits inside a cylindrical can. Three identical spherical balls need to fit entirely within the can. What is the maximum radius of each ball?

4   A cube has sides of length 3 cm. Find the length of a diagonal of the cube.

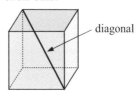

diagonal

5   A room is 5 m by 3 m and has a height of 3.5 m. Find the distance from a corner point on the floor to the opposite corner of the ceiling.

6   A rectangular box has internal dimensions 2 cm by 3 cm by 2 cm. Find the length of the longest toothpick that can be placed within the box.

7   Determine the length of the longest piece of timber which could be stored in a rectangular shed 6 m by 5 m by 2 m high.

Example 20 ◄》 **Self Tutor**

A pyramid of height 40 m has a square base with edges 50 m.
Determine the length of the slant edges.

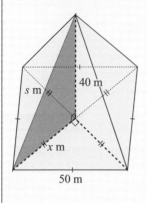

Let a slant edge have length s m.

Let half a diagonal have length x m.

Using $\qquad\qquad x^2 + x^2 = 50^2$ {Pythagoras}

$\therefore\quad 2x^2 = 2500$

$\therefore\quad x^2 = 1250$

Using $\qquad\qquad s^2 = x^2 + 40^2$ {Pythagoras}

$\therefore\quad s^2 = 1250 + 1600$

$\therefore\quad s^2 = 2850$

$\therefore\quad s = \sqrt{2850}$ {as $s > 0$}

$\therefore\quad s \approx 53.4$

So, each slant edge is about 53.4 m long.

8   ABCDE is a square-based pyramid. The apex of the pyramid is directly above M, the point of intersection of [AC] and [BD].

If an Egyptian Pharaoh wished to build a square-based pyramid with all edges 100 m, how high (to the nearest metre) would the pyramid reach above the desert sands?

9   A symmetrical square-based pyramid has height 10 cm and slant edges of 15 cm. Find the dimensions of its square base.

10   A cube has sides of length 2 m. B is at the centre of one face, and A is an opposite vertex. Find the direct distance from A to B.

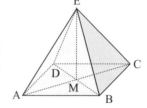

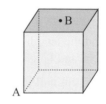

F   MORE DIFFICULT PROBLEMS (EXTENSION)

EXERCISE 4F

1   A highway runs east-west between two towns C and B that are 25 km apart. Town A lies 15 km directly north from C. A straight road is built from A to meet the highway at D which is equidistant from A and B. Find the position of D on the highway.

2 An aircraft hangar is semi-cylindrical with diameter 40 m and length 50 m. A helicopter places a cable across the top of the hangar, and one end is pinned to the corner at A. The cable is then pulled tight and pinned at the opposite corner B. Determine the length of the cable.

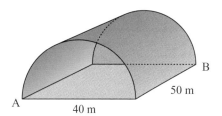

3 In 1876, President Garfield of the USA published a proof of the theorem of Pythagoras. Alongside is the figure he used. Write out the proof.

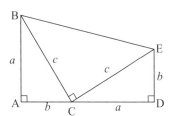

4 A rectangular piece of paper, 10 cm by 24 cm, is folded so that a pair of diagonally opposite corners coincide. Find the length of the crease.

5

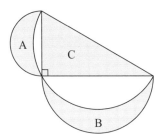

Show that Area A + Area B = Area C.

6 You are given a rectangle in which there is a point that is 3 cm, 4 cm and 5 cm from three of the vertices. How far is the point from the fourth vertex?

7 **a** A box has internal dimensions a cm by b cm by c cm. Show that the distance from one corner to the diametrically opposite corner is given by $\sqrt{a^2 + b^2 + c^2}$ cm.

  b A room is twice as long as it is wide, and half as high as it is wide. The distance from one corner of the floor to the diametrically opposite corner of the ceiling is 13.75 m. Find the height of the room.

8 The largest circle has radius a units. The smallest circles have radii c units. The other two circles have radii b units.

  a Given that the line joining the centres of the two touching circles passes through their point of contact, show that
  $$a : b : c = 6 : 3 : 2.$$

  b What fraction of the largest circle is occupied by the four inner circles?

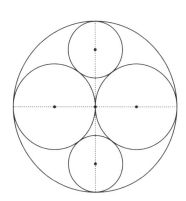

REVIEW SET 4A

1 Find the lengths of the unknown sides in the following triangles:

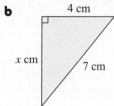

a 2 cm, 5 cm, x cm

b 4 cm, x cm, 7 cm

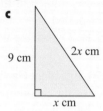

c 9 cm, $2x$ cm, x cm

2 Is the following triangle right angled? Give evidence.

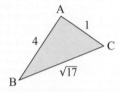

3 Show that $\{5, 11, 13\}$ is not a Pythagorean triple.

4 A rectangle has diagonal 15 cm and one side 8 cm. Find the perimeter of the rectangle.

5 A circle has a chord of length 10 cm. The shortest distance from the circle's centre to the chord is 5 cm. Find the radius of the circle.

6 A boat leaves X and travels due east for 10 km. It then sails 10 km south to Y. Find the distance and bearing of X from Y.

7 What is the length of the longest toothpick which can be placed inside a rectangular box that is 3 cm $\times$ 5 cm $\times$ 8 cm?

8 Two rally car drivers set off from town C at the same time. Driver A travels in the direction 63°T at 120 km h^{-1}, while driver B travels in the direction 333°T at 135 km h^{-1}. How far apart are they after one hour?

9 Find x in:

a

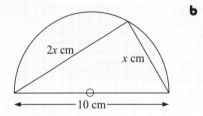

b

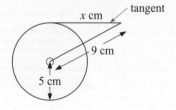

10

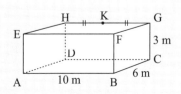

A room is 10 m by 6 m by 3 m. Find the shortest distance from:

a E to K

b A to K.

REVIEW SET 4B

1 Find the value of x in the following:

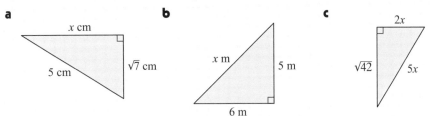

a x cm, 5 cm, $\sqrt{7}$ cm

b x m, 5 m, 6 m

c $2x$, $\sqrt{42}$, $5x$

2 Show that the following triangle is right angled and state which vertex is the right angle:

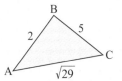

3 If the diameter of a circle is 20 cm, find the shortest distance from a chord of length 16 cm to the centre of the circle.

4 A rectangular gate is twice as wide as it is high. If a diagonal strut is 3.2 m long, find the height of the gate to the nearest millimetre.

5 If a softball diamond has sides of length 30 m, determine the distance a fielder must throw the ball from second base to reach home base.

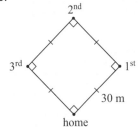

6 Town B is 27 km from town A in the direction 134^oT. Town C is 21 km from town B in a direction 224^oT. Find the distance between A and C.

7 If a 15 m ladder reaches twice as far up a vertical wall as the base is out from the wall, determine the distance up the wall to the top of the ladder.

8 Can an 11 m long piece of timber be placed in a rectangular shed of dimensions 8 m by 7 m by 3 m? Give evidence.

9 Two circles have a common tangent with points of contact X and Y.
The radii of the circles are 4 cm and 5 cm respectively.
The distance between the centres is 10 cm.
Find the length of the common tangent [XY].

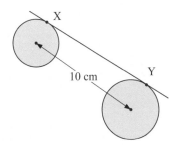

10 Find y in:

a

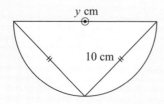

b

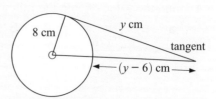

11 **a**

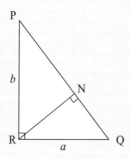

i What is the length of [PQ]?

ii Explain using triangle areas why
$$RN = \frac{ab}{\sqrt{a^2 + b^2}}.$$

b All edges of a square-based pyramid are 200 m long. O is the centre of base ABCD and M is the midpoint of [BC]. [ON] is a small shaft from face BCE to the King's chamber at O. How long is this shaft?

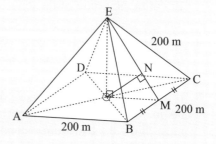

Chapter 5

Coordinate geometry

Contents:

THE NUMBER PLANE

The position of any point in the **number plane** can be specified in terms of an **ordered pair** of numbers (x, y), where:

> x is the **horizontal step** from a fixed point or **origin** O, and
> y is the **vertical step** from O.

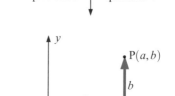

DEMO

Once the origin O has been given, two perpendicular axes are drawn. The **x-axis** is horizontal and the **y-axis** is vertical. The axes divide the number plane into four **quadrants**.

The **number plane** is also known as either:

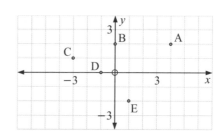

* the **2-dimensional plane**, or
* the **Cartesian plane**, named after **René Descartes**.

In the diagram, the point P is at (a, b).

a and b are referred to as the **coordinates** of P.

a is called the **x-coordinate**, and

b is called the **y-coordinate**.

Examples: The coordinates of the given points are

A(4, 2)
B(0, 2)
C(−3, 1)
D(−1, 0)
E(1, −2).

HISTORICAL NOTE

History now shows that the two Frenchmen René Descartes and Pierre de Fermat arrived at the idea of **analytical geometry** at about the same time. Descartes' work "*La Geometrie*", however, was published first, in 1637, while Fermat's "*Introduction to Loci*" was not published until after his death.

Pierre de Fermat

Today, they are considered the co-founders of this important branch of mathematics, which links algebra and geometry.

The initial approaches used by these mathematicians were quite opposite. Descartes began with a line or curve and then found the equation which described it. Fermat, to a large extent, started with an equation and investigated the shape of the curve it described. This interaction between algebra and geometry shows the power of **analytical geometry** as a branch of mathematics.

René Descartes

Analytical geometry and its use of coordinates provided the mathematical tools which enabled Isaac Newton to later develop another important branch of mathematics called calculus.

Newton humbly stated: *"If I have seen further than Descartes, it is because I have stood on the shoulders of giants."*

OPENING PROBLEM

Dirk and Imke live in two towns which are 60 km apart. They decide to rendezvous somewhere between the towns. Imke leaves Balen and rides her bike at a constant speed of 18 km h^{-1} towards Herstal. Dirk leaves 30 minutes later from Herstal and rides at a constant speed of 24 km h^{-1} towards Balen.

Things to think about:

- Can you write an equation for the distance travelled by each rider in terms of the time variable t hours?
- Can you graph each equation?
- Would each graph be linear?
- What would be the interpretation of the vertical axis intercept in each case?
- If the graphs are linear, what would be your interpretation of their gradients?
- What can be found from the point of intersection of the graphs?
- Can you use the graphs to find how far apart Dirk and Imke will be 30 minutes after Dirk has left Herstal?

A   DISTANCE BETWEEN TWO POINTS

Consider the points A(1, 3) and B(4, 1). We can join the points by a straight line segment of length d units. Suppose we draw a right angled triangle with hypotenuse [AB] and with sides parallel to the axes.

It is clear that $d^2 = 3^2 + 2^2$ {Pythagoras}

$$\therefore \quad d^2 = 13$$
$$\therefore \quad d = \sqrt{13} \qquad \{\text{as } d > 0\}$$

$\therefore$ the distance from A to B is $\sqrt{13}$ units.

EXERCISE 5A.1

1   If necessary, use Pythagoras' theorem to find the distance between:

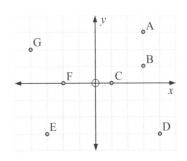

a A and B	b A and D	c C and A
d F and C	e G and F	f C and G
g E and C	h E and D	i B and G.

2 By plotting points and using Pythagoras' theorem, find the distance between:

     a A(3, 5) and B(2, 6)   **b** P(2, 4) and Q(−3, 2)   **c** R(0, 6) and S(3, 0)

THE DISTANCE FORMULA

To avoid drawing a diagram each time we wish to find a distance, a **distance formula** can be developed.

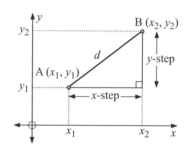

In going from A to B,   the x-step $= x_2 - x_1,$ and

                the y-step $= y_2 - y_1.$

Now, using Pythagoras' theorem,

$$(AB)^2 = (x\text{-step})^2 + (y\text{-step})^2$$

$$\therefore \quad AB = \sqrt{(x\text{-step})^2 + (y\text{-step})^2}$$

$$\therefore \quad d = \sqrt{(x_2 - x_1)^2 + (y_2 - y_1)^2}.$$

If A(x_1, y_1) and B(x_2, y_2) are two points in a plane, then the distance between these points is given by:

$$\mathbf{AB = \sqrt{(x_2 - x_1)^2 + (y_2 - y_1)^2}}$$

or $\mathbf{d = \sqrt{(x\text{-step})^2 + (y\text{-step})^2}.}$

> The distance formula saves us having to graph the points each time we want to find a distance.

Example 1   ◄)) Self Tutor

Find the distance between A(−2, 1) and B(3, 4).

    A(−2, 1)   B(3, 4)

      $x_1\, y_1$ $x_2\, y_2$

$$\begin{aligned} AB &= \sqrt{(3 - -2)^2 + (4 - 1)^2} \\ &= \sqrt{5^2 + 3^2} \\ &= \sqrt{25 + 9} \\ &= \sqrt{34} \text{ units} \end{aligned}$$

Example 2   ◄)) Self Tutor

Consider the points A(−2, 0), B(2, 1) and C(1, −3). Use the distance formula to determine if the triangle ABC is equilateral, isosceles or scalene.

$$\begin{aligned} AB &= \sqrt{(2 - -2)^2 + (1 - 0)^2} \\ &= \sqrt{4^2 + 1^2} \\ &= \sqrt{17} \text{ units} \end{aligned}$$

$$\begin{aligned} BC &= \sqrt{(1 - 2)^2 + (-3 - 1)^2} \\ &= \sqrt{(-1)^2 + (-4)^2} \\ &= \sqrt{17} \text{ units} \end{aligned}$$

$$\begin{aligned} AC &= \sqrt{(1 - -2)^2 + (-3 - 0)^2} \\ &= \sqrt{3^2 + (-3)^2} \\ &= \sqrt{18} \text{ units} \end{aligned}$$

As   AB = BC,   triangle ABC is isosceles.

Example 3 ◀ᴗ **Self Tutor**

Use the distance formula to show that triangle ABC is right angled
if A is (1, 2),   B is (2, 5),   and   C is (4, 1).

$AB = \sqrt{(2-1)^2 + (5-2)^2}$ $BC = \sqrt{(4-2)^2 + (1-5)^2}$

$\quad = \sqrt{1^2 + 3^2}$ $\quad\quad = \sqrt{2^2 + (-4)^2}$

$\quad = \sqrt{10}$ units $\quad\quad = \sqrt{20}$ units

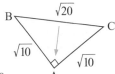

$AC = \sqrt{(4-1)^2 + (1-2)^2}$ So, $AB^2 + AC^2 = 10 + 10 = 20$

$\quad = \sqrt{3^2 + (-1)^2}$ $\quad$ and $BC^2 = 20$

$\quad = \sqrt{10}$ units $\quad\quad\quad \therefore$ triangle ABC is right angled at A.

The right angle is
opposite the
longest side.

Example 4 ◀ᴗ **Self Tutor**

Find b given that   A(3, −2)   and   B(b, 1)   are $\sqrt{13}$ units apart.

From A to B, x-step $= b - 3$

$\quad\quad\quad\quad\quad\quad\quad y$-step $= 1 - -2 = 3$

$\therefore \quad \sqrt{(b-3)^2 + 3^2} = \sqrt{13}$

$\therefore \quad (b-3)^2 + 9 = 13$

$\therefore \quad (b-3)^2 = 4$

$\therefore \quad b - 3 = \pm 2$

$\therefore \quad b = 3 \pm 2$

$\therefore \quad b = 5$ or 1.

There are two possible
solutions in this example.
Draw a diagram to see
why this is so.

EXERCISE 5A.2

1 Find the distance between the following pairs of points:

    a A(3, 1)   and   B(5, 3)
    b C(−1, 2)   and   D(6, 2)

    c O(0, 0)   and   P(−2, 4)
    d E(8, 0)   and   F(2, 0)

    e G(0, −2)   and   H(0, 5)
    f I(2, 0)   and   J(0, −1)

    g R(1, 2)   and   S(−2, 3)
    h W(5, −2)   and   Z(−1, −5)

2 Use the distance formula to classify triangle ABC as either equilateral, isosceles or
scalene:

    a A(3, −1),   B(1, 8),   C(−6, 1)
    b A(1, 0),   B(3, 1),   C(4, 5)

    c A(−1, 0),   B(2, −2),   C(4, 1)
    d A($\sqrt{2}$, 0),   B(−$\sqrt{2}$, 0),   C(0, −$\sqrt{5}$)

    e A($\sqrt{3}$, 1), B(−$\sqrt{3}$, 1), C(0, −2)
    f A(a, b),   B(−a, b),   C(0, 2)

3 Use the distance formula to show that the following triangles are right angled. In each case state the right angle.

    a A(-2, -1), B(3, -1), C(3, 3)
    b A(-1, 2), B(4, 2), C(4, -5)

    c A(1, -2), B(3, 0), C(-3, 2)
    d A(3, -4), B(-2, -5), C(2, 1)

4 Find a given that:

    a P(2, 3)   and   Q(a, -1)   are 4 units apart

    b P(-1, 1)   and   Q(a, -2)   are 5 units apart

    c X(a, a)   is $\sqrt{8}$ units from the origin

    d A(0, a)   is equidistant from   P(3, -3)   and   Q(-2, 2).

B   MIDPOINTS

THE MIDPOINT FORMULA

If point M is halfway between points A and B then M is the **midpoint** of [AB].

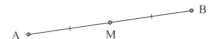

Consider the points   A(1, 2)   and   B(5, 4).

It is clear from the diagram alongside that the midpoint M of [AB] is (3, 3).

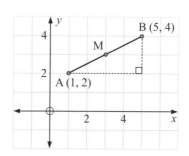

We notice that: $\dfrac{1+5}{2} = 3$ and $\dfrac{2+4}{2} = 3$.

So,   the x-coordinate of M is the *average* of the
       x-coordinates of A and B,

and   the y-coordinate of M is the *average* of the
       y-coordinates of A and B.

In general,   if A(x_1, y_1) and B(x_2, y_2) are two points then the **midpoint** M of [AB] has coordinates

$$\left(\frac{x_1 + x_2}{2}, \frac{y_1 + y_2}{2} \right).$$

Example 5   ◀» Self Tutor

Find the coordinates of the midpoint of [AB] for   A(-1, 3)   and   B(4, 7).

x-coordinate of midpoint y-coordinate of midpoint

$= \dfrac{-1+4}{2}$ $= \dfrac{3+7}{2}$

$= \dfrac{3}{2}$ $= 5$

$= 1\tfrac{1}{2}$ ∴   the midpoint of [AB] is ($1\tfrac{1}{2}$, 5).

Example 6   ◀ Self Tutor

M is the midpoint of [AB]. Find the coordinates of B if A is (1, 3) and M is (4, −2).

Let B be (a, b)

$\therefore \quad \dfrac{a+1}{2} = 4 \quad$ and $\quad \dfrac{b+3}{2} = -2$

$\therefore \quad a+1 = 8 \quad$ and $\quad b+3 = -4$

$\therefore \quad a = 7 \quad$ and $\quad b = -7$

$\therefore \quad$ B is (7, −7).

A (1, 3)

M (4, −2)

B (a, b)

Example 7   ◀ Self Tutor

Suppose A is (−2, 4) and M is (3, −1), where M is the midpoint of [AB].
Use *equal steps* to find the coordinates of B.

x-step: $-2 \xrightarrow{+5} 3 \xrightarrow{+5} 8$

y-step: $4 \xrightarrow{-5} -1 \xrightarrow{-5} -6$

$\therefore$ B is (8, −6).

A(−2, 4)   +5

M(3, −1)   −5
            +5

B(8, −6)   −5

EXERCISE 5B

1 Use this diagram only to find the coordinates
   of the midpoint of the line segment:

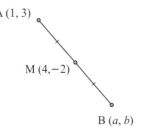

a [GA]   b [ED]

c [AC]   d [AD]

e [CD]   f [GF]

g [EG]   h [GD]

2 Find the coordinates of the midpoint of the line segment joining the pairs of points:

a (8, 1) and (2, 5)   b (2, −3) and (0, 1)

c (3, 0) and (0, 6)   d (−1, 4) and (1, 4)

e (5, −3) and (−1, 0)   f (−2, 4) and (4, −2)

g (5, 9) and (−3, −4)   h (3, −2) and (1, −5)

3 M is the midpoint of [AB]. Find the coordinates of B for:

a A(6, 4) and M(3, −1)   b A(−5, 0) and M(0, −1)

c A(3, −2) and M(1$\frac{1}{2}$, 2)   d A(−1, −2) and M(−$\frac{1}{2}$, 2$\frac{1}{2}$)

e A(7, −3) and M(0, 0)   f A(3, −1) and M(0, −$\frac{1}{2}$)

Check your answers using the *equal steps* method given in **Example 7**.

4 If T is the midpoint of [PQ], find the coordinates of P for:

   a   T(-3, 4) and Q(3, -2)   **b**   T(2, 0) and Q(-2, -3).

5 [AB] is the diameter of a circle with centre C. If A is (3, -2) and B is (-1, -4), find the coordinates of C.

6 [PQ] is a diameter of a circle with centre (3, $-\frac{1}{2}$). Find the coordinates of P given that Q is (-1, 2).

7 The diagonals of parallelogram PQRS bisect each other at X. Find the coordinates of S.

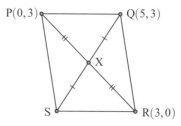

8 Triangle ABC has vertices   A(-1, 3),   B(1, -1),   and   C(5, 2).   Find the length of the line segment from A to the midpoint of [BC].

9 A, B, C and D are four points on the same straight line. The distances between successive points are equal, as shown. If A is (1, -3), C is (4, a) and D is (b, 5), find the values of a and b.

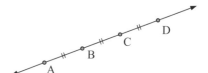

C | GRADIENT (OR SLOPE)

When looking at line segments drawn on a set of axes, it is clear that different line segments are inclined to the horizontal at different angles. Some appear to be *steeper* than others.

The gradient or slope of a line is a measure of its steepness.

If we choose any two distinct (different) points on the line, the **horizontal step** and **vertical step** between them may be determined.

Case 1:   *Case 2:*

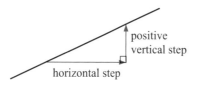

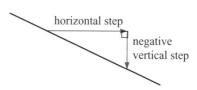

The **gradient** of a line may be determined by the fraction $\dfrac{\textbf{vertical step}}{\textbf{horizontal step}}$ or $\dfrac{\textbf{\textit{y}-step}}{\textbf{\textit{x}-step}}$.

Note:
   • In *Case 1*, both steps are positive and so the gradient is positive.
   • In *Case 2*, the steps are opposite in sign and so the gradient is negative.

Lines like

are forward sloping and have **positive gradients**.

Lines like

are backward sloping and have **negative gradients**.

Have you ever wondered why gradient is measured by y-step divided by x-step rather than x-step divided by y-step?

Perhaps it is because horizontal lines have no gradient and zero (0) should represent this. Also, as lines become steeper we want their numerical gradients to increase.

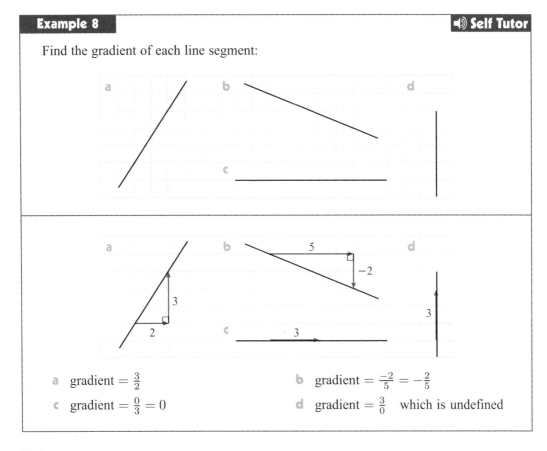

Example 8 ◀)) **Self Tutor**

Find the gradient of each line segment:

a gradient $= \frac{3}{2}$

b gradient $= \frac{-2}{5} = -\frac{2}{5}$

c gradient $= \frac{0}{3} = 0$

d gradient $= \frac{3}{0}$ which is undefined

Note:

- The gradient of any **horizontal** line is **0**, since the vertical step (the numerator) is 0.
- The gradient of any **vertical** line is **undefined**, since the horizontal step (the denominator) is 0.

THE GRADIENT FORMULA

If A is (x_1, y_1) and B is (x_2, y_2) then the

gradient of [AB] is $\dfrac{y_2 - y_1}{x_2 - x_1}$.

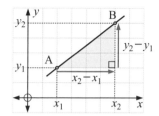

Example 9   ◀◑ **Self Tutor**

Find the gradient of the line through $(3, -2)$ and $(6, 4)$.

$$
\begin{array}{cc}
(3, -2) \quad (6, 4) & \text{gradient} = \dfrac{y_2 - y_1}{x_2 - x_1} \\
\uparrow \ \uparrow \quad \uparrow \ \uparrow & = \dfrac{4 - -2}{6 - 3} \\
x_1 \ y_1 \quad x_2 \ y_2 & = \dfrac{6}{3} \\
& = 2
\end{array}
$$

Example 10   ◀◑ **Self Tutor**

Through $(2, 4)$ draw a line with gradient $-\frac{2}{3}$.

It is a good idea to use a positive x-step.

Plot the point $(2, 4)$

gradient $= \dfrac{y\text{-step}}{x\text{-step}} = \dfrac{-2}{3}$

$\therefore$ let y-step $= -2$, x-step $= 3$.

Use these steps to find another point and draw the line through these points.

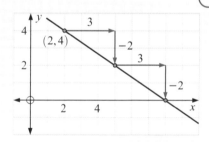

EXERCISE 5C.1

1 Find the gradient of each line segment:

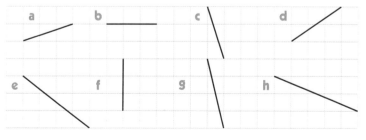

2 On grid paper draw a line segment with gradient:

   a $\frac{3}{4}$ b $-\frac{1}{2}$ c 2 d -3 e 0 f $-\frac{2}{5}$

3 Find the gradient of the line segment joining the following pairs of points:

    a (2, 3)   and   (7, 4)   **b** (5, 7)   and   (1, 6)

    c (1, −2)   and   (3, 6)   **d** (5, 5)   and   (−1, 5)

    e (3, −1)   and   (3, −4)   **f** (5, −1)   and   (−2, −3)

    g (−5, 2)   and   (2, 0)   **h** (0, −1)   and   (−2, −3)

4 On the same set of axes draw lines through (1, 2) with gradients of $\frac{3}{4}$, $\frac{1}{2}$, 1, 2 and 3.

5 On the same set of axes draw lines through (−2, −1) with gradients of 0, $-\frac{1}{2}$, −1 and −3.

PARALLEL LINES

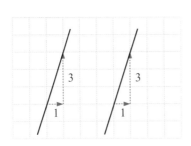

Notice that the given lines are parallel and both of them have a gradient or slope of 3.

In fact:

- if two lines are **parallel**, then they have **equal gradient**, and
- if two lines have **equal gradient**, then they are **parallel**.

PERPENDICULAR LINES

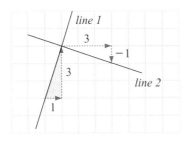

Notice that *line 1* and *line 2* are perpendicular.

Line 1 has gradient $\frac{3}{1} = 3$.

Line 2 has gradient $\frac{-1}{3} = -\frac{1}{3}$.

We see that the gradients are *negative reciprocals* of each other and their product is $3 \times -\frac{1}{3} = -1$.

For lines which are not horizontal or vertical:

- if the lines are **perpendicular** then their gradients are **negative reciprocals**
- if the gradients are **negative reciprocals** then the lines are **perpendicular**.

Proof:

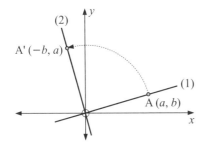

Suppose the two perpendicular lines are translated so that they intersect at the origin O. If A(a, b) lies on one line, then under an anticlockwise rotation about O of 90° it finishes on the other line and its coordinates are A$'$($-b$, a).

The gradient of line (1) is $\dfrac{b-0}{a-0} = \dfrac{b}{a}$.

The gradient of line (2) is $\dfrac{a-0}{-b-0} = -\dfrac{a}{b}$.

Example 11

If a line has gradient $\frac{2}{3}$, find the gradient of:

   a all lines parallel to the given line

   b all lines perpendicular to the given line.

$\frac{b}{a}$ and $-\frac{a}{b}$ are negative reciprocals.

   a Since the original line has gradient $\frac{2}{3}$, the gradient of all parallel lines is also $\frac{2}{3}$.

   b The gradient of all perpendicular lines is $-\frac{3}{2}$.   {the negative reciprocal}

Example 12 ◀⑴ **Self Tutor**

Find a given that the line joining A(2, 3) to B(a, -1) is parallel to a line with gradient -2.

$$\text{gradient of [AB]} = -2 \qquad \text{\{parallel lines have equal gradient\}}$$

$$\therefore \quad \frac{-1-3}{a-2} = -2 \qquad \text{\{gradient formula\}}$$

$$\therefore \quad \frac{-4}{a-2} = \frac{-2}{1}$$

$$\therefore \quad \frac{-4}{a-2} = \frac{-2}{1}\left(\frac{a-2}{a-2}\right) \qquad \text{\{achieving a common denominator\}}$$

$$\therefore \quad -4 = -2(a-2) \qquad \text{\{equating numerators\}}$$

$$\therefore \quad -4 = -2a+4$$

$$\therefore \quad 2a = 8$$

$$\therefore \quad a = 4$$

Example 13 ◀⑴ **Self Tutor**

Find t given that the line joining D(-1, -3) to C(1, t) is perpendicular to a line with gradient 2.

$$\text{gradient of [DC]} = -\tfrac{1}{2} \qquad \text{\{perpendicular to line of gradient 2\}}$$

$$\therefore \quad \frac{t--3}{1--1} = -\tfrac{1}{2} \qquad \text{\{gradient formula\}}$$

$$\therefore \quad \frac{t+3}{2} = \frac{-1}{2} \qquad \text{\{simplifying\}}$$

$$\therefore \quad t+3 = -1 \qquad \text{\{equating numerators\}}$$

$$\therefore \quad t = -4$$

EXERCISE 5C.2

1   Find the gradient of all lines perpendicular to a line with a gradient of:

   a $\frac{1}{2}$ b $\frac{2}{5}$ c 3   d 7

   e $-\frac{2}{5}$ f $-2\frac{1}{3}$ g -5 h -1

2   The gradients of two lines are listed below. Which of the line pairs are perpendicular?

   a $\frac{1}{3}, 3$ b $5, -5$ c $\frac{3}{7}, -2\frac{1}{3}$ d $4, -\frac{1}{4}$

   e $6, -\frac{5}{6}$ f $\frac{2}{3}, -\frac{3}{2}$ g $\frac{p}{q}, \frac{q}{p}$ h $\frac{a}{b}, -\frac{b}{a}$

3   Find a given that the line joining:

   a   A(1, 3)   to   B(3, a)   is parallel to a line with gradient 3

   b   P(a, -3)   to   Q(4, -2)   is parallel to a line with gradient $\frac{1}{3}$

   c   M(3, a)   to   N(a, 5)   is parallel to a line with gradient $-\frac{2}{5}$.

4   Find t given that the line joining:

   a   A(2, -3)   to   B(-2, t)   is perpendicular to a line with gradient $1\frac{1}{4}$

   b   C(t, -2)   to   D(1, 4)   is perpendicular to a line with gradient $\frac{2}{3}$

   c   P(t, -2)   to   Q(5, t)   is perpendicular to a line with gradient $-\frac{1}{4}$.

5   Given the points   A(1, 4),   B(-1, 0),   C(6, 3)   and   D(t, -1),   find t if:

   a   [AB] is parallel to [CD]   b   [AC] is parallel to [DB]

   c   [AB] is perpendicular to [CD]   d   [AD] is perpendicular to [BC].

COLLINEAR POINTS

   Three or more points are **collinear** if they lie on the same straight line.

If three points A, B and C are collinear, the gradient
of [AB] is equal to the gradient of [BC] and also the
gradient of [AC].

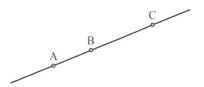

Example 14	◄) **Self Tutor**

   Show that the following points are collinear: A(1, -1),   B(6, 9),   C(3, 3).

gradient of [AB] $= \dfrac{9 - -1}{6 - 1}$ gradient of [BC] $= \dfrac{3 - 9}{3 - 6}$

$\qquad\qquad\qquad = \dfrac{10}{5}$ $\qquad\qquad = \dfrac{-6}{-3}$

$\qquad\qquad\qquad = 2$ $\qquad\qquad = 2$

$\therefore$ [AB] is parallel to [BC], and as point B is common to both line segments, A, B
and C are *collinear*.

EXERCISE 5C.3

1 Determine whether or not the following sets of three points are collinear:

   a A(1, 2), B(4, 6) and C(−4, −4)   **b** P(−6, −6), Q(−1, 0) and R(4, 6)

   c R(5, 2), S(−6, 5) and T(0, −4)   **d** A(0, −2), B(−1, −5) and C(3, 7)

2 Find c given that:

   a A(−4, −2), B(0, 2) and C(c, 5) are collinear

   b P(3, −2), Q(4, c) and R(−1, 10) are collinear.

D   USING COORDINATE GEOMETRY

Coordinate geometry is a powerful tool which can be used:

- to **check** the truth of a geometrical fact
- to **prove** a geometrical fact by using general cases.

TOOLS OF THE TRADE

We can find:
- **distances** using the **distance formula**
- **midpoints** using the **midpoint formula**
- **gradients** using the **gradient formula**.

Remember that:
- equal gradients indicate that the lines are parallel
- product of gradients $= -1$ indicates that the lines are perpendicular.

Example 15   ◀⑤ **Self Tutor**

P(3, −1), Q(1, 7) and R(−1, 5) are the vertices of triangle PQR.
M is the midpoint of [PQ] and N is the midpoint of [PR].

   a Find the coordinates of M and N.   **b** Find the gradients of [MN] and [QR].

   c What can be deduced from **b**?   **d** Find distances MN and QR.

   e What can be deduced from **d**?

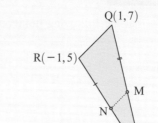

   a M is $\left(\dfrac{3+1}{2}, \dfrac{-1+7}{2}\right)$ which is (2, 3).

      N is $\left(\dfrac{3+-1}{2}, \dfrac{-1+5}{2}\right)$ which is (1, 2).

   b   gradient of [MN]   gradient of [QR]

        $= \dfrac{2-3}{1-2}$ $= \dfrac{5-7}{-1-1}$

        $= 1$ $= 1$

   c Equal gradients implies that [MN] ∥ [QR].

d $\quad MN = \sqrt{(1-2)^2 + (2-3)^2} \qquad QR = \sqrt{(-1-1)^2 + (5-7)^2}$

$\qquad\qquad = \sqrt{1+1} \qquad\qquad\qquad\qquad = \sqrt{4+4}$

$\qquad\qquad = \sqrt{2} \text{ units} \qquad\qquad\qquad\qquad = \sqrt{8}$

$\qquad\qquad\qquad\qquad\qquad\qquad\qquad\qquad = 2\sqrt{2} \text{ units}$

e From **d**, [QR] is twice as long as [MN].

EXERCISE 5D

1 Given P(1, 5), Q(5, 7), R(3, 1):

    a Show that triangle PQR is isosceles.

    b Find the midpoint M of [QR].

    c Use gradients to verify that [PM] is perpendicular to [QR].

    d Draw a sketch to illustrate what you have found in **a**, **b** and **c**.

2 Given A(6, 8), B(14, 6), C(−1, −3) and D(−9, −1):

    a Use gradients to show that:

        i [AB] is parallel to [DC]

        ii [BC] is parallel to [AD].

    b What kind of figure is ABCD?

    c Check that AB = DC and BC = AD using the distance formula.

    d Find the midpoints of diagonals: **i** [AC] **ii** [BD].

    e What property of parallelograms has been checked in **d**?

> For figures named ABCD, etc. the labelling is in cyclic order.

3 Given A(−1, 1), B(1, 5) and C(5, 1), where M is the midpoint of [AB] and N is the midpoint of [BC]:

    a Show that [MN] is parallel to [AC], using gradients.

    b Show that [MN] is half the length of [AC].

4 Given A(1, 3), B(6, 3), C(3, −1) and D(−2, −1):

    a Show that ABCD is a rhombus, using the distance formula.

    b Find the midpoints of [AC] and [BD].

    c Show that [AC] and [BD] are perpendicular, using gradients.

5 The sketch of quadrilateral ABCD is not drawn to scale. P, Q, R and S are the midpoints of [AB], [BC], [CD] and [DA] respectively.

    a Find the coordinates of:

        i P   **ii** Q   **iii** R   **iv** S.

    b Find the gradient of:

        i [PQ] **ii** [QR] **iii** [RS] **iv** [SP].

    c What can be deduced about quadrilateral PQRS from **b**?

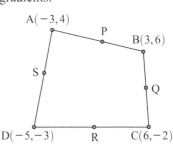

6 $S(s, 8)$ lies on a semi-circle as shown.

   a Find s.

   b Using this value of s, find the slope
      of: **i** [PS]   **ii** [SQ].

   c Use **b** to show that angle PSQ is a
      right angle.

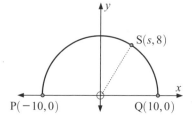

E | EQUATIONS OF STRAIGHT LINES

The **equation of a line** is an equation which connects the x and y values for every point
on the line.

THE GRADIENT-INTERCEPT FORM

> $y = mx + c$ is the **gradient-intercept form** of the equation of a line with
> gradient m and y-intercept c.

For example:

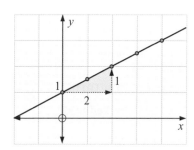

The illustrated line has

$$\text{gradient} = \frac{y\text{-step}}{x\text{-step}} = \tfrac{1}{2}$$

and the y-intercept is 1

$\therefore$ its equation is $y = \tfrac{1}{2}x + 1$.

THE GENERAL FORM

> $Ax + By = C$ is the **general form** of the equation of a line.

For the line $y = \tfrac{1}{2}x + 1,$

            $2y = x + 2$ {multiplying both sides by 2}

  $\therefore$ $x - 2y = -2$ is the equation of the line in general form.

FINDING THE EQUATION OF A LINE

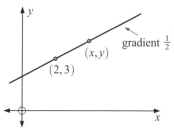

Consider the illustrated line which has gradient
$\tfrac{1}{2}$ and passes through the point $(2, 3)$.

Suppose (x, y) is any point on the line.

The gradient between $(2, 3)$ and (x, y) is $\dfrac{y - 3}{x - 2}$.

Equating gradients gives us $\dfrac{y - 3}{x - 2} = \tfrac{1}{2}$ {gradient formula}

Consider two rearrangements of this equation of the line:

$$\frac{y-3}{x-2} = \tfrac{1}{2}$$

or

$$\frac{y-3}{x-2} = \tfrac{1}{2}$$

$$\therefore \quad y - 3 = \tfrac{1}{2}(x-2)$$

$$\therefore \quad 2(y-3) = 1(x-2)$$

$$\therefore \quad y - 3 = \tfrac{1}{2}x - 1$$

$$\therefore \quad 2y - 6 = x - 2$$

$$\therefore \quad y = \tfrac{1}{2}x + 2$$

$$\therefore \quad x - 2y = -4$$

which is in the form $y = mx + c$ called the **gradient-intercept** form.

which is in the form $Ax + By = C$ called the **general** form.

In this case $A = 1$, $B = -2$, and $C = -4$.

To find the equation of a line we need to know:

- the **gradient**
- the coordinates of any **point** on the line.

Summary:

If a straight line has gradient m and passes through (a, b) then it has equation $\dfrac{y-b}{x-a} = m$

which can be rearranged into   **gradient-intercept** form $y = mx + c$

or   **general** form $Ax + By = C$.

Reminder:

All **vertical lines** have equations of the form $x = a$ where a is a constant.

All **horizontal lines** have equations of the form $y = c$ where c is a constant.

Example 16   ◄⋙ Self Tutor

Find, in *gradient-intercept form*, the equation of the line through $(-1, 3)$ with a gradient of 5.

The equation of the line is $\dfrac{y-3}{x--1} = 5$

$$\therefore \quad \frac{y-3}{x+1} = 5$$

$$\therefore \quad y - 3 = 5(x+1)$$

$$\therefore \quad y - 3 = 5x + 5$$

$$\therefore \quad y = 5x + 8$$

To find the equation of a line we need to know its gradient and a point which lies on it.

Example 17   ◀ᴗ) **Self Tutor**

Find, in *general form*, the equation of the line with gradient $\frac{3}{4}$ that passes through $(5, -2)$.

The equation of the line is
$$\frac{y - -2}{x - 5} = \frac{3}{4}$$

$$\therefore \quad \frac{y + 2}{x - 5} = \frac{3}{4}$$

$$\therefore \quad 4(y + 2) = 3(x - 5)$$

$$\therefore \quad 4y + 8 = 3x - 15$$

$$\therefore \quad 3x - 4y = 23$$

Example 18   ◀ᴗ) **Self Tutor**

Find the equation of the line which passes through the points $A(-1, 5)$ and $B(2, 3)$.

The gradient of the line is
$$\frac{3 - 5}{2 - -1} = \frac{-2}{3}$$

Using point A, the equation is
$$\frac{y - 5}{x - -1} = -\frac{2}{3}$$

$$\therefore \quad \frac{y - 5}{x + 1} = -\frac{2}{3}$$

$$\therefore \quad 3(y - 5) = -2(x + 1)$$

$$\therefore \quad 3y - 15 = -2x - 2$$

$$\therefore \quad 2x + 3y = 13$$

Check that you get the same final answer using point B instead of A.

If we are given the equation of a line in general form, one way to find the slope is to rearrange it into gradient-intercept form.

Example 19   ◀ᴗ) **Self Tutor**

Find the gradient of the line $2x + 5y = 17$.

$$2x + 5y = 17$$

$$\therefore \quad 5y = 17 - 2x \qquad \text{\{subtracting } 2x \text{ from both sides\}}$$

$$\therefore \quad y = \frac{17}{5} - \frac{2x}{5} \qquad \text{\{dividing both sides by 5\}}$$

$$\therefore \quad y = -\frac{2}{5}x + \frac{17}{5} \qquad \text{and so the gradient is } -\frac{2}{5}.$$

EXERCISE 5E.1

1   Find, in *gradient-intercept form*, the equation of the line through:

    a $(2, -5)$ having a gradient of 5   **b** $(-1, -2)$ having a gradient of -2

    c $(7, -3)$ having a gradient of -4 **d** $(3, 4)$ having a gradient of $\frac{1}{2}$

    e $(-2, 3)$ having a gradient of $-\frac{1}{3}$ **f** $(5, -1)$ having a gradient of 0.

2   Find, in *general form*, the equation of the line through:

    a $(2, 5)$ with gradient $\frac{3}{4}$ **b** $(-1, 4)$ with gradient $\frac{2}{5}$

    c $(5, 0)$ with gradient $-\frac{1}{2}$ **d** $(6, -2)$ with gradient $-\frac{3}{4}$

    e $(-3, -1)$ with gradient 5   **f** $(5, -3)$ with gradient -3.

3   Find the equation of the line which passes through the points:

    a $A(1, 5)$ and $B(4, 8)$ **b** $A(0, 4)$ and $B(-1, 5)$

    c $M(2, 7)$ and $N(-3, 7)$ **d** $P(-3, 2)$ and $Q(-3, 10)$

    e $A(-3, -2)$ and $B(4, -2)$ **f** $C(-3, 1)$ and $D(6, 0)$

    g $P(2, -1)$ and $Q(-1, -2)$ **h** $R(-2, 3)$ and $S(-4, -1)$

4   Find the equation of the line:

    a which has gradient $\frac{1}{2}$ and cuts the y-axis at 3

    b which is parallel to a line with slope 2, and passes through the point $(-1, 4)$

    c which cuts the x-axis at 5 and the y-axis at -2

    d which cuts the x axis at -1, and passes through $(-3, 4)$

    e which is perpendicular to a line with gradient $\frac{3}{4}$, and cuts the x-axis at 5

    f which is perpendicular to a line with gradient -2, and passes through $(-2, 3)$.

5   Find the gradient of the line with equation:

    a $y = 3x + 5$ **b** $y = 1 - 2x$ **c** $y = 0$

    d $x = 2$ **e** $y = \dfrac{2x - 5}{3}$ **f** $3x + y = 4$

    g $2x - 7y = 3$ **h** $2x + 7y = 4$ **i** $3x - 4y = 1$

    j $3x + 4y = 7$ **k** $Ax - By = C$ **l** $Ax + By = C$

6

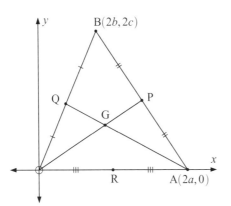

A **median** of a triangle is a line segment from a vertex to the midpoint of the opposite side.

    a Show that [OP] has equation $cx - (a + b)y = 0$.

    b Show that [AQ] has equation $cx - (b - 2a)y = 2ac$.

    c Prove that the third median [BR] passes through the point of intersection G of medians [OP] and [AQ].

7 **a** Show that the perpendicular bisector of [OB] has equation $bx + cy = b^2 + c^2$.

b Show that the perpendicular bisector of [AB] has equation $(a - b)x - cy = a^2 - b^2 - c^2$.

c Prove that the perpendicular bisector of [OA] passes through the point of intersection of the other two perpendicular bisectors of $\triangle OAB$.

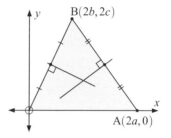

8

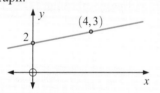

The perpendicular bisector of a chord of a circle passes through the circle's centre.

Find the coordinates of the centre of the circle which passes through the points A(5, 7), B(7, 1) and C(−1, 5).

EQUATIONS FROM GRAPHS

If a graph contains sufficient information then we can determine its equation.

Remember that we must have at least one point and we must be able to determine the line's gradient.

Example 20   ◀) **Self Tutor**

Find, in gradient-intercept form, the equation of the line with graph:

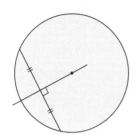

Two points on the line are (0, 2) and (4, 3)

$\therefore$ the gradient $m = \dfrac{3 - 2}{4 - 0} = \dfrac{1}{4}$

and the y-intercept $c = 2$.

$\therefore$ the equation is $y = \dfrac{1}{4}x + 2$.

Example 21   ◀) **Self Tutor**

Find, in general form, the equation of the line with graph:

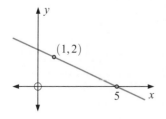

Two points on the line are (1, 2) and (5, 0)

$\therefore$ the gradient $m = \dfrac{0 - 2}{5 - 1} = \dfrac{-2}{4} = \dfrac{-1}{2}$

As we do not know the y-intercept we equate

gradients: $\dfrac{y - 2}{x - 1} = -\dfrac{1}{2}$

$\therefore$ $2(y - 2) = -1(x - 1)$

$\therefore$ $2y - 4 = -x + 1$

$\therefore$ $x + 2y = 5$

Example 22

Find the equation connecting the variables in:

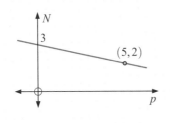

$(0, 3)$ and $(5, 2)$ lie on the straight line.

$\therefore$ the gradient $m = \dfrac{2-3}{5-0} = -\dfrac{1}{5}$

and the Y-intercept is $c = 3$.

The equation is of the form $Y = mX + c$
where $Y \equiv N$ and $X \equiv p$.

$\therefore$ the equation is $N = -\frac{1}{5}p + 3$.

The symbol $\equiv$ means 'is equivalent to'

EXERCISE 5E.2

1 Find the equation of the line with:

  a gradient 3 and y-intercept 5
  b gradient 2 and y-intercept -5
  c gradient -3 and y-intercept -2
  d gradient $-\frac{1}{2}$ and y-intercept -1
  e gradient 0 and y-intercept 4
  f undefined gradient, through $(-1, -4)$

2 Find the equations of the illustrated lines:

a 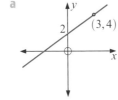 b 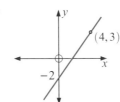 c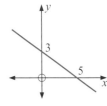

d 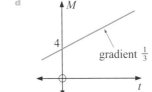 e 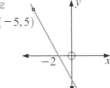 f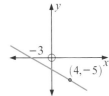

3 Find the equation connecting the variables given:

a 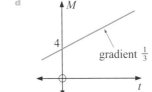 b 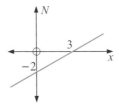 c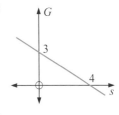

d 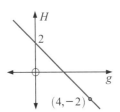 e 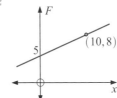 f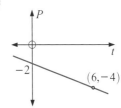

FINDING THE EQUATION OF A LINE QUICKLY

If a line has gradient $\frac{3}{4}$, it must have form $y = \frac{3}{4}x + c$.

We can rearrange this into the form $4y = 3x + 4c$ or $3x - 4y = C$.

If a line has gradient $-\frac{3}{4}$, using the same working we would obtain $3x + 4y = C$.

This suggests that:

- for gradient $\dfrac{A}{B}$ the general form of the line is $Ax - By = C$

- for gradient $-\dfrac{A}{B}$ the general form of the line is $Ax + By = C$.

The constant term C on the RHS is obtained by substituting the coordinates of a point which lies on the line.

Example 23   ◀ϻ **Self Tutor**

Find the equation of the line:

  a   with gradient $\frac{3}{4}$, that passes through $(5, -2)$

  b   with gradient $-\frac{3}{4}$, that passes through $(1, 7)$.

> You will find with practice that you can write down the equation very quickly.

  a   The equation is $3x - 4y = 3(5) - 4(-2)$

          $\therefore$ $3x - 4y = 23$

  b   The equation is $3x + 4y = 3(1) + 4(7)$

          $\therefore$ $3x + 4y = 31$

Example 24   ◀ϻ **Self Tutor**

Find the equation of the tangent to the circle with centre $(2, 3)$ at the point $(-1, 5)$.

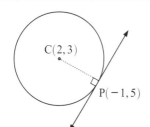

gradient of CP is $\dfrac{5 - 3}{(-1) - 2} = \dfrac{2}{-3} = -\dfrac{2}{3}$

$\therefore$ the gradient of the tangent at P is $\frac{3}{2}$

$\therefore$ the equation of the tangent is
$$3x - 2y = 3(-1) - 2(5)$$
or $3x - 2y = -13$

> The tangent is perpendicular to the radius at the point of contact.

EXERCISE 5E.3

1   Find the equation of the line:

  a   through $(4, 1)$ with gradient $\frac{1}{2}$
        b   through $(-2, 5)$ with gradient $\frac{2}{3}$

  c   through $(5, 0)$ with gradient $\frac{3}{4}$
        d   through $(3, -2)$ with gradient 3

  e   through $(1, 4)$ with gradient $-\frac{1}{3}$
        f   through $(2, -3)$ with gradient $-\frac{3}{4}$

  g   through $(3, -2)$ with gradient -2
        h   through $(0, 4)$ with gradient -3.

2 We can use the reverse process to question **1** to write down the gradient of a line given in general form. Find the gradient of the line with equation:

    a $2x + 3y = 8$ **b** $3x - 7y = 11$ **c** $6x - 11y = 4$

    d $5x + 6y = -1$ **e** $3x + 6y = -1$ **f** $15x - 5y = 17$

3 Explain why:

    a any line parallel to $3x + 5y = 2$ has the form $3x + 5y = C$

    b any line perpendicular to $3x + 5y = 2$ has the form $5x - 3y = C$.

4 Find the equation of the line which is:

    a parallel to the line $3x + 4y = 6$ and passes through $(2, 1)$

    b perpendicular to the line $5x + 2y = 10$ and passes through $(-1, -1)$

    c perpendicular to the line $x - 3y + 6 = 0$ and passes through $(-4, 0)$

    d parallel to the line $x - 3y = 11$ and passes through $(0, 0)$.

5 $2x - 3y = 6$ and $6x + ky = 4$ are two straight lines.

    a Write down the gradient of each line.   **b** Find k if the lines are parallel.

    c Find k if the lines are perpendicular.

6 Find the equation of the tangent to the circle with centre:

    a $(0, 2)$ at the point $(-1, 5)$ **b** $(0, 0)$ at the point $(3, -2)$

    c $(3, -1)$ at the point $(-1, 1)$ **d** $(2, -2)$ at the point $(5, -2)$.

PERPENDICULAR BISECTORS

The **perpendicular bisector** of two points A and B divides the number plane into two regions. On one side of the line are points that are closer to B than to A, and vice versa on the other side.

We observe that the midpoint of line segment [AB] must lie on the perpendicular bisector of [AB].

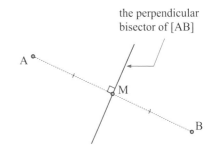

Points on the perpendicular bisector of [AB] are **equidistant** from A and B.

Example 25   ◀⟩ **Self Tutor**

Find the equation of the perpendicular bisector of [AB] for A$(-1, 2)$ and B$(3, 4)$.

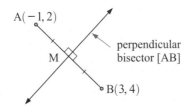

M is $\left(\dfrac{-1 + 3}{2}, \dfrac{2 + 4}{2} \right)$ or $(1, 3)$.

The gradient of [AB] is $\dfrac{4 - 2}{3 - -1} = \dfrac{2}{4} = \dfrac{1}{2}$

$\therefore$ the gradient of any perpendicular line is $-\dfrac{2}{1}$

∴   the equation of the perpendicular bisector is $2x + y = 2(1) + (3)$

or $2x + y = 5.$

EXERCISE 5E.4

1 Find the equation of the perpendicular bisector of [AB] for:

  a A(3, −3) and B(1, −1)
  b A(1, 3) and B(−3, 5)
  c A(3, 1) and B(−3, 6)
  d A(4, −2) and B(4, 4).

2 Two Post Offices are located at P(3, 8) and Q(7, 2) on a Council map. What is the equation of the line which should form the boundary between the two regions being serviced by the Post Offices?

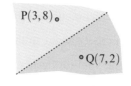

3 The **Voronoi** diagram alongside shows the location of three Post Offices and the corresponding regions of closest proximity. The Voronoi edges are the perpendicular bisectors of [AB], [BC] and [CA] respectively. Find:

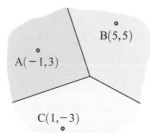

  a the equations of the Voronoi edges
  b the coordinates of the Voronoi vertex.

4

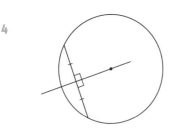

The perpendicular bisector of a chord of a circle passes through its centre.

Find the centre of a circle passing through points P(5, 7), Q(7, 1) and R(−1, 5) by finding the perpendicular bisectors of [PQ] and [QR] and solving them simultaneously.

5 Triangle ABC has the vertices shown. Find:

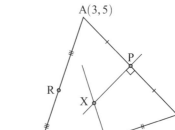

  a the coordinates of P, Q and R, the midpoints of [AB], [BC] and [AC] respectively
  b the equation of the perpendicular bisector of
    i [AB]   **ii** [BC]   **iii** [AC]
  c the coordinates of X, the point of intersection of the perpendicular bisector of [AB] and the perpendicular bisector of [BC].
  d Does the point X lie on the perpendicular bisector of [AC]?
  e What does your result from **d** suggest about the perpendicular bisectors of the sides of a triangle?
  f What is special about the point X in relation to the vertices of the triangle ABC?

F DISTANCE FROM A POINT TO A LINE

When we talk about the distance from a point to a line, we actually mean the *shortest* distance from the point to the line.

Suppose that N is the foot of the perpendicular from P to the line l.

If M is any point on the line other than at N, then $\triangle MNP$ is right angled with hypotenuse [MP], and so $MP \geqslant NP$.

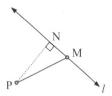

Consequently, NP is the shortest distance from P to line l.

So, the distance from a point to a line is the distance from the point to the foot of the perpendicular from P to the line.

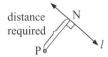

FINDING THE DISTANCE

To find the shortest distance from a point P to a line l we follow these steps:

Step 1: Find the gradient of the line l and the gradient of [PN].

Step 2: Find the equation of line segment [PN].

Step 3: Solve simultaneously the equations of line l and line segment [PN].

Step 4: Write down the coordinates of N.

Step 5: Find distance PN using the distance formula.

Example 26   ◀ᴖ) **Self Tutor**

Find the distance from P(7, -4) to the line with equation $2x + y = 5$.

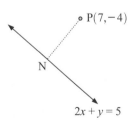

The gradient of $2x + y = 5$ is $-\frac{2}{1}$

$\therefore$ the gradient of [NP] is $\frac{1}{2}$

$\therefore$ the equation of (NP) is

$$x - 2y = (7) - 2(-4)$$

i.e., $x - 2y = 15$

So, we now solve simultaneously $\begin{cases} 2x + y = 5 \ \text{......} \ (1) \\ x - 2y = 15 \ \text{......} \ (2). \end{cases}$

$\quad\quad 4x + 2y = 10 \quad \{(1) \times 2\}$

$\quad\quad\ \ x - 2y = 15 \quad \{(2)\}$ When $x = 5$, $2(5) + y = 5$

$\therefore \ \ 5x \quad\quad = 25$ $\therefore \ \ 10 + y = 5$

$\therefore \quad x \quad\quad = 5$ $\therefore \quad\ \ y = -5$

$\therefore$ N is $(5, -5)$ So, $PN = \sqrt{(7-5)^2 + (-4--5)^2}$

$$= \sqrt{2^2 + 1^2}$$
$$= \sqrt{5} \text{ units}$$

EXERCISE 5F

1 Find the distance from:

   a $(7, -4)$ to $y = 3x - 5$ **b** $(-6, 0)$ to $y = 3 - 2x$

   c $(8, -5)$ to $y = -2x - 4$ **d** $(-10, 9)$ to $y = -4x + 3$

   e $(-2, 8)$ to $3x - y = 6$ **f** $(1, 7)$ to $4x - 3y = 8$

2 Find the distance between the following pairs of parallel lines:

   a $y = 3x + 2$ and $y = 3x - 8$ **b** $3x + 4y = 4$ and $3x + 4y = -16$

   Hint: Find a point on one of the lines and find the distance from this point to the other line.

3 A straight water pipeline passes through two points with map references $(3, 2)$ and $(7, -1)$ respectively. The shortest spur pipe from the pipeline to the farm P at $(9, 7)$ is [PN]. Find:

   a the coordinates of N

   b the length of the pipeline [PN] given that the grid reference scale is 1 unit $\equiv$ 0.5 km.

4 The distance from (h, k) to the lines $Ax + By + C = 0$ can be found using the formula $d = \dfrac{|Ah + Bk + C|}{\sqrt{A^2 + B^2}}.$

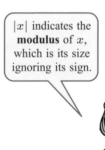

$|x|$ indicates the **modulus** of x, which is its size ignoring its sign.

So, in **Example 26**, the distance from $2x + y = 5$ to

$(7, -4)$ is $d = \dfrac{|2(7) + (-4) - 5|}{\sqrt{4 + 1}} = \dfrac{5}{\sqrt{5}} = \sqrt{5}$ units.

   a Use this formula to check your answers to question **1** above.

   b Prove 'the distance from a point to line' formula using the following steps:

     i Find the area of the shaded triangle using two different altitudes.

     ii Equate the areas to show that the distance from O$(0, 0)$ to

          $Ax + By + C = 0$ is $\dfrac{|C|}{\sqrt{A^2 + B^2}}.$

     iii Consider the second figure. Translate (h, k) and the line $Ax + By + C = 0$ by the same amount so that (h, k) moves to O$(0, 0)$. What is the equation of line 2?

     iv Use **ii** and **iii** to find d.

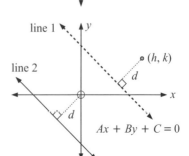

G | 3-DIMENSIONAL COORDINATE GEOMETRY (EXTENSION)

In 3-D coordinate geometry we need to specify an origin O and three mutually perpendicular axes, called the X-axis, the Y-axis and the Z-axis.

3D-POINT PLOTTER

Any point in space is specified using an ordered triple in the form (x, y, z).

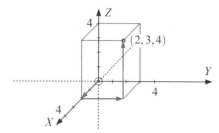

We generally suppose that the Y and Z-axes are in the plane of the page, and the X-axis is coming out of the page as shown.

The point $(2, 3, 4)$ is found by starting at the origin $O(0, 0, 0)$, moving 2 units along the x-axis, 3 units in the y-direction, and then 4 units in the z-direction.

We see that $(2, 3, 4)$ is located on the corner of a rectangular prism opposite O.

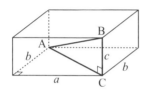

Now consider the rectangular prism illustrated, in which A is opposite B.

$$AC^2 = a^2 + b^2 \qquad \text{\{Pythagoras\}}$$
$$\text{and} \quad AB^2 = AC^2 + c^2 \quad \text{\{Pythagoras\}}$$
$$\therefore \quad AB^2 = a^2 + b^2 + c^2$$
$$\text{and so} \quad AB = \sqrt{a^2 + b^2 + c^2}$$

Consequently,

If A is (x_1, y_1, z_1) and B is (x_2, y_2, z_2) then
$$AB = \sqrt{(x_2 - x_1)^2 + (y_2 - y_1)^2 + (z_2 - z_1)^2}.$$

The **midpoint** of [AB] is $\left(\dfrac{x_1 + x_2}{2}, \dfrac{y_1 + y_2}{2}, \dfrac{z_1 + z_2}{2} \right)$.

Example 27 | ◀ૢ Self Tutor

For A(3, −1, 2) and B(−1, 2, 4), find:

  a the distance AB   **b** the midpoint of [AB].

---

a $\begin{aligned} AB &= \sqrt{(-1 - 3)^2 + (2 - -1)^2 + (4 - 2)^2} \\ &= \sqrt{(-4)^2 + 3^2 + 2^2} \\ &= \sqrt{16 + 9 + 4} \\ &= \sqrt{29} \text{ units} \end{aligned}$

b The midpoint is $\left(\dfrac{3 + -1}{2}, \dfrac{-1 + 2}{2}, \dfrac{2 + 4}{2} \right)$,

which is $(1, \frac{1}{2}, 3)$.

EXERCISE 5G

PRINTABLE 3-D
PLOTTER PAPER

1 On separate axes, plot the points:

   a $(4, 0, 0)$ **b** $(0, 2, 0)$ **c** $(0, 0, -3)$ **d** $(1, 2, 0)$

   e $(2, 0, 4)$ **f** $(0, 3, -1)$ **g** $(2, 2, 2)$ **h** $(2, -1, 3)$

   i $(4, 1, 2)$ **j** $(-2, 2, 3)$ **k** $(-1, 1, -1)$ **l** $(-3, 2, -1)$

2 For these pairs of points find: **i** the distance AB **ii** the midpoint of [AB].

   a $A(2, 3, -4)$ and $B(0, -1, 2)$ **b** $A(0, 0, 0)$ and $B(2, -4, 4)$

   c $A(1, 1, 1)$ and $B(3, 3, 3)$ **d** $A(-1, 2, 4)$ and $B(4, -1, 3)$

3 Find the nature of triangle ABC given that:

   a A is $(3, -3, 6)$, B is $(6, 2, 4)$ and C is $(4, -1, 3)$

   b A is $(1, -2, 2)$, B is $(-8, 4, 17)$ and C is $(3, 6, 0)$.

4 Find k if the distance from $P(1, 2, 3)$ to $Q(k, 1, -1)$ is 6 units.

5 Find the relationship between x, y and z if the point $P(x, y, z)$:

   a is always 2 units from $O(0, 0, 0)$

   b is always 4 units from $A(1, 2, 3)$.

Comment on your answers in each case.

6 Illustrate and describe these sets:

   a $\{(x, y, z) \mid y = 2\}$ **b** $\{(x, y, z) \mid x = 1, y = 2\}$

   c $\{(x, y, z) \mid x^2 + y^2 = 1, z = 0\}$ **d** $\{(x, y, z) \mid x^2 + y^2 + z^2 = 4\}$

   e $\{(x, y, z) \mid 0 \leqslant x \leqslant 2, 0 \leqslant y \leqslant 2, z = 3\}$

   f $\{(x, y, z) \mid 0 \leqslant x \leqslant 2, 0 \leqslant y \leqslant 2, 0 \leqslant z \leqslant 1\}$.

WHERE DOES THE FIGHTER CROSS THE COAST?

LINKS
click here

Areas of interaction:
Human ingenuity

REVIEW SET 5A

1 **a** Find the equation of the vertical line through $(-1, 5)$.

   b Find the distance between the points $S(7, -2)$ and $T(-1, 1)$.

   c Given $P(-3, 2)$ and $Q(3, -1)$, find the midpoint of [PQ].

   d Find the gradient of all lines perpendicular to a line with gradient $-\frac{1}{2}$.

   e Find the y-intercept for the line $4x - 3y = -9$.

   f Determine the gradient of the line with equation $4x + 5y = 11$.

   g Find the axes intercepts and gradient of the line with equation $2x + 3y = 6$.

2 If $X(-2, 3)$ and $Y(a, -1)$ are 6 units apart, find the value of a.

3 Determine the equation of the illustrated line:

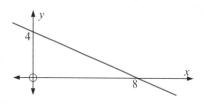

4 Find the equation of the line through $(1, -2)$ and $(3, 4)$.

5 Show that A$(1, -2)$, B$(4, 4)$ and C$(5, 6)$ are collinear.

6 Find b given that A$(-6, 2)$, B$(b, 0)$ and C$(3, -4)$ are collinear.

7 Find the axes intercepts for the line with equation $2x - 5y = 10$,   and hence draw a graph of this line.

8 Given A$(-3, 1)$, B$(1, 4)$ and C$(4, 0)$:

   a Show that triangle ABC is isosceles.

   b Find the midpoint X of [AC].

   c Use gradients to verify that [BX] is perpendicular to [AC].

9 Find the equation of the:

   a tangent to the circle with centre $(-1, 2)$ at the point $(3, 1)$

   b perpendicular bisector of [AB] for A$(2, 6)$ and B$(5, -2)$.

10 Find the shortest distance from A$(3, 5)$ to the line with equation $3x + 2y = 6$.

11 **a** For P$(-1, 2, 3)$ and Q$(1, -2, -3)$, find:

     i the distance PQ   **ii** the midpoint of [PQ].

   b Find k if P is $(1, 3, -1)$, Q is $(2, 1, k)$, and PQ $= \sqrt{30}$ units.

REVIEW SET 5B

1 **a** Find the midpoint of the line segment joining A$(-2, 3)$ to B$(-4, 3)$.

   b Find the distance from C$(-3, -2)$ to D$(0, 5)$.

   c Find the equation of the x-axis.

   d Find the gradient of all lines perpendicular to a line with slope $\frac{2}{3}$.

   e Write down the gradient and y-intercept of the line with equation $y = 5 - 2x$.

2 Determine the equation of the illustrated line:

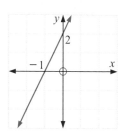

3 K$(-3, 2)$ and L$(3, m)$ are 9 units apart. Find m.

4 A$(-1, 2)$, B$(3, a)$ and C$(-3, 7)$ are collinear. Find a.

5 Find the equation of the line:

    a with gradient -2 and y-intercept 7

    b passing through $(-1, 3)$ and $(2, 1)$

    c parallel to a line with gradient $\frac{3}{2}$ and passing through $(5, 0)$.

6 If $(k, 5)$ lies on the line with equation $3x - y = -8$, find k.

7 Find the equation connecting the variables for the graph given.

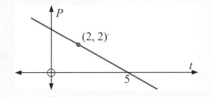

8 Given A$(-3, 2)$, B$(2, 3)$, C$(4, -1)$ and D$(-1, -2)$ are the vertices of quadrilateral ABCD:

    a Find the gradient of [AB] and [DC].

    b Find the gradient of [AD] and [BC].

    c What do you deduce from your answers to **a** and **b**?

    d Find the midpoints of the diagonals of the quadrilateral. What property of parallelograms does this check?

9 Find the equation of the:

    a tangent to the circle with centre $(-1, -3)$ at the point $(2, -1)$

    b perpendicular bisector of [PQ] for P$(-3, 7)$ and Q$(1, -1)$.

10 Find:

    a the coordinates of point N

    b the shortest distance from A to N.

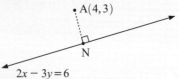

11 **a** How far is A$(-1, -2, 5)$ from the origin O?

    b P(x, y, z) is equidistant from $(-1, 1, 0)$ and $(2, 0, 0)$.
Deduce that $y = 3x - 1$.

Congruence and similarity

Contents:

CONGRUENCE AND SIMILARITY

We are similar.

We are congruent.

Two figures are **congruent** if they are identical in every respect, apart from position.

Two figures are **similar** if one figure is an enlargement of the other.

OPENING PROBLEM

If a group of people were each asked to draw triangle ABC in which $A\widehat{B}C = 40^o$, $B\widehat{C}A = 65^o$ and $C\widehat{A}B = 75^o$, would every person draw an identical triangle? In other words, if each triangle was cut out with a pair of scissors, would they match perfectly when placed on top of each other?

The question arises: "What information is sufficient to draw a **unique** triangle?"

You should find that:

- knowing the lengths of its three sides is sufficient
- knowing the size of its three angles is not sufficient.

A   CONGRUENCE OF FIGURES

In mathematics we use the term **congruent** to describe things which have the same shape and size. The closest we get to congruence in humans is identical twins.

EXERCISE 6A

1   Which of the following figures are congruent?

   a   b   c   d   e

2   Which of the following geometric figures are congruent?

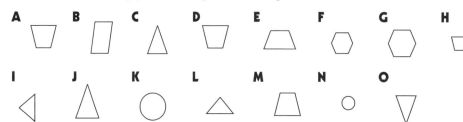

3 Here are some pairs of congruent geometric figures.

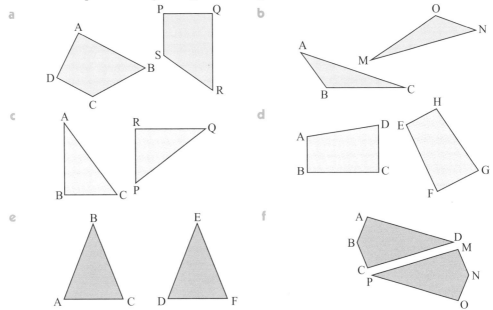

For each pair:

i identify the side in the second figure corresponding to the side [AB] in the first figure

ii identify the angle in the second figure corresponding to $A\widehat{B}C$ in the first figure.

B   CONSTRUCTING TRIANGLES

If several people are asked to accurately draw triangle ABC in which AB = 3 cm and BC = 2 cm, many different shaped triangles would probably be drawn.

Here are three such triangles:

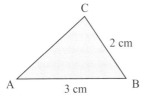
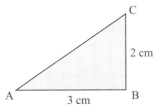
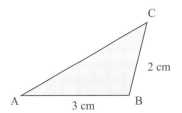

The information given is insufficient to draw a triangle of one particular shape.

However, if we are asked to accurately draw triangle ABC in which AB = 3 cm, BC = 2 cm and AC = 4 cm, one and only one triangular shape can be drawn.

The easiest way to draw this triangle is to use a ruler and compass construction.

Everyone using this construction would draw **the same** figure.

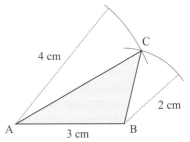

EXERCISE 6B

1 Construct a triangle which has sides of length:

   a 2 cm, 3 cm and 3 cm   b 2 cm, 3 cm and 4 cm
   c 2 cm, 3 cm and 5 cm   d 2 cm, 3 cm and 7 cm.

2 Copy and complete:
   "The sum of the lengths of any two sides of a triangle must be .... the length of the third side".

3 Draw a triangle ABC with all sides greater than 6 cm in length and with the angles at A, B and C being 60°, 50° and 70° respectively.

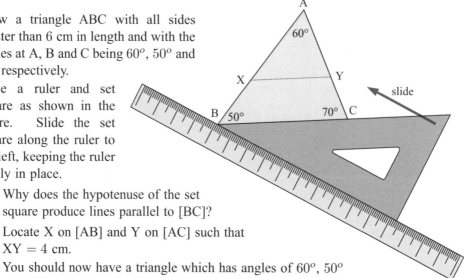

   Place a ruler and set square as shown in the figure.   Slide the set square along the ruler to the left, keeping the ruler firmly in place.

   a Why does the hypotenuse of the set square produce lines parallel to [BC]?

   b Locate X on [AB] and Y on [AC] such that XY = 4 cm.

   You should now have a triangle which has angles of 60°, 50° and 70°, and where the side opposite the 60° angle is 4 cm long.

INVESTIGATION   **CONSTRUCTING TRIANGLES**

You will need: a ruler, a sharp pencil, a protractor, and a compass.

What to do:

A   Given two sides and the included angle between them

1 Accurately draw triangle ABC in which AB = 5 cm, BC = 4 cm and $A\widehat{B}C = 50°$ by following these steps:

   a Draw [AB] first.
   b At B, use your protractor to draw the 50° angle.
   c From B measure 4 cm to locate C.   Join [AC].

   COMPUTER DEMO

2 Is it possible to draw this triangle just as accurately, in some other way, without using trial and error?

B   Given one angle is a right angle, the hypotenuse, and one other side

1   Accurately draw triangle PQR in which $P\widehat{Q}R = 90^o$, the hypotenuse PR is 4 cm and RQ is 2 cm by following these steps:

  a   Draw [RQ] first.

  b   At Q, use your protractor to draw a right angle.

  c   With your compass set at 4 cm and with its point at R, draw an arc to intersect the perpendicular at P.   Join [RP].

2   Is it possible to draw this triangle just as accurately, in some other way, without using trial and error?

C   Given two sides and a non-included angle

1   Accurately draw triangle XYZ in which XY = 6 cm, $Y\widehat{X}Z = 45^o$ and YZ = 5 cm by following these steps:

  a   Draw [XY] first.

  b   Use your protractor to draw an angle at X of 45°.

  c   With your compass set at 5 cm and with its point at Y, draw a circle.

  d   Locate Z on your figure. Show that there are *two* triangles which can be drawn which satisfy the original conditions.

D   Given two angles and a side

When given two angles, we are really given all three since the angles of a triangle sum to 180°. We saw earlier that this is not sufficient to draw a unique triangle. However, having one given side will fix the triangle's shape.

1   Draw triangle CDE where $C\widehat{D}E = 80^o$, $D\widehat{E}C = 40^o$,   and

  a   DE = 5 cm   **b**   CE = 5 cm   **c**   CD = 5 cm.

2   In each case, is one and only one triangle formed?

C   CONGRUENT TRIANGLES

Two triangles are **congruent** if they are identical in every respect except for position.

If one triangle was cut out with scissors and placed on the top of the other, they would match each other perfectly.

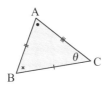
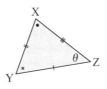

The above triangles are congruent.

We write $\triangle ABC \cong \triangle XYZ$,   where $\cong$ reads *"is congruent to"*.

Note: When writing the congruence statement above, we label the vertices that are in corresponding positions in the same order,   i.e., we write $\triangle ABC \cong \triangle XYZ$ but **not** $\triangle YXZ$ **or** $\triangle ZYX$, etc.

We have already seen how triangles being equiangular (having all three angles equal) is *not* a test for congruence.

For example, these triangles are equiangular but clearly triangle **B** is much larger than triangle **A**.

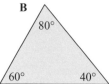

If we are given two sides and a non-included angle, more than one triangle can be drawn.

For example, triangles **C** and **D** have two equal sides and the same non-included angle, but they are *not* the same triangle.

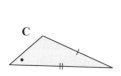
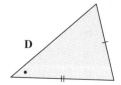

In the **Investigation** on *Constructing and drawing triangles* we saw that one and only one triangle can be drawn if we are given:

- two sides and the included angle between them
- one angle is a right angle, the hypotenuse, and one other side
- two angles and a side.

There are, however, four acceptable tests for the **congruence** of two triangles.

TESTS FOR TRIANGLE CONGRUENCE

Two triangles are congruent if one of the following is true:

- All corresponding sides are equal in length. (**SSS**)

- Two sides and the **included** angle are equal. (**SAS**)

- Two angles and a pair of **corresponding sides** are equal. (**AAcorS**)

- For right angled triangles, the hypotenuses and one other pair of sides are equal (**RHS**).

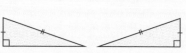

The information we are given will help us decide which test to use to prove two triangles are congruent. The diagrams in the following exercise are sketches only and **are not** drawn to scale. However, the information on them is **correct**.

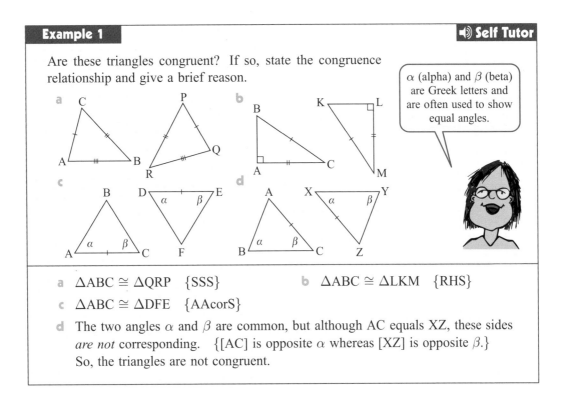

Example 1   🔊 **Self Tutor**

Are these triangles congruent? If so, state the congruence relationship and give a brief reason.

α (alpha) and *β* (beta) are Greek letters and are often used to show equal angles.

a △ABC ≅ △QRP {SSS}   **b** △ABC ≅ △LKM {RHS}

c △ABC ≅ △DFE {AAcorS}

d The two angles *α* and *β* are common, but although AC equals XZ, these sides *are not* corresponding.   {[AC] is opposite *α* whereas [XZ] is opposite *β*.}
  So, the triangles are not congruent.

EXERCISE 6C.1

1   In each set of three triangles, two are congruent. The diagrams are *not* drawn to scale. State which pair is congruent, together with a reason (SSS, SAS, AAcorS or RHS).

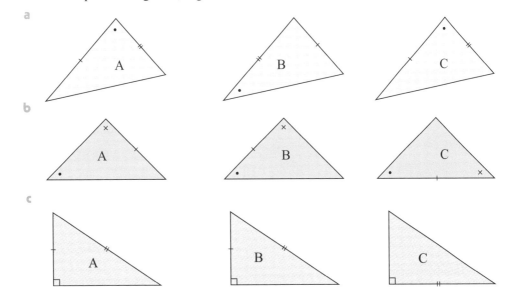

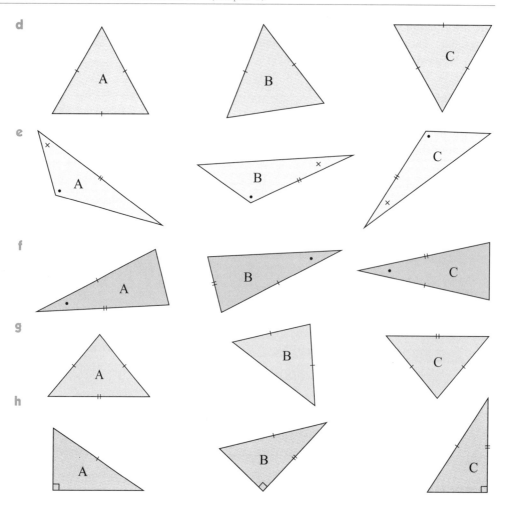

2 Are the following pairs of triangles congruent? If so, state the congruence relationship and give a brief reason.

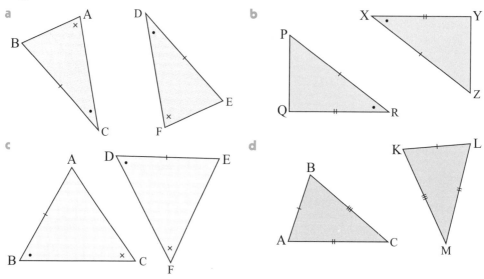

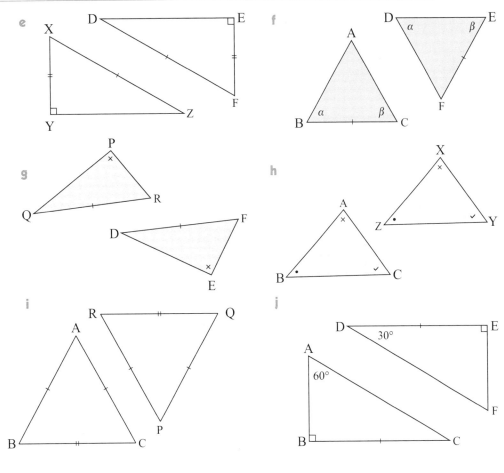

USING CONGRUENCE

Consider the figure opposite:

Are the two triangles congruent?

If so, what can we deduce about the length DE?

What else can we deduce about [DE]?

We could give this answer:

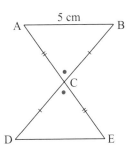

In △s ABC and EDC:

- BC = DC   {given}
- AC = EC   {given}
- A$\hat{C}$B = D$\hat{C}$E   {vertically opposite}

∴   △ABC ≅ △EDC: {SAS}

Consequently,   (1)   DE = BA = 5 cm

(2)   B$\hat{A}$C = D$\hat{E}$C   and so AB ∥ DE
{equal alternate angles}

We see from this example that congruence arguments give us a powerful tool for proving geometrical observations.

Example 2   ◀)) **Self Tutor**

Explain why △ABC and
△DBC are congruent:

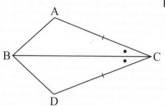

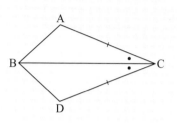

In △s ABC and DBC:

- AC = DC
- $A\widehat{C}B = D\widehat{C}B$
- [BC] is common to both.

∴   the triangles are congruent (SAS).

Example 3   ◀)) **Self Tutor**

Are there congruent triangles in
the given figure?

If so, what can be deduced?

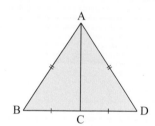

In △s ABC and ADC:
- AB = AD   {given}
- BC = DC   {given}
- [AC] is a common side.

∴   △s ABC and ADC are congruent {SSS}

Consequently,
- $B\widehat{A}C = D\widehat{A}C$
- $A\widehat{B}C = A\widehat{D}C$
- $A\widehat{C}B = A\widehat{C}D$,   and so   [AC] ⊥ [BD].

{the angles are equal and add to 180°}

Example 4   ◀)) **Self Tutor**

Triangle ABC is isosceles with AC = BC.
[BC] and [AC] are produced to E and D
respectively so that CE = CD.
Prove that AE = BD.

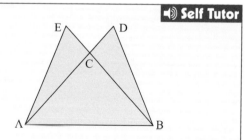

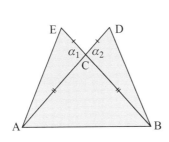

In triangles ACE and BCD:

- $AC = BC$ {given}
- $\alpha_1 = \alpha_2$ {vertically opposite}
- $CE = CD$ {given}

$\therefore$ the triangles are congruent (SAS) and in particular, $AE = BD$.

EXERCISE 6C.2

1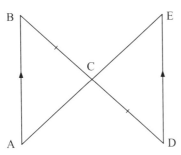

a   Explain why triangles ABC and EDC are congruent.

b   If $AC = 5$ cm and $\widehat{BAC} = 37°$, find:

   i   the length of [CE]

   ii   the size of $\widehat{DEC}$.

2   PQRS is a kite with longer diagonal [QS].

a   Show that the triangles are congruent.

b   What other facts can then be deduced about the figure?

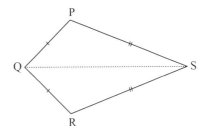

3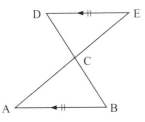

In the given figure, [DE] is parallel to [AB] and $DE = AB$.

a   Show that the triangles are congruent.

b   What other facts can then be deduced about the figure?

4   C is the centre of the circle.

a   Show that the figure contains congruent triangles.

b   What other facts can then be deduced about the figure?

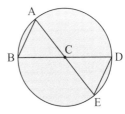

5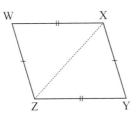

WXYZ is a quadrilateral with opposite sides equal. [XZ] is added to the figure.

a   Show that the two triangles created are congruent.

b   Hence deduce that WXYZ is a parallelogram.

6 Point P is equidistant from both [AB] and [AC]. Use congruence to show that P lies on the bisector of $B\hat{A}C$.

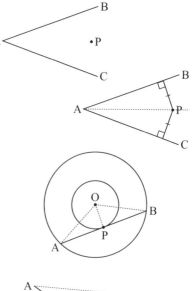

> **Note:** To find the distance from P to either line we draw perpendiculars from the point to each line.

7 Two concentric circles are drawn as shown. A tangent is drawn at P on the inner circle, and it meets the other circle at A and B.

Use triangle congruence to prove that P is the midpoint of [AB].

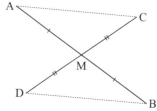

8 **a** Prove that triangles AMC and BMD are congruent.

  b Deduce that [AC] and [DB] are parallel and equal in length.

  c What can be deduced about the quadrilateral ACBD?

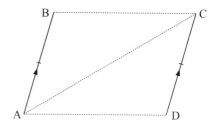

9 [AB] and [DC] are parallel and equal in length.

  a Show that Δs ABC and CDA are congruent.

  b Hence show that ABCD is a parallelogram.

  c Copy and complete: *"If a pair of opposite sides of a quadrilateral are parallel and equal in length, then the quadrilateral is ......"*

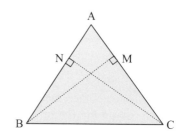

10 In ΔABC, [BM] is drawn perpendicular to [AC] and [CN] is drawn perpendicular to [AB].

Now if these perpendiculars are equal in length:

  a prove that Δs BCM and CBN are congruent

  b prove that ΔABC is isosceles.

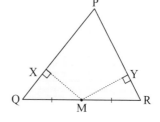

11 For ΔPQR, M is the midpoint of [QR] and [MX] is drawn perpendicular to [PQ]. [MY] is drawn perpendicular to [PR].

If the perpendiculars are equal in length:

  a prove that ΔMQX is congruent to ΔMRY

  b prove that ΔPQR is isosceles.

THE ISOSCELES TRIANGLE THEOREM AND ITS CONVERSES

Recall that:

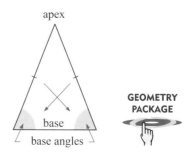

An **isosceles triangle** is a triangle in which two sides are equal in length.

The angles opposite the two equal sides are called the **base angles**.

The vertex where the two equal sides meet is called the **apex**.

THE ISOSCELES TRIANGLE THEOREM

In an isosceles triangle:
- the base angles are equal
- the line joining the apex to the midpoint of the base bisects the vertical angle and meets the base at right angles.

We actually proved this result in **Example 3**. You should look back at the working given.

CONVERSES OF THE ISOSCELES TRIANGLE THEOREM

With many theorems there are converses which we can use in problem solving. We have already seen one example in the converse to Pythagoras' theorem.

The isosceles triangle theorem has these converses:

Converse 1:   If a triangle has two equal angles then it is isosceles.

Converse 2:   The angle bisector of the apex of an isosceles triangle bisects the base at right angles.

Converse 3:   The perpendicular bisector of the base of an isosceles triangle passes through its apex.

EXERCISE 6C.3

1   Prove *Converse 2*.

2   In order to prove *Converse 1*, Sam draws a line from the apex to the midpoint of the base. He hopes to use congruence.

   a   Will he be successful?

   b   Will Sam be successful if he uses the second construction shown, which includes the perpendicular from the apex on the base?

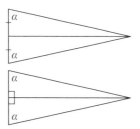

3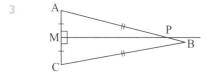

Mustafa is trying to prove *Converse 3*. He draws the perpendicular bisector of the base so that it does not pass through vertex B, but instead meets [AB] at some other point P. By joining [CP], help Mustafa complete his proof.

D   SIMILARITY

Two figures are **similar** if one is an enlargement of the other (regardless of orientation).

DISCUSSION

- Discuss whether the following pairs of figures are similar:

a   b    c

d    e    f

- Are congruent figures similar? Give reasons for your answer.

If two figures are similar then their corresponding sides are *in proportion*. This means that the lengths of sides will be increased (or decreased) by the same ratio from one figure to the next. This ratio is called the **enlargement factor**. We often denote it by k.

Consider the enlargement below for which the enlargement factor is 1.5.

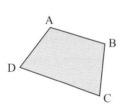

Since $k = 1.5$,   notice that $\dfrac{A'B'}{AB} = \dfrac{B'C'}{BC} = \dfrac{C'D'}{CD} = \dfrac{D'A'}{DA} = \dfrac{B'D'}{BD} = 1.5$.

Angle sizes do not change under enlargements.

> If two figures are **similar** then:
> - the figures are equiangular, and
> - the corresponding sides are *in proportion*.

SIMILAR TRIANGLES

> If two triangles are equiangular then they are **similar**.
>
> Similar triangles have corresponding sides in the same ratio.

To test if two triangles are similar, we need to show that:

- at least two pairs of angles are equal in size   *or*
- their sides are in proportion.

Example 5   ◀) **Self Tutor**

Show that the following figures possess similar triangles:

a

b

---

a

Δs ABC and ADE are equiangular as:

- $\alpha_1 = \alpha_2$ {equal corresponding angles}
- $\widehat{A}$ is common to both triangles

$\therefore$ the triangles are similar.

b

Δs ABC, EDC are equiangular as

- $\alpha_1 = \alpha_2$ {equal alternate angles}
- $\beta_1 = \beta_2$ {vertically opposite angles}

$\therefore$ the triangles are similar.

Example 6   ◀) **Self Tutor**

In the diagram given, establish that a
pair of triangles is similar and find x:

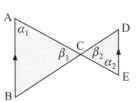

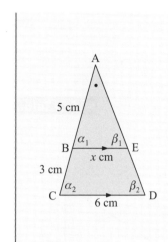

Δs ABE and ACD are similar as

$$\alpha_1 = \alpha_2 \quad \text{and} \quad \beta_1 = \beta_2 \quad \{\text{corresponding angles}\}$$

Corresponding sides must be in the same ratio, and so

$$\frac{AB}{AC} = \frac{BE}{CD}$$

$$\therefore \quad \frac{5}{5+3} = \frac{x}{6}$$

$$\therefore \quad \frac{x}{6} = \frac{5}{8}$$

$$\therefore \quad x = \frac{5}{8} \times 6$$

$$\therefore \quad x = 3.75$$

We label the vertices of the figure so that we can easily refer to them.

USEFUL TABLE

In similar triangle problems it is often useful to set up a table of side lengths that are opposite equal angles.

In **Example 6** this would be

	•	α	β
ΔABE	x	-	5
ΔACD	6	-	8

$$\therefore \quad \frac{x}{6} = \frac{5}{8}$$

EXERCISE 6D

1   Show that the following figures possess similar triangles:

a
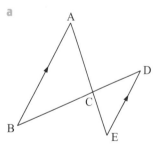

b
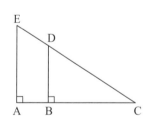

c
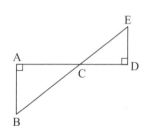

2   For the following figures, establish that a pair of triangles is similar, and hence find x:

a
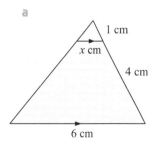

b
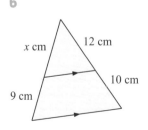

c
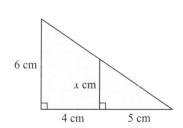

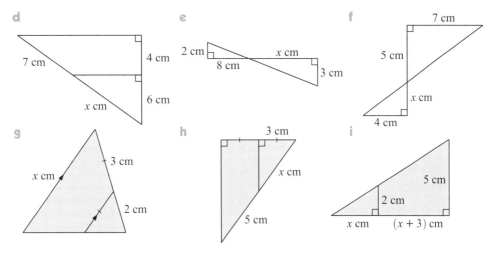

3 A ramp is built to enable wheel-chair access to a building that is 24 cm above ground level. The ramp has a constant slope of 2 in 15, which means that for every 15 cm horizontally it rises 2 cm. Calculate the length of the base of the ramp.

4 A boy who is 1.6 m tall casts a 2.4 m shadow when he stands 8.1 m from the base of an electric light pole. How high above the ground is the light globe?

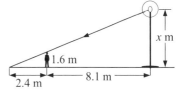

5

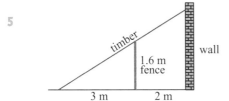

A piece of timber leaning against a wall, just touches the top of a fence, as shown. Find how far up the wall the timber reaches.

6 At the same time as the shadow cast by a vertical 30 cm long ruler is 45 cm long, Rafael's shadow is 264 cm long.

   a Draw a fully labelled sketch of the situation.   **b** Find Rafael's height.

7 There is an electric light post E on one side of a straight road, and a mail box M directly opposite on the other side of the road.

Taj walks 30 metres along the road away from E to point T.

Kanvar is 8 metres away from M at point S, so that E, M, and S are in a straight line. Kanvar walks 6 m parallel to the road in the opposite direction to Taj, to K. Now T, M and K are in a straight line.

Explain why triangles TEM and KSM are similar. Find the width of the road.

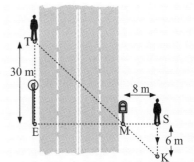

8 A 3.5 m ladder leans on a 2.4 m high fence. One
end is on the ground and the other end touches
a vertical wall 2.9 m from the ground.
How far is the bottom of the ladder
from the fence?

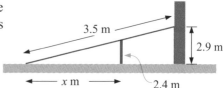

9 Two surveyors estimate the height of a nearby hill. One stands 5 m away from the other
on horizontal ground holding a 3 m stick vertically. The other surveyor finds a "line
of sight" to the top of the hill, and observes this line passes the vertical stick at 2.4 m.
They measure the distance from the stick to the top of the hill to be 1500 m using laser
equipment.
How high, correct to the nearest metre, is
their estimate of the height of the hill?

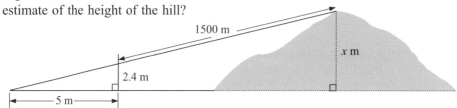

AREAS AND VOLUMES
OF SIMILAR FIGURES

RELATED AREAS

Consider the triangle illustrated with base b cm and
altitude a cm. If the base and altitude are multiplied
by the same positive constant k, a figure is obtained
which is *similar*.

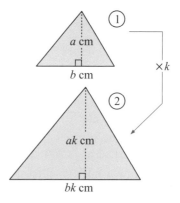

Notice that:

$$\frac{\text{Area (2)}}{\text{Area (1)}} = \frac{\frac{1}{2}(bk)(ak)}{\frac{1}{2}ba} = k^2.$$

This suggests that:

> If the corresponding sides of similar figures are in the ratio k, then:
>
> Area of image $= k^2 \times$ area of object.

For example, for the similar triangles alongside:

$$\frac{A}{6.2} = \left(\frac{8}{5}\right)^2$$

$$\therefore \quad A = 6.2 \times \tfrac{64}{25} = 15.872 \text{ cm}^2$$

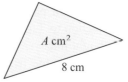

Example 7   ◀》 **Self Tutor**

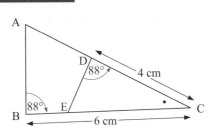

Triangle DEC has area 4.2 cm^2.

a   Find the area of triangle ABC.

b   Find the area of quadrilateral ABED.

The $\triangle$s DEC and BAC are equiangular and so are similar.

a $\dfrac{\text{area } \triangle \text{ABC}}{\text{area } \triangle \text{DEC}} = \left(\frac{6}{4}\right)^2 = 2.25$

$\therefore \quad \dfrac{\text{area } \triangle \text{ABC}}{4.2 \text{ cm}^2} = 2.25$

$\therefore \quad \text{area } \triangle \text{ABC} = 2.25 \times 4.2 \text{ cm}^2$

$= 9.45 \text{ cm}^2$

b   Area of ABED $= (9.45 - 4.2) \text{ cm}^2 = 5.25 \text{ cm}^2$

RELATED VOLUMES

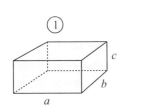

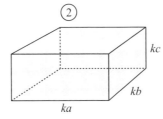

If the sides of a rectangular prism are all multiplied by k then

$$\frac{\text{Volume (2)}}{\text{Volume (1)}} = \frac{k^3 abc}{abc} = k^3.$$

This suggests that:

> If the corresponding sides of similar solids are in the ratio k, then:
>
> Volume of image $= k^3 \times$ volume of object.

EXERCISE 6E

1   For each pair of similar figures, find the unknown area.

a
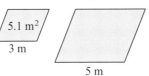

b
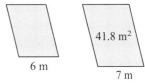

c

d
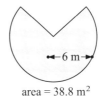

2 In the given figure, the area of $\triangle BCD$ is 6.4 cm². Find the area of:

    a $\triangle ACE$ **b** quadrilateral ABDE.

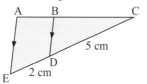

3 Find:

    a the value of x

    b the area of $\triangle PQT$ given quadrilateral QRST has area 22 m².

4 What will happen to the volume of:

    a a sphere if the radius is doubled

    b a sphere if the radius is increased by 20%

    c a cylinder if the radius and height are halved

    d a cylinder if the radius and height are increased by 50%?

5 A scale model is made of a 300 year old sailing ship. The model is a 1 : 200 reduction of the original. Find:

    a the height of the mast in the model if the original mast was 20 m high

    b the area of a sail in the model if the original sail was 120 m²

    c the height and radius of a keg in the model if the original was 1.2 m high and 0.9 m in diameter

    d the capacity of the water tank in the model if the capacity of the original was 10 000 litres.

THE USE OF MODELLING

LINKS
click here

Areas of interaction:
Approaches to learning

REVIEW SET 6A

1 Which of the following figures are congruent?

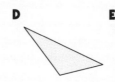

2 Using a ruler and compass, construct a triangle with sides of length 3 cm, 5 cm and 6 cm.

3 In each set of three triangles, two are congruent. The diagrams are not drawn to scale. State which pair is congruent, giving a reason (SSS, SAS, AAcorS or RHS).

    a **A**

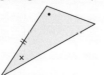
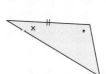

b **A**   **B**   **C**

4 ABCD is a quadrilateral with [AB] ∥ [DC].

  a Show that triangles ABC and ADC are congruent.

  b Deduce that ABCD is a parallelogram.

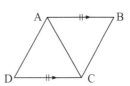

5 Show that the following figures possess similar triangles.

  a 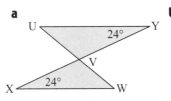 **b** 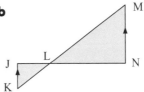 **c**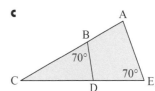

6 A, B and C are pegs on the bank of a canal which has parallel straight sides. C and D are directly opposite each other. AB = 30 m and BC = 140 m.

When I walk from A directly away from the bank, I reach a point E, 25 m from A, where E, B and D line up. How wide is the canal?

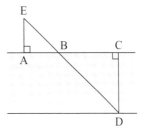

7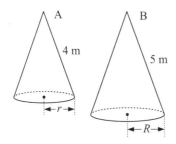

The slant heights of two similar cones are 4 m and 5 m respectively.

  a Find the ratio $R : r$.

  b What is the ratio of the surface areas for the curved part of each figure?

  c What is the ratio of the volumes of the cones?

8 If △ABC has area 15 cm²:

  a find the area of △CDE

  b find the area of PQED.

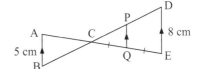

REVIEW SET 6B

1 In this pair of congruent figures:

  a Identify the side in the second figure corresponding to the side [AB] in the first figure.

  b Identify the angle in the second figure corresponding to A$\widehat{B}$C in the first figure.

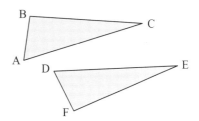

2 [AB] is a diameter of the circle.

  a Show that the figure contains congruent triangles.

  b What other facts can then be deduced about the figure?

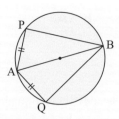

3 Using a compass and ruler, construct a triangle with sides of length 12 cm, 5 cm and 13 cm. What do you notice about this triangle?

4 In each the following figures, establish that a pair of triangles is similar, and find x:

a

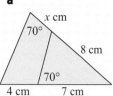

b

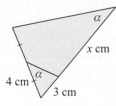

c

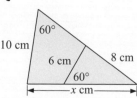

5

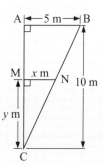

  a Show that $\triangle$s ABC and MNC are similar.

  b Hence, show that $y = 2x$.

  c The volume of a cone is given by $V = \frac{1}{3}\pi r^2 h$.

  Find the volume of water in the cone in terms of x.

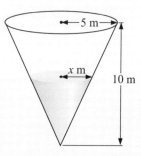

6 A sphere of lead is melted into 125 identical smaller spheres. If the radius of the original sphere was 10 cm, what is the radius of each new sphere?

7 In the given figure, triangle BCD has area 8 m^2 and quadrilateral ABDE has area 12 m^2.

Find the length of side [AE] correct to the nearest cm.

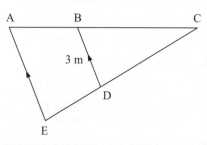

8

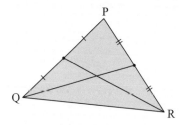

In triangle PQR, X is the midpoint of [PQ] and Y is the midpoint of [PR]. If [XR] and [QY] are equal in length:

  a prove that triangles XQR and YQR are congruent

  b prove that triangle PQR is isosceles.

Chapter 7

Transformation geometry

Contents:

TRANSFORMATIONS

A change in the size, shape, orientation or position of an object is called a **transformation**.

Reflections, rotations, translations and enlargements are all examples of transformations. We can describe these transformations mathematically using **transformation geometry**.

Many trees, plants, flowers, animals and insects are **symmetrical** in some way. Such symmetry results from a reflection, so we can describe symmetry using transformations.

In **transformation geometry** figures are changed (or transformed) in size, shape, orientation or position according to certain rules.

The original figure is called the **object** and the new figure is called the **image**.

We will consider the following **transformations**:

- **Translations** where every point moves a fixed distance in a given direction
- **Reflections** or mirror images
- **Rotations** about the origin O throught a given angle
- **Dilations** (enlargements and reductions) of three kinds:
  - ▸ with centre the origin
  - ▸ vertical, with x-axis fixed
  - ▸ horizontal, with y-axis fixed.

Here are some examples:

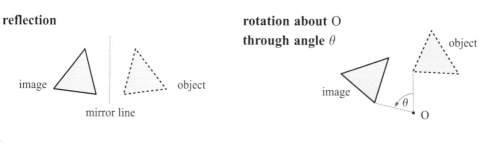

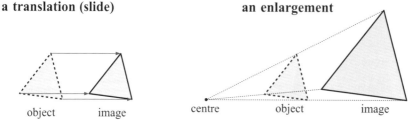

COMPUTER DEMO

A **TRANSLATIONS**

A **translation** moves an object from one place to another. Every point on the object moves the same distance in the same direction.

If P(x, y) is **translated** h units in the x-direction and k units in the y-direction to become P$'(x', y')$, then $x' = x + h$ and $y' = y + k$.

We write P(x, y) $\begin{pmatrix} h \\ k \end{pmatrix}$ P$'(x + h, y + k)$

where P$'$ is the **image** of the object P and $\begin{pmatrix} h \\ k \end{pmatrix}$ is called the **translation vector**.

$\left. \begin{array}{l} x' = x + h \\ y' = y + k \end{array} \right\}$ are called the **transformation equations**.

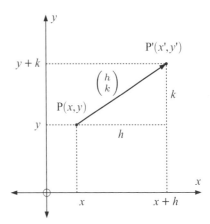

Example 1 ◀) **Self Tutor**

Triangle OAB with vertices O$(0, 0)$, A$(2, 3)$ and B$(-1, 2)$ is translated $\begin{pmatrix} 3 \\ 2 \end{pmatrix}$.

Find the image vertices and illustrate the object and image.

O$(0, 0)$ $\xrightarrow{\begin{pmatrix} 3 \\ 2 \end{pmatrix}}$ O$'(3, 2)$

A$(2, 3)$ $\xrightarrow{\begin{pmatrix} 3 \\ 2 \end{pmatrix}}$ A$'(5, 5)$

B$(-1, 2)$ $\xrightarrow{\begin{pmatrix} 3 \\ 2 \end{pmatrix}}$ B$'(2, 4)$

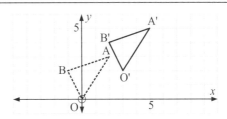

Example 2 ◀) **Self Tutor**

Find the image equation when $2x - 3y = 6$ is translated $\begin{pmatrix} -1 \\ 2 \end{pmatrix}$.
Check your result by graphing.

The transformation equations are
$$x' = x - 1 \quad \text{and} \quad y' = y + 2$$
$$\therefore \quad x = x' + 1 \quad \text{and} \quad y = y' - 2$$

So, we replace x by $(x + 1)$ and y by $(y - 2)$,
and $2x - 3y = 6$ becomes
$$2(x + 1) - 3(y - 2) = 6$$
$$\therefore \quad 2x + 2 - 3y + 6 = 6$$
$$\therefore \quad 2x - 3y = -2$$

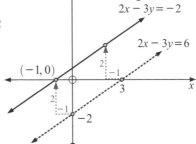

> The image line is parallel to the object line.

Example 3   ◀) **Self Tutor**

Find the image of $y = 2x^2$ under a translation with vector $\begin{pmatrix} 3 \\ -2 \end{pmatrix}$.

The transformation equations are $x' = x + 3$ and $y' = y - 2$
$$\therefore \quad x = x' - 3 \quad \text{and} \quad y = y' + 2$$

So, we replace x by $(x - 3)$ and y by $(y + 2)$
and $y = 2x^2$ becomes $(y + 2) = 2(x - 3)^2$
$$\therefore \quad y + 2 = 2(x^2 - 6x + 9)$$
$$\therefore \quad y = 2x^2 - 12x + 16$$

EXERCISE 7A

1 Copy and complete:

a $(2, -1) \underset{\begin{pmatrix} 3 \\ 4 \end{pmatrix}}{\longrightarrow} (\dots , \dots)$

b $(5, 2) \underset{\begin{pmatrix} -1 \\ 4 \end{pmatrix}}{\longrightarrow} (\dots , \dots)$

c $(3, -2) \underset{\begin{pmatrix} \dots \\ \dots \end{pmatrix}}{\longrightarrow} (3, 1)$

d $(\dots , \dots) \underset{\begin{pmatrix} -3 \\ 1 \end{pmatrix}}{\longrightarrow} (-3, 2)$

2 Find the image equations of the following, and if possible give your answers in the form $y = f(x)$. Use the transformation geometry package to check your answers.

TRANSFORMATION GEOMETRY

a $3x + 2y = 8$ under $\begin{pmatrix} -1 \\ 3 \end{pmatrix}$

b $x = 4$ under $\begin{pmatrix} 2 \\ 1 \end{pmatrix}$

c $2x - y = 6$ under $\begin{pmatrix} -3 \\ 0 \end{pmatrix}$

d $y = 5$ under $\begin{pmatrix} 2 \\ -5 \end{pmatrix}$

e $y = x^2$ under $\begin{pmatrix} 0 \\ 3 \end{pmatrix}$

f $y = -2x^2$ under $\begin{pmatrix} 3 \\ 2 \end{pmatrix}$

g $xy = 5$ under $\begin{pmatrix} -4 \\ 1 \end{pmatrix}$

h $xy = -8$ under $\begin{pmatrix} 3 \\ -2 \end{pmatrix}$

i $y = 2^x$ under $\begin{pmatrix} 0 \\ -3 \end{pmatrix}$

j $y = 3^{-x}$ under $\begin{pmatrix} 2 \\ 0 \end{pmatrix}$

3 What single transformation is equivalent to a translation of $\begin{pmatrix} 2 \\ 1 \end{pmatrix}$ followed by a translation of $\begin{pmatrix} 3 \\ 4 \end{pmatrix}$?

B   REFLECTIONS

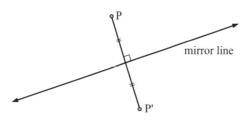

mirror line

When $P(x, y)$ is **reflected** in the **mirror line** to become $P'(x', y')$, the mirror line perpendicularly bisects $[PP']$.

Thus, for every point on an object, the mirror line perpendicularly bisects the line segment joining the point with its image.

We will concentrate on the following reflections:

$$\mathbf{M}_x \quad \text{the reflection in the } x\text{-axis}$$
$$\mathbf{M}_y \quad \text{the reflection in the } y\text{-axis}$$
$$\mathbf{M}_{y=x} \quad \text{the reflection in the line } y = x$$
$$\mathbf{M}_{y=-x} \quad \text{the reflection in the line } y = -x.$$

Example 4 ◀》 **Self Tutor**

Find the image of the point $(3, 1)$ in:

a $\mathbf{M}_x$ 　　　　 b $\mathbf{M}_y$ 　　　　 c $\mathbf{M}_{y=x}$ 　　　　 d $\mathbf{M}_{y=-x}$

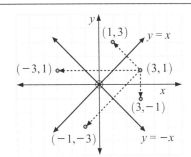

a $(3, 1) \xrightarrow{\mathbf{M}_x} (3, -1)$

b $(3, 1) \xrightarrow{\mathbf{M}_y} (-3, 1)$

c $(3, 1) \xrightarrow{\mathbf{M}_{y=x}} (1, 3)$

d $(3, 1) \xrightarrow{\mathbf{M}_{y=-x}} (-1, -3)$

The diagram in **Example 4** is useful for deducing the general equations of the four basic reflections.

For example,　from　$(3, 1) \xrightarrow{\mathbf{M}_{y=x}} (1, 3)$　we can see

that in general,　$(x, y) \xrightarrow{\mathbf{M}_{y=x}} (y, x)$.

$$\therefore \quad x' = y \quad \text{and} \quad y' = x$$

If you forget these or want to check any of them, choose a point such as $(3, 1)$.

$(x, y) \xrightarrow{\mathbf{M}_x} (x, -y)$ 　　　 $\therefore \quad x' = x$ 　and 　$y' = -y$

$(x, y) \xrightarrow{\mathbf{M}_y} (-x, y)$ 　　　 $\therefore \quad x' = -x$ 　and 　$y' = y$

$(x, y) \xrightarrow{\mathbf{M}_{y=x}} (y, x)$ 　　　 $\therefore \quad x' = y$ 　and 　$y' = x$

$(x, y) \xrightarrow{\mathbf{M}_{y=-x}} (-y, -x)$ 　　 $\therefore \quad x' = -y$ 　and 　$y' = -x$

Example 5 ◀》 **Self Tutor**

Find the image equation of $2x - 3y = 8$ reflected in the y-axis.

The transformation equations are 　　$x' = -x$ 　and 　$y' = y$

$$\therefore \quad x = -x' \quad \text{and} \quad y = y'$$

So, we replace x by $(-x)$ and leave y as is,

and $2x - 3y = 8$ becomes $2(-x) - 3(y) = 8$

$$\therefore \quad -2x - 3y = 8$$
$$\therefore \quad 2x + 3y = -8$$

EXERCISE 7B

1 Find, by graphical means, the image of:

   a $(4, -1)$ under $\mathbf{M}_x$

   b $(4, -1)$ under $\mathbf{M}_y$

   c $(4, -1)$ under $\mathbf{M}_{y=x}$

   d $(4, -1)$ under $\mathbf{M}_{y=-x}$

   e $(-1, -3)$ under $\mathbf{M}_x$

   f $(-1, -3)$ under $\mathbf{M}_y$

   g $(-1, -3)$ under $\mathbf{M}_{y=x}$

   h $(-1, -3)$ under $\mathbf{M}_{y=-x}$

2 Find the image equation of:

   a $y = 2x + 3$ under $\mathbf{M}_x$

   b $y = x^2$ under $\mathbf{M}_x$

   c $y = \dfrac{5}{x}$ under $\mathbf{M}_y$

   d $y = 2^x$ under $\mathbf{M}_{y=x}$

   e $2x + 3y = 4$ under $\mathbf{M}_{y=-x}$

   f $x^2 + y^2 = 4$ under $\mathbf{M}_x$

   g $y = -x^2$ under $\mathbf{M}_x$

   h $2x - 3y = 4$ under $\mathbf{M}_y$

   i $x = 3$ under $\mathbf{M}_{y=-x}$

   j $y = 2x^2$ under $\mathbf{M}_{y=x}$

3 Find the image of:

   a $(2, 3)$ under $\mathbf{M}_x$ followed by translation $\begin{pmatrix} -1 \\ 2 \end{pmatrix}$

   b $(4, -1)$ under $\mathbf{M}_{y=-x}$ followed by translation $\begin{pmatrix} 4 \\ 3 \end{pmatrix}$

   c $(-1, 5)$ under $\mathbf{M}_y$ followed by $\mathbf{M}_x$ followed by translation $\begin{pmatrix} 2 \\ -4 \end{pmatrix}$

   d $(3, -2)$ under $\mathbf{M}_{y=x}$ followed by translation $\begin{pmatrix} 3 \\ 4 \end{pmatrix}$

   e $(4, 3)$ under translation $\begin{pmatrix} 1 \\ -4 \end{pmatrix}$ followed by $\mathbf{M}_x$.

C   ROTATIONS

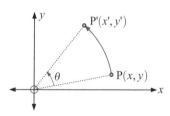

When $P(x, y)$ moves under a **rotation** about O through an angle of θ to a new position $P'(x', y')$, then $OP = OP'$ and $\widehat{POP'} = \theta$ where **positive** θ is measured **anticlockwise**.

O is the only point which does not move under the rotation.

Notation: $\mathbf{R}_\theta$ means "a rotation about O through an angle of θ^o".

We will concentrate on the following rotations:

(x, y) $\underset{\longrightarrow}{\mathbf{R}_{90}}$ $(-y, x)$ $\therefore$ $x' = -y$ and $y' = x$

(x, y) $\underset{\longrightarrow}{\mathbf{R}_{-90}}$ $(y, -x)$ $\therefore$ $x' - y$ and $y' = -x$

(x, y) $\underset{\longrightarrow}{\mathbf{R}_{180}}$ $(-x, -y)$ $\therefore$ $x' = -x$ and $y' = -y$

Example 6   ◄)) Self Tutor

Find the image of the point (3, 1) under: a R_{90} b R_{-90} c R_{180}

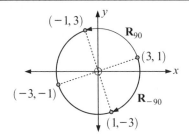

a (3, 1) $\underset{\longrightarrow}{R_{90}}$ (−1, 3)   anticlockwise

b (3, 1) $\underset{\longrightarrow}{R_{-90}}$ (1, −3)   clockwise

c (3, 1) $\underset{\longrightarrow}{R_{180}}$ (−3, −1)

Example 7   ◄)) Self Tutor

Find the image equation of the line $2x - 3y = -6$ under a clockwise rotation about O through $90°$.   Check by graphing.

Under the clockwise rotation R_{-90}, $x' = y$ and $y' = -x$

$$\therefore \quad x = -y' \quad \text{and} \quad y = x'$$

So, we replace x by $(-y)$ and y by (x), and $2x - 3y = -6$ becomes

$$2(-y) - 3(x) = -6$$
$$\therefore \quad -2y - 3x = -6$$
$$\therefore \quad 3x + 2y = 6$$

Check:

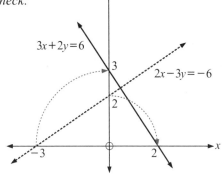

The image line has x-intercept 2 and y-intercept 3

$\therefore$ the slope is $-\frac{3}{2}$

$\therefore$ the equation is $3x + 2y = 3(2) + 2(0)$

$$\therefore \quad 3x + 2y = 6$$

EXERCISE 7C

1 Find the image of the point:

    a (−2, 3)   under R_θ where $\theta = 90°, -90°, 180°$

    b (4, −1)   under R_θ where $\theta = 90°, -90°, 180°$.

2 Find the image equation when:

    a $3x - 4y = 7$ is rotated clockwise through a quarter turn about O

    b $y = -3$ is rotated anticlockwise through $90°$ about O c $x = 7$ is rotated through 180° about O

    d $y = x^2$ is rotated through 180° about O

    e $2x + 3y = 12$ is rotated about O through 90° in a clockwise direction.

3 Find the image of:

    a $(2, 3)$ under $\mathbf{R}_{90}$ followed by $\mathbf{M}_x$

    b $(-2, 5)$ under $\mathbf{M}_{y=-x}$ followed by $\mathbf{R}_{-90}$

    c $(-3, -1)$ under $\mathbf{M}_{y=x}$ followed by $\mathbf{R}_{180}$

    d $(4, -2)$ under $\mathbf{R}_{90}$ followed by translation $\begin{pmatrix} -2 \\ -3 \end{pmatrix}$

    e $x - y = 8$ under $\mathbf{M}_{y=-x}$ followed by translation $\begin{pmatrix} 4 \\ -1 \end{pmatrix}$

    f $x + 2y = -4$ under $\mathbf{R}_{-90}$ followed by translation $\begin{pmatrix} 2 \\ -5 \end{pmatrix}$

    g $x + y = 1$ under $\mathbf{R}_{90}$ followed by $\mathbf{M}_{y=x}$ followed by translation $\begin{pmatrix} 3 \\ 1 \end{pmatrix}$.

DILATIONS

Dilations are enlargements or reductions. There are *three* types to consider:

DILATIONS WITH CENTRE THE ORIGIN

Suppose $P(x, y)$ moves to $P'(x', y')$ such that P' lies on the line (OP), and $\overrightarrow{OP'} = k\overrightarrow{OP}$.

We call this a **dilation** with centre O and factor k.

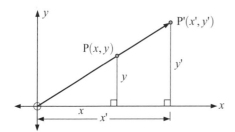

From the similar triangles

$$\frac{x'}{x} = \frac{y'}{y} = \frac{OP'}{OP} = k$$

$$\therefore \quad \begin{cases} x' = kx \\ y' = ky \end{cases}$$

The **transformation equations** for a **dilation** with

centre O$(0, 0)$ and **factor** k are: $\begin{cases} x' = kx \\ y' = ky. \end{cases}$

Example 8   ◀》 **Self Tutor**

Consider the triangle ABC with vertices A$(1, 1)$, B$(4, 1)$ and C$(1, 4)$ under a dilation with centre O and factor   a $k = 2$ b $k = \frac{1}{2}$.

Find the position of the image of $\triangle$ABC under each dilation.

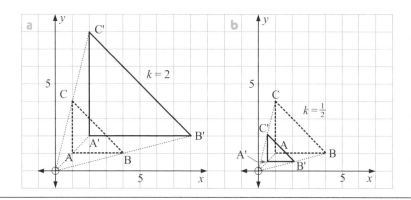

We can see from the examples above that:

> If $k > 1$, the image figure is an **enlargement** of the object.

> If $0 < k < 1$, the image figure is a **reduction** of the object.

INVESTIGATION 1   NEGATIVE DILATION FACTORS

Your task is to investigate dilations with centre O and with *negative* dilation factor k.

What to do:

1 Consider the rectangle with coordinates A(2, 1), B(6, 1), C(2, 3) and D(6, 3).
   Dilate the rectangle with centre O and factor:
   a $k = -2$ **b** $k = -\frac{1}{2}$.

2 Generalise your results in **1** to describe the effect of a dilation with centre O and factor k where:
   a $-1 < k < 0$ **b** $k < -1$.

Example 9   ◀ᴺ) Self Tutor

Find the equation of the image figure when $y = x^2$ is dilated with centre O and factor 3. Illustrate.

Since $k = 3$, $x' = 3x$ and $y' = 3y$

$\therefore \quad x = \frac{x'}{3}$ and $y = \frac{y'}{3}$

So, we replace x by $\left(\frac{x}{3}\right)$ and y by $\left(\frac{y}{3}\right)$,

and $y = x^2$ becomes $\frac{y}{3} = \left(\frac{x}{3}\right)^2$

$\therefore \quad \frac{y}{3} = \frac{x^2}{9}$

$\therefore \quad y = \frac{1}{3}x^2$

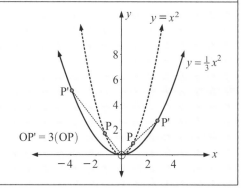

VERTICAL DILATIONS WITH FIXED x-AXIS

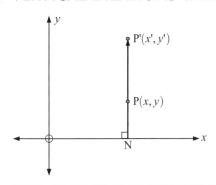

Suppose P(x, y) moves to P$'(x', y')$ such that P$'$ lies on the line through N$(x, 0)$ and P, and $\overrightarrow{NP'} = k\overrightarrow{NP}$.

We call this a **vertical dilation** with factor k.

For a **vertical dilation** with **factor** k, the **transformation equations** are:
$$\begin{cases} x' = x \\ y' = ky. \end{cases}$$

| **Example 10** | ◀) **Self Tutor** |

Consider the triangle ABC with   A(1, 1),   B(5, 1)   and   C(1, 4)   under a vertical dilation with factor   **a** $k = 2$ **b** $k = \frac{1}{2}$.

Find the position of the image of $\triangle$ABC under each dilation.

a 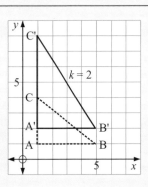   **b**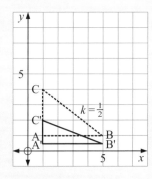

HORIZONTAL DILATIONS WITH FIXED y-AXIS

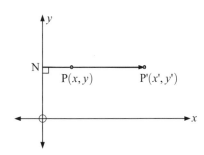

Suppose P(x, y) moves to P$'(x', y')$ such that P$'$ lies on the line through N$(0, y)$ and P, and $\overrightarrow{NP'} = k\overrightarrow{NP}$.

We call this a **horizontal dilation** with factor k.

For a **horizontal dilation** with **factor** k, the **transformation equations** are:
$$\begin{cases} x' = kx \\ y' = y. \end{cases}$$

| **Example 11** | ◀) **Self Tutor** |

Consider the triangle ABC with   A(1, 1), B(5, 1) and C(1, 4)   under a horizontal dilation with factor   **a** $k = 2$ **b** $k = \frac{1}{2}$.

Find the position of the image of $\triangle$ABC under each dilation.

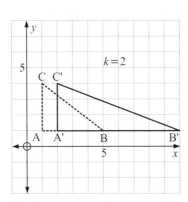

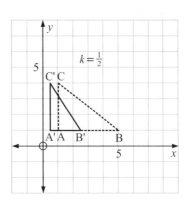

Example 12

Find the image of a circle with centre O and radius 3 units, under a horizontal dilation with factor 2.

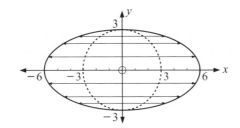

$x' = 2x$ and $y' = y$

∴   the horizontal distances from the y-axis are doubled, whilst the y-values remain the same.

The image is an ellipse.

EXERCISE 7D

1   Find the image of:

   a   (2, 3) under a dilation with centre O and factor 3

   b   (−1, 4) under a dilation with centre O and factor $\frac{1}{3}$

   c   (3, −1) under a vertical dilation with factor 4

   d   (4, 5) under a vertical dilation with factor 2

   e   (−2, 1) under a horizontal dilation with factor $\frac{1}{2}$

   f   (3, −4) under a horizontal dilation with factor $\frac{3}{2}$.

2   Find the image equation of:

   a $y = 2x + 3$ under a dilation with centre O and factor 2

   b $y = -x^2$ under a dilation with centre O and factor $\frac{1}{2}$

   c $y = 2x^2$ under a horizontal dilation with factor 4

   d $xy = 2$ under a horizontal dilation with factor 2

   e $y = 2^x$ under a vertical dilation with factor 2.

3   Find the image of a circle with centre O and radius 2 units under:

    a   a dilation with centre O and factor $\frac{3}{2}$

    b   a vertical dilation with factor $\frac{3}{2}$

    c   a horizontal dilation with factor $\frac{3}{2}$.

INVESTIGATION 2   LINEAR TRANSFORMATIONS

If $P(x, y)$ moves to $P'(x', y')$ under a transformation with equations

$$\begin{cases} x' = ax + by \\ y' = cx + dy \end{cases}$$

where a, b, c, and d are real numbers, then we say we have a **linear transformation**.

The purpose of this investigation is to examine the effect of a linear transformation on the **sense** and **area** of the image compared with the object.

What to do:

1   Alongside is the **unit square** with vertices O(0, 0), A(1, 0), B(1, 1), and C(0, 1).

If we perform the linear transformation

$$\begin{cases} x' = 3x + y \\ y' = x + 2y \end{cases}$$

then $O(0,0) \rightarrow O'(0,0)$
$\quad\quad\quad A(1,0) \rightarrow A'(3,1)$
$\quad\quad\quad B(1,1) \rightarrow B'(4,3)$
$\quad\quad\quad C(0,1) \rightarrow C'(1,2)$.

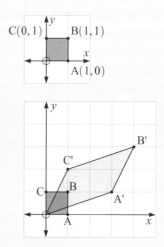

Notice that:

- OABC is labelled anticlockwise and O'A'B'C' is also labelled anticlockwise. In this case we say that the **sense** of the object has been **preserved**. Otherwise, we would say the sense was **reversed**.

- We can show that O'A'B'C' has area 5 units^2.
  So, the area of the image $= 5\times$ the area of the object.

For the following linear transformations, determine the effect that each has on the unit square's sense and area:

    a $\begin{cases} x' = 2x + y \\ y' = x + 2y \end{cases}$ **b** $\begin{cases} x' = x + y \\ y' = x - y \end{cases}$ **c** $\begin{cases} x' = 2x \\ y' = 2y \end{cases}$

    d $\begin{cases} x' = 2x \\ y' = y \end{cases}$ **e** $\begin{cases} x' = x - 3y \\ y' = x + y \end{cases}$ **f** $\begin{cases} x' = -2x + y \\ y' = 3x + 2y \end{cases}$

2 Consider the general linear transformation $\begin{cases} x' = ax + by \\ y' = cx + dy. \end{cases}$

   a Show that sense is preserved if $ad - bc > 0$,   and is reversed if $ad - bc < 0$.
   Does this result agree with your answers in **1**?

   b If k is the modulus or absolute value of $ad - bc$,   i.e., $k = |ad - bc|$,   show
   that the area of the image $= k \times$ the area of the object.

TRANSFORMING ART

LINKS
click here

Areas of interaction:
Environments/Human ingenuity

REVIEW SET 7A

1 Find the image equation of the following translations:

   a $3x - 2y = 6$ under $\begin{pmatrix} -1 \\ 4 \end{pmatrix}$
   b $y = 2$ under $\begin{pmatrix} -4 \\ 1 \end{pmatrix}$

   c $2x + y = 5$ under $\begin{pmatrix} 2 \\ 3 \end{pmatrix}$
   d $y = 2x^2$ under $\begin{pmatrix} 2 \\ -5 \end{pmatrix}$.

2 Find the image of:

   a $(2, -5)$ under $\mathbf{M}_y$
   b $(-3, 6)$ under $\mathbf{M}_{y=x}$

   c $(-1, 5)$ under $\mathbf{R}_{-90}$
   d $(3, -5)$ under $\mathbf{R}_{90}$.

3 Find the equation of the image of:

   a $y = 3x + 2$ under $\mathbf{M}_y$
   b $y = 3x^2$ under $\mathbf{M}_x$

   c $y = 3^x$ under $\mathbf{M}_{y=x}$
   d $xy = 6$ under $\mathbf{M}_{y=-x}$.

4 Find the image of:

   a $(5, 1)$ under $\mathbf{R}_{180}$ followed by translation $\begin{pmatrix} 2 \\ 3 \end{pmatrix}$

   b $(-2, 4)$ under $\mathbf{M}_y$ followed by $\mathbf{M}_x$.

5 Find the image of:

   a $(2, -1)$ under a dilation with centre O and factor 2

   b $(3, 5)$ under a vertical dilation with factor 4

   c $(-4, -7)$ under a horizontal dilation with factor 2.

6 Find the image equation of:

   a $y = 3x + 2$ under a dilation with centre O and factor 3

   b $2x - 5y = 10$ under a vertical dilation with factor 2

   c $y = -2x + 1$ under a horizontal dilation with factor $\frac{1}{2}$

   d $y = x^2 - 3x + 5$ under a reflection in the x-axis

   e $x^2 + y^2 = 4$ under the translation $\begin{pmatrix} 5 \\ -2 \end{pmatrix}$.

REVIEW SET 7B

1 Find the image of:

   a $(3, -2)$ under $\mathbf{M}_x$

   b $(5, -4)$ under $\mathbf{M}_{y=-x}$

   c $(-2, -5)$ under $\mathbf{R}_{180}$

   d $(-2, 7)$ under $\mathbf{R}_{-90}$.

2 Find the image equation for the translation:

   a $5x - 2y = 8$ under $\begin{pmatrix} 3 \\ -2 \end{pmatrix}$

   b $y = -x^2$ under $\begin{pmatrix} -2 \\ 5 \end{pmatrix}$

   c $xy = -4$ under $\begin{pmatrix} 1 \\ -2 \end{pmatrix}$

   d $x^2 + y^2 = 9$ under $\begin{pmatrix} -3 \\ -4 \end{pmatrix}$.

3 Find the equation of the image of:

   a $3x - 4y = 8$ under $\mathbf{M}_{y=x}$

   b $xy = -12$ under $\mathbf{R}_{180}$

   c $2x + 3y = 9$ under $\mathbf{R}_{90}$

   d $y = -2x^2$ under $\mathbf{M}_x$.

4 Find the image of:

   a $(3, -7)$ under $\mathbf{M}_y$ followed by translation $\begin{pmatrix} 2 \\ -6 \end{pmatrix}$

   b $(3, -2)$ under $\mathbf{M}_{y=-x}$ followed by $\mathbf{R}_{-90}$.

5 Find the image of:

   a $(3, 5)$ under a dilation with centre O and factor 3

   b $(-2, 3)$ under a horizontal dilation with factor 2

   c $(-5, -3)$ under a vertical dilation with factor $\frac{1}{2}$.

6 Find the image equation of:

   a $y = -2x + 1$ under a vertical dilation with factor 3

   b $y = 2 - 5x$ under a horizontal dilation with factor $\frac{1}{3}$

   c $2x - 6y = 7$ under a dilation with centre O and factor 2

   d $y = 2x^2 - 3x - 1$ under $\mathbf{R}_{90}$

   e $x^2 + y^2 = 8$ under the translation $\begin{pmatrix} -3 \\ -4 \end{pmatrix}$.

Chapter 8

Univariate data analysis

Contents:

HISTORICAL NOTE

- Florence Nightingale (1820-1910), the famous "lady with the lamp", developed and used graphs to represent data relating to hospitals and public health.

- Today about 92% of all nations conduct a census at regular intervals. The UN gives assistance to developing countries to help them with census procedures, so that accurate and comparable worldwide statistics can be collected.

OPENING PROBLEM 1

Kelly grows pumpkins and wishes to investigate the effect of an organic fertiliser on the number of pumpkins harvested.

She hopes that the fertiliser will significantly increase the number of pumpkins harvested per plant.

In identical soils she has planted many seeds in two patches, one using the fertiliser and the other not. All other factors such as watering have been kept the same for both patches.

Random plants are selected and the number of pumpkins counted. The results are:

Without fertiliser

4 7 8 3 9	8 6 5 9 7	8 7 8 4 6
7 6 8 6 7	6 6 7 8 8	4 7 7 7 3
5 5 8 9 7	4 9 6 9 7	

With fertiliser

8 10 4 10 15	4 9 7 11 10	8 8 6 10 10
9 5 9 6 7	5 7 7 9 8	6 5 7 8 7
2 6 9 7 10	6 8 7 10 8	

For you to consider:

- Can you state clearly the problem that Kelly wants to solve?
- How has Kelly tried to make a fair comparison?
- How could Kelly have made sure that her selection was at random?
- What is the best way of organising this data?
- What are suitable methods for displaying the data?
- Are there any abnormally high or low results, and how should they be treated?
- How can she best indicate the most typical yield per plant?
- How can we best indicate the spread of the data?
- Can a satisfactory conclusion be made?

STATISTICAL TERMINOLOGY

STATISTICS

Statistics is the art of solving problems and answering questions by collecting and analysing data.

The facts or pieces of information we collect are called **data**. Data is the plural of the word *datum*, which means a single piece of information.

A list of information is called a **data set** and because it is not in an organised form it is called **raw data**.

THE STATISTICAL METHOD

The process of **statistical enquiry** (or **investigation**) includes the following steps:

Step 1: Examining a problem which may be solved using data and posing the correct question(s).

Step 2: Collecting data.

Step 3: Organising the data.

Step 4: Summarising and displaying the data.

Step 5: Analysing the data, making a conclusion in the form of a conjecture.

Step 6: Writing a report.

VARIABLES

There are two types of variables that we commonly deal with:

- A **categorical variable** is one which describes a particular quality or characteristic. It can be divided into **categories**. The information collected is called **categorical data**.

  Examples of categorical variables are:

  Getting to school: the categories could be train, bus, car and walking.
      Colour of eyes: the categories could be blue, brown, hazel, green, and grey.

- A **quantitative variable** is one which has a numerical value, and is often called a **numerical variable**. The information collected is called **numerical data**.

  Quantitative variables can be either discrete or continuous.

  A **quantitative discrete variable** takes exact number values and is often a result of **counting**.

  Examples of discrete quantitative variables are:

  The number of people in a household: the variable could take the values 1, 2, 3,...
          The score out of 30 for a test: the variable could take the values
                          0, 1, 2, 3, ..., 30.

- A **quantitative continuous variable** takes numerical values within a certain continuous range. It is usually a result of **measuring**.

  Examples of quantitative continuous variables are:

  ▶ *The weight of newborn babies:*   the variable could take any positive value on the number line but is likely to be in the range 0.5 kg to 7 kg.

  ▶ *The heights of Year 10 students:*   the variable would be measured in centimetres. A student whose height is recorded as 145 cm could have exact height anywhere between 144.5 cm and 145.5 cm.

CENSUS OR SAMPLE

The two types of data collection are by census or sample.

> A **census** is a method which involves collecting data about every individual in a *whole population*.

The individuals in a population may be people or objects. A census is detailed and accurate but is expensive, time consuming, and often impractical.

> A **sample** is a method which involves collecting data about a *part of the population* only.

A sample is cheaper and quicker than a census but is not as detailed or as accurate. Conclusions drawn from samples always involve some error.

A sample must truly reflect the characteristics of the whole population. It must therefore be **unbiased** and **sufficiently large**.

> A **biased sample** is one in which the data has been unfairly influenced by the collection process and is not truly representative of the whole population.

EXERCISE 8A.1

1 Classify the following variables as either categorical or numerical:

    a the time taken to travel to school

    b the number of cousins a person has

    c voting intention at the next election

    d the number of cars in a household

    e the speed of cars on a particular stretch of highway

    f favourite type of apple

    g town or city where a person was born

    h the weight of three-year-old children.

2 Write down the possible categories for the following categorical variables:

    a gender   b favourite football code

    c hair colour   d type of fuel used in a car.

3 For each of the following possible investigations, classify the variable as categorical, quantitative discrete or quantitative continuous:

  a the number of goals scored each week by a hockey team

  b the weights of the members of a basketball team

  c the most popular TV station

  d the number of kittens in each litter

  e the number of bread rolls bought each week by a family

  f the pets owned by students in your class

  g the number of leaves on a rose plant stem

  h the number of hours of daylight each day in winter

  i the number of people who die from heart attacks each year in a given city

  j the amount of rainfall in each month of the year

  k the countries of origin of refugees

  l the reasons people use public transport

  m the stopping distances of cars doing 80 km h^{-1}

  n the number of cars passing through an intersection per hour

  o the pulse rates of a group of hockey players at rest.

4 State whether a census or a sample would be used for these investigations:

  a the reasons for people using taxis

  b the heights of the basketballers at a particular school

  c finding the percentage of people in a city who suffer from asthma

  d the resting pulse rates of members of your favourite sporting team

  e finding the country of origin of immigrants

  f the amount of daylight each month where you live.

5 Discuss any possible bias in the following situations:

  a only Year 12 students are interviewed about changes to the school uniform

  b motorists stopped in peak hour are interviewed about traffic problems

  c real estate agents are interviewed about the prices of houses

  d a 'who will you vote for' survey at an expensive city restaurant.

STATISTICAL GRAPHS

Two variables under consideration are usually linked by one being *dependent* on the other.

For example, the *total cost of a dinner* depends on *the number of guests present.*
We say that *the total cost of a dinner* is the **dependent variable**, and *the number of guests present* is the **independent variable**.

In general, when we draw **graphs** involving two variables, the *independent variable* is placed on the **horizontal axis** and the *dependent variable* is placed on the **vertical axis**. An exception to this is when we draw a horizontal bar chart.

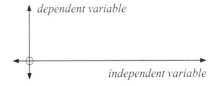

Acceptable graphs to display categorical data are:

Vertical column graph   **Horizontal bar chart**   **Pie chart**   **Segment bar chart**

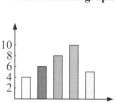   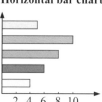   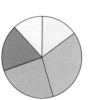   

For categorical data, the **mode** is the category which occurs most frequently. In the graphs above, the mode is the green category.

INTERNET STATISTICS

There are thousands of sites worldwide which display statistics for everyone to see. Sites which show statistics that are important on a global scale include:

- www.un.org   for the United Nations
- www.who.int   for the World Health Organisation

GRAPHING STATISTICS USING A COMPUTER PACKAGE

There are many available software packages which enable us to graph data.

One common way to store and display data is to use a spreadsheet. Click on the icon to obtain instructions for graphing data using a computer spreadsheet.

SPREADSHEET

Now click on the other icon to obtain a graphing package for statistics. Experiment with the different types of graphs it can produce. Enter some data of your own and print the results.

STATISTICS PACKAGE

EXERCISE 8A.2

1 At a school, children were randomly chosen and asked to nominate their favourite fruit. The following data was collected:

Type of fruit	Frequency
Apple	20
Banana	24
Grapes	3
Orange	11
Mandarin	10
Nectarine	7
Pear	2
Peach	3

  a What are the variables in this investigation?
  b What is the dependent variable?
  c What is the sample size?
  d If we are trying to find out the favourite fruit of children in general, is the sample unbiased?
  e If we are only interested in the favourite fruit of 368 children within the school, is the sample unbiased?
  f What is the mode?
  g Using a computer package, construct a vertical column graph to illustrate the data.

2 55 randomly selected Year 10 students were asked to nominate their favourite subject studied at school. The results of the survey are displayed in the bar chart shown.

a   What are the variables in this investigation?

b   What are the dependent and independent variables?

c   What is the mode?

d   What given information indicates that the sample was unbiased?

e   If there are 173 Year 10 students at the school, is the sample size sufficient?

f   Construct a pie chart for the data. If possible, use a spreadsheet.

3 Warren read the following report from the local paper:

OUR CHANGING POPULATION

A spokesperson from the Statistics Bureau reported today that the number of persons per household has reached an all time low. Some of the reasons suggested for this decline were: women having fewer children and at a later stage in their lives because they want to establish their careers, more couples choosing not to have children at all, and it being more expensive than at any time previously to raise children.

In the past large families were common. It was cheaper to raise children as the 'necessities' of life were basic compared with the current times. Few married women had paid employment outside the home.

Whilst there have been fluctuations in family size over the last hundred years, such as the 'baby boom' following World War II, it is now seen as unlikely that we will ever return to the large families of the past.

Warren decided to put this statement to the test in his local town of Boodernut. He applied for and received census data from the Statistics Bureau, a copy of which is given alongside.

a   Find the population sizes of the town in:
  i   1935   ii   1960   iii   1985

b   Prepare a table of percentages for the town's population data (correct to 1 decimal place).

Private household size of Boodernut			
Number of	*Year*		
persons	1935	1960	1985
1	9	8	69
2	68	177	184
3	73	162	248
4	109	374	162
5+	178	283	38
Totals			

c   Using the data, write a brief discussion and conclusion which compares the changes in the household sizes over the 1935 to 1985 period.

B   QUANTITATIVE (NUMERICAL) DATA

Recall that:

> A **quantitative variable** is one which has a numerical value, and is often called a **numerical variable**. The information collected is called **numerical data**.

Quantitative variables can be either discrete or continuous and they each have an appropriate way to organise and display the data collected for them.

> A **quantitative discrete variable** takes exact number values and is often a result of **counting**.

Some examples are:

- *The number of pets in a household:*   the variable could take the values of 0, 1, 2, 3, 4, ...

- *Shoe size:*   the variable could take the values of 3, $3\frac{1}{2}$, 4, $4\frac{1}{2}$, 5, $5\frac{1}{2}$, ...

> A **quantitative continuous variable** takes numerical values within a certain continuous range. It is usually a result of **measuring**.

Some examples are:

- *The weight of Year 10 students:*   the variable can take any positive value from about 40 kg to 120 kg. Theoretically the variable could take any value on the number line but is very unlikely to take a value outside the range given.

- *The time taken to get to school:*   the variable can take any value from about 1 minute to 80 minutes.

ORGANISATION AND DISPLAY OF DISCRETE DATA

In the **Opening Problem** on page **170**, the quantitative discrete variable is: *the number of pumpkins per plant*.

To organise the data a **tally-frequency table** could be used. We count the data systematically and use a '|' to indicate each data value. We use ⦀⦀ to represent 5.

Below is the table for *Without fertiliser*:

Number of pumpkins/plant	Tally	Frequency
3	||	2
4	||||	4
5	|||	3
6	⦀⦀ ||	7
7	⦀⦀ ⦀⦀ |	11
8	⦀⦀ |||	8
9	⦀⦀	5

A **column graph** or **dot plot** could be used to display the results.

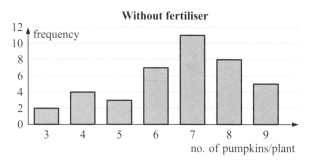

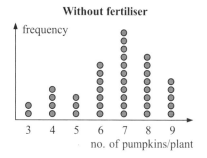

DISCUSSION

Are there any advantages or disadvantages in using a dot plot rather than a column graph?

From both graphs we can make observations and calculations such as:

- 7 pumpkins per plant is the **mode** of the *Without fertiliser* data since this is the value which occurred most frequently.

- 5% of the plants with no fertiliser had fewer than 4 pumpkins on them.

DESCRIBING THE DISTRIBUTION OF THE DATA SET

The **mode** of a data set is the most frequently occurring value(s).   Many data sets show **symmetry** or **partial symmetry** about the mode.

If we place a curve over the column graph we see that this curve shows symmetry. We say that we have a **symmetrical distribution**.

For the *Without fertiliser* data we have the distribution alongside. It is said to be **negatively skewed** because, by comparison with the symmetrical distribution, it has been 'stretched' on the left (or negative) side of the mode.

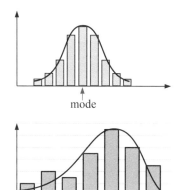

So, we have:

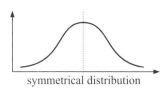

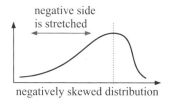

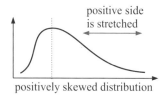

OUTLIERS

Outliers are data values that are either much larger or much smaller than the general body of data. Outliers appear separated from the body of data on a frequency graph.

For example, in the data set: 3, 1, 7, 6, 8, 18, 2, 6, 7, 7, the data value 18 is an outlier. Some outliers are genuine and must be included in an analysis of the whole data set. However, other outliers may not reflect the truth and should not be considered. These may be due to human error or some other factor.

EXERCISE 8B

1   State whether these quantitative (or numerical) variables are discrete or continuous:

   a   the time taken to run 1500 metres

   b   the maximum temperature reached on a March day

   c   the weight of cargo taken on a ship

   d   the time taken for a battery to run down

   e   the number of trips made by a taxi

   f   the number of people in a theatre

   g   the number of minutes spent sending text messages per day.

2   20 students were asked "How many TV sets do you have in your household?" and the following data was collected: 2 1 0 3 1 2 1 3 4 0 0 2 2 0 1 1 0 1 0 1

   a   What is the variable in this investigation?

   b   Is the data discrete or continuous? Why?

   c   Construct a dot plot to display the data. Use a heading for the graph, and add an appropriate scale and label to each axis.

   d   How would you describe the distribution of the data? Is it symmetrical, positively skewed or negatively skewed? Are there any outliers?

   e   What percentage of the households had no TV sets?

   f   What percentage of the households had three or more TV sets?

3   A randomly selected sample of shoppers was asked, 'How many times did you shop at a supermarket in the past week?' A column graph was constructed for the results.

   a   How many shoppers gave data in the survey?

   b   How many of the shoppers shopped once or twice?

   c   What percentage of the shoppers shopped more than four times?

   d   Describe the distribution of the data.

4   Employees of a company were asked to record the number of times they left the company office on business appointments during one week. The following dot plot was constructed from the data:

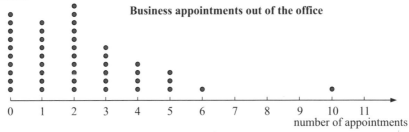

Business appointments out of the office

    a What is the variable in this investigation?

    b Explain why the data is discrete numerical data.

    c What percentage of the employees did not leave the office?

    d What percentage of the employees left the office more than 5 times?

    e What was the most frequent number of business appointments out of the office?

    f Describe the distribution of the data.

    g How would you describe the data value '10'?

5 The number of toothpicks in a box is stated as 50 but the actual number of toothpicks has been found to vary. To investigate this, the number of toothpicks in a box was counted for a sample of 60 boxes:

50 52 51 50 50 51 52 49 50 48 51 50 47 50 52 48 50 49 51 50
49 50 52 51 50 50 52 50 53 48 50 51 50 50 49 48 51 49 52 50
49 49 50 52 50 51 49 52 52 50 49 50 49 51 50 50 51 50 53 48

    a What is the variable in this investigation?

    b Is the data continuous or discrete numerical data?

    c Construct a frequency table for this data.

    d Display the data using a bar chart.

    e Describe the distribution of the data.

    f What percentage of the boxes contained exactly 50 toothpicks?

6 Revisit the **Opening Problem** on page **170**. Using the *With fertiliser* data:

    a Organise the data in a tally-frequency table.

    b Draw a column graph of the data.

    c Are there any outliers?

    d Is the data skewed?

    e What evidence is there that the fertiliser increases the number of pumpkins per plant?

    f Can it be said that the fertiliser will increase the farmer's pumpkin crop and therefore her profits?

C   GROUPED DISCRETE DATA

In situations where there are lots of different numerical values recorded, it may not be practical to use an ordinary tally-frequency table, or to display the data using a dot plot or column graph.

For example, a local hardware store is concerned about the number of people visiting the store at lunch time.

Over 30 consecutive week days they recorded data.

The results were:

37, 30, 17, 13, 46, 23, 40, 28, 38, 24, 23, 22, 18, 29, 16,
35, 24, 18, 24, 44, 32, 54, 31, 39, 32, 38, 41, 38, 24, 32.

In situations like this, grouping the data into **class intervals** is appropriate. It seems sensible to use class intervals of length 10 in this case.

The tally-frequency table is:

Number of people	Tally	Frequency
10 to 19	⦚⦚⦚	5
20 to 29	⦚⦚⦚ ||||	9
30 to 39	⦚⦚⦚ ⦚⦚⦚ |	11
40 to 49	||||	4
50 to 59	|	1
	Total	30

STEM-AND-LEAF PLOTS

A **stem-and-leaf plot** (often called a stem-plot) is a way of writing down the data in groups and is used for small data sets. It shows actual data values and gives a visual comparison of frequencies.

For numbers with two digits, the first digit forms part of the **stem** and the second digit forms a **leaf**.

For example, for the data value 17,   1 is recorded on the stem, and the 7 is a leaf value.

The **stem-and-leaf plot** is:

Stem	Leaf
1	73868
2	384329444
3	70852192882
4	6041
5	4 **Note:** 1 | 7 means 17.

The **ordered stem-and-leaf plot** is:

Stem	Leaf
1	36788
2	233444489
3	01222578889
4	0146
5	4

The ordered stemplot arranges all data from smallest to largest.

Notice the following features:

- all the actual data is shown
- the minimum (smallest) data value is 13
- the maximum (largest) data value is 54
- the 'thirties' interval (30 to 39) occurred most often, and is the **modal class**.

EXERCISE 8C

1 The data set below is the test scores (out of 100) for a Science test for 50 students.

92	29	78	67	68	58	80	89	92
69	66	56	88	81	70	73	63	55
67	64	62	74	56	75	90	56	47
59	64	89	39	51	87	89	76	59
72	80	95	68	80	64	53	43	61
71	38	44	88	62				

a Construct a tally and frequency table for this data using class intervals 0 - 9, 10 - 19, 20 - 29, ..., 90 - 100.

b What percentage of the students scored 80 or more for the test?

c What percentage of students scored less than 50 for the test?

d Copy and complete the following:
   More students had a test score in the interval .... than in any other interval.

2 **a** Draw a stem-and-leaf plot using stems 2, 3, 4, and 5 for the following data:
   29, 27, 33, 30, 46, 40, 35, 24, 21, 58, 27, 34, 25, 36, 57, 34, 42, 51, 50, 48

  b Redraw the stem-and-leaf plot from **a** so that it is ordered.

3 For the ordered stem-and-leaf plot given, find:

Stem	Leaf
0	1 3 7
1	0 3 4 7 8 8 9
2	0 0 1 2 2 3 5 5 6 8 9
3	2 4 4 5 8 9
4	3

1 | 8   represents 18

a the minimum value

b the maximum value

c the number of data with a value greater than 25

d the number of data with a value of at least 40

e the percentage of the data which is less than 15.

4 A test score out of 60 marks is recorded for a group of 45 students:

34	37	44	51	53	39	33	58	40	42	43	43	47	37	35
41	43	48	50	55	44	44	52	54	59	39	31	29	44	57
45	34	29	27	18	49	41	42	37	42	43	43	45	34	51

a Construct a stem-and-leaf plot for this data using 0, 1, 2, 3, 4, and 5 as the stems.

b Redraw the stem-and-leaf plot so that it is ordered.

c What advantage does a stem-and-leaf plot have over a frequency table?

d What is the **i** highest **ii** lowest   mark scored for the test?

e If an 'A' is awarded to students who scored 50 or more for the test, what percentage of students scored an 'A'?

f What percentage of students scored less than half marks for the test?

g Describe the distribution of the data.

D   CONTINUOUS DATA

A **continuous numerical variable** can theoretically take any value on part of the number line. A continuous variable often has to be **measured** so that data can be recorded.

Examples of continuous numerical variables are:

The height of Year 10 students: the variable can take any value from about 100 cm to 200 cm.

The speed of cars on a stretch of highway: the variable can take any value from 0 km h^{-1} to the fastest speed that a car can travel, but is most likely to be in the range 50 km h^{-1} to 150 km h^{-1}.

ORGANISATION AND DISPLAY OF CONTINUOUS DATA

When data is recorded for a continuous variable there are likely to be many different values. This data is therefore organised using **class intervals**. A special type of graph called a **frequency histogram** is used to display the data.

A histogram is similar to a column graph but, to account for the continuous nature of the variable, the 'columns' are joined together.

An example is given alongside:

The **modal class**, which is the class of values that appears most often, is easy to identify from a histogram.

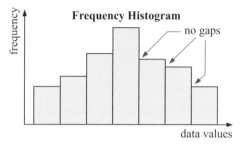

SUMMARY OF COLUMN GRAPHS AND FREQUENCY HISTOGRAMS

Column graphs and frequency histograms both have the following features:

- on the **vertical axis** we have the **frequency** of occurrence
- on the **horizontal axis** we have the range of scores
- **column widths are equal** and the height varies according to frequency.

Histograms have no gaps between the columns because they are used for **continuous** data.

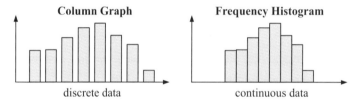

Column Graph	Frequency Histogram
discrete data	continuous data

Example 1   ◀ᴈ **Self Tutor**

The weights of parcels sent on a given day from a post office were, in kilograms:
2.9, 4.0, 1.6, 3.5, 2.9, 3.4, 3.2, 5.2, 4.6, 3.1, 2.8, 3.7, 4.9, 3.4, 1.3, 2.5, 2.2
Organise the data using a frequency table and graph the data.

The data is *continuous* since the weight could be any value from 0.1 kg up to 6 kg. The lowest weight recorded is 1.3 kg and the highest is 5.2 kg so we will use class intervals of 1 kg. The class interval $2 - < 3$ includes all weights from 2 kg up to, but not including, 3 kg.

A frequency histogram is used to graph this continuous data.

Weight (kg)	Frequency
$1 - < 2$	2
$2 - < 3$	5
$3 - < 4$	6
$4 - < 5$	3
$5 - < 6$	1

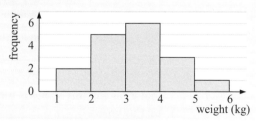

A stemplot could also be used to organise the data:

Note: The modal class is (3 - < 4) kg as this occurred most frequently.

Stem	Leaf
1	3 6
2	2 5 8 9 9
3	1 2 4 4 5 7
4	0 6 9
5	2 *Scale:* 2	9 means 2.9 kg.

EXERCISE 8D

1   A frequency table for the weights of a volleyball squad is given below.

   a   Explain why 'weight' is a continuous variable.

   b   Construct a frequency histogram for the data. The axes should be carefully marked and labelled, and you should include a heading for the graph.

   c   What is the modal class? Explain what this means.

   d   Describe the distribution of the data.

Weight (kg)	Frequency
75 - < 80	2
80 - < 85	5
85 - < 90	8
90 - < 95	7
95 - < 100	5
100 - < 105	1

2   A school has conducted a survey of 50 students to investigate the time it takes for them to travel to school. The following data gives the travel times to the nearest minute:

16	8	10	17	25	34	42	18	24	18	45	33	40
3	20	12	10	10	27	16	37	45	15	16	26	16
14	18	15	27	19	32	6	12	14	20	10	16	
21	25	8	32	46	14	15	20	18	8	10	25	

   a   Is travel time a discrete or continuous variable?

   b   Construct an ordered stemplot for the data using stems   0, 1, 2, ...

   c   Describe the distribution of the data.

   d   Copy and complete:
   "The modal travelling time was between ..... and ..... minutes."

3   For the following data, state whether a frequency histogram or a column graph should be used and draw the appropriate graph.

   a   Most appealing car colour:

Colour	white	red	blue	black	other
Frequency	47	44	31	23	18

   b   The number of students in classes:

Number of students	21	22	23	24	25	26	27
Frequency	1	4	7	9	15	8	2

   c   The time taken to make a pizza (to the nearest min):

Time (min)	5	6	7	8	9	10	11
Frequency	1	2	3	7	10	8	5

d The heights of 25 netball players (to the nearest cm):

Height (cm)	140 - 149	150 - 159	160 - 169	170 - 179	180 - 189
Frequency	2	3	7	9	4

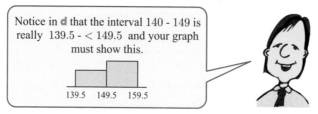

Notice in **d** that the interval 140 - 149 is really 139.5 - < 149.5 and your graph must show this.

139.5   149.5   159.5

e The 'best times' of 45 swimmers:

Time (sec)	50 - < 60	60 - < 70	70 - < 80	80 - < 90	90 - < 100
Frequency	8	23	7	4	3

4 A plant inspector takes a random sample of ten week old plants from a nursery and measures their height in millimetres.

The results are shown in the table alongside.

Height (mm)	Frequency
20 - < 40	4
40 - < 60	17
60 - < 80	15
80 - < 100	8
100 - < 120	2
120 - < 140	4

a Represent the data on a frequency histogram.

b How many of the seedlings are 40 mm or more?

c What percentage of the seedlings are between 60 and 80 mm?

d The total number of seedlings in the nursery is 857. Estimate the number of seedlings which measure: **i** less than 100 mm   **ii** between 40 and 100 mm.

E   MEASURING THE CENTRE

We can get a better understanding of a data set if we can locate the **middle** or **centre** of the data and get an indication of its **spread**. Knowing one of these without the other is often of little use.

There are *three statistics* that are used to measure the **centre** of a data set. These are: the **mean**, the **median** and the **mode**.

THE MEAN

The **mean** of a data set is the statistical name for the arithmetic average.

$$\text{mean} = \frac{\textbf{the sum of all data values}}{\textbf{the number of data values}}$$

or $\bar{x} = \dfrac{\sum x}{n}$ where $\sum x$ is the sum of the data

The mean gives us a single number which indicates a centre of the data set. It is not necessarily a member of the data set.

For example, a mean test mark of 67% tells us that there are several marks below 67% and several above it. 67% is at the centre, but it does not mean that one of the students scored 67%.

THE MEDIAN

The **median** is the *middle value* of an ordered data set.

An ordered data set is obtained by listing the data, usually from smallest to largest.
The median splits the data in halves. Half of the data are less than or equal to the median and half are greater than or equal to it.

For example, if the median mark for a test is 67% then you know that half the class scored less than or equal to 67% and half scored greater than or equal to 67%.

Note: For an **odd number** of data, the median is one of the data.
For an **even number** of data, the median is the average of the two middle values and may not be one of the original data.

If there are n data values, find the value of $\dfrac{n+1}{2}$.

The median is the $\left(\dfrac{n+1}{2}\right)$th data value.

For example:

If $n = 13$, $\frac{13+1}{2} = 7$,   so the median = 7th ordered data value.

If $n = 14$, $\frac{14+1}{2} = 7.5$,   so the median = average of 7th and 8th ordered data values.

THE MODE

The **mode** is the most frequently occurring value in the data set.

Example 2   ◀) Self Tutor

The number of small aeroplanes flying into a remote airstrip over a 15-day period
is   5 7 0 3 4 6 4 0 5 3 6 9 4 2 8.   For this data set, find:

  a   the mean   b   the median   c   the mode.

---

a   mean $= \dfrac{5+7+0+3+4+6+4+0+5+3+6+9+4+2+8}{15}$ $\longleftarrow \Sigma x$

$\hspace{8em}\longleftarrow n$

$\hspace{3em} = \frac{66}{15}$

$\hspace{3em} = 4.4$ aeroplanes

b   The ordered data set is: 0̶ 0̶ 2̶ 3̶ 3̶ 4̶ 4̶ 4̶ 5̶ 5̶ 6̶ 6̶ 7̶ 8̶ 9̶ $\{$as $n = 15$, $\frac{n+1}{2} = 8\}$

$\hspace{3em} \therefore$ median = 4 aeroplanes

c   4 is the score which occurs the most often $\therefore$ mode = 4 aeroplanes

Suppose that on the next day, 6 aeroplanes land on the airstrip in **Example 2**. We need to recalculate the measures of the centre to see the effect of this new data value.

We expect the mean to rise as the new data value is greater than the old mean.

In fact, the new mean $= \dfrac{66+6}{16} = \dfrac{72}{16} = 4.5$ aeroplanes.

The new ordered data set is: $\cancel{0\,0}\,2\,3\,3\,4\,4\ \underbrace{4\,5}_{\text{two middle scores}}\ \cancel{5\,6\,6\,6\,7\,8\,9}$

$\therefore\quad$ median $= \dfrac{4+5}{2} = 4.5$ aeroplanes

This new data set has two modes, 4 and 6 aeroplanes, and we say that the data set is **bimodal**.

Note:

- If a data set has three or more modes, we do not use the mode as a measure of the middle.
- Consider the data: 2 4 7 3 5 8 5 6 5 6 4 3 7 6 5 4

    The dot plot of this data is:

    For this data the mean, median and mode are all 5.

Equal or approximately equal values of the mean, mode and median *may* indicate a *symmetrical distribution* of data. However, we should always check using a graph before calling a data set symmetric.

Example 3   ◀ Self Tutor

The mean of six scores is 78.5. What is the sum of the scores?

$$\dfrac{\text{sum}}{6} = 78.5$$

$\therefore\quad$ sum $= 78.5 \times 6$

$\qquad\quad = 471$

$\therefore\quad$ the sum of the scores is 471.

Example 4   ◀ Self Tutor

Find x if 10, 7, 3, 6 and x have a mean of 8.

There are 5 scores.

$\therefore\quad \dfrac{10+7+3+6+x}{5} = 8$

$\therefore\quad \dfrac{26+x}{5} = 8$

$\therefore\quad 26+x = 40$

$\therefore\quad x = 14$

EXERCISE 8E.1

1 Find the i mean ii median iii mode for each of the following data sets:

  a 12, 17, 20, 24, 25, 30, 40

  b 8, 8, 8, 10, 11, 11, 12, 12, 16, 20, 20, 24

  c 7.9, 8.5, 9.1, 9.2, 9.9, 10.0, 11.1, 11.2, 11.2, 12.6, 12.9

  d 427, 423, 415, 405, 445, 433, 442, 415, 435, 448, 429, 427, 403, 430, 446, 440, 425, 424, 419, 428, 441

2 Consider the following   *Data set A:*   5, 6, 6, 7, 7, 7, 8, 8, 9, 10, 12
  two data sets: *Data set B:*   5, 6, 6, 7, 7, 7, 8, 8, 9, 10, 20

  a Find the mean for both *Data set A* and *Data set B*.

  b Find the median of both *Data set A* and *Data set B*.

  c Explain why the mean of *Data set A* is less than the mean of *Data set B*.

  d Explain why the median of *Data set A* is the same as the median of *Data set B*.

3 The selling price of $158 000, $290 000, $290 000, $1.1 million, $900 000,
  nine houses are: $395 000, $925 000, $420 000, $760 000

  a Find the mean, median and modal selling prices.

  b Explain why the mode is an unsatisfactory measure of the middle in this case.

  c Is the median a satisfactory measure of the middle of this data set?

4 The following raw data is the daily rainfall (to the nearest millimetre) for the month of February 2007 in a city in China:

  0, 4, 1, 0, 0, 0, 2, 9, 3, 0, 0, 0, 8, 27, 5, 0, 0, 0, 0, 8, 1, 3, 0, 0, 15, 1, 0, 0

  a Find the mean, median and mode for the data.

  b Give a reason why the median is not the most suitable measure of centre for this set of data.

  c Give a reason why the mode is not the most suitable measure of centre for this set of data.

  d Are there any outliers in this data set?

  e On some occasions outliers are removed because they are not typical of the rest of the data and are often due to errors in observation and/or calculation. If the outliers in the data set were accurately found, should they be removed before finding the measures of the middle?

5 A basketball team scored 38, 52, 43, 54, 41 and 36 points in their first six matches.

  a Find the mean number of points scored for the first six matches.

  b What score does the team need to shoot in their next match to maintain the same mean score?

  c The team scores only 20 points in the seventh match. What is the mean number of points scored for the seven matches?

  d If the team scores 42 points in their eighth and final match, will their previous mean score increase or decrease? Find the mean score for all eight matches.

6 The mean of 12 scores is 8.8. What is the sum of the scores?

7 While on a camping holiday, Daffyd drove on average, 325 km per day for a period of 7 days. How far did Daffyd drive in total while on holiday?

8 The mean monthly sales for a CD store are $216 000. Calculate the total sales for the store for the year.

9 Find x if 7, 15, 6, 10, 4 and x have a mean of 9.

10 Find a, given that 10, a, 15, 20, a, a, 17, 7 and 15 have a mean of 12.

11 Over a semester, Jamie did 8 science tests. Each was marked out of 30 and Jamie averaged 25. However, when checking his files, he could only find 7 of the 8 tests. For these he scored 29, 26, 18, 20, 27, 24 and 29. Determine how many marks out of 30 he scored for the eighth test.

12 On the first four days of her holiday Benita drove an average of 424 kilometres per day and on the next three days she drove an average of 544 kilometres per day.

   a What is the total distance that Benita drove in the first four days?

   b What is the total distance that Benita drove in the next three days?

   c What is the mean distance Benita travelled per day over the seven day period?

13 A sample of 12 measurements has a mean of 8.5 and a sample of 20 measurements has a mean of 7.5. Find the mean of all 32 measurements.

14 The mean, median and mode of seven numbers are 8, 7 and 6 respectively. Two of the numbers are 8 and 10. If the smallest of the seven numbers is 4, find the largest of the seven numbers.

DISCUSSION

Which of the measures of the middle is more affected by the presence of an outlier? Develop at least two examples to show how the measures of the middle can be altered by outliers.

MEASURES OF THE CENTRE FROM OTHER SOURCES

When the same data appears several times we often summarise the data in table form. We can find then find the measures of the centre directly from the table.

Consider the data in the given table:

THE MODE

There are 14 of data value 6 which is more than any other data value.

The mode is therefore 6.

THE MEAN

A 'Product' column helps to add all scores.

The mean $= \frac{258}{40} = 6.45$.

Data value	Frequency	Product
3	1	$1 \times 3 = 3$
4	2	$2 \times 4 = 8$
5	4	$4 \times 5 = 20$
6	14	$14 \times 6 = 84$
7	11	$11 \times 7 = 77$
8	6	$6 \times 8 = 48$
9	2	$2 \times 9 = 18$
Total	40	258

THE MEDIAN

There are 40 data values, an even number, so there are *two* *middle* data values.

As the sample size $n = 40$, $\frac{n+1}{2} = \frac{41}{2} = 20.5$

Remember that the median is the middle of the *ordered* data set.

∴   the median is the average of the 20th and 21st data values.

In the table, the blue numbers show us accumulated values.

Data Value	Frequency
3	1
4	2
5	4
6	14
7	11
8	6
9	2
Total	40

1 ← one number is 3
3 ← 3 numbers are 4 or less
7 ← 7 numbers are 5 or less
21 ← 21 numbers are 6 or less
32 ← 32 numbers are 7 or less

We can see that the 20th and 21st data values (in order) are both 6's.

∴   median $= \dfrac{6+6}{2} = 6$

Notice that we have a skewed distribution for which the mean, median and mode are nearly equal. This is why we need to be careful when we use measures of the middle to call distributions symmetric.

Example 5   ◄⑴ Self Tutor

Each student in a class of 20 is assigned a number between 1 and 10 to indicate his or her fitness.

Calculate the: **a** mean
                  b median
                  c mode

of the scores.

Score	Number of students
5	1
6	2
7	4
8	7
9	4
10	2
Total	20

a

Score	Number of students	Product
5	1	$5 \times 1 = 5$
6	2	$6 \times 2 = 12$
7	4	$7 \times 4 = 28$
8	7	$8 \times 7 = 56$
9	4	$9 \times 4 = 36$
10	2	$10 \times 2 = 20$
Total	20	157

The mean score

$= \dfrac{\text{total of scores}}{\text{number of scores}}$

$= \dfrac{157}{20}$

$= 7.85$

b There are 20 scores, and so the median is the average of the 10th and 11th.

Score	Number of Students	
5	1	← ─── 1st student
6	2	← ─── 2nd and 3rd student
7	4	← ─── 4th, 5th, 6th and 7th student
8	7	← ─── 8th, 9th, **10th**, **11th**, 12th,
9	4	13th, 14th student
10	2	

STATISTICS PACKAGE

The 10th and 11th students both scored 8 $\therefore$ median = 8.

c Looking down the 'number of students' column, the highest frequency is 7.
This corresponds to a score of 8, so the mode = 8.

EXERCISE 8E.2

1 The table given shows the results when 3 coins were tossed simultaneously 40 times.
The number of heads appearing was recorded.

Number of heads	Number of times occurred
0	6
1	16
2	14
3	4
Total	40

Calculate the: **a** mode   **b** median   **c** mean.

2 The following frequency table records the number of text messages sent in a day by 50 fifteen-year-olds.

No. of messages	Frequency
0	2
1	4
2	7
3	4
4	2
5	0
6	1
7	8
8	13
9	7
10	2

a For this data, find the:
   i mean   **ii** median   **iii** mode.

b Construct a column graph for the data and show the position of the measures of centre (mean, median and mode) on the horizontal axis.

c Describe the distribution of the data.

d Why is the mean smaller than the median for this data?

e Which measure of centre would be the most suitable for this data set?

3 The frequency column graph alongside gives the value of donations for an overseas aid organisation, collected in a particular street.

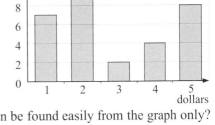

   a Construct a frequency table from the graph.

   b Determine the total number of donations.

   c For the donations find the:

      i mean   **ii** median   **iii** mode.

   d Which of the measures of central tendency can be found easily from the graph only?

4 Hui breeds ducks. The number of ducklings surviving for each pair after one month is recorded in the table.

   a Calculate the:

      i mean   **ii** mode   **iii** median.

   b Is the data skewed?

   c How does the skewness of the data affect the measures of the middle of the distribution?

Number of survivors	Frequency
0	1
1	2
2	5
3	9
4	20
5	30
6	9
Total	76

F   CUMULATIVE DATA

Sometimes it is useful to know the number of scores that lie above or below a particular value. In such situations it is convenient to construct a **cumulative frequency distribution table** and a **cumulative frequency graph** to represent the data.

The cumulative frequency gives a *running total* of the scores up to a particular value.

Example 6   ◀) **Self Tutor**

The data shown gives the weights of 80 male basketball players.

   a Construct a cumulative frequency distribution table.

   b Represent the data on a cumulative frequency graph.

   c Use your graph to estimate the:

      i median weight

      ii number of men weighing less than 83 kg

      iii number of men weighing more than 92 kg.

Weight (w kg)	Frequency
$65 \leqslant w < 70$	1
$70 \leqslant w < 75$	2
$75 \leqslant w < 80$	8
$80 \leqslant w < 85$	16
$85 \leqslant w < 90$	21
$90 \leqslant w < 95$	19
$95 \leqslant w < 100$	8
$100 \leqslant w < 105$	3
$105 \leqslant w < 110$	1
$110 \leqslant w < 115$	1

a

Weight (w kg)	frequency	cumulative frequency
$65 \leqslant w < 70$	1	1
$70 \leqslant w < 75$	2	3
$75 \leqslant w < 80$	8	11
$80 \leqslant w < 85$	16	27
$85 \leqslant w < 90$	21	48
$90 \leqslant w < 95$	19	67
$95 \leqslant w < 100$	8	75
$100 \leqslant w < 105$	3	78
$105 \leqslant w < 110$	1	79
$110 \leqslant w < 115$	1	80

this is $1 + 2$

this is $1 + 2 + 8$

this 48 means that there are 48 players who weigh less than 90 kg

STATISTICS PACKAGE

b **Cumulative frequency graph of basketballers' weights**

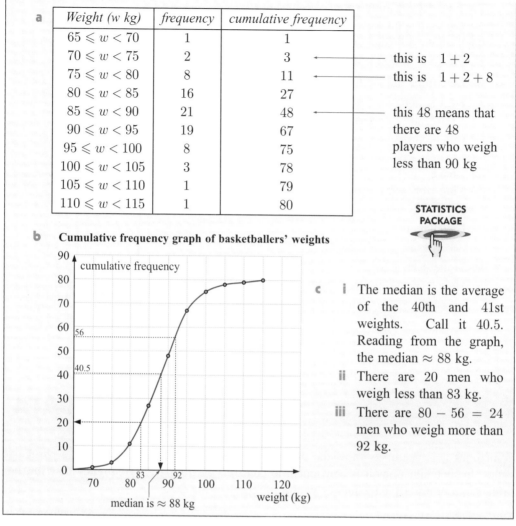

c i The median is the average of the 40th and 41st weights.   Call it 40.5. Reading from the graph, the median $\approx$ 88 kg.

ii There are 20 men who weigh less than 83 kg.

iii There are $80 - 56 = 24$ men who weigh more than 92 kg.

median is $\approx$ 88 kg

EXERCISE 8F

1 For each of the following distributions:

   i construct a cumulative frequency table

   ii draw a cumulative frequency graph

   iii use your graph to find the median of the data.

a

Age	Freq.
0 - < 1	1
1 - < 2	3
2 - < 3	3
3 - < 4	6
4 - < 5	12
5 - < 6	15
6 - < 7	8
7 - < 8	5
8 - < 9	2

b

Time	Freq.
$0 \leqslant t < 1$	7
$1 \leqslant t < 2$	11
$2 \leqslant t < 3$	20
$3 \leqslant t < 4$	22
$4 \leqslant t < 5$	12
$5 \leqslant t < 6$	9
$6 \leqslant t < 7$	5

c

Height	Freq.
$0 \leqslant h < 5$	4
$5 \leqslant h < 10$	8
$10 \leqslant h < 15$	14
$15 \leqslant h < 20$	16
$20 \leqslant h < 25$	10
$25 \leqslant h < 30$	6
$30 \leqslant h < 35$	2

2 The following data shows the lengths, in centimetres, of 40 salmon caught in a lake during a fishing competition.

30 26 38 28 27 31 38 34 40 24 33 30 36 38 32 35 32 36 27 35
36 37 29 31 33 40 34 37 44 38 36 34 33 31 38 35 36 33 33 28

  a Construct a cumulative frequency table for salmon lengths, x cm, using the intervals:
     $24 \leqslant x < 27$, $27 \leqslant x < 30$, ... etc.

  b Draw a cumulative frequency graph.

  c Use **b** to find the median length.

  d Use the original data to find its median and compare your answer with **c**. Comment!

3 In an examination the following scores were achieved by a group of students:

Draw a cumulative frequency graph of the data and use it to find:

  a the median examination mark

  b how many students scored less than 75 marks

  c how many students scored between 60 and 80 marks

  d how many students failed, given that the pass mark was 55

  e the credit mark, given that the top 16% of students were awarded credits.

Score	Frequency
$10 \leqslant x < 20$	2
$20 \leqslant x < 30$	6
$30 \leqslant x < 40$	4
$40 \leqslant x < 50$	8
$50 \leqslant x < 60$	12
$60 \leqslant x < 70$	27
$70 \leqslant x < 80$	34
$80 \leqslant x < 90$	18
$90 \leqslant x < 100$	9

4 The following frequency distribution was obtained by asking 50 randomly selected people the size of their shoes.

Shoe size	5	$5\frac{1}{2}$	6	$6\frac{1}{2}$	7	$7\frac{1}{2}$	8	$8\frac{1}{2}$	9	$9\frac{1}{2}$	10
Frequency	2	0	1	4	6	12	11	7	3	2	2

Draw a cumulative frequency graph of the data and use it to find:

  a the median shoe size

  b how many people had a shoe size of: **i**   7 or more   **ii** $8\frac{1}{2}$ or less.

5 In a cross-country race, the times (in minutes) of 160 competitors were recorded as follows:

Draw a cumulative frequency graph of the data and use it to find:

  a the median time

  b the approximate number of runners whose time was not more than 32 minutes

  c the approximate time in which the fastest 40 runners completed the course.

Times (min)	Frequency
$20 \leqslant t < 25$	18
$25 \leqslant t < 30$	45
$30 \leqslant t < 35$	37
$35 \leqslant t < 40$	33
$40 \leqslant t < 45$	19
$45 \leqslant t < 50$	8

6 The following table summarises distances a baseball was thrown by a number of different students.

Distance (m)	$30 \leqslant d < 40$	$40 \leqslant d < 50$	$50 \leqslant d < 60$	$60 \leqslant d < 70$	$70 \leqslant d < 80$	$80 \leqslant d < 90$
Frequency	7	17	28	15	13	4

Draw a cumulative frequency graph of the data and use it to find:

   a   the median distance thrown by the students

   b   the number of students who threw the ball less than 45 m

   c   the number of students who threw the ball between 55 and 70 m.

   d   If only students who threw the ball further than 55 m were considered for further coaching, how many students were considered?

G   MEASURING THE SPREAD

Knowing the middle of a data set can be quite useful, but for a more accurate picture of the data set we also need to know its spread.

For example,   2, 3, 4, 5, 6, 7, 8, 9, 10   has a mean value of 6 and so does

                4, 5, 5, 6, 6, 6, 7, 7, 8.   However, the first data set is more widely spread than the second one.

Three commonly used statistics that indicate the spread of a set of data are the

     •   **range**   •   **interquartile range**   •   **standard deviation**.

THE RANGE

> The **range** is the difference between the **maximum** (largest) data value and the **minimum** (smallest) data value.
>
> **range = maximum data value − minimum data value**

Example 7	◀) Self Tutor

Find the range of the data set: 5, 3, 8, 4, 9, 7, 5, 6, 2, 3, 6, 8, 4.

range = maximum value − minimum value = 9 − 2 = 7

THE UPPER AND LOWER QUARTILES AND THE INTERQUARTILE RANGE

The median divides an ordered data set into halves, and these halves are divided in half again by the **quartiles**.

The middle value of the lower half is called the **lower quartile**. One quarter, or 25%, of the data have values less than or equal to the lower quartile. 75% of the data have values greater than or equal to the lower quartile.

The middle value of the upper half is called the **upper quartile**. One quarter, or 25%, of the data have values greater than or equal to the upper quartile. 75% of the data have values less than or equal to the upper quartile.

The **interquartile range** is the range of the middle half (50%) of the data.

$$\text{interquartile range} = \text{upper quartile} - \text{lower quartile}$$

The data set is thus divided into quarters by the lower quartile (Q_1), the median (Q_2), and the upper quartile (Q_3).

So, the interquartile range, $$IQR = Q_3 - Q_1.$$

Example 8   ◀ぅ **Self Tutor**

For the data set: 7, 3, 4, 2, 5, 6, 7, 5, 5, 9, 3, 8, 3, 5, 6   find the:

  a   median   **b**   lower quartile

  c   upper quartile   **d**   interquartile range.

The ordered data set is:

      2 3 3 3 4 5 5 5 5 6 6 7 7 8 9   (15 of them)

a   As $n = 15$, $\dfrac{n+1}{2} = 8$

    The median = 8th score = 5

b/c   As the median is a data value, we now ignore it and split the remaining data into two:

        lower   upper Q_1 = median of lower half = 3

     $\overbrace{2\ 3\ 3\ 3\ 4\ 5\ 5}$ $\overbrace{5\ 6\ 6\ 7\ 7\ 8\ 9}$ Q_3 = median of upper half = 7

d $IQR = Q_3 - Q_1 = 7 - 3 = 4$

Example 9   ◀ぅ **Self Tutor**

For the data set: 6, 10, 7, 8, 13, 7, 10, 8, 1, 7, 5, 4, 9, 4, 2, 5, 9, 6, 3, 2   find the:

  a   median   **b**   lower quartile

  c   upper quartile   **d**   interquartile range.

The ordered data set is:

      1 2 2 3 4 4 5 5 6 6 7 7 7 8 8 9 9 10 10 13   (20 of them)

a   As $n = 20$, $\dfrac{n+1}{2} = 10.5$

    $\therefore$ median $= \dfrac{\text{10th value} + \text{11th value}}{2} = \dfrac{6+7}{2} = 6.5$

b/c   As the median is not a data value we split the data into two:

        lower   upper

   $\overbrace{1\ 2\ 2\ 3\ \underbrace{4\ 4}\ 5\ 5\ 6\ 6}$ $\overbrace{7\ 7\ 7\ 8\ \underbrace{8\ 9}\ 9\ 10\ 10\ 13}$

         $Q_1 = 4$ $Q_3 = 8.5$

> **d** $IQR = Q_3 - Q_1$ **Note:** Some computer packages (for example, **MS Excel**)
> $\quad\quad\quad = 8.5 - 4$ calculate quartiles in a different way from this
> $\quad\quad\quad = 4.5$ example.

EXERCISE 8G

1 For each of the following data sets, make sure the data is ordered and then find:

    i the median   **ii** the upper and lower quartiles

   iii the range   **iv** the interquartile range.

  a 5, 6, 6, 6, 7, 7, 7, 8, 8, 8, 8, 9, 9, 9, 9, 9, 10, 10, 11, 11, 11, 12, 12

  b 11, 13, 16, 13, 25, 19, 20, 19, 19, 16, 17, 21, 22, 18, 19, 17, 23, 15

  c 23.8, 24.4, 25.5, 25.5, 26.6, 26.9, 27, 27.3, 28.1, 28.4, 31.5

2 The times spent (in minutes) by 24 people in a queue at a supermarket, waiting to be served at the checkout, were:

1.4 5.2 2.4 2.8 3.4 3.8 2.2 1.5
0.8 0.8 3.9 2.3 4.5 1.4 0.5 0.1
1.6 4.8 1.9 0.2 3.6 5.2 2.7 3.0

  a Find the median waiting time and the upper and lower quartiles.

  b Find the range and interquartile range of the waiting time.

  c Copy and complete the following statements:

    i "50% of the waiting times were greater than .... minutes."

    ii "75% of the waiting times were less than ...... minutes."

    iii "The minimum waiting time was .... minutes and the maximum waiting time was ..... minutes. The waiting times were spread over ...... minutes."

3

Stem	Leaf
2	0 1 2 2
3	0 0 1 4 4 5 8
4	0 2 3 4 6 6 9
5	1 1 4 5 8

    $5 \mid 1$ represents 51

For the data set given, find:

  a the minimum value   **b** the maximum value

  c the median   **d** the lower quartile

  e the upper quartile   **f** the range

  g the interquartile range.

H   BOX-AND-WHISKER PLOTS

A **box-and-whisker plot** (or simply a **boxplot**) is a visual display of some of the descriptive statistics of a data set. It shows:

  • the minimum value   • the lower quartile (Q_1)   • the median (Q_2)

  • the upper quartile (Q_3)   • the maximum value

These five numbers form the **five-number summary** of a data set.

Here is the boxplot for **Example 8**:

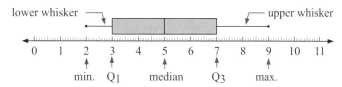

lower whisker — upper whisker

0 1 2 3 4 5 6 7 8 9 10 11

min. Q1 median Q3 max.

The rectangular box represents the 'middle' half of the data set.
The lower whisker represents the 25% of the data with smallest values.
The upper whisker represents the 25% of the data with greatest values.

Example 10 ◀️)) **Self Tutor**

For the data set: 5 1 6 8 1 7 4 5 6 11 3 4 4 2 5 5

a construct the five-number summary   b draw a boxplot

c find the i range ii interquartile range

d find the percentage of data values less than 4.

---

a The ordered data set is:

1 1 2 3 4 4 4 5 | 5 5 5 6 6 7 8 11 (16 of them)

$Q_1 = 3.5$ median $= 5$ $Q_3 = 6$

So the 5-number summary is:
$$\begin{cases} \text{min value} = 1 & Q_1 = 3.5 \\ \text{median} = 5 & Q_3 = 6 \\ \text{max value} = 11 \end{cases}$$

b

0 1 2 3 4 5 6 7 8 9 10 11

c i range $=$ max value $-$ min value   ii IQR $= Q_3 - Q_1$
$= 11 - 1$ $= 6 - 3.5$
$= 10$ $= 2.5$

STATISTICS PACKAGE

d 25% of the data values are less than 4.

EXERCISE 8H.1

1

0 10 20 30 40 50 60 70 80

goals scored by a netball team

a The boxplot given summarises the goals scored by a netball team. Locate:

i the median   ii the maximum value   iii the minimum value

iv the upper quartile   v the lower quartile.

b Calculate: i the range   ii the interquartile range.

2

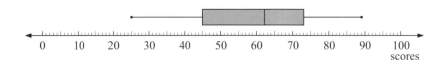

The boxplot shown summarises the points scored by a basketball team. Copy and complete the following statements about their results:

a The highest score was ..... points.   b The lowest score was ..... points.

c Half of the scores were greater than or equal to ..... points.

d The top 25% of the scores were at least ..... points.

e The middle half of the scores were between ..... and ..... points.

f Find the range of the data set.

g Find the interquartile range of the data set.

3 For the following data sets:

    i construct a 5-number summary   ii draw a boxplot

    iii find the range   iv find the interquartile range

a 5, 5, 10, 9, 4, 2, 8, 6, 5, 8, 6, 7, 9, 6, 10, 3, 11

b 7, 0, 4, 6, 8, 8, 9, 5, 6, 8, 8, 8, 9, 8, 1, 8, 3, 7, 2, 7, 4, 5, 9, 4

4 The weight, in kilograms, of a particular brand of bags of firewood is stated to be 20 kg. However, some bags weigh more than this and some weigh less. A sample of bags is carefully weighed, and the measurements are given in the ordered stem-and-leaf plot shown.

Stem	Leaf
18	8
19	5 7 7 8 8 9
20	1 1 1 2 2 5 6 8
21	0 1 1 2 4 6
22	3

20 | 5   represents   20.5 kg

a Locate the median, upper and lower quartiles, and maximum and minimum weights for the sample.

b Draw a boxplot for the data.

c Find: i the interquartile range   ii the range.

d Copy and complete the following statements about the distribution of weights for the bags of firewood in this sample:

    i Half of the bags of firewood weighed at least ..... kg.

    ii .....% of the bags had a weight less than 20 kg.

    iii The weights of the middle 50% of the bags were spread over ..... kg.

    iv The lightest 25% of the bags had a weight of ..... kg or less.

e Is the distribution of weights in this sample symmetrical, or positively or negatively skewed?

PARALLEL BOXPLOTS

Parallel boxplots enable us to make a *visual comparison* of the distributions of two sets of data and their descriptive statistics (median, range and interquartile range).

Parallel boxplots could be horizontal or vertical.

Example 11 ◀)) **Self Tutor**

An office worker has the choice of travelling to work by car or bus and has collected data giving the travel times from recent journeys using both of these types of transport. He is interested to know which type of transport is the quickest to get him to work and which is the most reliable.

Car travel times (min): 13, 14, 18, 18, 19, 21, 22, 22, 24, 25, 27, 28, 30, 33, 43

Bus travel times (min): 16, 16, 16, 17, 17, 18, 18, 18, 20, 20, 21, 21, 23, 28, 30

Prepare parallel boxplots for the data sets and use them to compare the two methods of transport for speed and reliability.

For car travel: min $= 13$ $Q_1 = 18$ median $= 22$ $Q_3 = 28$ max $= 43$

For bus travel: min $= 16$ $Q_1 = 17$ median $= 18$ $Q_3 = 21$ max $= 30$

In the data sets we identify some outliers: 28 and 30 mins by bus and 43 mins by car. They are represented as asterisks on the boxplot, and are not included in the whiskers.

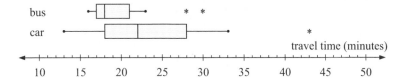

Using the medians, 50% of the time bus travel takes 18 minutes or less, compared with car travel at 22 minutes or less. Bus travel is therefore generally *quicker*.

Comparing spread: range for car $= 43 - 13$ range for bus $= 30 - 16$

$$= 30 \qquad\qquad\qquad = 14$$

$$\text{IQR} = Q_3 - Q_1 \qquad\qquad \text{IQR} = Q_3 - Q_1$$

$$= 28 - 18 \qquad\qquad\qquad = 21 - 17$$

$$= 10 \qquad\qquad\qquad = 4$$

Comparing these spread measures, the bus travel times are less 'spread out' than the car travel times. They are *more predictable or reliable*.

EXERCISE 8H.2

1 The following boxplots compare the numbers of students on school buses A and C over a one month period.

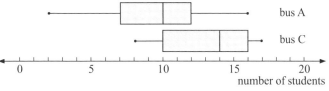

    a Find the 5-number summaries for the students on both buses.

    b Determine the i range ii interquartile range   for each group of students.

2 Two classes have completed the same test. Boxplots have been drawn to summarise and display the results. They have been drawn on the same set of axes so that the results can be compared.

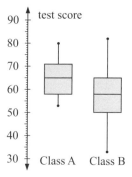

  a In which class was:

   i the highest mark   **ii** the lowest mark

   iii there a larger spread of marks?

  b Find:

   i the range of marks in class B

   ii the interquartile range for class A.

  c If the top 50% of class B passed the test, what percentage of class A passed?

  d Describe the distribution of marks in: **i** class A   **ii** class B.

  e Copy and complete: The students in class .... generally scored higher marks. The marks in class ...... were more varied.

3 The heights (to the nearest centimetre) of boys and girls in a Year 10 class in Norway are as follows:

  Boys   165 171 169 169 172 171 171 180 168 168 166 168 170 165 171 173 187
      181 175 174 165 167 163 160 169 167 172 174 177 188 177 185 167 160

  Girls   162 171 156 166 168 163 170 171 177 169 168 165 156 159 165 164 154
      171 172 166 152 169 170 163 162 165 163 168 155 175 176 170 166

  a Find the five-number summary for each of the data sets.

  b Compare and comment on the distribution of the data.

▌ STATISTICS FROM TECHNOLOGY

GRAPHICS CALCULATOR

A **graphics calculator** can be used to find descriptive statistics and to draw some types of graphs.

Consider the data set: 5 2 3 3 6 4 5 3 7 5 7 1 8 9 5

No matter what brand of calculator you use you should be able to:

- Enter the data as a list.
- Enter the statistics calculation part of the menu and obtain the descriptive statistics like these shown. $\bar{x}$ is the mean
- Obtain a box-and-whisker plot such as:

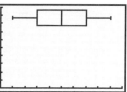

These screen dumps are from a TI-83.

- Obtain a vertical barchart if required.

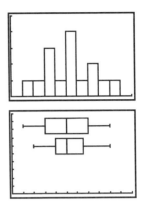

- Enter a second data set into another list and obtain a side-by-side boxplot for comparison with the first one.

Instructions for these tasks can be found at the front of the book in the **Graphics Calculator Instructions** section.

EXERCISE 8I.1

1 For your calculator enter the data set: 5 2 3 3 6 4 5 3 7 5 7 1 8 9 5   and obtain the mean and the 5-number summary. This is the first example above and you should check your results from it.

2 Obtain the boxplot for question 1.

3 Obtain the vertical bar chart for question 1.

4 Enter the data set: 9 6 2 3 5 5 7 5 6 7 6 3 4 4 5 8 4   into a second list. Find the mean and 5-number summary. Now create a side-by-side boxplot for both sets of data.

COMPUTER PACKAGE

Various statistical packages are available for computer use, but many are expensive and often not easy to use. Click on the icon to use the statistics package on the CD.

Enter data set 1:   5 2 3 3 6 4 5 3 7 5 7 1 8 9 5

Enter data set 2:   9 6 2 3 5 5 7 5 6 7 6 3 4 4 5 8 4

STATISTICS PACKAGE

Examine the side-by-side column graphs.
Click on the Box & whisker tab to view the side-by-side boxplots.
Click on the Statistics tab to obtain the descriptive statistics.
Select Print ... from the File menu to print all of these on one sheet of paper.

EXERCISE 8I.2

1 Enter the **Opening Problem** data on page **170** for the *Without fertiliser* data in Set 1 and the *With fertiliser* data in Set 2. Print out the page of graphs, boxplots and descriptive statistics.

2 Enter these grouped continuous data sets:

Set 1:

Value	Frequency
11.6	1
11.7	3
11.8	16
11.9	28
12.0	11
12.1	7
12.2	9

Set 2:

Value	Frequency
11.5	1
11.6	8
11.7	17
11.8	31
11.9	16
12.0	8
12.1	10
12.2	3

Examine the graphs, boxplots and descriptive statistics for each and print the results.

STANDARD DEVIATION

The problem with the range and the IQR as measures of spread is that both only use two values in their calculation.

Some data sets can have their characteristics hidden when the IQR is quoted. It would be helpful to have a measure of spread that used *all* of the data values in its calculation. One such statistic is the **standard deviation**, s.

The **deviation** of a data value x from the mean $\overline{x}$ is given by $x - \overline{x}$.

So, $\sqrt{\dfrac{\sum (x - \overline{x})^2}{n}}$ is the average of the sum of the squares of the deviations from the mean.

Notice that in $\dfrac{\sum (x - \overline{x})^2}{n}$ we are squaring the units, so if we take the square root of this quantity then we convert back to the original units.

We hence define:

the **standard deviation** $s = \sqrt{\dfrac{\sum (x - \overline{x})^2}{n}}$ where $\begin{aligned} &x \text{ is a data value} \\ &\overline{x} \text{ is the mean of the sample} \\ &n \text{ is the sample size.} \end{aligned}$

If we are considering an entire population, we usually call the mean μ (the Greek letter *mu*) and the standard deviation σ (*sigma*).

In general, the population standard deviation σ is unknown, so we use the standard deviation of a sample s as an estimate for σ.

Note: The IQR is a more appropriate tool for measuring spread if the distribution is considerably skewed.

Example 12   ◀) **Self Tutor**

A greengrocer chain is to purchase oranges from two different wholesalers. They take five random samples of 40 oranges to examine them for skin blemishes. The counts for the number of blemished oranges are:

| Wholesaler Sunblessed | 4 | 16 | 14 | 8 | 8 |
| Wholesaler Valencia Star | 9 | 12 | 11 | 10 | 13 |

Find the mean and standard deviation for each data set, and hence compare the wholesale suppliers.

Wholesaler Sunblessed

x	$x - \overline{x}$	$(x - \overline{x})^2$
4	-6	36
16	6	36
14	4	16
8	-2	4
8	-2	4
50	*Total*	96

$$\therefore \quad \overline{x} = \frac{50}{5} \qquad s = \sqrt{\frac{\sum(x - \overline{x})^2}{n}}$$
$$= 10 \qquad\qquad = \sqrt{\frac{96}{5}}$$
$$\approx 4.38$$

For **TI** the standard deviation required is σX. For **CASIO** the standard deviation is $x\sigma n$. For the H&H statistics package, use σn.

Wholesaler Valencia Star

x	$x - \overline{x}$	$(x - \overline{x})^2$
9	-2	4
12	1	1
11	0	0
10	-1	1
13	2	4
55	*Total*	10

$$\therefore \quad \overline{x} = \frac{55}{5} \qquad s = \sqrt{\frac{\sum(x - \overline{x})^2}{n}}$$
$$= 11 \qquad\qquad = \sqrt{\frac{10}{5}}$$
$$\approx 1.41$$

On average, Valencia Star supplied oranges with more blemishes but less variability than those supplied by Sunblessed.

EXERCISE 8J.1

1   Consider the following two samples:

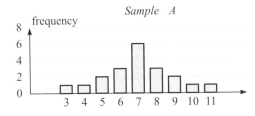

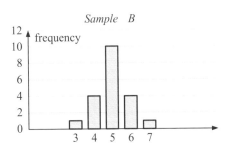

a   By looking at the graphs, which distribution has the wider spread?

b   Find the mean of each sample.

c   For each sample, find   i   the range   ii   the interquartile range.

d   Calculate the standard deviation for each sample.

e   Explain why s provides a better measure of spread than the other two measures.

2 **a** Find the standard deviation of the data: 3, 4, 5, 6, 7, 20.

   b Recalculate the standard deviation with the outlier removed.

   c What is the effect on the standard deviation if an outlier is removed?

3 Basketballers Colin and Imran compare their points scores for the last 10 matches.

Points by Colin	24	18	30	28	25	17	28	32	24	28
Points by Imran	10	30	40	29	14	42	38	43	31	21

   a Find the mean and standard deviation for the number of points scored by each player for these matches.

   b Which measure is used to determine which of the players is more consistent?

4 Two baseballers compare their batting performances for a ten game stretch. The numbers of safe hits per game were recorded as:

Mickey	5	4	1	0	5	4	0	5	4	2
Julio	1	2	3	3	3	4	6	2	3	3

   a Show that each baseballer has the same mean and range.

   b Whose performance do you suspect is more variable?

   c Check your answer to **b** by finding the standard deviation for each distribution.

   d Does the range or the standard deviation give a better indication of variability?

STANDARD DEVIATION FOR GROUPED DATA

For grouped data $s = \sqrt{\dfrac{\sum f(x - \bar{x})^2}{\sum f}}$ where s is the **standard deviation**

   x is **any score**

   $\bar{x}$ is the **mean**

   f is the **frequency** of each score.

Example 13   ◀) **Self Tutor**

Find the standard deviation
of the distribution:

score	0	1	2	3	4
frequency	1	2	4	2	1

x	f	fx	$x - \bar{x}$	$(x - \bar{x})^2$	$f(x - \bar{x})^2$
0	1	0	-2	4	4
1	2	2	-1	1	2
2	4	8	0	0	0
3	2	6	1	1	2
4	1	4	2	4	4
Total	10	20			12

$\bar{x} = \dfrac{\sum fx}{\sum f} = \dfrac{20}{10} = 2$

$s = \sqrt{\dfrac{\sum f(x - \bar{x})^2}{\sum f}}$

$= \sqrt{\dfrac{12}{10}}$

≈ 1.10

Example 14   ◀)) **Self Tutor**

The weights (in kilograms) of 25 calves were measured and the results placed in the table shown.

a   Estimate the standard deviation by using interval midpoints.

b   Can the range be found?

Weight (kg)	Frequency
50 - < 60	1
60 - < 70	3
70 - < 80	9
80 - < 90	6
90 - < 100	4
100 - < 110	2

a

Weight class (kg)	Centre of class (x)	Frequency	$f\,x$	$f(x - \bar{x})^2$
50 - < 60	55	1	55	676
60 - < 70	65	3	195	768
70 - < 80	75	9	675	324
80 - < 90	85	6	510	96
90 - < 100	95	4	380	784
100 - < 110	105	2	210	1152
	Totals	25	2025	3800

$$\bar{x} = \frac{\sum f\,x}{\sum f} \qquad\qquad s = \sqrt{\frac{\sum f(x - \bar{x})^2}{\sum f}}$$

$$\approx \frac{2025}{25} \qquad\qquad\qquad \approx \sqrt{\frac{3800}{25}}$$

$$\approx 81 \qquad\qquad\qquad\qquad \approx 12.3$$

b   As the data has been grouped in classes, we do not know the smallest and largest data values. Consequently, the range cannot be found.

EXERCISE 8J.2

1   Find the standard deviation of the following test results.

Test score, x	10	11	12	13	14	15
Frequency, f	4	6	7	2	3	2

2   The number of chocolates in 60 boxes was counted and the results tabulated.

Number of chocolates	25	26	27	28	29	30	31	32
Frequency	1	5	7	13	12	12	8	2

Find the mean and standard deviation of the distribution.

3   The lengths of 30 trout were measured to the nearest cm. The following data was obtained:

Length (cm)	30 - < 32	32 - < 34	34 - < 36	36 - < 38	38 - < 40	40 - < 42	42 - < 44
Frequency	1	1	3	7	11	5	2

Estimate the mean length and the standard deviation of the lengths.

4 The weekly wages of 90 department store workers are given alongside:

Estimate the mean wage and the standard deviation of the wages.

Wage (€)	Number of Workers
380-389.99	5
390-399.99	16
400-409.99	27
410-419.99	16
420-429.99	12
430-439.99	8
440-449.99	4
450-459.99	2

K   THE NORMAL DISTRIBUTION

The normal distribution is the most important distribution for a continuous random variable, and lies at the heart of statistics. Many natural and synthetic phenomena have distributions that are normal or approximately normal.

Some examples are:
- the heights of 16 year old males
- the distribution of volumes in soft drink cans
- the lengths of adult sharks
- the lengths of cilia on a cell
- scores on tests taken by a large population
- repeated measurements of the same quantity
- yields of corn or wheat
- life time of batteries

The graphs of the above distributions would be **bell-shaped**, which indicates a normal distribution.

A TYPICAL NORMAL DISTRIBUTION

A large sample of cockle shells was collected and the maximum distance across each shell was measured. Click on the video clip icon to see how a histogram of the data is built up.

VIDEO CLIP

Now click on the demo icon to observe the effect of changing the class interval lengths for normally distributed data.

COMPUTER DEMO

HOW THE NORMAL DISTRIBUTION ARISES

Example 1:

Consider the apples harvested from an apple tree. They do not all have the same weight. This variation may be due to genetic factors, different times when the flowers were fertilised, different amounts of sunlight reaching the leaves and fruit, different weather conditions, and so on.

The result is that much of the fruit will have weights centred about the mean weight, and there will be fewer apples that are much heavier or much lighter than this mean.

A bell-shaped distribution of weights results which the normal distribution models closely.

Example 2:

In the manufacturing of 50 mm nails, the machines are set to produce nails of average length 50 mm. However there is always minor variation due to random errors in the manufacturing process. A small standard deviation of 0.3 mm, say, may be observed, but once again a bell-shaped distribution models the situation.

In this case the bell-shaped curve shown could represent the distribution of nail lengths.

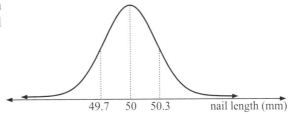

THE SIGNIFICANCE OF STANDARD DEVIATION

If a large sample from a typical bell-shaped data distribution is taken, what percentage of the data values would lie between $\bar{x} - s$ and $\bar{x} + s$?

Click on the icon and try to answer this question. Repeat the sampling many times.

Now try to determine the percentage of data values which would lie between $\bar{x} - 2s$ and $\bar{x} + 2s$ and between $\bar{x} - 3s$ and $\bar{x} + 3s$.

COMPUTER
DEMO

It can be shown that for any measured variable from any population that is normally distributed, no matter the values of the mean and standard deviation:

- approximately **68%** of the population will have a measure that falls between **1** standard deviation either side of the mean
- approximately **95%** of the population will have a measure that falls between **2** standard deviations either side of the mean
- approximately **99.7%** of the population will have a measure that falls between **3** standard deviations either side of the mean.

The proportion of data values that lie within different ranges relative to the mean are shown below:

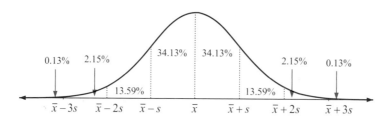

Example 15   ◀) **Self Tutor**

A sample of 200 cans of peaches was taken from a warehouse and the contents of each can measured for net weight. The sample mean was 486 g with standard deviation 6.2 g. What proportion of the cans will lie within:

  a 1 standard deviation of the mean   **b** 3 standard deviations of the mean?

For a manufacturing process such as this, the distribution of weights in the cans is approximately normal.

  a About 68% of the cans would be expected to have contents between
     486 ± 6.2 g   i.e., between 479.8 g and 492.2 g.

  b Nearly all of the cans would be expected to have contents between
     $486 \pm 3 \times 6.2$ g   i.e., between 467.4 g and 504.6 g.

EXERCISE 8K

1 Five hundred year 10 students sat for a Mathematics examination. Their marks were normally distributed with a mean of 75 and a standard deviation of 8.

  a Copy and complete this bell-shaped curve, assigning scores to the markings on the horizontal axis:

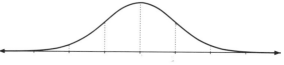

  b How many students would you expect scored marks:
     i more than 83   **ii** less than 59   **iii** between 67 and 91?

2 A sample of 300 bottles of soft drink was taken from a production line and the contents of each bottle measured for net volume. The sample mean was 377 mL with standard deviation 1.5 mL.

  a Represent this information on a bell-shaped curve.

  b How many bottles in the sample would you expect to have contents
     i between 374 and 380 mL   **ii** more than 375.5 mL?

  c What proportion of bottles in the production line would you expect to have contents less than 375.5 mL?

3   The mean height of players in a basketball competition is 181 cm. If the standard deviation is 4 cm, what percentage of them are likely to be:

    a   taller than 189 cm   b   taller than 177 cm

    c   between 169 cm and 189 cm   d   shorter than 185 cm?

4   The mean average rainfall of Charlesville for August is 68 mm with standard deviation 8 mm. Over a 40 year period, how many times would you expect there to be less than 52 mm of rainfall during August?

DECODING A SECRET MESSAGE

LINKS
click here

Areas of interaction:
Human ingenuity

REVIEW SET 8A

1   Classify the following variables as either categorical or numerical:

    a   the country of origin of a person

    b   the heights of seedlings after two weeks

    c   the scores of team members in a darts competition.

2   A randomly selected sample of small businesses has been asked, "How many full-time employees are there in your business?". A column graph has been constructed for the results.

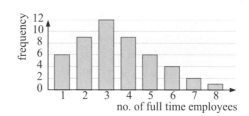

    a   How many small businesses gave data in the survey?

    b   How many of the businesses had only one or two full-time employees?

    c   What percentage of the businesses had five or more full-time employees?

    d   Describe the distribution of the data.

3   A class of 20 students was asked "How many children are there in your household?" and the following data was collected:

    1 2 3 3 2 4 5 4 2 3 8 1 2 1 3 2 1 2 1 2

    a   What is the variable in the investigation?

    b   Is the data discrete or continuous? Why?

    c   Construct a dot plot to display the data showing a heading for the graph, a scale and clearly labelled axes.

    d   How would you describe the distribution of the data? Is it symmetrical, or positively or negatively skewed? Are there any outliers?

4 The test score out of 40 marks was recorded for a group of 30 students:

25 18 35 32 34 28 24 39 29 33
22 34 39 31 36 35 36 33 35 40
26 25 20 18 9 40 32 23 28 27

   a Construct a stem-and-leaf plot for this data using 0, 1, 2, 3 and 4 as the stems.

   b Redraw the stem-and-leaf plot so that it is ordered.

   c What advantage does the stem-and-leaf plot have over a frequency table?

   d What was the **i** highest **ii** lowest mark scored for the test?

   e If an 'A' was awarded to students who scored 36 or more for the test, what percentage of students scored an 'A'?

5 Eight scores have an average of six. Scores of 15 and x increase the average to 7. Find x.

6 For the following sample of weights (in kg) of year 10 students, find:

   a the minimum weight

   b the maximum weight

   c the number of students with a weight greater than 52 kg

   d the number of students with a weight of at least 70 kg

   e the percentage of students with a weight less than 48 kg.

Stem	Leaf
3	2 4 8
4	0 4 4 7 9 9 9
5	0 0 1 2 2 3 3 5 5 6 8 8
6	0 1 2 4 4 5 7 9
7	0 2 6
8	4
9	1 9 | 1 represents 91

7 A frequency table for the masses of eggs in a carton marked '50 g eggs' is given below.

   a Explain why 'mass' is a continuous variable.

   b Construct a frequency histogram for the data. The axes should be carefully marked and labelled, and you should include a heading for the graph.

   c What is the modal class? Explain what this means.

   d Describe the distribution of the data.

Mass (g)	Frequency
48 - < 49	1
49 - < 50	1
50 - < 51	16
51 - < 52	4
52 - < 53	3

8 For the following data set of the number of points scored by a rugby team, find:

   a the mean   **b** the mode   **c** the median   **d** the range

   e the upper and lower quartiles   **f** the interquartile range.

   28, 24, 16, 6, 46, 34, 43, 16, 36, 49, 30, 28, 4, 31, 47, 41, 26, 25, 20, 29, 42

9

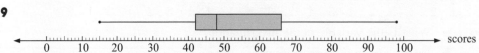

   a From the boxplot that shows the scores out of 100 for an exam, state:

      i the median score   **ii** the maximum score   **iii** the minimum score

      iv the upper quartile   **v** the lower quartile

   b Calculate: **i** the range   **ii** the interquartile range of scores.

10 The weights to the nearest 0.1 kg of a sample of three month old chickens were:

0.8,   0.7,   1.0,   0.9,   0.9,   0.8,   0.9,   1.0,   1.0,   0.8

    a Find the sample mean and standard deviation.

    b In the next 3 months, the weights of the chickens doubled. Find the new sample mean and standard deviation.

    c Comment, in general terms, on your findings from **a** and **b**.

REVIEW SET 8B

1   **a** State whether a census or a sample would be used to find the preferred time of day for shopping at a supermarket.

    b Comment on possible bias when conducting this investigation.

2 The data below are the scores (out of 100) for a Mathematics examination for 45 students.

58   31   80   69   70   71   82   91   94   60   68   58   90   83   72
75   65   76   69   66   64   57   58   77   92   94   49   61   66   91
64   53   89   91   78   61   74   82   97   70   82   66   55   45   63

Construct a stem-and-leaf plot for this data using the numbers 3 to 9 as the stems.

    a Redraw the stem-and-leaf plot so that it is ordered.

    b What is the **i** highest **ii** lowest mark scored for the examination?

    c If an 'A' was awarded to students who scored 85 or more for the examination, what percentage of students scored an 'A'?

    d Would you describe this distribution as:

       i symmetric   **ii** skewed   **iii** neither symmetric nor skewed?

3 Find the **a** mean **b** median **c** mode for the following data set:

13   16   15   17   14   13   13   15   16   14
16   14   15   15   15   13   17   14   12   14

4 A sample of 15 measurements has a mean of 14.2 and a sample of 10 measurements has a mean of 12.6. Find the mean of the total sample of 25 measurements.

5 Determine the mean of the numbers 7, 5, 7, 2, 8 and 7. If two additional numbers, 2 and x, reduce the mean by 1, find x.

6 The given table shows the distribution of scores for a year 10 spelling test in Australia.

    a Calculate the:

       i mean   **ii** mode

       iii median   **iv** range of the scores

    b The average score for all year 10 students across Australia in this spelling test was 6.2. How does this class compare to the national average?

    c Describe the skewness of the data set.

Score	Frequency
6	2
7	4
8	7
9	12
10	5
Total	30

7 In a one month period at a particular hospital the lengths of newborn babies were recorded. The results are shown in the table given.

a Represent the data on a frequency histogram.

b How many babies are 52 cm or more?

c What percentage of babies have lengths in the interval 50 cm $\leqslant l < 53$ cm?

d Construct a cumulative frequency distribution table.

e Represent the data on a cumulative frequency graph.

f Use your graph to estimate the:

   i median length

   ii number of babies with length less than 51.5 cm.

length (cm)	frequency
$48 \leqslant l < 49$	1
$49 \leqslant l < 50$	3
$50 \leqslant l < 51$	9
$51 \leqslant l < 52$	10
$52 \leqslant l < 53$	16
$53 \leqslant l < 54$	4
$54 \leqslant l < 55$	5
$55 \leqslant l < 56$	2

8 The following data set that shows the amount of money spent on lunch by a sample of office workers. For this data:

a construct a 5-number summary

b draw a boxplot

c find the range of money spent.

d What was the range of money spent by the middle 50% of office workers surveyed?

Stem	Leaf
8	6
9	0 2 5 5 7
10	0 1 1 1 2 4 4 6
11	3 6 6 8 8
12	0

8 | 6   represents $8.60

9 The given parallel boxplots represent the 100-metre swim times for the members of a swimming squad.

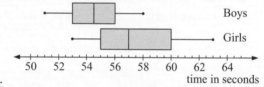

Copy and complete the following:

a Comparing the median swim times for girls and boys shows that, in general, the ...... swim ...... seconds faster than the ......

b The range of the girls' swim times is ...... seconds compared to the range of ...... seconds for the boys.

c The fastest 25% of the boys swim faster than ......% of the girls.

d ......% of the boys swim faster than 60 seconds whereas ......% of the girls swim faster than 60 seconds.

10 The life of a clock battery is found to be normally distributed with a mean of 35.4 weeks and a standard deviation of 6.8 weeks.

In a batch of 500 batteries, find the number that will probably last:

a at least 42.2 weeks

b less than 21.8 weeks

c between 35.4 and 49 weeks.

Chapter **9**

Quadratic equations

OPENING PROBLEM

Diadro Dress Company makes and sells dresses.

If x dresses are sold each week then their profit for the week is given by
$P = -11x^2 + 450x - 800$ euros.

Things to think about:

- How many dresses must be sold in order to make a profit of €3000?
- How many dresses must be sold each week in order to make a profit?

Equations of the form $ax + b = 0$ where $a \neq 0$ are called **linear equations** and have *only one* solution.

For example, $3x - 2 = 0$ is the linear equation with $a = 3$ and $b = -2$. It has the solution $x = \frac{2}{3}$.

Equations of the form $ax^2 + bx + c = 0$ where $a \neq 0$ are called **quadratic equations**. They may have *two*, *one* or *zero* solutions.

Here are some simple quadratic equations which clearly show the truth of this statement:

Equation	$ax^2 + bx + c = 0$ form	a	b	c	Solutions	
$x^2 - 4 = 0$	$x^2 + 0x - 4 = 0$	1	0	-4	$x = 2$ or $x = -2$	**two**
$(x - 2)^2 = 0$	$x^2 - 4x + 4 = 0$	1	-4	4	$x = 2$	**one**
$x^2 + 4 = 0$	$x^2 + 0x + 4 = 0$	1	0	4	none as x^2 is always $\geqslant 0$	**zero**

Now consider the example $x^2 + 3x - 10 = 0$.

If $x = 2$, $\quad x^2 + 3x - 10$ $\qquad$ and if $x = -5$, $\quad x^2 + 3x - 10$
$\qquad\qquad = 2^2 + 3 \times 2 - 10$ $\qquad\qquad\qquad\qquad = (-5)^2 + 3 \times (-5) - 10$
$\qquad\qquad = 4 + 6 - 10$ $\qquad\qquad\qquad\qquad\qquad = 25 - 15 - 10$
$\qquad\qquad = 0$ $\qquad\qquad\qquad\qquad\qquad\qquad = 0$

$x = 2$ and $x = -5$ both satisfy the equation $x^2 + 3x - 10 = 0$, so we say that they are both **solutions**.

But, how do we find these solutions without using trial and error?

In this chapter we will discuss several methods for solving quadratic equations, and apply them to practical problems.

A   QUADRATIC EQUATIONS OF THE FORM $x^2 = k$

Consider the equation $x^2 = 7$.

Now $\sqrt{7} \times \sqrt{7} = 7$, so $x = \sqrt{7}$ is one solution,

and $(-\sqrt{7}) \times (-\sqrt{7}) = 7$, so $x = -\sqrt{7}$ is also a solution.

Thus, if $x^2 = 7$, then $x = \pm\sqrt{7}$.

$\pm\sqrt{7}$ is read as 'plus or minus the square root of 7'

SOLUTION OF $x^2 = k$

If $x^2 = k$ then $\begin{cases} x = \pm\sqrt{k} & \text{if } k > 0 \\ x = 0 & \text{if } k = 0 \\ \text{there are } \textbf{no real solutions} & \text{if } k < 0. \end{cases}$

Example 1   ◀ Self Tutor

Solve for x: **a** $2x^2 + 1 = 15$ **b** $2 - 3x^2 = 8$

a $2x^2 + 1 = 15$
$\therefore \quad 2x^2 = 14$ {take 1 from both sides}
$\therefore \quad x^2 = 7$ {divide both sides by 2}
$\therefore \quad x = \pm\sqrt{7}$

b $2 - 3x^2 = 8$
$\therefore \quad -3x^2 = 6$ {take 2 from both sides}
$\therefore \quad x^2 = -2$ {divide both sides by -3}
which has no solutions as x^2 cannot be < 0.

Example 2   ◀ Self Tutor

Solve for x:

a $(x - 3)^2 = 16$ **b** $(x + 2)^2 = 11$

For equations of the form $(x \pm a)^2 = k$ we do not expand the LHS.

a $(x - 3)^2 = 16$
$\therefore \quad x - 3 = \pm\sqrt{16}$
$\therefore \quad x - 3 = \pm 4$
$\therefore \quad x = 3 \pm 4$
$\therefore \quad x = 7 \text{ or } -1$

b $(x + 2)^2 = 11$
$\therefore \quad x + 2 = \pm\sqrt{11}$
$\therefore \quad x = -2 \pm \sqrt{11}$

EXERCISE 9A

1 Solve for x:

    a $\quad x^2 = 100$ b $\quad 2x^2 = 50$ c $\quad 5x^2 = 20$

    d $\quad 6x^2 = 54$ e $\quad 5x^2 = -45$ f $\quad 7x^2 = 0$

    g $\quad 3x^2 - 2 = 25$ h $\quad 4 - 2x^2 = 12$ i $\quad 4x^2 + 2 = 10$

2 Solve for x:

    a $\quad (x-1)^2 = 9$ b $\quad (x+4)^2 = 16$ c $\quad (x+2)^2 = -1$

    d $\quad (x-4)^2 = 5$ e $\quad (x-6)^2 = -4$ f $\quad (x+2)^2 = 0$

    g $\quad (2x-5)^2 = 0$ h $\quad (3x+2)^2 = 4$ i $\quad \frac{1}{3}(2x+3)^2 = 2$

B   SOLUTION BY FACTORISATION

THE NULL FACTOR LAW

For quadratic equations which are not of the form $\quad x^2 = k,\quad$ we need an alternative method of solution. One method is to factorise the quadratic and then apply the **Null Factor** law.

The Null Factor law states that:

> When the product of two (or more) numbers is zero, then *at least one* of them must be zero.

So, if $ab = 0$ then $a = 0$ or $b = 0$.

Example 3   ◀) **Self Tutor**

Solve for x using the Null Factor law:

    a $\quad 3x(x-5) = 0$ b $\quad (x-4)(3x+7) = 0$

    a $3x(x-5) = 0$ b $(x-4)(3x+7) = 0$

      $\therefore \quad 3x = 0$ or $x - 5 = 0$ $\therefore \quad x - 4 = 0$ or $3x + 7 = 0$

            $\therefore \quad x = 0$ or 5 $\therefore \quad x = 4$ or $3x = -7$

                                          $\therefore \quad x = 4$ or $-\frac{7}{3}$

EXERCISE 9B.1

1 Solve for the unknown using the Null Factor law:

    a $\quad 3x = 0$ b $\quad a \times 8 = 0$ c $\quad -7y = 0$

    d $\quad ab = 0$ e $\quad 2xy = 0$ f $\quad abc = 0$

    g $\quad a^2 = 0$ h $\quad pqrs = 0$ i $\quad a^2 b = 0$

2 Solve for x using the Null Factor law:

   a $x(x-5) = 0$ **b** $2x(x+3) = 0$ **c** $(x+1)(x-3) = 0$

   d $3x(7-x) = 0$ **e** $-2x(x+1) = 0$ **f** $4(x+6)(2x-3) = 0$

   g $(2x+1)(2x-1) = 0$ **h** $11(x+2)(x-7) = 0$ **i** $-6(x-5)(3x+2) = 0$

   j $x^2 = 0$ **k** $4(5-x)^2 = 0$ **l** $-3(3x-1)^2 = 0$

STEPS FOR SOLVING QUADRATIC EQUATIONS

To use the **Null Factor** law when solving equations, we must have one side of the equation *equal to zero*.

    Step 1:   If necessary, rearrange the equation so one side is **zero**.

    Step 2:   **Fully factorise** the other side (usually the LHS).

    Step 3:   Use the **Null Factor** law.

    Step 4:   **Solve** the resulting linear equations.

    Step 5:   **Check** at least one of your solutions.

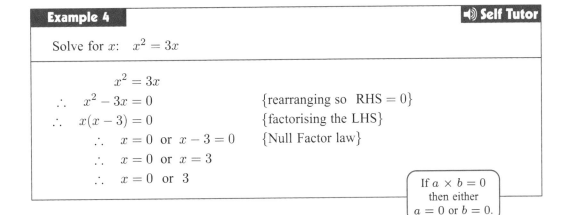

Example 4   **◀)) Self Tutor**

Solve for x: $x^2 = 3x$

$$x^2 = 3x$$
$$\therefore \quad x^2 - 3x = 0 \qquad \text{\{rearranging so } RHS = 0\}$$
$$\therefore \quad x(x-3) = 0 \qquad \text{\{factorising the LHS\}}$$
$$\therefore \quad x = 0 \text{ or } x - 3 = 0 \qquad \text{\{Null Factor law\}}$$
$$\therefore \quad x = 0 \text{ or } x = 3$$
$$\therefore \quad x = 0 \text{ or } 3$$

If $a \times b = 0$ then either $a = 0$ or $b = 0$.

ILLEGAL CANCELLING

Let us reconsider the equation $x^2 = 3x$ from **Example 4**.

We notice that there is a common factor of x on both sides.

If we cancel x from both sides, we will have $\dfrac{x^2}{x} = \dfrac{3x}{x}$ and thus $x = 3$.

Consequently, we will 'lose' the solution $x = 0$.

From this example we conclude that:

We must never cancel a variable that is a common factor from both sides of an equation unless we know that the factor cannot be zero.

Example 5   ◀)) **Self Tutor**

Solve for x: $x^2 + 3x = 28$

$$x^2 + 3x = 28$$
$$\therefore \quad x^2 + 3x - 28 = 0 \qquad \{\text{rearranging so RHS } = 0\}$$
$$\therefore \quad (x + 7)(x - 4) = 0 \qquad \{\text{sum} = +3 \text{ and product } = -28$$
$$\therefore \quad \text{the numbers are } +7 \text{ and } -4\}$$
$$\therefore \quad x + 7 = 0 \quad \text{or} \quad x - 4 = 0 \qquad \{\text{Null Factor law}\}$$
$$\therefore \quad x = -7 \quad \text{or} \quad 4$$

Example 6   ◀)) **Self Tutor**

Solve for x: $5x^2 = 3x + 2$

$$5x^2 = 3x + 2$$
$$\therefore \quad 5x^2 - 3x - 2 = 0 \qquad \{\text{rearranging so RHS } = 0\}$$
$$\therefore \quad 5x^2 - 5x + 2x - 2 = 0 \qquad \{ac = -10, \quad b = -3$$
$$\therefore \quad 5x(x - 1) + 2(x - 1) = 0 \qquad \therefore \quad \text{the numbers are } -5 \text{ and } +2\}$$
$$\therefore \quad (x - 1)(5x + 2) = 0$$
$$\therefore \quad x - 1 = 0 \quad \text{or} \quad 5x + 2 = 0 \qquad \{\text{Null Factor law}\}$$
$$\therefore \quad x = 1 \quad \text{or} \quad -\tfrac{2}{5}$$

Example 7   ◀)) **Self Tutor**

Solve for x: $\dfrac{x + 5}{4} = \dfrac{9 - x}{x}$

$$\frac{x + 5}{4} = \frac{9 - x}{x}$$
$$\therefore \quad x(x + 5) = 4(9 - x) \qquad \{\text{removing the fractions}\}$$
$$\therefore \quad x^2 + 5x = 36 - 4x \qquad Check: \text{ if } x = 3, \quad \text{LHS} = \tfrac{8}{4} = 2$$
$$\therefore \quad x^2 + 9x - 36 = 0 \qquad\qquad\qquad\qquad \text{RHS} = \tfrac{6}{3} = 2 \ \checkmark$$
$$\therefore \quad (x - 3)(x + 12) = 0 \qquad \text{if } x = -12, \quad \text{LHS} = -\tfrac{7}{4}$$
$$\therefore \quad x = 3 \quad \text{or} \quad -12 \qquad\qquad\qquad\qquad \text{RHS} = \tfrac{21}{-12} = -\tfrac{7}{4} \ \checkmark$$

EXERCISE 9B.2

1 Solve for x:

a $x^2 - 7x = 0$ **b** $x^2 - 5x = 0$ **c** $x^2 = 8x$

d $x^2 = 4x$ **e** $3x^2 + 6x = 0$ **f** $2x^2 + 5x = 0$

g $4x^2 - 3x = 0$ **h** $4x^2 = 5x$ **i** $3x^2 = 9x$

2 Solve for x:

- **a** $x^2 - 1 = 0$
- **b** $x^2 - 9 = 0$
- **c** $(x - 5)^2 = 0$
- **d** $(x + 2)^2 = 0$
- **e** $x^2 + 3x + 2 = 0$
- **f** $x^2 - 3x + 2 = 0$
- **g** $x^2 + 5x + 6 = 0$
- **h** $x^2 - 5x + 6 = 0$
- **i** $x^2 + 7x + 6 = 0$
- **j** $x^2 + 9x + 14 = 0$
- **k** $x^2 + 11x = -30$
- **l** $x^2 + 2x = 15$
- **m** $x^2 + 4x = 12$
- **n** $x^2 = 11x - 24$
- **o** $x^2 = 14x - 49$

3 Solve for x:

- **a** $x^2 + 9x + 20 = 0$
- **b** $x^2 + 11x + 28 = 0$
- **c** $x^2 + 2x = 8$
- **d** $x^2 + x = 12$
- **e** $x^2 + 6 = 5x$
- **f** $x^2 + 4 = 4x$
- **g** $x^2 = x + 6$
- **h** $x^2 = 7x + 60$
- **i** $x^2 = 3x + 70$
- **j** $10 - 3x = x^2$
- **k** $x^2 + 12 = 7x$
- **l** $9x + 36 = x^2$

4 Solve for x:

- **a** $2x^2 + 2 = 5x$
- **b** $3x^2 + 8x = 3$
- **c** $3x^2 + 17x + 20 = 0$
- **d** $2x^2 + 5x = 3$
- **e** $2x^2 + 5 = 11x$
- **f** $2x^2 + 7x + 5 = 0$
- **g** $3x^2 + 13x + 4 = 0$
- **h** $5x^2 = 13x + 6$
- **i** $2x^2 + 17x = 9$
- **j** $2x^2 + 3x = 5$
- **k** $3x^2 + 2x = 8$
- **l** $2x^2 + 9x = 18$

5 Solve for x:

- **a** $6x^2 + 13x = 5$
- **b** $6x^2 = x + 2$
- **c** $6x^2 + 5x + 1 = 0$
- **d** $21x^2 = 62x + 3$
- **e** $10x^2 + x = 2$
- **f** $10x^2 = 7x + 3$

6 Solve for x by first expanding brackets and then making one side of the equation zero:

- **a** $x(x + 5) + 2(x + 6) = 0$
- **b** $x(1 + x) + x = 3$
- **c** $(x - 1)(x + 9) = 8x$
- **d** $3x(x + 2) - 5(x - 3) = 17$
- **e** $4x(x + 1) = -1$
- **f** $2x(x - 6) = x - 20$

7 Solve for x by first eliminating the algebraic fractions:

- **a** $\dfrac{x}{3} = \dfrac{2}{x}$
- **b** $\dfrac{4}{x} = \dfrac{x}{2}$
- **c** $\dfrac{x}{5} = \dfrac{2}{x}$
- **d** $\dfrac{x - 1}{4} = \dfrac{3}{x}$
- **e** $\dfrac{x - 1}{x} = \dfrac{x + 11}{5}$
- **f** $\dfrac{x}{x + 2} = \dfrac{1}{x}$
- **g** $\dfrac{2x}{3x + 1} = \dfrac{1}{x + 2}$
- **h** $\dfrac{2x + 1}{x} = 3x$
- **i** $\dfrac{x + 2}{x - 1} = \dfrac{x}{2}$

8 Solve for x:

- **a** $x^4 - 5x^2 + 4 = 0$
- **b** $x^4 - 7x^2 + 12 = 0$
- **c** $x^4 = 4x^2 + 5$

Hint: Treat them as quadratics in the variable x^2.

C   COMPLETING THE SQUARE

Try as much as we like, we will not be able to solve quadratic equations such as $x^2 + 4x - 7 = 0$ using the factorisation methods already practised. This is because the solutions are not rationals.

To solve this equation we need a different technique.

We saw in **Example 2** that if $(x + 2)^2 = 11$

$$\text{then} \quad x + 2 = \pm\sqrt{11}$$
$$\therefore \quad x = -2 \pm \sqrt{11}$$

So, we can solve $x^2 + 4x - 7 = 0$ if we can rearrange it so there is a perfect square on the left hand side.

Consider $x^2 + 4x - 7 = 0$

$$\therefore \quad x^2 + 4x = 7$$
$$\therefore \quad x^2 + 4x + 4 = 7 + 4$$
$$\therefore \quad (x + 2)^2 = 11$$
$$\therefore \quad x + 2 = \pm\sqrt{11}$$
$$\therefore \quad x = -2 \pm \sqrt{11}$$

> We add 4 to both sides to 'complete' a perfect square on the LHS.

Hence the solutions to $x^2 + 4x - 7 = 0$ are $x = -2 \pm \sqrt{11}$.

The process of creating a **perfect square** on the left hand side is called **completing the square**.

From our previous study of perfect squares we observe that:

$$(x + 3)^2 = x^2 + 2 \times 3 \times x + 3^2$$
$$(x - 5)^2 = x^2 - 2 \times 5 \times x + 5^2$$
$$(x + p)^2 = x^2 + 2 \times p \times x + p^2$$

So,   the constant term is "**the square of half the coefficient of x**".

Example 8   ◀ **Self Tutor**

To create a perfect square on the LHS, what must be added to both sides of the equation:

  a $x^2 + 8x = -5$ **b** $x^2 - 6x = 13$?

What does the equation become in each case?

> We keep the equation balanced by adding the same number to both sides of the equation.

---

  a In $x^2 + 8x = -5$, half the coefficient of x is $\frac{8}{2} = 4$.

   So, we add 4^2 to both sides

   and the equation becomes $x^2 + 8x + 4^2 = -5 + 4^2$

$$\therefore \quad (x + 4)^2 = -5 + 16$$
$$\therefore \quad (x + 4)^2 = 11$$

b In $x^2 - 6x = 13$, half the coefficient of x is $\frac{-6}{2} = -3$.

So, we add $(-3)^2 = 3^2$ to both sides

and the equation becomes $x^2 - 6x + 3^2 = 13 + 3^2$

$$\therefore \quad (x-3)^2 = 13 + 9$$

$$\therefore \quad (x-3)^2 = 22$$

Example 9 ◀) **Self Tutor**

Solve for x by completing the square, leaving answers in simplest radical form:

a $x^2 + 2x - 2 = 0$ **b** $x^2 - 4x + 6 = 0$

a $\qquad x^2 + 2x - 2 = 0$

$\therefore \quad x^2 + 2x \quad = 2$ {move constant term to RHS}

$\therefore \quad x^2 + 2x + 1^2 = 2 + 1^2$ {add $(\frac{2}{2})^2 = 1^2$ to both sides}

$\therefore \quad (x+1)^2 = 3$ {factorise LHS, simplify RHS}

$\therefore \quad x + 1 = \pm\sqrt{3}$

$\therefore \quad x = -1 \pm \sqrt{3}$

b $\qquad x^2 - 4x + 6 = 0$

$\therefore \quad x^2 - 4x \quad = -6$ {move constant term to the RHS}

$\therefore \quad x^2 - 4x + 2^2 = -6 + 2^2$ {add $(-\frac{4}{2})^2 = 2^2$ to both sides}

$\therefore \quad (x-2)^2 = -2$ {factorise LHS, simplify RHS}

which is impossible as no perfect square can be negative.

$\therefore \quad$ no real solutions exist.

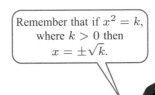

Remember that if $x^2 = k$, where $k > 0$ then $x = \pm\sqrt{k}$.

EXERCISE 9C

1 For each of the following equations:

    i find what must be added to both sides of the equation to create a perfect square on the LHS

    ii write each equation in the form $(x+p)^2 = k$.

a $x^2 + 2x = 5$ **b** $x^2 - 2x = -7$ **c** $x^2 + 6x = 2$

d $x^2 - 6x = -3$ **e** $x^2 + 10x = 1$ **f** $x^2 - 8x = 5$

g $x^2 + 12x = 13$ **h** $x^2 + 5x = -2$ **i** $x^2 - 7x = 4$

2 If possible, solve for x by completing the square, leaving answers in simplest radical form:

a $x^2 - 4x + 1 = 0$
b $x^2 - 2x - 2 = 0$
c $x^2 - 4x - 3 = 0$

d $x^2 + 2x - 1 = 0$
e $x^2 + 2x + 4 = 0$
f $x^2 + 4x + 1 = 0$

g $x^2 + 6x + 3 = 0$
h $x^2 - 6x + 11 = 0$
i $x^2 + 8x + 14 = 0$

3 Solve for x by completing the square, leaving answers in simplest radical form:

a $x^2 + 3x + 2 = 0$
b $x^2 = 4x + 8$
c $x^2 - 5x + 6 = 0$

d $x^2 + x - 1 = 0$
e $x^2 + 3x - 1 = 0$
f $x^2 + 5x - 2 = 0$

4 a To solve $3x^2 + 6x - 1 = 0$ by completing the square, our first step must be to divide both sides by 3. Explain why this statement is true.

   b Solve by completing the square:

   i $2x^2 + 4x - 1 = 0$
   ii $3x^2 - 12x + 7 = 0$
   iii $5x^2 - 10x + 3 = 0$

   iv $x - \dfrac{1}{x} = 1$
   v $2x - \dfrac{1}{x} = 3$
   vi $\dfrac{x - 1}{2 - x} = 2x + 1$

D   **PROBLEM SOLVING**

The problems in this section can all be converted to algebraic form as **quadratic equations**. They can all be solved using **factorisation** or **completing the square**.

PROBLEM SOLVING METHOD

Step 1:   Carefully read the question until you understand the problem. A rough sketch may be useful.

Step 2:   Decide on the unknown quantity and label it x, say.

Step 3:   Use the information given to find an equation which contains x.

Step 4:   Solve the equation.

Step 5:   Check that any solutions satisfy the equation and are realistic to the problem.

Step 6:   Write your answer to the question in sentence form.

Example 10   ◀ **Self Tutor**

The sum of a number and its square is 42. Find the number.

Let the number be x.   Therefore its square is x^2.

$$x + x^2 = 42$$
$$\therefore \quad x^2 + x - 42 = 0 \qquad \text{\{rearranging\}}$$
$$\therefore \quad (x + 7)(x - 6) = 0 \qquad \text{\{factorising\}}$$
$$\therefore \quad x = -7 \quad \text{or} \quad x = 6$$

So, the number is -7 or 6.   *Check:* If $x = -7$, $-7 + (-7)^2 = -7 + 49 = 42$ ✓

　　　　　　　　　　　　　　　　　　　If $x = 6$, $\quad 6 + 6^2 = 6 + 36 = 42$ ✓

Example 11 ◀)) Self Tutor

A rectangle has length 5 cm greater than its width. If it has an area of 84 cm^2, find the dimensions of the rectangle.

If x cm is the width, then $(x+5)$ cm is the length.

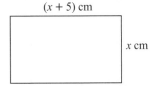

Now area $= 84$ cm^2

$\therefore \quad x(x+5) = 84$

$\therefore \quad x^2 + 5x = 84$

$\therefore \quad x^2 + 5x - 84 = 0$

$\therefore \quad (x+12)(x-7) = 0$

$\therefore \quad x = -12 \text{ or } 7$

But $x > 0$ as lengths are positive quantities, so $x = 7$

$\therefore$ the rectangle is 7 cm by 12 cm.

Example 12 ◀)) Self Tutor

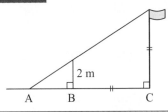

Given that [BC] is 3 m longer than [AB], find the height of the flag pole.

Let the height of the pole be x m.

$\therefore \quad$ BC $= x$ m and AB $= (x-3)$ m

The triangles are equiangular, so they are similar.

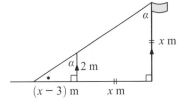

Hence $\dfrac{2}{x-3} = \dfrac{x}{(x-3)+x}$

$\therefore \quad 2(2x-3) = x(x-3)$

$\therefore \quad 4x - 6 = x^2 - 3x$

$\therefore \quad 0 = x^2 - 7x + 6$

$\therefore \quad (x-1)(x-6) = 0$

$\therefore \quad x = 1 \text{ or } 6$

However, x cannot be 1 as $x - 3 > 0$

$\therefore \quad x = 6$

So, the flag pole is 6 m high.

EXERCISE 9D

1   The sum of a number and its square is 110. Find the number.

2   The product of a number and the number increased by 4 is 117. Find the two possible values of the number.

3   When 24 is subtracted from the square of a number, the result is five times the original number. Find the number.

4   The sum of two numbers is 6 and the sum of their squares is 28. Find the exact values of these numbers.

5   Two numbers differ by 7 and the sum of their squares is 29. Find the numbers.

6   A rectangle has length 4 cm greater than its width. Find its width given that its area is 96 cm^2.

7   A triangle has base 4 m more than its altitude. If its area is 70 m^2, find its altitude.

8   A rectangular enclosure is made from 60 m of fencing. The area enclosed is 216 m^2. Find the dimensions of the enclosure.

9   A rectangular garden bed was built against an existing brick wall. 24 m of edging was used to enclose 60 m^2. Find the dimensions of the garden bed to the nearest cm.

10   A right angled triangle has sides 3 cm and 8 cm respectively less than its hypotenuse. Find the length of the hypotenuse to the nearest mm.

11   ABCD is a rectangle in which AB = 21 cm. The square AXYD is removed and the remaining rectangle has area 80 cm^2. Find the length of [BC].

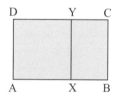

12   Find x in:

a

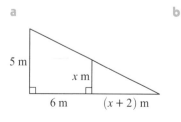

b

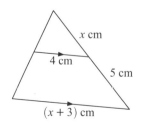

c

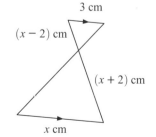

13 A, B, C and D are posts on the banks of a 20 m wide canal. A and B are 1 m apart. If OA = CD, find how far C and D are apart.

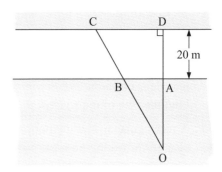

14

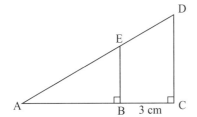

[AB] is 2 cm longer than [BE]. [DC] is 3 cm less than twice the length of [BE].

  a Explain why triangles ABE and ACD are similar.

  b If BE = x cm, show that $x^2 - 4x - 6 = 0$.

  c Hence, show that BE = $2 + \sqrt{10}$ cm.

15 Sarah has a brother who is 5 years younger than herself and another brother who is 8 years younger than herself. She observes that the product of her brothers' ages is equal to the age of her 40 year old father. How old is Sarah?

16 In a theatre there is a central block of seats with n seats per row. Blocks on either side contain 4 seats per row. The number of rows is 5 less than the total number of seats per row. If there are 126 seats in the theatre, find the value of n.

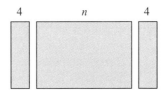

17 In a 42 km marathon race a runner took $(n - 4)$ hours to run the race, running at a constant speed of $(n + 7)$ km h^{-1}. Find:

  a the value of n

  b the time the runner took to run the race

  c the speed of the runner.

18 The numerator of a fraction is 3 less than the denominator. If the numerator is increased by 6 and the denominator is increased by 5, the fraction is doubled in value. Find the original fraction.

19 182 sweets are equally divided among a certain number of children at a party. If the number of sweets each child receives is one more than the number of children, find the number of children at the party.

20 At a fruit market John bought k oranges for a total of \$20. If Jenny had bought oranges at another stall, 10 more oranges could have been bought for the same price. Given that the difference in price per orange was 10 cents, find how many oranges were purchased by John.

21 The sum of a number and its reciprocal is $2\frac{1}{12}$. Find the number.

22 The sum of a number and twice its reciprocal is $3\frac{2}{3}$. Find the number.

23 A sheet of cardboard is 15 cm long and 10 cm wide. It is to be made into an open box which has a base area of 66 cm², by cutting out equal squares from the four corners and then bending the edges upwards.

Find the size of the squares to be cut out.

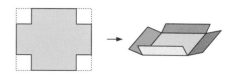

24 A rectangular swimming pool is 12 m long by 6 m wide. It is surrounded by a pavement of uniform width, the area of the pavement being $\frac{7}{8}$ of the area of the pool.

   a If the pavement is x m wide, show that the area of the pavement is $4x^2 + 36x$ m².

   b Hence, show that $4x^2 + 36x - 63 = 0$.

   c How wide is the pavement?

25 A circular magnet has an inner radius of x cm, an outer radius 2 cm larger, and its depth is the same as the inner radius.

If the total volume of the magnet is 120π cm³, find x.

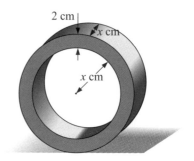

E   THE QUADRATIC FORMULA

Many quadratic equations cannot be solved by factorisation, and completing the square is rather tedious. Consequently, the **quadratic formula** has been developed.

$$\text{If} \quad ax^2 + bx + c = 0 \quad \text{where} \quad a \neq 0, \quad \text{then} \quad x = \frac{-b \pm \sqrt{b^2 - 4ac}}{2a}.$$

Proof: If $\quad ax^2 + bx + c = 0$

$$\text{then} \quad x^2 + \frac{b}{a}x + \frac{c}{a} = 0 \qquad \{\text{dividing each term by } a, \text{ as } a \neq 0\}$$

$$\therefore \quad x^2 + \frac{b}{a}x \quad = -\frac{c}{a}$$

$$\therefore \quad x^2 + \frac{b}{a}x + \left(\frac{b}{2a}\right)^2 = -\frac{c}{a} + \left(\frac{b}{2a}\right)^2 \qquad \{\text{completing the square on LHS}\}$$

$$\therefore \quad \left(x + \frac{b}{2a}\right)^2 = -\frac{c}{a}\left(\frac{4a}{4a}\right) + \frac{b^2}{4a^2}$$

$$\therefore \quad \left(x + \frac{b}{2a}\right)^2 = \frac{b^2 - 4ac}{4a^2}$$

$$\therefore \quad x + \frac{b}{2a} = \pm\sqrt{\frac{b^2 - 4ac}{4a^2}}$$

$$\therefore \quad x = -\frac{b}{2a} \pm \frac{\sqrt{b^2 - 4ac}}{2a}$$

$$\therefore \quad x = \frac{-b \pm \sqrt{b^2 - 4ac}}{2a}$$

Consider the **Opening Problem** on page **214** which involves the Diadro Dress Company. The equation we need to solve is: $\quad -11x^2 + 450x - 800 = 3000$.

$$\therefore \quad 11x^2 - 450x + 3800 = 0 \quad \text{where} \quad a = 11, \quad b = -450, \quad \text{and} \quad c = 3800.$$

Using the formula we obtain $\quad x = \dfrac{450 \pm \sqrt{450^2 - 4 \times 11 \times 3800}}{22} \quad$ which simplifies to $x \approx 11.9 \quad \text{or} \quad 29.0$.

So, the sale of either 12 or 29 dresses a week would produce a profit of about €3000.

USE OF THE QUADRATIC FORMULA

If $b^2 - 4ac$ is a rational perfect square then $\sqrt{b^2 - 4ac}$ will be rational, and so the solutions of the quadratic will also be rational. In such instances, it is preferable to solve the quadratic by factorisation.

For example, $6x^2 - 13x - 8 = 0$ has $b^2 - 4ac = 169 - 4(6)(-8) = 361 = 19^2$, so we should solve this equation by factorising $6x^2 - 13x - 8$ into $(3x - 8)(2x + 1)$.

Example 13   ◆⟩ **Self Tutor**

Solve for x: **a** $x^2 - 2x - 2 = 0$ **b** $2x^2 + 3x - 4 = 0$

a $x^2 - 2x - 2 = 0$ has
$a = 1$, $b = -2$, $c = -2$

$$\therefore \quad x = \frac{-(-2) \pm \sqrt{(-2)^2 - 4(1)(-2)}}{2(1)}$$

$$\therefore \quad x = \frac{2 \pm \sqrt{4 + 8}}{2}$$

$$\therefore \quad x = \frac{2 \pm \sqrt{12}}{2}$$

$$\therefore \quad x = \frac{2 \pm 2\sqrt{3}}{2}$$

$$\therefore \quad x = 1 \pm \sqrt{3}$$

b $2x^2 + 3x - 4 = 0$ has
$a = 2$, $b = 3$, $c = -4$

$$\therefore \quad x = \frac{-3 \pm \sqrt{3^2 - 4(2)(-4)}}{2(2)}$$

$$\therefore \quad x = \frac{-3 \pm \sqrt{9 + 32}}{4}$$

$$\therefore \quad x = \frac{-3 \pm \sqrt{41}}{4}$$

EXERCISE 9E.1

1 Use the quadratic formula to solve for x:

a $x^2 + 2x = 2$
b $x^2 + 2 = 6x$
c $x^2 = 4x + 1$

d $x^2 + 1 = 3x$
e $x^2 + 8x + 5 = 0$
f $2x^2 = 2x + 1$

g $9x^2 = 6x + 1$
h $25x^2 + 1 = 20x$
i $2x^2 + 6x + 1 = 0$

j $3x^2 + 2x - 2 = 0$
k $x + \dfrac{1}{x} = 3$
l $x - \dfrac{3}{x} = 1$

2 Use the quadratic formula to solve for x:

a $(x + 2)(x - 1) = 5$
b $(x + 1)^2 = 3 - x^2$
c $\dfrac{x + 1}{x} = \dfrac{x}{2}$

d $x + \dfrac{1}{x + 2} = 4$
e $3x - \dfrac{4}{x + 1} = 10$
f $\dfrac{x + 2}{x - 1} = \dfrac{3x}{x + 1}$

3 Find x in:

a
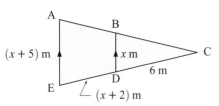

b
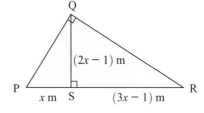

4 Two numbers have a sum of 4, and the sum of their reciprocals is 8. Find the numbers.

5 A rectangular enclosure is built against an existing wall. 48 m of fencing is used for the other 3 sides. What dimensions does the rectangle have if the area is 254 m²? Give your answer correct to the nearest centimetre.

QUADRATIC EQUATIONS WITH NO REAL SOLUTIONS

Consider $x^2 + 2x + 5 = 0$.

Using the quadratic formula, the solutions are:

$$x = \frac{-2 \pm \sqrt{4 - 4(1)(5)}}{2(1)}$$

$$\therefore \quad x = \frac{-2 \pm \sqrt{-16}}{2}$$

However, in the real number system, $\sqrt{-16}$ does not exist. We therefore say that $x^2 + 2x + 5 = 0$ has no real solutions.

If we graph $y = x^2 + 2x + 5$ we get:

The graph does not cut the x-axis, and this further justifies the fact that $x^2 + 2x + 5 = 0$ has no real solutions.

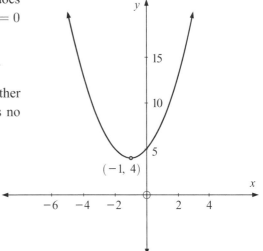

EXERCISE 9E.2

1 Show that the following quadratic equations have no real solutions:

    a $x^2 - 3x + 12 = 0$ b $x^2 + 2x + 4 = 0$ c $-2x^2 + x - 1 = 0$

2 Solve for x, where possible:

    a $x^2 - 25 = 0$ b $x^2 + 25 = 0$ c $x^2 - 7 = 0$

    d $x^2 + 7 = 0$ e $4x^2 - 9 = 0$ f $4x^2 + 9 = 0$

    g $x^2 - 4x + 5 = 0$ h $x^2 - 4x - 5 = 0$ i $x^2 - 10x + 29 = 0$

    j $x^2 + 6x + 25 = 0$ k $2x^2 - 6x - 5 = 0$ l $2x^2 + x - 2 = 0$

THE DISCRIMINANT, Δ

In the quadratic formula, the quantity $b^2 - 4ac$ under the square root sign is called the **discriminant**.

The symbol **delta** or Δ is used to represent the discriminant, so $\Delta = b^2 - 4ac$.

The quadratic formula can be written as $x = \dfrac{-b \pm \sqrt{\Delta}}{2a}$ where Δ replaces $b^2 - 4ac$.

Notice that:

- if $\Delta = 0$, $x = \dfrac{-b}{2a}$ is the **only solution** and is known as a **repeated root**
- if $\Delta > 0$, $\sqrt{\Delta}$ is a real number and so there are **two distinct real roots**
$$\dfrac{-b + \sqrt{\Delta}}{2a} \quad \text{and} \quad \dfrac{-b - \sqrt{\Delta}}{2a}$$
- if $\Delta < 0$, $\sqrt{\Delta}$ does not exist and so we have **no real solutions**
- if a, b and c are rational and Δ is a **perfect square** then the equation has two rational roots which can be found by factorisation.

Example 14   ◀)) **Self Tutor**

Use the discriminant to determine the nature of the roots of:

a $2x^2 - 3x + 4 = 0$ 　　　　　　 b $4x^2 - 4x - 1 = 0$

a $\Delta = b^2 - 4ac$
$= (-3)^2 - 4(2)(4)$
$= -23$ which is < 0
$\therefore$ there are no real roots

b $\Delta = b^2 - 4ac$
$= (-4)^2 - 4(4)(-1)$
$= 32$ which is > 0
$\therefore$ there are 2 distinct real roots

Example 15   ◀)) **Self Tutor**

$kx^2 + 6x - 3 = 0$ has a repeated root. Find k.

The discriminant $\Delta = 6^2 - 4(k)(-3) = 36 + 12k$.

A quadratic has a repeated root when $\Delta = 0$

$\therefore \quad 36 + 12k = 0$

$\therefore \quad 12k = -36$

$\therefore \quad k = -3$

EXERCISE 9E.3

1 Find the discriminant of:

　　a $x^2 - 2x - 7 = 0$ 　　　　 b $2x^2 - 3x + 6 = 0$ 　　　　 c $x^2 - 11 = 0$

　　d $2x^2 - 6x - 4 = 0$ 　　　　 e $3x^2 + 7x - 1 = 0$ 　　　　 f $4x^2 - 7x + 11 = 0$

2 Using the discriminant only, state the nature of the solutions of:

　　a $x^2 + 7x - 2 = 0$ 　　　　 b $x^2 + 4\sqrt{2}x + 8 = 0$ 　　　 c $2x^2 + 3x - 1 = 0$

　　d $6x^2 + 5x - 4 = 0$ 　　　　 e $x^2 + x + 6 = 0$ 　　　　　 f $9x^2 + 6x + 1 = 0$

3 Using the discriminant only, determine which of the following quadratic equations have rational roots which can be found by factorisation.

　　a $2x^2 + 7x - 4 = 0$ 　　　　 b $3x^2 - 7x - 6 = 0$ 　　　　 c $2x^2 + 6x + 1 = 0$

　　d $6x^2 + 19x + 10 = 0$ 　　　 e $4x^2 - 3x + 3 = 0$ 　　　　 f $8x^2 - 10x - 3 = 0$

4 Find values of k such that:

    a $kx^2 + 12x + 2 = 0$ has a repeated root

    b $3x^2 + 16x + k = 0$ has a repeated root

    c $kx^2 + 6x - 3 = 0$ has two distinct real roots

    d $4x^2 - 12x + k = 0$ has two distinct real roots

    e $2x^2 - 5x + k = 0$ has no real solutions

    f $kx^2 - 11x - k = 0$ has no real roots.

MINIMISING THE COSTS

LINKS
click here

Areas of interaction:
Environments/Human ingenuity

REVIEW SET 9A

1 Solve for x:

    a $2x^2 = 4$ **b** $3x^2 + 18 = 0$ **c** $5x(x - 3) = 0$

    d $x^2 + 24 = 11x$ **e** $10x^2 - 11x - 6 = 0$ **f** $3x^2 = 2x + 21$

2 Solve for x:

    a $x^2 = x$ **b** $(x + 3)^2 = -1$ **c** $3(x - 2)^2 = 15$

3 Solve by completing the square: **a** $x^2 + 8x + 5 = 0$ **b** $x^2 - 14x + 7 = 0$

4 The length of a rectangle is three times its width, and its area is 9 cm^2. Find the dimensions of the rectangle.

5 The sum of a number and its reciprocal is 3. Find the number.

6 When the square of a number is increased by one, the result is four times the original number. Find the number.

7 Using the discriminant only, state the nature of the solutions of:

    a $x^2 + 3x - 6 = 0$ **b** $2x^2 + 5x + 7 = 0$

8 Use the quadratic formula to solve:

    a $2x^2 + 2x - 1 = 0$ **b** $\dfrac{1}{x} - \dfrac{1}{1 - x} = 2$

9 In a right angled triangle, the second to longest side is 5 cm longer than the shortest side, and the hypotenuse is three times longer than the shortest side. Find the exact length of the hypotenuse.

10 Consider $kx^2 + 10x - 5 = 0$. Find k for which the equation has:

    a a repeated root   **b** two distinct real roots.

11 **a** A straight length of wire is 20 cm long. It is bent at right angles to form the two shorter sides of a right angled triangle. If the triangle's area is 30 cm², find:

      i the length of the hypotenuse   **ii** the triangle's perimeter.

  b Is it possible for a right angled triangle with shorter sides made from a 20 cm length of wire to have an area of 51 cm²?

REVIEW SET 9B

1 Solve for x:

  a $-2(x-3)^2 = 0$ **b** $(x+5)(x-4) = 0$ **c** $(2-x)^2 = -1$

  d $x^2 - 5x = 24$ **e** $2x^2 = 8$ **f** $6x^2 - x - 2 = 0$

2 Solve by completing the square: **a** $x^2 - 4x = 10$ **b** $x^2 + x - 9 = 0$

3 A rectangle has length 5 cm greater than its width. If it has an area of 80 cm², find the dimensions of the rectangle.

4 The sum of a number and five times its square, is equal to four. Find the number.

5 A right angled triangle has hypotenuse two centimetres shorter than three times the length of the shortest side. The other side is 7 cm longer than the shortest side. Find the length of each side of the triangle.

6 Using the discriminant only, state the nature of the solutions of:

  a $x^2 + \sqrt{3}x + 1 = 0$ **b** $2x^2 + 5x + 2 = 0$

7 Use the quadratic formula to solve for x:

  a $x^2 - 2x - 7 = 0$ **b** $4x^2 - x + 1 = 0$ **c** $\dfrac{3x}{1-x} = \dfrac{5}{x}$

8 Consider $2x^2 + kx + 9 = 0$. Find the values of k for which the equation has a repeated root.

9 Find the unknown in:

a 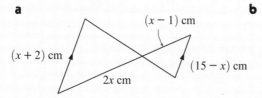   **b**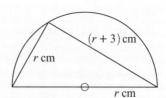

10 Two numbers differ by 3 and the difference between their reciprocals is 4. Find the exact values of the numbers given that they are both positive.

11 A group of friends hire a bus for a day for €480. At the last minute, two more people decide to go on the trip, and as a result each person pays €8 less.

How many people went on the trip?

Chapter 10

Trigonometry

Contents:

Trigonometry is a branch of mathematics that deals with triangles. In particular, it considers the relationship between their side lengths and angles.

We can apply trigonometry in engineering, astronomy, architecture, navigation, surveying, the building industry, and in many other branches of applied science.

HISTORICAL NOTE   ASTRONOMY AND TRIGONOMETRY

The Greek astronomer **Hipparchus** (140 BC) is credited with being the founder of trigonometry. To aid his astronomical calculations, he produced a table of numbers in which the lengths of chords of a circle were related to the length of the radius.

Ptolemy, another great Greek astronomer of the time, extended this table in his major published work *Almagest* which was used by astronomers for the next 1000 years. In fact, much of Hipparchus' work is known through the writings of Ptolemy. These writings found their way to Hindu and Arab scholars.

Aryabhata, a Hindu mathematician in the 6th Century AD, constructed a table of the lengths of half-chords of a circle with radius one unit. After completing this chapter you will see that the length of the half-chord is a **sine** function. So, Aryabhata actually drew up the first table of sine values.

In the late 16th century, **Rhaeticus** produced comprehensive and remarkably accurate tables of all six trigonometric ratios, three of which you will learn about in this chapter. These involved a tremendous number of tedious calculations, all without the aid of calculators or computers.

OPENING PROBLEM

A surveyor is standing on horizontal ground and wishes to find the height of a mountain some distance away on the other side of a lake. In order to do this he uses a theodolite to accurately measure:

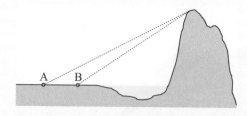

- the angle between the horizontal ground at A and the line of sight to the top of the mountain to be 33.7^o
- the angle between the horizontal ground at B and the line of sight to the top of the mountain to be 41.6^o
- the distance from A to B to be 400 m.

For your consideration:

- Can you draw a labelled diagram of the situation showing all information given?
- Can you solve this problem using right angled triangle trigonometry?
- Can you solve this problem faster using the sine or cosine rules?

A · TRIGONOMETRIC RATIOS

In previous years we have defined the following basic trigonometric ratios for right-angled triangles:

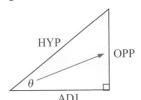

$$\sin \theta = \frac{\text{OPP}}{\text{HYP}}, \quad \cos \theta = \frac{\text{ADJ}}{\text{HYP}}, \quad \frac{\sin \theta}{\cos \theta} = \frac{\text{OPP}}{\text{ADJ}}$$

where $\qquad \tan \theta = \dfrac{\sin \theta}{\cos \theta}.$

We can use these ratios to find unknown side lengths and angles in right angled triangles.

INVESTIGATION 1 · COMPLEMENTARY ANGLES

Two angles are **complementary** if their sum is 90°. We say that θ and $(90^o - \theta)$ are **complements** of each other.

PRINTABLE WORKSHEET

Your task is to determine if a relationship exists between the sines and cosines of an angle and its complement.

What to do:

1 Use your calculator to complete a table like the one shown. Include some angles of your choice.

θ	$\sin \theta$	$\cos \theta$	$90^o - \theta$	$\sin(90^o - \theta)$	$\cos(90^o - \theta)$
17°			73°		
38°					
59°					

2 Write down your observations from the tabled values.

3 Use the figure alongside to prove that your observations are true for all angles θ where $0^o < \theta < 90^o$.

4 Investigate possible connections between $\tan \theta$ and $\tan(90^o - \theta)$.

FINDING TRIGONOMETRIC RATIOS

Example 1	◀) Self Tutor

For the following triangle find:

   a $\sin \theta$ **b** $\cos \phi$ **c** $\tan \theta$

a $\sin \theta = \dfrac{\text{OPP}}{\text{HYP}} = \dfrac{b}{c}$ **b** $\cos \phi = \dfrac{\text{ADJ}}{\text{HYP}} = \dfrac{b}{c}$ **c** $\tan \theta = \dfrac{\text{OPP}}{\text{ADJ}} = \dfrac{b}{a}$

FINDING SIDES

In a right angled triangle, if we are given another angle and a side we can find:

- the third angle using the 'angle sum of a triangle is $180°$'
- the other sides using trigonometry.

Step 1:   Redraw the figure and mark on it HYP, OPP, ADJ relative to the given angle.

Step 2:   Choose the correct trigonometric ratio and use it to set up an equation.

Step 3:   Solve to find the unknown.

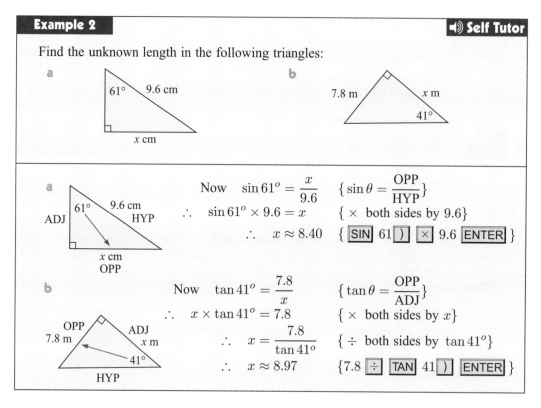

EXERCISE 10A.1

1 For each of the following triangles find:

    i $\sin\theta$ ii $\cos\theta$ iii $\tan\theta$ iv $\sin\phi$ v $\cos\phi$ vi $\tan\phi$

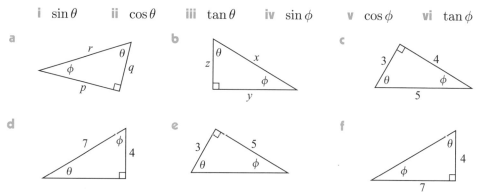

2 Construct a trigonometric equation connecting the angle with the sides given:

a
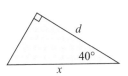

b
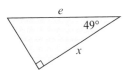

c
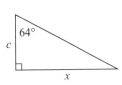

d
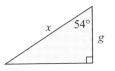

e
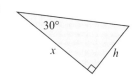

f
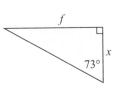

g
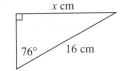

h
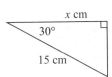

i
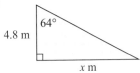

3 Find, to 2 decimal places, the unknown length in:

a
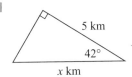

b
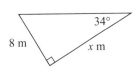

c
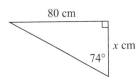

d
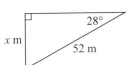

e
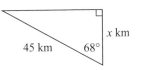

f
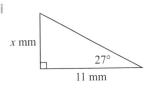

g
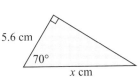

h
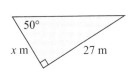

i
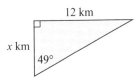

j

k

l

4 Find *all* the unknown angles and sides of:

a
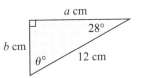

b
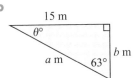

c
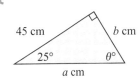

FINDING ANGLES

In the right angled triangle shown, $\sin \theta = \frac{3}{5}$.

So, we are looking for the angle θ with a sine of $\frac{3}{5}$.

If $\sin^{-1}(......)$ reads   "the angle with a sine of ......",   we can write $\theta = \sin^{-1}\left(\frac{3}{5}\right)$.
Another way of describing this is to say   "θ is the *inverse sine* of $\frac{3}{5}$".

> If $\sin \theta = x$ then θ is the **inverse sine** of x.

You can find graphics calculator instructions for finding these inverse trigonometric functions on page **14**.

We can define **inverse cosine** and **inverse tangent** in a similar way.

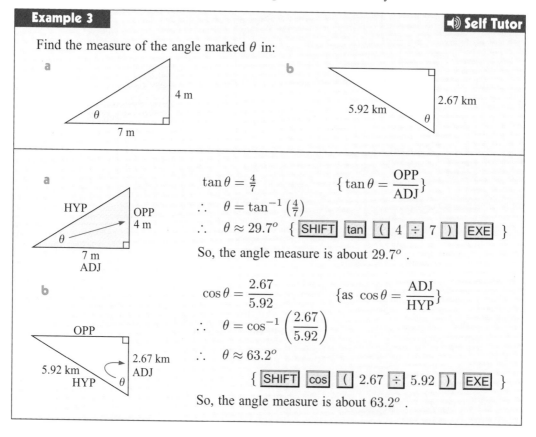

Example 3   ◄) **Self Tutor**

Find the measure of the angle marked θ in:

a

4 m

θ

7 m

b

5.92 km   2.67 km

θ

---

a

HYP   OPP
4 m

θ

7 m
ADJ

$\tan \theta = \frac{4}{7}$ $\{ \tan \theta = \dfrac{\text{OPP}}{\text{ADJ}} \}$

$\therefore \quad \theta = \tan^{-1}\left(\frac{4}{7}\right)$

$\therefore \quad \theta \approx 29.7°$ { [SHIFT] [tan] [(] 4 [÷] 7 [)] [EXE] }

So, the angle measure is about $29.7°$.

b

OPP

2.67 km
ADJ

5.92 km
HYP θ

$\cos \theta = \dfrac{2.67}{5.92}$ $\{$as $\cos \theta = \dfrac{\text{ADJ}}{\text{HYP}}\}$

$\therefore \quad \theta = \cos^{-1}\left(\dfrac{2.67}{5.92}\right)$

$\therefore \quad \theta \approx 63.2°$

{ [SHIFT] [cos] [(] 2.67 [÷] 5.92 [)] [EXE] }

So, the angle measure is about $63.2°$.

EXERCISE 10A.2

1 Find the measure of the angle marked θ in:

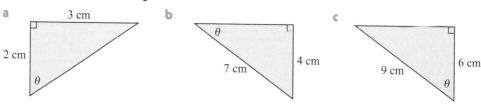

a   3 cm

2 cm

θ

b θ

7 cm   4 cm

c

9 cm   6 cm

θ

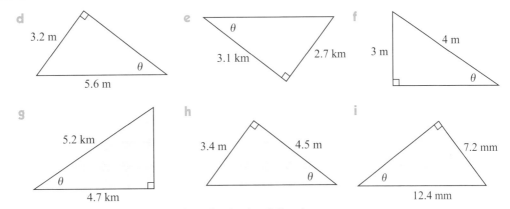

2   Find all the unknown sides and angles in the following:

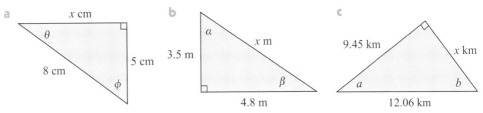

3   Check your answers for x in question **2** using Pythagoras' theorem.

4   Find θ using trigonometry in the following. What conclusions can you draw?

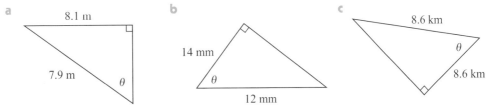

 INVESTIGATION 2   **HIPPARCHUS AND THE UNIVERSE**

Hipparchus was a Greek astronomer and mathematician born in Nicaea in the 2nd century BC. He is considered among the greatest astronomers of antiquity.

Part 1:   How Hipparchus measured the distance to the moon

Consider two towns A and B on the earth's equator.   The moon is directly overhead town A. From B the moon is just visible, since MB is a tangent to the earth and is therefore perpendicular to BC. Angle C is the difference in longitude between towns A and B, which Hipparchus calculated to be approximately 89° in the 2nd century BC.

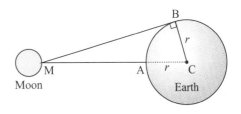

We know today that the radius of the earth is approximately 6378 km. Hipparchus would have used a less accurate figure, probably based on Eratosthenes' measure of the earth's circumference.

What to do:

1 Use $r = 6378$ km and $\widehat{BCM} = 89^o$ to estimate the distance from the centre of the earth C to the moon.

2 Now calculate the distance AM **between** the earth and the moon.

3 In calculating just one distance between the earth and the moon, Hipparchus was assuming that the orbit of the moon was circular. In fact it is not. Research the shortest and greatest distances to the moon. How were these distances determined? How do they compare with Hipparchus' method?

Part 2: How Hipparchus measured the radius of the moon

From town A on the earth's surface, the angle between an imaginary line to the centre of the moon and an imaginary line to the edge of the moon (a tangent to the moon) is about 0.25^o.

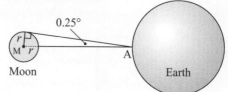

The average distance from the earth to the moon is about 384 403 km.

What to do:

1 Confirm from the diagram that $\sin 0.25^o = \dfrac{r}{r + 384\,403}$.

2 Solve this equation to find r, the radius of the moon.

3 Research the actual radius of the moon, and if possible find out how it was calculated. How does your answer to **2** compare?

B   TRIGONOMETRIC PROBLEM SOLVING

The trigonometric ratios can be used to solve a wide variety of problems involving right angled triangles. When solving such problems it is important to follow the steps below:

Step 1:   Read the question carefully.

Step 2:   Draw a diagram, not necessarily to scale, with the given information clearly marked.

Step 3:   If necessary, label the vertices of triangles in the figure.

Step 4:   State clearly any assumptions you make which will enable you to use right angled triangles or properties of other geometric figures.

Step 5:   Choose an appropriate trigonometric ratio and use it to generate an equation connecting the quantities. On some occasions more than one equation may be needed.

Step 6:   Solve the equation(s) to find the unknown.

Step 7:   Answer the question in words.

ANGLES OF ELEVATION AND DEPRESSION

The angle between the horizontal and your
line of sight is called the **angle of elevation**
if you are looking upwards, or the **angle of
depression** if you are looking downwards.

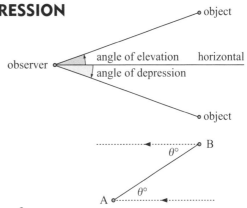

If the angle of elevation from A to B is θ^o,
then the angle of depression from B to A is
also θ^o.

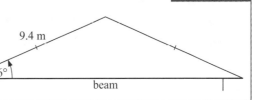

When using trigonometry to solve problems we often use:

- the properties of isosceles and right angled triangles
- the properties of circles and tangents
- true bearings
- angles of elevation and depression.

Example 4 ◀) **Self Tutor**

Determine the length of the horizontal
roofing beam required to support a roof
of pitch 16° as shown alongside:

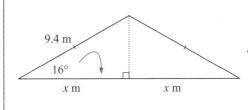

$$\cos \theta = \frac{\text{ADJ}}{\text{HYP}}$$

$$\therefore \quad \cos 16^o = \frac{x}{9.4}$$

$$\therefore \quad x = 9.4 \times \cos 16^o$$

$$\therefore \quad x \approx 9.036$$

{*Calculator:* 9.4 $\boxed{\times}$ $\boxed{\text{COS}}$ 16 $\boxed{)}$ $\boxed{\text{ENTER}}$ }

$$\therefore \quad \text{the length of the beam} = 2 \times 9.036 \text{ m}$$

$$\approx 18.1 \text{ m}$$

Example 5 ◀) **Self Tutor**

A ladder 4.1 m in length rests against a vertical
wall and reaches 3.5 m up from ground level. Find:

  a the angle the ladder makes with the ground

  b the distance from the foot of the ladder to the
wall using trigonometry.

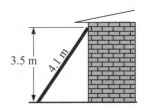

a $\sin \theta = \dfrac{\text{OPP}}{\text{HYP}} = \dfrac{3.5}{4.1}$

$\therefore \quad \theta = \sin^{-1}\left(\dfrac{3.5}{4.1}\right)$

$\therefore \quad \theta \approx 58.6^o$

{ SHIFT sin (3.5 ÷ 4.1) EXE }

$\therefore$ the ladder makes an angle of about 58.6^o with the ground.

b $\cos \theta = \dfrac{\text{ADJ}}{\text{HYP}}$

$\therefore \quad \cos 58.61^o = \dfrac{x}{4.1}$

$\therefore \quad 4.1 \times \cos 58.61^o = x$

$\therefore \quad 2.14 \approx x$

$\therefore$ the foot of the ladder is about 2.14 m from the wall.

Example 6   ◀)) Self Tutor

The angle between a tangent from point P to a circle and the line from P to the centre of the circle is 27°. Determine the length of the line from P to the centre of the circle if the radius is 3 cm.

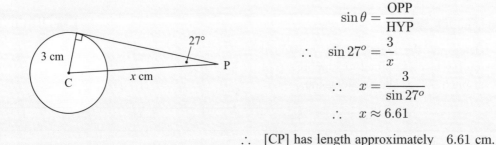

$\sin \theta = \dfrac{\text{OPP}}{\text{HYP}}$

$\therefore \quad \sin 27^o = \dfrac{3}{x}$

$\therefore \quad x = \dfrac{3}{\sin 27^o}$

$\therefore \quad x \approx 6.61$

$\therefore$ [CP] has length approximately   6.61 cm.

EXERCISE 10B.1

1   From a point 235 m from the base of a cliff, the angle of elevation to the cliff top is 25°. Find the height of the cliff.

2   What angle will a 5 m ladder make with a wall if it reaches 4.2 m up the wall?

3   The angle of elevation from a fishing boat to the top of a lighthouse 25 m above sea-level is 6°. Calculate the horizontal distance from the boat to the lighthouse.

4   A rectangular gate has a diagonal strut of length 3 m. The angle between the diagonal and a side is 28°. Find the length of the longer side of the gate.

5   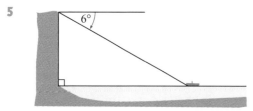   From a vertical cliff 80 m above sea level, a fishing boat is observed at an angle of depression of 6°. How far out to sea is the boat?

6   A railway line goes up an incline of constant angle 4° over a horizontal distance of 4 km. How much altitude has the train gained by the end of the incline?

7 At the entrance to a building there is a ramp for wheelchair access. The length of the ramp is 5 metres, and it rises to a height of 0.6 metres. Find the angle θ that the ramp makes with the ground.

8

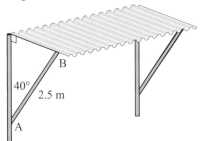

The roof of a bus shelter is supported by a metal strut 2.5 m in length. The strut is attached to the back wall of the shelter at an angle of 40°. Calculate how far below the roof of the shelter the strut is attached to the wall.

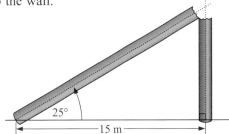

9 A goalpost was hit by lightning and snapped in two. The top of the post is now resting 15 m from its base at an angle of 25°. Find the height of the goal post before it snapped.

10

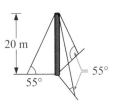

Three strong cables are used to brace a 20 m tall pole against movement due to the wind. Each rope is attached so that the angle of elevation to the top of the pole is 55°. Find the total length of cable.

11 A tangent from point P to a circle of radius 4 cm is 10 cm long. Find:

   a the distance of P from the centre of the circle

   b the size of the angle between the tangent and the line joining P to the centre of the circle.

12 [AB] is a chord of a circle with centre O and radius of length 5 cm. [AB] has length 8 cm. What angle does [AB] subtend at the centre of the circle, i.e., what is the size of angle AOB?

13 A rhombus has sides of length 10 cm, and the angle between two adjacent sides is 76°. Find the length of the longer diagonal of the rhombus.

14 The dimensions of a double garage are shown in the diagram alongside. Calculate the height of the top of the roof above the ground.

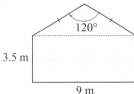

15 A tree casts a shadow 6 m long when the sun is at an elevation of 70°. A gardener wishes to fell the tree at ground level and needs to cut the trunk into 4 m lengths to cart it away. How many cuts must he make?

16 An aeroplane takes off from the ground at an angle of 27° and its average speed in the first 10 seconds is 200 km h^{-1}. What is the altitude of the plane at the end of this time?

17 An observer notices that an aeroplane flies directly overhead. Two minutes later the aeroplane is at an angle of elevation of 27°. Assuming the aeroplane is travelling with constant speed, what will be its angle of elevation after another two minutes?

18 Determine the measure of the base angles of an isosceles triangle in which the equal sides are $\frac{2}{3}$ of the length of the base.

19 An isosceles triangle is drawn with base angles 24° and base 28 cm. Find the base angles of the isosceles triangle with the same base length but with treble the area.

20 The angle of elevation from a point on level ground to the top of a building 100 m high is 22°. Find:

  a the distance of the point from the base of the building

  b the distance the point must be moved towards the building in order that the angle of elevation becomes 40°.

21 From a point A which is 30 m from the base of a building B, the angle of elevation to the top of the building C is 56°, and to the top of the flag pole [CD] is 60°.
Find the length of the flag pole.

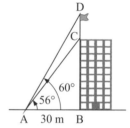

22

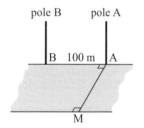

A man, M, positions himself on a river bank as in the diagram alongside, so he can observe two poles A and B of equal height on the opposite bank of the river.
He finds the angle of elevation to the top of pole A is 22°, and the angle of elevation to the top of pole B is 19°.
Show how he could use these facts to determine the width of the river, if he knows that A and B are 100 m apart.

23 A surveyor standing on a horizontal plain can see a volcano in the distance. The angle of elevation of the top of the volcano is 23°. If the surveyor moves 750 m closer, the angle of elevation is now 37°. Determine the height of the volcano.

24 Find the shortest distance between the two parallel lines.

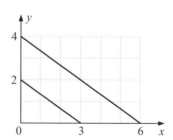

TRUE BEARINGS

In **Chapter 4** we saw that:

the **true bearing** of B from A is the clockwise measure of the angle between [AB] and the 'north' line through A.

Example 7   ◀)) **Self Tutor**

An aeroplane departs A and flies on a 143° course for 368 km. It then changes direction
to a 233° course and flies a further 472 km to town C. Find:

  a the distance of C from A   b the bearing of C from A.

First, we draw a fully labelled diagram of
the flight. On the figure, we show angles
found using parallel lines.   Angle ABC
measures 90°.

  a $AC = \sqrt{368^2 + 472^2}$ {Pythagoras}

       ≈ 598.5

  So, C is about 598.5 km from A.

  b To find the required angle we first need to find θ.

      Now $\tan \theta = \dfrac{\text{OPP}}{\text{ADJ}} = \dfrac{472}{368}$

            $\therefore\quad \theta = \tan^{-1}\left(\frac{472}{368}\right)$

            $\therefore\quad \theta \approx 52.06°$

  The required angle is $143° + 52.06° \approx 195.06°$

  $\therefore$ the bearing of C from A is about 195°.

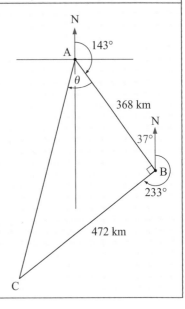

EXERCISE 10B.2

1 Draw diagrams to represent bearings from O of:

      a 136°   b 240°   c 051°   d 327°

2 Find the bearing of Q from P if the bearing of P from Q is:

      a 054°   b 113°   c 263°   d 304°

3 A, B and C are the checkpoints of a triangular orienteering course. For each of the
   following courses, find the bearing of:

      i   B from A   ii   C from B   iii   B from C
      iv C from A   v   A from B   vi   A from C.

  a   b

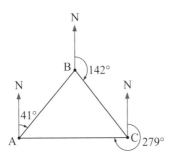

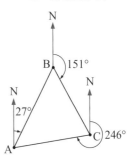

4 A bush-walker walks 14 km east and then 9 km south. Find the bearing of his finishing
   position from his starting point.

5 Runner A runs at 10 km h^{-1} due north. Runner B leaves the same spot and runs at 12 km h^{-1} due east. Find the distance and bearing of runner B from runner A after 30 minutes.

6 A hiker walks in the direction 153° and stops when she is 20 km south of her starting point. How far did she walk?

7 A ship sails for 60 km on a bearing 040°. How far east of its starting point is the ship?

8 An aeroplane travels on a bearing of 295° so that it is 200 km west of its starting point. How far has it travelled on this bearing?

9 A fishing trawler sails from port P in the direction 024° for 30 km, and then in the direction 114° for 20 km. Calculate:

 a the distance and bearing of the trawler from P

 b the direction in which the trawler must sail in order to return to P.

C   3-DIMENSIONAL PROBLEM SOLVING

Right angled triangles occur frequently in 3-dimensional figures. We can use Pythagoras' theorem and trigonometry to find unknown angles and lengths.

Example 8   ◀) **Self Tutor**

A cube has sides of length 10 cm. Find the angle between the diagonal AB of the cube and one of the edges at B.

The angle between [AB] and *any* of the edges at B is the same.

∴   the required angle is $\widehat{ABC}$.

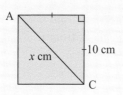

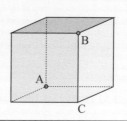

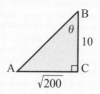

By Pythagoras:

$$x^2 = 10^2 + 10^2$$
$$\therefore \quad x^2 = 200$$
$$\therefore \quad x = \sqrt{200}$$

$$\tan\theta = \frac{\text{OPP}}{\text{ADJ}} = \frac{\sqrt{200}}{10}$$
$$\therefore \quad \theta = \tan^{-1}\left(\frac{\sqrt{200}}{10}\right)$$
$$\therefore \quad \theta \approx 54.7^o$$

∴   the required angle is about 54.7^o.

EXERCISE 10C.1

1 The figure alongside is a cube with sides of length 15 cm. Find:

   a EG   **b** $A\widehat{G}E$.

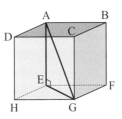

2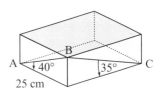

The figure alongside is a rectangular prism. X and Y are the midpoints of the edges [EF] and [FG] respectively. Find:

   a HX   **b** $D\widehat{X}H$

   c HY   **d** $D\widehat{Y}H$.

3 In the triangular prism alongside, find:

   a DF

   b $A\widehat{F}D$.

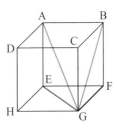

4 [AB] and [BC] are wooden support struts on a crate. Find the total length of wood required to make the two struts.

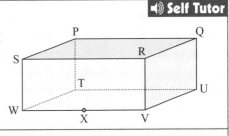

5 All edges of a square-based pyramid are 12 m in length.

   a Find the angle between a slant edge and a base diagonal.

   b Show that this angle is the same for any square-based pyramid with all edge lengths equal.

SHADOW LINES (PROJECTIONS)

Consider a wire frame in the shape of a cube as shown in the diagram alongside. Imagine a light source shining down directly on this cube from above.

The shadow cast by wire [AG] would be [EG]. This is called the **projection** of [AG] onto the base plane EFGH.

Similarly, the projection of [BG] onto the base plane is [FG].

Example 9   ◀ϑ **Self Tutor**

Find the shadow or projection of the following onto the base plane if a light is shone from directly above the figure:

   a [UP]   **b** [WP]

   c [VP]   **d** [XP].

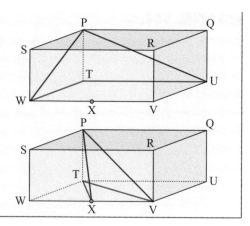

a The projection of [UP] onto the base plane is [UT].

b The projection of [WP] onto the base plane is [WT].

c The projection of [VP] onto the base plane is [VT].

d The projection of [XP] onto the base plane is [XT].

THE ANGLE BETWEEN A LINE AND A PLANE

The angle between a line and a plane is the angle between the line and its projection on the plane.

Example 10   ◀)) **Self Tutor**

Name the angle between the following line segments and the base plane EFGH:

a [AH]   b [AG].

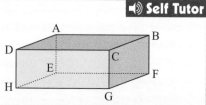

---

a The projection of [AH] onto the base plane EFGH is [EH]

∴ the required angle is $A\widehat{H}E$.

b The projection of [AG] onto the base plane EFGH is [EG]

∴ the required angle is $A\widehat{G}E$.

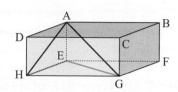

Example 11   ◀)) **Self Tutor**

Find the angle between the following line segments and the base plane EFGH:

a [DG]   b [BH]

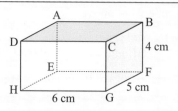

---

a The required angle is $D\widehat{G}H$.

∴ $\tan\theta = \dfrac{\text{OPP}}{\text{ADJ}} = \dfrac{4}{6}$

∴ $\theta = \tan^{-1}\left(\dfrac{4}{6}\right)$

∴ $\theta \approx 33.69°$

∴ the angle is about $33.7°$

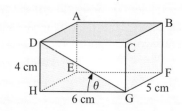

b The required angle is $\widehat{BHF}$.

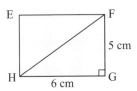

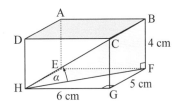

By Pythagoras,

$$(HF)^2 = 6^2 + 5^2$$

$$\therefore \quad (HF)^2 = 61$$

$$\therefore \quad HF = \sqrt{61} \text{ cm}$$

$$\tan\alpha = \frac{OPP}{ADJ} = \frac{4}{\sqrt{61}}$$

$$\therefore \quad \alpha = \tan^{-1}\left(\frac{4}{\sqrt{61}}\right)$$

$$\therefore \quad \alpha \approx 27.12^o$$

$$\therefore \quad \text{the angle is about } 27.1^o.$$

EXERCISE 10C.2

1 Find the following projections onto the base planes of the given figures:

a

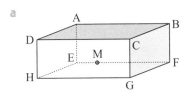

   i [CF]

   ii [DG]

   iii [DF]

   iv [CM]

b

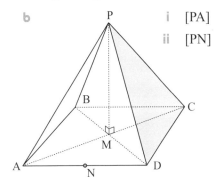

   i [PA]

   ii [PN]

c

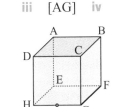

   i [BD]

   ii [AE]

   iii [AF]

   iv [AX]

2 For each of the following figures, name the angle between the given line segment and the base plane:

   a **i** [DE]   **ii** [CE]   **b** **i** [PY]   **ii** [QW]   **c** **i** [AQ]   **ii** [AY]

      iii [AG] **iv** [BX]   **iii** [QX] **iv** [YQ]

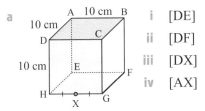

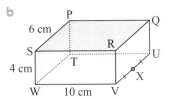

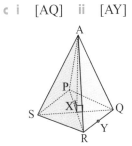

3 For each of the following figures, find the angle between the given line segments and the base plane:

a

   i [DE]

   ii [DF]

   iii [DX]

   iv [AX]

b

   i [PU]

   ii [PV]

   iii [SX]

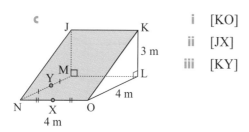

c

i [KO]
ii [JX]
iii [KY]

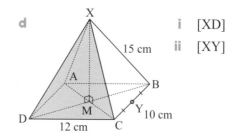

d

i [XD]
ii [XY]

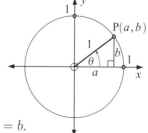

D   THE UNIT CIRCLE

Consider the circle of radius 1 unit with its centre at the origin O. This circle is called the **unit circle**. It has equation $x^2 + y^2 = 1$.

Suppose P lies on the circle so that [OP] makes angle θ with the positive x-axis. θ is always measured in the anticlockwise direction.

For any acute angle θ, notice that $\cos \theta = \dfrac{a}{1} = a$ and $\sin \theta = \dfrac{b}{1} = b$.

In fact, for any angle θ: The x-coordinate of P is called the **cosine** of angle θ or $\cos \theta$.

The y-coordinate of P is called the **sine** of angle θ or $\sin \theta$.

Using the equation of the circle, we can immediately establish that: $$\cos^2 \theta + \sin^2 \theta = 1 \quad \text{for all } \theta.$$

Alongside is a unit circle diagram:

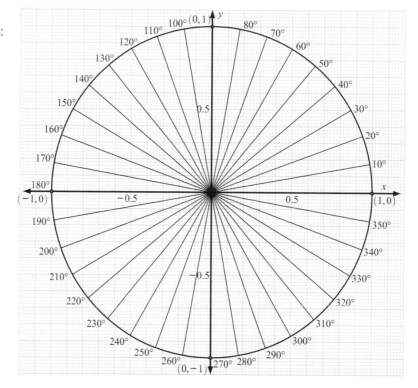

Example 12

◀)) Self Tutor

Given that $0° \leqslant \theta \leqslant 180°$,   solve these equations to 1 decimal place:

   a $\cos \theta = 0.623$ b $\cos \theta = -0.317$ c $\sin \theta = 0.814$

a $\cos \theta = 0.623$

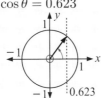

$\theta = \cos^{-1}(0.623)$

$\therefore \quad \theta \approx 51.5°$

b $\cos \theta = -0.317$

$\theta = \cos^{-1}(-0.317)$

$\therefore \quad \theta \approx 108.5°$

c $\sin \theta = 0.814$

$\theta = \sin^{-1}(0.814)$

or $180° - \sin^{-1}(0.814)$

$\therefore \quad \theta \approx 54.5°$ or $125.5°$

TANGENT

Suppose [OP] is extended to meet the tangent from the x-axis at point T.

As P moves around the circle, the length of the tangent changes.

The **tangent** of angle θ or $\tan \theta$ is the length of the tangent from the x-axis to the extension of [OP].

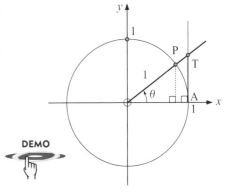

DEMO

EXERCISE 10D

1   Use the unit circle diagram to find:

  a $\cos 0°$ b $\sin 0°$ c $\cos 90°$ d $\sin 90°$

  e $\sin 180°$ f $\cos 180°$ g $\sin 270°$ h $\cos 270°$

  i $\cos 360°$ j $\sin 360°$ k $\cos 450°$ l $\sin 450°$

2   Use the unit circle diagram to estimate, to 2 decimal places:

  a $\cos 50°$ b $\sin 50°$ c $\cos 110°$ d $\sin 110°$

  e $\sin 170°$ f $\cos 170°$ g $\sin 230°$ h $\cos 230°$

  i $\cos 320°$ j $\sin 320°$ k $\cos(-30°)$ l $\sin(-30°)$

3   Check your answers to **2** using your calculator.

4   Explain, using a unit circle diagram, why:

  a $\sin(180° - \theta) = \sin \theta$ b $\cos(180° - \theta) = -\cos \theta$

  c $\cos(-\theta) = \cos \theta$ d $\sin(-\theta) = -\sin \theta$.

5   Simplify:

  a $\sin(180° + \theta)$ b $\cos(180° + \theta)$

6   **a** If $\cos\theta = \frac{1}{2}$, what value does θ have for $0° \leqslant \theta \leqslant 180°$?

    b If $\cos\theta = -\frac{1}{2}$, what value does θ have for $0° \leqslant \theta \leqslant 180°$?

    c If $\sin\theta = \frac{1}{2}$, what values may θ have for $0° \leqslant \theta \leqslant 180°$?

7   Given that $0° \leqslant \theta \leqslant 180°$, solve these equations to 1 decimal place:

    a $\cos\theta = 0.672$ **b** $\cos\theta = -0.672$ **c** $\cos\theta = 0.138$

    d $\cos\theta = -0.138$ **e** $\sin\theta = 0.317$ **f** $\sin\theta = 0.887$

    g $\cos\theta = 0.077$ **h** $\cos\theta = -0.369$ **i** $\sin\theta = 0.929$

8   Find $\tan\theta$ for:

    a $\theta = 0°$ **b** $\theta = 45°$ **c** θ acute but very close to $90°$

9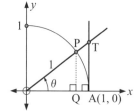

    a Suppose θ is any acute angle. Find the length of:

        i [OQ]   **ii** [PQ]   **iii** [AT].

    b Deduce that $\tan\theta = \dfrac{\sin\theta}{\cos\theta}$ using similar triangles.

10 By considering $\tan(180° - \theta) = \dfrac{\sin(180° - \theta)}{\cos(180° - \theta)}$, find the connection between $\tan(180° - \theta)$ and $\tan\theta$.

Check your answer using your calculator with $\theta = 23°$.

E   AREA OF A TRIANGLE USING SINE

Consider the triangle alongside, in which the sides opposite angles A, B and C are labelled a, b and c respectively.

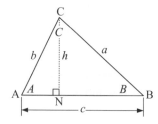

Area of triangle ABC $= \frac{1}{2} \times AB \times CN = \frac{1}{2}ch$

    But $\sin A = \dfrac{h}{b}$

      $\therefore$ $h = b\sin A$

    $\therefore$ area $= \frac{1}{2}c(b\sin A)$ or $\frac{1}{2}bc\sin A$

If the altitudes from A and B were drawn, we could also show that

    area $= \frac{1}{2}ac\sin B = \frac{1}{2}ab\sin C$.   **area $= \frac{1}{2}ab\sin C$**   is worth remembering.

Summary:

    The area of a triangle is:

    a half of the product of two sides and the sine of the included angle.

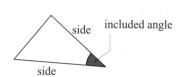

Example 13

🔊 **Self Tutor**

Find the area of
triangle ABC.

A

11 cm

28°

B   15 cm   C

Area $= \frac{1}{2}ac\sin B$

$\quad = \frac{1}{2} \times 15 \times 11 \times \sin 28^o$

$\quad \approx 38.7 \text{ cm}^2$

EXERCISE 10E

1   Find the area of:

a

12 cm

45°

13 cm

b

28 km

82°

25 km

c

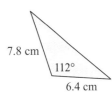

7.8 cm

112°

6.4 cm

d

32 m   84°   27 m

e

10.6 cm   125°   12.2 cm

f

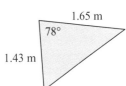

1.65 m

78°

1.43 m

2   Find the area of a parallelogram with sides 6.4 cm and 8.7 cm and one interior angle
    64°.

3

A

14 cm

75°

B

x cm

C

If triangle ABC has area 150 cm², find the value of x.

4   Triangle PQR has $P\widehat{Q}R = \theta$.   PQ = 10 m,   QR = 12 m,   and the area of the triangle
    is 30 m². Find the possible values of θ.

5   Triangle ABC has   AB = 13 cm   and   BC = 17 cm,   and its area is 73.4 cm².   Find
    the measure of $A\widehat{B}C$.

6

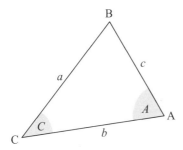

a   Find the area of triangle ABC using:

    i   angle A ii   angle C

b   Hence, show that $\dfrac{a}{c} = \dfrac{\sin A}{\sin C}$.

INVESTIGATION 3   SINE AND COSINE RULES

Part A: The Sine Rule

We have established that the area of a triangle is a half of the product of any two sides and the sine of the included angle.

This can be written in symbolic form as:

$$\text{Area } \triangle ABC = \tfrac{1}{2}ab\sin C = \tfrac{1}{2}ac\sin B = \tfrac{1}{2}bc\sin A$$

What to do:

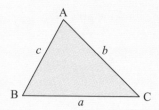

1 Using this relationship, show that

$$\frac{\sin A}{a} = \frac{\sin B}{b} = \frac{\sin C}{c}.$$

This relationship is known as the **sine rule**.

2 Copy and complete the following statement using **1**:
In any triangle the ratio of the sines of angles and their .... sides is constant.

Part B: The Cosine Rule

What to do:

1 For the figure alongside, copy and complete:

In $\triangle ANC$, $b^2 = ... + ...$ {Pythagoras}

$\therefore \ h^2 = ... - .....$ (1)

In $\triangle BNC$, $a^2 = ... + ...$ {Pythagoras}

$\therefore \ h^2 = ... - .....$ (2)

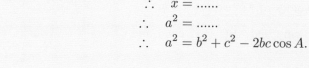

By equating (1) and (2), $a^2 - ...... = b^2 - ......$

Expanding and collecting terms gives $a^2 = ...$

But in $\triangle ACN$, $\cos A = \dfrac{....}{....}$

$\therefore \quad x = ...$

$\therefore \quad a^2 = ...$

$\therefore \quad a^2 = b^2 + c^2 - 2bc\cos A.$

2 Copy and complete the following: In any triangle with sides a, b and c units and opposite angles A, B and C respectively,

$$a^2 = b^2 + c^2 - ......$$
$$b^2 = a^2 + c^2 - ......$$
$$c^2 = a^2 + b^2 - ......$$

This rule is called the **cosine rule**.

F | THE SINE RULE

The **sine rule** is a set of equations which connects the lengths of the sides of any triangle with the sines of the opposite angles.

The triangle does not have to be right angled for the sine rule to be used.

THE SINE RULE

In any triangle ABC with sides a, b and c units, and opposite angles A, B and C respectively,

$$\frac{\sin A}{a} = \frac{\sin B}{b} = \frac{\sin C}{c} \quad \text{or} \quad \frac{a}{\sin A} = \frac{b}{\sin B} = \frac{c}{\sin C}.$$

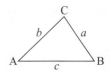

Proof: The area of any triangle ABC is given by $\frac{1}{2}bc \sin A = \frac{1}{2}ac \sin B = \frac{1}{2}ab \sin C$.

Dividing each expression by $\frac{1}{2}abc$ gives $\frac{\sin A}{a} = \frac{\sin B}{b} = \frac{\sin C}{c}$.

The sine rule is used to solve problems involving triangles when angles and sides opposite those angles are to be related.

GEOMETRY PACKAGE

FINDING SIDES

Example 14   ◀)) **Self Tutor**

Find the length of side [BC], correct to 2 decimal places:

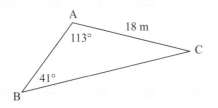

By the sine rule,

$$\frac{BC}{\sin 113^o} = \frac{18}{\sin 41^o}$$

$$\therefore \quad BC = \frac{18 \times \sin 113^o}{\sin 41^o}$$

$$\therefore \quad BC \approx 25.26$$

$\therefore$ [BC] is about 25.26 m long.

EXERCISE 10F

1   Find the value of x:

a
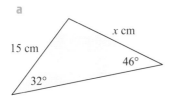

b
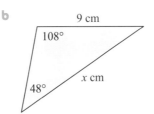

c
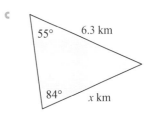

2 In triangle ABC find:

    a a if $A = 65^o$, $B = 35^o$, $b = 18$ cm   **b** b if $A = 72^o$, $C = 27^o$, $c = 24$ cm

    c c if $B = 25^o$, $C = 42^o$, $a = 7.2$ cm.

FINDING ANGLES

The problem of finding angles using the sine rule is more complicated because there may be two possible answers. We discovered this in **Exercise 10D**.

This is because an equation of the form

$$\sin \theta = a \quad \text{produces answers of the form} \quad \theta = \sin^{-1} a \quad \text{or} \quad (180^o - \sin^{-1} a).$$

Example 15   ◀) **Self Tutor**

Find, correct to 1 decimal place, the measure of angle C in triangle ABC if
AC = 8 cm, AB = 12 cm, and angle B measures 28°.

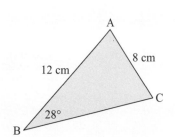

$$\frac{\sin C}{c} = \frac{\sin B}{b} \quad \text{\{sine rule\}}$$

$$\therefore \quad \frac{\sin C}{12} = \frac{\sin 28^o}{8}$$

$$\therefore \quad \sin C = \frac{12 \times \sin 28^o}{8}$$

Now $\quad \sin^{-1}\left(\dfrac{12 \times \sin 28^o}{8}\right) \approx 44.8^o$

> This is called the "ambiguous case".

and since the angle at C could be acute or obtuse,

$$\therefore \quad C \approx 44.8^o \quad \text{or} \quad (180 - 44.8)^o$$

$$\therefore \quad C \text{ measures } 44.8^o \text{ if it is acute, or } 135.2^o \text{ if it is obtuse.}$$

In this case there is insufficient information to determine the actual shape of the triangle.

The validity of the two answers in the above example can be demonstrated by a simple construction.

Step 1:   Draw AB of length 12 cm and construct an angle of 28° at B.

Step 2:   From A, draw an arc of radius 8 cm.

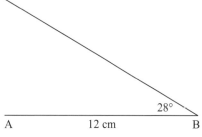

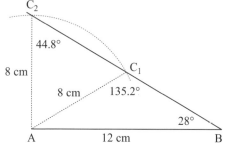

Sometimes there is information given in the question which enables us to **reject** one of the answers.

Example 16   ◀) **Self Tutor**

Find the measure of angle L in triangle KLM given that $L\widehat{K}M$ measures 52°, LM = 158 m, and KM = 128 m.

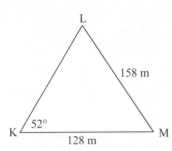

By the sine rule, $\dfrac{\sin L}{128} = \dfrac{\sin 52^o}{158}$

$\therefore$ $\sin L = \dfrac{128 \times \sin 52^o}{158}$

Now $\sin^{-1}\left(\dfrac{128 \times \sin 52^o}{158}\right) \approx 39.7^o$

$\therefore$ since L could be acute or obtuse,

$L \approx 39.7^o$ or $(180 - 39.7)^o \approx 140.3^o$

However, we can reject $L = 140.3^o$ as $140.3^o + 52^o > 180^o$ which is impossible.

$\therefore$ the angle $L \approx 39.7^o$.

3 Find the value of θ:

a

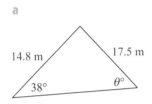

b

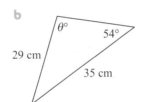

c

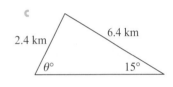

4 In triangle ABC, find the measure of:

  a angle A if $a = 12.6$ cm, $b = 15.1$ cm   and $A\widehat{B}C = 65^o$

  b angle B if $b = 38.4$ cm, $c = 27.6$ cm   and $A\widehat{C}B = 43^o$

  c angle C if $a = 5.5$ km, $c = 4.1$ km   and $B\widehat{A}C = 71^o$.

There may be two possible solutions.

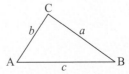

G   THE COSINE RULE

THE COSINE RULE

In any triangle ABC with sides a, b and c units and opposite angles A, B and C respectively,

$$a^2 = b^2 + c^2 - 2bc\cos A$$
$$b^2 = a^2 + c^2 - 2ac\cos B$$
$$c^2 = a^2 + b^2 - 2ab\cos C.$$

In **Investigation 3** on page **254** we established the cosine rule by using Pythagoras' Theorem and right angled triangle trigonometry.

The **cosine rule** can be used to solve problems involving triangles given

- **two sides** and the **included angle**   or • **three sides**.

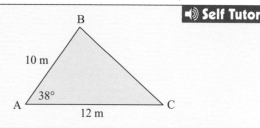

Example 17	◀ৰ) Self Tutor

Find, correct to 2 decimal places, the length of [BC].

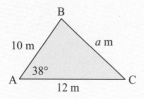

By the cosine rule:

$$a^2 = b^2 + c^2 - 2bc \cos A$$
$$\therefore \quad a = \sqrt{12^2 + 10^2 - 2 \times 12 \times 10 \times \cos 38^\circ}$$
$$\therefore \quad a \approx 7.41$$

$\therefore$ [BC] is 7.41 m in length.

EXERCISE 10G

GEOMETRY PACKAGE

1   Find the length of the remaining side in the given triangle:

a
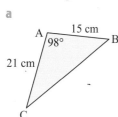

b
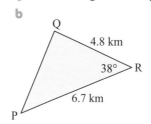

c
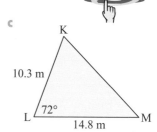

2   Find the measure of all angles of:

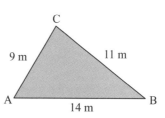

3   Find:

   a   the smallest angle of a triangle with sides 9 cm, 11 cm and 13 cm

   b   the largest angle of a triangle with sides 3 cm, 5 cm and 7 cm.

4

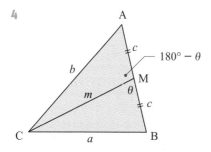

   a   Use the cosine rule in triangle BCM to find $\cos \theta$ in terms of a, c and m.

   b   Use the cosine rule in triangle ACM to find $\cos(180^\circ - \theta)$ in terms of b, c and m.

   c   Use the fact that $\cos(180^\circ - \theta) = -\cos \theta$ to prove **Apollonius' median theorem**:
$$a^2 + b^2 = 2m^2 + 2c^2.$$

d Find x in the following:

i

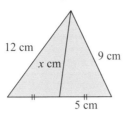

ii

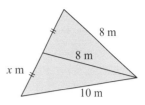

5 In triangle ABC,   AB $= 10$ cm,   AC $= 9$ cm   and $A\widehat{B}C = 60^o$.   Let BC $= x$ cm.

    a Use the cosine rule to show that x is a solution of $x^2 - 10x + 19 = 0$.

    b Solve the above equation for x.

    c Use a scale diagram and a compass to explain why there are two possible values of x.

PROBLEM SOLVING WITH THE SINE AND COSINE RULES

Whenever there is a choice between using the sine rule or the cosine rule, always use the **cosine rule** to avoid the ambiguous case.

Example 18　　　　　　　　　　　　　　　　　　◀) **Self Tutor**

An aircraft flies 74 km on a bearing 038° and then 63 km on a bearing 160°.
Find the distance of the aircraft from its starting point.

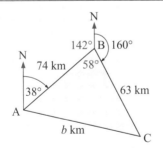

By the cosine rule,

$$b^2 = a^2 + c^2 - 2ac\cos B$$

$\therefore \quad b^2 = 63^2 + 74^2 - 2 \times 63 \times 74 \times \cos 58^o$

$\therefore \quad b^2 \approx 4504.03$

$\therefore \quad b \approx 67.1$

$\therefore$ the aircraft is 67.1 km from its starting point.

EXERCISE 10H

1 Two farm houses A and B are 10.3 km apart. A third farm house C is located such that $B\widehat{A}C = 83^o$ and $A\widehat{B}C = 59^o$.   How far is C from A?

2 A roadway is horizontal for 524 m from A to B, followed by a 23° incline 786 m long from B to C. How far is it directly from A to C?

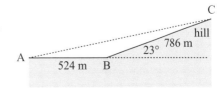

3 Towns A, B and C are located such that $\widehat{BAC} = 50°$ and B is twice as far from C as A is from C. Find the measure of $\widehat{BCA}$.

4 Hazel's property is triangular with dimensions as shown in the figure.

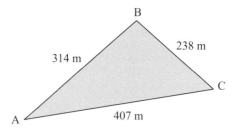

    a Find the measure of the angle at A, correct to 2 decimal places.

    b Hence, find the area of her property to the nearest hectare.

5 An orienteer runs for 450 m then turns through an angle of 32° and runs for another 600 m. How far is she from her starting point?

6 A yacht sails 6 km on a bearing 127° and then 4 km on a bearing 053°. Find the distance and bearing of the yacht from its starting point.

7 Mount X is 9 km from Mount Y on a bearing 146°. Mount Z is 14 km away from Mount X and on a bearing 072° from Mount Y. Find the bearing of X from Z.

8 From points A and B at sea, the angles of elevation to the top of the mountain T are 37° and 41° respectively. A and B are 1200 m apart.

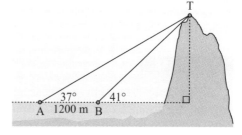

    a What is the size of $\widehat{ATB}$?

    b Find the distance from A to T.

    c Find the distance from B to T.

    d Find the height of the mountain.

    e Use the given figure to show that

$$d = h\left(\frac{1}{\tan\theta} - \frac{1}{\tan\phi}\right).$$

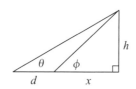

    f Use **e** to check your answer to **d**.

9 Bushwalkers leave point P and walk in the direction 238° for 11.3 km to point Q. At Q they change direction to 107° and walk for 18.9 km to point R. How far is R from the starting point P?

10

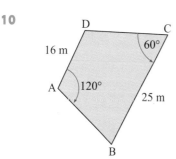

David's garden plot is in the shape of a quadrilateral. If the corner points are A, B, C and D then the angles at A and C are 120° and 60° respectively. AD = 16 m, BC = 25 m, and [DC] is 5 m longer than [AB]. A fence runs around the entire boundary of the plot. How long is the fence?

TRIGONOMETRIC IDENTITIES

We have already discovered that $\sin(180^\circ - \theta) = \sin\theta$ and that $\tan\theta = \dfrac{\sin\theta}{\cos\theta}$ and these are true *for all values of* θ.

We call such relationships **trigonometric identities**.

Consider the unit circle again.

Remember that if P(x, y) moves around the unit circle such that [OP] makes an angle of θ with the positive x-axis, then:

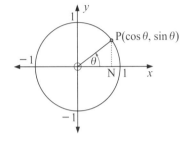

the x-coordinate of P is $\cos\theta$ and
the y-coordinate of P is $\sin\theta$.

Notice that: $\cos\theta = \dfrac{\text{ON}}{\text{OP}} = \dfrac{x}{1} = x$

$\therefore \quad \sin\theta = \dfrac{\text{PN}}{\text{OP}} = \dfrac{y}{1} = y.$

GEOMETRY PACKAGE

Notice also that in $\triangle$ONP, $\quad x^2 + y^2 = 1 \qquad \{\text{Pythagoras}\}$

$\therefore \quad [\cos\theta]^2 + [\sin\theta]^2 = 1$

We write: $\quad \boldsymbol{\cos^2\theta + \sin^2\theta = 1}.$

Notice also that as $-1 \leqslant x \leqslant 1$ and $-1 \leqslant y \leqslant 1$ for all points on the unit circle,

$$-1 \leqslant \cos\theta \leqslant 1 \quad \text{and} \quad -1 \leqslant \sin\theta \leqslant 1 \quad \text{for all } \theta.$$

Example 19 ◀) Self Tutor

Find the exact value of $\cos\theta$ if $\sin\theta = \frac{1}{3}$ and:

  a $0^\circ < \theta < 90^\circ$ **b** $90^\circ < \theta < 180^\circ$.

Using $\cos^2\theta + \sin^2\theta = 1$,

$\cos^2\theta + \left(\frac{1}{3}\right)^2 = 1$

$\therefore \quad \cos^2\theta + \frac{1}{9} = 1$

$\therefore \quad \cos^2\theta = \frac{8}{9}$

$\therefore \quad \cos\theta = \pm\sqrt{\frac{8}{9}}$

$\therefore \quad \cos\theta = \pm\frac{2\sqrt{2}}{3}$

a For $0^\circ < \theta < 90^\circ$,
$\cos\theta$ is positive

$\therefore \quad \cos\theta = \frac{2\sqrt{2}}{3}$

b For $90^\circ < \theta < 180^\circ$,
$\cos\theta$ is negative

$\therefore \quad \cos\theta = \frac{-2\sqrt{2}}{3}$

EXERCISE 10I.1

1 Find the exact value of $\cos\theta$ if $\sin\theta = \frac{2}{3}$ and:

    a $0^o < \theta < 90^o$ **b** $90^o < \theta < 180^o$.

2 If $\sin\theta = \frac{1}{\sqrt{3}}$ and $90^o < \theta < 180^o$, find the exact value of $\cos\theta$.

3 If $\cos\theta = -\frac{3}{5}$ and $90^o < \theta < 180^o$, find the exact value of $\sin\theta$.

SIMPLIFYING TRIGONOMETRIC EXPRESSIONS

For a given angle θ, $\sin\theta$ and $\cos\theta$ are real numbers, so the algebra of trigonometry is identical to the algebra of real numbers.

Consequently, we can simplify $2\sin\theta + 3\sin\theta$ in the same way as $2x + 3x$,

i.e., $2\sin\theta + 3\sin\theta = 5\sin\theta$.

Example 20	◀)) **Self Tutor**
Simplify: **a** $2\cos\theta + 5\cos\theta$	**b** $2\sin\alpha - 7\sin\alpha$
a $2\cos\theta + 5\cos\theta = 7\cos\theta$ $\{2x + 5x = 7x\}$	**b** $2\sin\alpha - 7\sin\alpha = -5\sin\alpha$ $\{2x - 7x = -5x\}$

To simplify more complicated trigonometric expressions involving $\sin\theta$ and $\cos\theta$ we often use $\sin^2\theta + \cos^2\theta = 1$.

It is worth graphing $y = \sin^2\theta$, $y = \cos^2\theta$ and $y = \sin^2\theta + \cos^2\theta$ using technology.

Notice that: $\sin^2\theta + \cos^2\theta$ could be replaced by 1

                      1 could be replaced by $\sin^2\theta + \cos^2\theta$

               $\sin^2\theta$ could be replaced by $1 - \cos^2\theta$

          $1 - \cos^2\theta$ could be replaced by $\sin^2\theta$

              $\cos^2\theta$ could be replaced by $1 - \sin^2\theta$

         $1 - \sin^2\theta$ could be replaced by $\cos^2\theta$.

GRAPHING PACKAGE

Example 21	◀)) **Self Tutor**
Simplify: **a** $3 - 3\cos^2\theta$	**b** $\cos^3\theta + \cos\theta\sin^2\theta$
a $3 - 3\cos^2\theta$ $= 3(1 - \cos^2\theta)$ $= 3\sin^2\theta$ $\{$as $\cos^2\theta + \sin^2\theta = 1\}$	**b** $\cos^3\theta + \cos\theta\sin^2\theta$ $= \cos\theta(\cos^2\theta + \sin^2\theta)$ $= \cos\theta \times 1$ $= \cos\theta$

We can **expand** and **factorise** expressions in the same way as normal algebra.

Example 22   ◀)) **Self Tutor**

Expand and simplify if possible: $(\cos\theta + \sin\theta)^2$

$(\cos\theta + \sin\theta)^2$
$= \cos^2\theta + 2\cos\theta\sin\theta + \sin^2\theta$ {using $(a+b)^2 = a^2 + 2ab + b^2$}
$= \cos^2\theta + \sin^2\theta + 2\cos\theta\sin\theta$
$= 1 + 2\cos\theta\sin\theta$

Example 23   ◀)) **Self Tutor**

Factorise: a $\sin^2\alpha - \cos^2\alpha$ b $\sin^2\theta - 5\sin\theta + 4$

a $\sin^2\alpha - \cos^2\alpha$
$= (\sin\alpha + \cos\alpha)(\sin\alpha - \cos\alpha)$ $\{a^2 - b^2 = (a+b)(a-b)\}$

b $\sin^2\theta - 5\sin\theta + 4$
$= (\sin\theta - 4)(\sin\theta - 1)$ $\{x^2 - 5x + 4 = (x-4)(x-1)\}$

Example 24   ◀)) **Self Tutor**

Simplify: a $\dfrac{3 - 3\sin^2\theta}{1 + \sin\theta}$ b $\dfrac{\cos^2\theta - \sin^2\theta}{\cos\theta - \sin\theta}$

a $\dfrac{3 - 3\sin^2\theta}{1 + \sin\theta}$

$= \dfrac{3(1 - \sin^2\theta)}{1 + \sin\theta}$

$= \dfrac{3(1 + \sin\theta)(1 - \sin\theta)}{(1 + \sin\theta)}$

$= 3(1 - \sin\theta)$

b $\dfrac{\cos^2\theta - \sin^2\theta}{\cos\theta - \sin\theta}$

$= \dfrac{(\cos\theta + \sin\theta)(\cos\theta - \sin\theta)}{(\cos\theta - \sin\theta)}$

$= \cos\theta + \sin\theta$

EXERCISE 10I.2

1 Simplify:

  a $\cos\theta + \cos\theta$ b $2\sin\theta + 3\sin\theta$ c $4\sin\theta - \sin\theta$

  d $5\sin\theta - 3\sin\theta$ e $2\cos\theta - 5\cos\theta$ f $12\cos\theta - 7\cos\theta$

2 Simplify:

  a $5\sin^2\theta + 5\cos^2\theta$ b $-3\sin^2\theta - 3\cos^2\theta$ c $-\sin^2\theta - \cos^2\theta$

  d $7 - 7\sin^2\theta$ e $6 - 6\cos^2\theta$ f $\sin\theta\cos^2\theta + \sin^3\theta$

  g $\sin^2\theta - 1$ h $3 - 3\sin^2\theta$ i $6\cos^2\theta - 6$

  j $\dfrac{1 - \cos^2\theta}{\sin^2\theta}$ k $\dfrac{2 - 2\cos^2\theta}{\sin\theta}$ l $\dfrac{\cos^2\theta - 1}{\sin\theta}$

3 Expand and simplify if possible:

    a $(2 + \sin\theta)^2$ **b** $(\sin\alpha - 3)^2$ **c** $(\cos\alpha - 4)^2$

    d $(\sin\beta + \cos\beta)^2$ **e** $(\sin\phi - \cos\phi)^2$ **f** $-(1 - \cos\alpha)^2$

4 Factorise:

    a $1 - \sin^2\phi$ **b** $\sin^2\theta - \cos^2\theta$ **c** $\cos^2\beta - 1$

    d $3\sin^2\beta - \sin\beta$ **e** $6\cos\phi + 3\cos^2\phi$ **f** $4\sin^2\theta - 2\sin\theta$

    g $\sin^2\theta + 6\sin\theta + 8$ **h** $2\cos^2\theta + 7\cos\theta + 6$ **i** $8\cos^2\alpha + 2\cos\alpha - 1$

5 Simplify:

    a $\dfrac{1 - \cos^2\alpha}{1 - \cos\alpha}$ **b** $\dfrac{\sin^2\theta - 1}{\sin\theta + 1}$ **c** $\dfrac{\cos\alpha - \sin\alpha}{\cos^2\alpha - \sin^2\alpha}$

    d $\dfrac{\cos^2\theta - \sin^2\theta}{\cos\theta + \sin\theta}$ **e** $\dfrac{\sin\phi + \cos\phi}{\cos^2\phi - \sin^2\phi}$ **f** $\dfrac{4 - 4\sin^2\theta}{2\cos\theta}$

6 By starting with the left hand side, prove the following identities:

    a $(\cos\theta + \sin\theta)^2 - (\cos\theta - \sin\theta)^2 = 4\sin\theta\cos\theta$

    b $(4\sin\theta + 3\cos\theta)^2 + (3\sin\theta - 4\cos\theta)^2 = 25$

    c $(1 - \sin\theta)\left(1 + \dfrac{1}{\sin\theta}\right) = \dfrac{\cos^2\theta}{\sin\theta}$ **d** $\left(1 + \dfrac{1}{\cos\theta}\right)(\cos\theta - \cos^2\theta) = \sin^2\theta$

    e $\dfrac{\cos\theta}{1 + \sin\theta} + \dfrac{1 + \sin\theta}{\cos\theta} = \dfrac{2}{\cos\theta}$ **f** $\dfrac{\cos\theta}{1 - \sin\theta} - \dfrac{\cos\theta}{1 + \sin\theta} = 2\tan\theta$

LINKS
click here

WHERE ARE WE?

Areas of interaction:
Approaches to learning/Human ingenuity

REVIEW SET 10A

1 Find $\sin\theta$, $\cos\theta$ and $\tan\theta$ for the triangle:

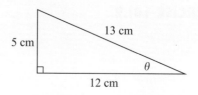

2 Find the value of x:

    a

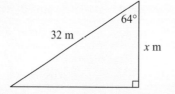

    b

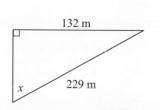

3 Find the measure of all unknown sides and angles in triangle CDE:

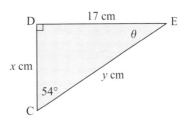

4 From a point 120 m horizontally from the base of a building, the angle of elevation to the top of the building is 34°. Find the height of the building.

5 If $\cos\theta = -0.5781$ and $0^o \leqslant \theta \leqslant 180^o$,   find θ.

6 A ship sails 40 km on the bearing 056°. How far is it north of its starting point?

7 Find the angle that:

   a [BG] makes with [FG]

   b [AG] makes with the base plane EFGH.

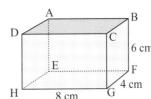

8 Find the area of:

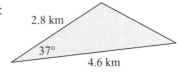

9 Use the diagram alongside to write, in terms of a and b, a value for:

   a $\cos\theta$ **b** $\sin\theta$

   c $\tan\theta$ **d** $\sin(180^o - \theta)$

   e $\cos(180^o - \theta)$ **f** $\tan(180^o - \theta)$

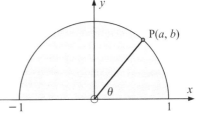

10 Two long straight roads intersect at P at an angle of 53°. Starting at P, cyclist A rides for 16.2 km along one of the roads, while cyclist B rides 18.9 km along the other road. How far apart are the cyclists now? Assume $A\widehat{P}B$ is acute.

11

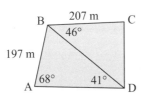

   Find:

   a the length of [BD]

   b the total area of quadrilateral ABCD.

12 Simplify: **a** $\dfrac{\cos^2\theta - 1}{\cos\theta + 1}$ **b** $\dfrac{4\cos\theta}{2\sin^2\theta + 2\cos^2\theta}$

13 By starting with the left hand side, prove the identity $\dfrac{\sin\theta}{1 - \cos\theta} + \dfrac{1 - \cos\theta}{\sin\theta} = \dfrac{2}{\sin\theta}$.

REVIEW SET 10B

1 Use your calculator to find, correct to 4 decimal places:

   a $\cos 74^o$ **b** $\sin 132^o$ **c** $\tan 97^o$.

2 Find the value of x in the following:

a

8 m
5 m
x

b

7.5 cm
x
9.4 cm

3 Find the measure of all unknown sides and
angles in triangle KLM:

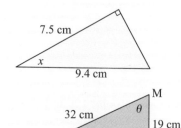

32 cm
θ
M
19 cm
K
α
x cm
L

4 The angle of elevation from a point 2 km from the base of the vertical cliff to the
top of the cliff is $17.7°$. Find the height of the cliff, in metres.

5 A tangent to a circle from a point 13 cm from the centre is 11 cm in length. Find
the angle between the tangent and the line from the point to the centre of the circle.

6 If $\sin\theta = \frac{3}{4}$ and θ is obtuse, and find the exact value of $\cos\theta$.

7 A ship leaves port P and travels for 50 km in the direction $181°$. It then sails 60 km
in the direction $274°$ to an island port Q.

  a How far is Q from P?

  b To sail back directly from Q to P, in what direction must the ship sail?

8 The figure alongside is a square-based
pyramid in which all edges are 20 cm in
length. Find:

  a $\widehat{ADM}$

  b $\widehat{ACD}$.

A
B
M
E
C
D

9

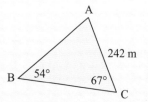

A
242 m
B
$54°$
$67°$
C

Jason's sketch of his father's triangular
vegetable patch is shown alongside. Find:

  a the length of the fence [AB].

  b the area of the patch in hectares.

10 Triangle ABC has $AB = 12$ m, $BC = 10$ m, $AC = x$ m, and $\widehat{BAC} = 40°$.
Show that there are two possible values for x.

11 Write in simplest form:

  a $\dfrac{\sin\theta}{\cos\theta}$

  b $\dfrac{1 - \sin^2\theta}{1 + \sin\theta}$

  c $\dfrac{3 - 3\cos^2\theta}{\sin\theta}$

12 By starting with the left hand side, prove the following identities:

  a $(\sin\theta + 2\cos\theta)^2 + (2\sin\theta - \cos\theta)^2 = 5$

  b $(1 + \sin\theta)\left(1 - \dfrac{1}{\sin\theta}\right) = -\dfrac{\cos^2\theta}{\sin\theta}$

Chapter 11

Probability

Contents:

Consider these statements:

"The Wildcats will probably beat the Tigers on Saturday."
"It is unlikely that it will rain today."
"I will probably make the team."

Each of these statements indicates a **likelihood** or **chance** of a particular event happening.

We can indicate the likelihood of an event happening in the future by using a percentage.

    0%   indicates we believe the event **will not occur**.
  100%   indicates we believe the event **is certain to occur**.

All events can therefore be assigned a percentage between 0% and 100% (inclusive).

A number close to 0% indicates the event is **unlikely** to occur, whereas a number close to 100% means that it is **highly likely** to occur.

In mathematics, we usually write probabilities as either decimals or fractions rather than percentages. However, as $100\% = 1$, comparisons or conversions from percentages to fractions or decimals are very simple.

An **impossible** event which has 0% chance of happening is assigned a probability of 0.

A **certain** event which has 100% chance of happening is assigned a probability of 1.

All other events can be assigned a probability between 0 and 1.

The assigning of probabilities is usually based on either:

- observing the results of an experiment (experimental probability),   or
- using arguments of symmetry (theoretical probability).

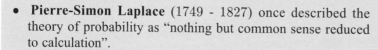

HISTORICAL NOTE

- **Girolamo Cardan** (1501 to 1576) admitted in his autobiography that he gambled "not only every year, but .... every day, and with the loss at once of thought, of substance, and of time". He wrote a handbook on gambling with tips on cheating and how to detect it. His book included discussion on equally likely events, frequency tables for dice probabilities, and expectations.

Girolamo Cardan

- **Pierre-Simon Laplace** (1749 - 1827) once described the theory of probability as "nothing but common sense reduced to calculation".

- **Blaise Pascal** (1623 - 1662) invented the first mechanical digital calculator. Pascal and his friend **Pierre de Fermat** (1601 - 1665) were first to develop probability theory as we know it today. Pascal also developed the syringe and the hydraulic press. He wrote a large number of articles on Christian beliefs and ethics.

OPENING PROBLEM

When Karla dropped some metal nuts she noticed that they finished either on their ends or on their sides. She was interested to know what the probability was that a nut would finish on its end. So, she tossed a nut 200 times, and found that it finished on its end 137 times.

side   end

Later Sam repeated the experiment and the nut finished on its end 145 times.

For you to consider:

- What would Karla's best estimate be of the chance that the nut will finish on its end?
- What would Sam's estimate be?
- How can we obtain a better estimate of the chance of an end occurring?
- Hilda said that the best estimate would be obtained when the nut is tossed thousands of times. Is she correct?

A   EXPERIMENTAL PROBABILITY

We should use suitable language to help us describe what we are doing and the results we expect and get.

- The **number of trials** is the total number of times the experiment is repeated.
- The **outcomes** are the different results possible for one trial of the experiment.
- The **frequency** of a particular outcome is the number of times that this outcome is observed.
- The **relative frequency** of an outcome is the frequency of that outcome divided by the total number of trials.

For example, when tossing a tin can in the air 250 times, it comes to rest on an end 37 times. We say:

- the number of trials is 250
- the outcomes are *ends* and *sides*
- the frequency of *ends* is 37 and *sides* is 213
- the relative frequency of *ends* $= \frac{37}{250} \approx 0.148$
- the relative frequency of *sides* $= \frac{213}{250} \approx 0.852$.

EXPERIMENTAL PROBABILITY

Sometimes the only way of finding the probability of a particular event occurring is by experimentation.

Tossing a tin can is one such example. The probability of a can of this shape finishing on its end is the relative frequency found by experimentation.

We say that:

the **estimated experimental probability** is the relative frequency of the event.

We write: Experimental P(end) ≈ 0.148.

The larger the number of trials, the more confident we are that the experimental probability obtained is accurate.

Example 1   ◀◤ **Self Tutor**

Find the experimental probability of:

  a   tossing a head with one toss of a coin if it falls heads 96 times in 200 tosses

  b   rolling a *six* with a die given that when it was rolled 300 times, a *six* occurred 54 times.

a	Experimental P(getting a head)	**b** Experimental P(rolling a *six*)

        a   Experimental P(getting a head)   **b**   Experimental P(rolling a *six*)

$$= \text{relative frequency of getting a head} \qquad = \text{relative frequency of rolling a } six$$

$$= \frac{96}{200} \qquad\qquad\qquad\qquad = \frac{54}{300}$$

$$= 0.48 \qquad\qquad\qquad\qquad = 0.18$$

EXERCISE 11A

1 Find the experimental probability of rolling *an odd number* with a die if *an odd number* occurred 33 times when the die was rolled 60 times.

2 Clem fired 200 arrows at a target and hit the target 168 times. Find the experimental probability of Clem hitting the target.

3 Ivy has free-range hens. Out of the first 123 eggs that they laid she found that 11 had double-yolks. Calculate the experimental probability of getting a double-yolk egg from her hens.

4 Jackson leaves for work at the same time each day. Over a period of 227 working days, on his way to work he had to wait for a train at the railway crossing on 58 days. Calculate the experimental probability that Jackson has to wait for a train on his way to work.

5 Ravi has a circular spinner marked P, Q and R on 3 equal sectors. Find the experimental probability of getting a Q if the spinner was twirled 417 times and finished on Q on 138 occasions.

6 Each time Claude shuffled a pack of cards before a game, he recorded the suit of the top card of the pack.

His results for 140 games were 34 Hearts, 36 Diamonds, 38 Spades and 32 Clubs.

Find the experimental probability that the top card of a shuffled pack is:

  a   a Heart   **b**   a Club or Diamond.

B PROBABILITIES FROM TABLED DATA

If we are given a table of frequencies then we use **relative frequencies** to estimate the probabilities of the events.

Remember that: $\text{relative frequency} = \dfrac{\textbf{frequency}}{\textbf{number of trials}}$

Example 2 ◀) **Self Tutor**

A marketing company surveys 80 randomly selected people to discover what brand of shoe cleaner they use. The results are shown in the table alongside:

Brand	Frequency
Shine	27
Brite	22
Cleano	20
No scuff	11

a Based on these results, what is the experimental probability of a community member using:
 i Brite ii Cleano?

b Would you classify the estimate of a to be very good, good, or poor? Why?

---

a We start by calculating the relative frequency for each brand.

 i Experimental P(Brite) = 0.275
 ii Experimental P(Cleano) = 0.250

b Poor, as the sample size is very small.

Brand	Frequency	Relative Frequency
Shine	27	0.3375
Brite	22	0.2750
Cleano	20	0.2500
No scuff	11	0.1375

EXERCISE 11B

1 A marketing company was commissioned to investigate brands of products usually found in the bathroom. The results of a soap survey are given below:

 a How many people were randomly selected in this survey?

 b Calculate the relative frequency of use of each brand of soap.

 c Using the results obtained by the marketing company, what is the experimental probability that the soap used by a randomly selected person is:
  i Just Soap ii Indulgence iii Silktouch?

Brand	Freq	Relative Frequency
Silktouch	125	
Super	107	
Just Soap	93	
Indulgence	82	
Total		

2 Two coins were tossed 489 times and the *number of heads* occurring at each toss was recorded. The results are shown opposite:

 a Copy and complete the table given.

 b Estimate the chance of the following events occurring: i 0 heads ii 1 head iii 2 heads.

Outcome	Freq	Rel Freq
0 heads	121	
1 head		
2 heads	109	
Total		

3 At the Annual Show the toffee apple vendor estimated that three times as many people preferred red toffee apples to green toffee apples.

   a If 361 people wanted green toffee apples, estimate how many wanted red.

   b Copy and complete the table given.

   c Estimate the probability that the next customer will ask for:

      i a green toffee apple   **ii** a red toffee apple.

Colour	Freq	Rel Freq
Green	361	
Red		
Total		

4 The tickets sold for a tennis match were recorded as people entered the stadium. The results are shown:

   a How many tickets were sold in total?

   b Copy and complete the table given.

   c If a person in the stadium is selected at random, what is the probability that the person bought a Concession ticket?

Ticket Type	Freq	Rel Freq
Adult	3762	
Concession	1084	
Child	389	
Total		

5 The results of a local Council election are shown in the table. It is known that 6000 people voted in the election.

   a Copy and complete the table given.

   b What is the chance that a randomly selected person from this electorate voted for a female councillor?

Councillor	Freq	Rel Freq
Mr Tony Trimboli	2167	
Mrs Andrea Sims	724	
Mrs Sara Chong	2389	
Mr John Henry		
Total		

C   REPRESENTING COMBINED EVENTS

The possible outcomes for tossing two coins are listed below:

   two heads   head and tail   tail and head   two tails

These results are the combination of two events: tossing coin 1 and tossing coin 2. If H represents a 'head' and T a 'tail', the sample space of possible outcomes is   HH, HT, TH and TT.

> A **sample space** is the set of all possible outcomes of an experiment.

Possible ways of representing sample spaces are:

- listing them
- using a 2-dimensional grid
- using a tree diagram
- using a Venn diagram.

Example 3   🔊 Self Tutor

Represent the sample space for tossing two coins using:

a   a list   b   a 2-D grid   c   a tree diagram

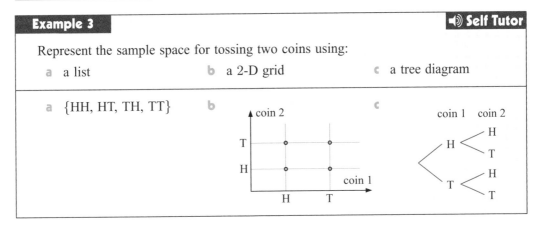

Example 4   🔊 Self Tutor

Illustrate, using a tree diagram, the possible outcomes when drawing two marbles from a bag containing several marbles of each of the colours red, green and yellow.

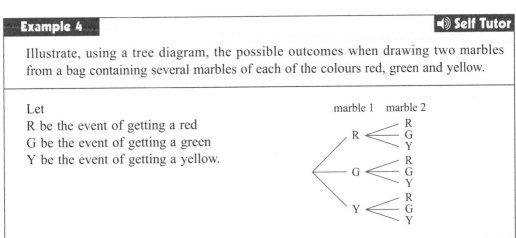

EXERCISE 11C

1   List the sample space for the following:

   a   twirling a square spinner labelled A, B, C, D

   b   the sexes of a 2-child family

   c   the order in which 4 blocks A, B, C and D can be lined up

   d   the 8 different 3-child families.

   e   spinning a coin   i   twice   ii   three times   iii   four times.

2   Illustrate on a 2-dimensional grid the sample space for:

   a   rolling a die and tossing a coin simultaneously

   b   rolling two dice

   c   rolling a die and spinning a spinner with sides A, B, C, D

   d   twirling two square spinners: one labelled A, B, C, D and the other 1, 2, 3, 4.

3   Illustrate on a tree diagram the sample space for:

   a   tossing a 5-cent and 10-cent coin simultaneously

   b   tossing a coin and twirling an equilateral triangular spinner labelled A, B and C

   c   twirling two equilateral triangular spinners labelled 1, 2 and 3 and X, Y and Z

  d drawing two tickets from a hat containing a number of pink, blue and white tickets.

  e drawing two beads from a bag containing 3 red and 4 blue beads.

4 Draw a Venn diagram to show a class of 20 students where 7 study History and Geography, 10 study History, 15 study Geography, and 2 study neither subject.

D THEORETICAL PROBABILITY

From the methods of showing sample spaces in the previous section, we can find the probabilities of combined events.

These are theoretical probabilities which are calculated using

$$P(\text{event happens}) = \frac{\text{number of ways the event can happen}}{\text{total number of possible outcomes}}.$$

Example 5   ◀)) Self Tutor

Three coins are tossed. Write down a list of all possible outcomes. Find the probability of getting:

  a 3 heads   **b** at least one head

  c 3 heads if it is known that there is at least one head.

Notice how we list the outcomes in a systematic way.

The sample space is: HHH   HHT   TTH   TTT
                         HTH   THT
                         THH   HTT

  a P(3 heads) $= \frac{1}{8}$

  b P(at least one H) $= \frac{7}{8}$ {all except TTT}

  c P(HHH knowing at least one H) $= \frac{1}{7}$
       {The sample space now excludes TTT}

Example 6   ◀)) Self Tutor

A die has the numbers 0, 0, 1, 1, 4 and 5. It is rolled *twice*. Illustrate the sample space using a 2-D grid. Hence find the probability of getting:

  a a total of 5   **b** two numbers which are the same.

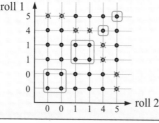

There are $6 \times 6 = 36$ possible outcomes.

  a P(total of 5)
        $= \frac{8}{36}$ {those with a $\times$}

  b P(same numbers)
        $= \frac{10}{36}$ {those circled}

EXERCISE 11D

1   a   List all possible orderings of the letters O, D and G.

   b   If these three letters are placed at random in a row, what is the probability of:

      i   spelling DOG
      ii   O appearing first
      iii   O not appearing first
      iv   spelling DOG or GOD?

2   The Venn diagram shows the sports played by boys at the local high school.

   A student is chosen at random. Find the probability that he:

   a   plays football

   c   plays football or rugby

   e   plays neither of these sports

   f   plays football, given that he is in at least one team

   g   plays rugby, given that he plays football.

   b   plays both codes

   d   plays exactly one of these sports

Venn diagram: F (football) and R (rugby); 12, 5, 7 in the circles; 19 outside. U is the universal set.
$F \equiv$ football
$R \equiv$ rugby

3   Draw the grid of the sample space when a 10-cent and a 50-cent coin are tossed simultaneously. Hence determine the probability of getting:

   a   two heads
   b   two tails
   c   exactly one head
   d   at least one head.

4   A coin and a pentagonal spinner with sectors 1, 2, 3, 4 and 5 are tossed and spun respectively.

   a   Draw a grid to illustrate the sample space of possible outcomes.

   b   How many outcomes are possible?

   c   Use your grid to determine the chance of getting:

      i   a head and a 4
      ii   a tail and an odd number
      iii   an even number
      iv   a tail or a 3.

5   List the six different orders in which Alex, Bodi and Kek may sit in a row. If the three of them sit randomly in a row, determine the probability that:

   a   Alex sits in the middle
   b   Alex sits at the left end
   c   Alex sits at the right end
   d   Bodi and Kek are seated together.

6   a   List the 8 possible 3-child families, according to the gender of the children. For example, BGB means *"the first is a boy, the second is a girl, and the third is a boy"*.

   b   Assuming that each of these is equally likely to occur, determine the probability that a randomly selected 3-child family consists of:

      i   all boys
      ii   all girls
      iii   boy, then girl, then girl
      iv   two girls and a boy
      v   a girl for the eldest
      vi   at least one boy.

7 In a class of 24 students, 10 take Biology, 12 take Chemistry, and 5 take neither Biology nor Chemistry. Find the probability that a student picked at random from the class takes:

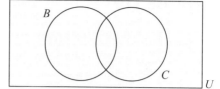

  a Chemistry but not Biology

  b Chemistry or Biology.

8 **a** List, in systematic order, the 24 different orders in which four people P, Q, R and S may sit in a row.

  b Hence, determine the probability that when the four people sit at random in a row:

    i P sits on one end

    ii Q sits on one of the two middle seats

    iii P and Q are seated together

    iv P, Q and R are seated together, not necessarily in that order.

9 A pair of dice is rolled.

  a Show that there are 36 members in the sample space of possible outcomes by displaying them on a grid.

  b Hence, determine the probability of a result with:

    i one die showing a 4 and the other a 5

    ii both dice showing the same result

    iii at least one of the dice showing a result of 3

    iv either a 4 or 6 being displayed

    v both dice showing even numbers

    vi the sum of the values being 7.

10 60 married men were asked whether they gave their wife flowers or chocolates for their last birthday. The results were: 26 gave chocolates, 21 gave flowers, and 5 gave both chocolates and flowers. If one of the married men was chosen at random, determine the probability that he gave his wife:

  a flowers but not chocolates   **b** neither chocolates nor flowers

  c chocolates or flowers.

11 List the possible outcomes when four coins are tossed simultaneously. Hence determine the probability of getting:

  a all heads   **b** two heads and two tails

  c more tails than heads   **d** at least one tail   **e** exactly one head.

12 **a** Copy and complete the grid alongside for the sample space of drawing one card from an ordinary pack.

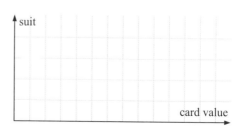

b Use your grid to determine the probability of getting:

  i   a Queen   ii   the Jack of hearts   iii a spade
  iv a picture card   v   a red 7   vi   a diamond or a club
  vii a King or a heart   viii a Queen and a 3.

13 The medical records for a class of 28 children show whether they had previously had measles or mumps. The records show 22 have had measles, 13 have had measles and mumps, and 27 have had measles or mumps. If one child from the class is selected at random, determine the probability that he or she has had:

  a measles   b mumps but not measles   c neither mumps nor measles.

E   COMPOUND EVENTS

We have previously used two-dimensional grids to represent sample spaces and hence find answers to certain probability problems.

Consider again a simple example of tossing a coin and rolling a die simultaneously.

To determine the probability of getting a head and a '5', we can illustrate the sample space on the two-dimensional grid shown. We can see that there are 12 possible outcomes but only one with the property that we want, so the answer is $\frac{1}{12}$.

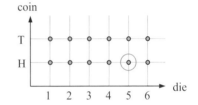

However, notice that $P(\text{a head}) = \frac{1}{2}$, $P(\text{a '5'}) = \frac{1}{6}$ and $\frac{1}{2} \times \frac{1}{6} = \frac{1}{12}$.

This suggests that $P(\text{a head } \textbf{and} \text{ a '5'}) = P(\text{a head}) \times P(\text{a '5'})$, i.e., we multiply the separate probabilities.

It seems that if A and B are two events for which the occurrence of each one does not affect the occurence of the other, then $P(A \text{ and } B) = P(A) \times P(B)$.

The two events 'getting a head' and 'rolling a 5' are events with this property, as the occurrence or non-occurrence of either one cannot affect the occurence of the other. We say they are **independent**.

If two events A and B are **independent** then $P(A \textbf{ and } B) = P(A) \times P(B)$.

Example 7	◀)) Self Tutor

A coin is tossed and a die rolled simultaneously. Find the probability that a tail and a '2' result.

'Getting a tail' and 'rolling a 2' are independent events.

$\therefore$ $P(\text{a tail } \textbf{and} \text{ a '2'}) = P(\text{a tail}) \times P(\text{a '2'})$
$= \frac{1}{2} \times \frac{1}{6}$
$= \frac{1}{12}$

Example 8   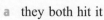 **Self Tutor**

Sunil has probability $\frac{4}{5}$ of hitting a target and Monika has probability $\frac{5}{6}$.

If they both fire simultaneously at the target, determine the probability that:

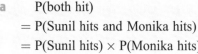

a   they both hit it   b   they both miss it.

a	P(both hit)	b	P(both miss)
	= P(Sunil hits and Monika hits)		= P(Sunil misses and Monika misses)
	= P(Sunil hits) × P(Monika hits)		= P(Sunil misses) × P(Monika misses)
	= $\frac{4}{5} \times \frac{5}{6}$		= $\frac{1}{5} \times \frac{1}{6}$
	= $\frac{2}{3}$		= $\frac{1}{30}$

EXERCISE 11E.1

1   A coin and a pentagonal spinner with edges marked A, B, C, D and E are tossed and twirled simultaneously. Find the probabilities of getting:

   a   a head and a D   b   a tail and either an A or a D.

2   A spinner with 6 equal sides has 3 red, 2 blue and 1 yellow edge. A second spinner with 7 equal sides has 4 purple and 3 green edges. Both spinners are twirled simultaneously. Find the probability of getting:

   a   a red and a green   b   a blue and a purple.

3   Janice and Lee take set shots at a netball goal from 3 m. From past experience, Janice throws a goal on average 2 times in every 3 shots, whereas Lee throws a goal 4 times in every 7. If they both shoot for goals, determine the probability that:

   a   both score a goal   b   both miss

   c   Janice goals but Lee misses.

4   When a nut was tossed 400 times it finished on its edge 84 times and on its side for the rest. Use this information to estimate the probability that when two identical nuts are tossed:

edge   side

   a   they both fall on their edges   b   they both fall on their sides.

5   Tei has probability $\frac{1}{3}$ of hitting a target with an arrow, while See has probability $\frac{2}{5}$. If they both fire at the target, determine the probability that:

   a   both hit the target   b   both miss the target

   c   Tei hits the target and See misses   d   Tei misses the target and See hits.

6   A certain brand of drawing pin was tossed into the air 600 times. It landed on its back ⏚ 243 times and on its side ⚲ for the remainder. Use this information to estimate the probability that:

   a   one drawing pin, when tossed, will fall on its   i   back   ii   side

   b   two drawing pins, when tossed, will both fall on their backs

   c   two drawing pins, when tossed, will both fall on their sides.

DEPENDENT EVENTS

Suppose a cup contains 4 red and 2 green marbles. One marble is randomly chosen, its colour is noted, and it is then put aside. A second marble is then randomly selected. What is the chance that it is red?

If the first marble was red,   P(second is red) $= \frac{3}{5}$ ⟵ 3 reds remaining
⟵ 5 to choose from

If the first marble was green,   P(second is red) $= \frac{4}{5}$ ⟵ 4 reds remaining
⟵ 5 to choose from

So, the probability of the second marble being red **depends** on what colour the first marble was. We therefore have **dependent events**.

> Two or more events are **dependent** if they are **not independent**.
>
> **Dependent** events are events for which the occurrence of one of the events *does affect* the occurrence of the other event.

For compound events which are dependent, a similar product rule applies as to that for independent events:

> If A and B are dependent events then
>
> P(A **then** B) = P(A) $\times$ P(B given that A has occurred).

Example 9   🔊 **Self Tutor**

A box contains 4 blue and 3 yellow buttons of the same size. Two buttons are randomly selected from the box without replacement. Find the probability that:

   a   both are yellow   b   the first is yellow and the second is blue.

---

a   P(both are yellow)

    = P(first is yellow *and* second is yellow)

    = P(first is yellow) $\times$ P(second is yellow given that the first is yellow)

    $= \frac{3}{7} \times \frac{2}{6}$ ⟵ 2 yellows remaining
             ⟵ 6 to choose from

    $= \frac{1}{7}$

b   P(first is Y and second is B)

    = P(first is Y) $\times$ P(second is B given that the first is Y)

    $= \frac{3}{7} \times \frac{4}{6}$ ⟵ 4 blues remaining
             ⟵ 6 to choose from

    $= \frac{2}{7}$

EXERCISE 11E.2

1   A packet contains 8 identically shaped jelly beans. 5 are green and 3 are yellow. Two jelly beans are randomly selected without replacing the first before the second is drawn.

   a   Determine the probability of getting:

      i   two greens   ii   a green then a yellow

      iii   a yellow then a green   iv   two yellows

   b   Why do your answers in a add up to 1?

2   A pocket in a golf bag contains 6 white and 4 yellow golf balls. Two of them are selected at random without replacement.

   a   Determine the probability that:

      i   both are white   ii   the first is white and the second is yellow

      iii   one of each colour is selected.

   b   Why do your answers in a not add up to 1?

3   A container has 4 purple, 3 blue and 1 gold ticket. Three tickets are selected without replacement. Find the probability that:

   a   all are purple   b   all are blue   c   the first two are purple and the third is gold.

F   USING TREE DIAGRAMS

Tree diagrams can be used to illustrate sample spaces, provided that the alternatives are not too numerous.

Once the sample space is illustrated, the tree diagram can be used for determining probabilities. Consider **Example 8** again. The tree diagram for this information is:

H = hits
M = misses

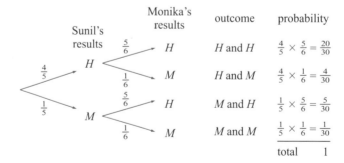

Notice that:

- The probabilities for hitting and missing are marked on the branches.
- There are *four* alternative paths and each path shows a particular outcome.
- All outcomes are represented and the probabilities of each outcome are obtained by **multiplying** the probabilities along that path.

Example 10 ◀⟩ **Self Tutor**

Stephano is having problems. His desktop computer will only boot up 90% of the time and his laptop will only boot up 70% of the time.

  a Draw a tree diagram to illustrate this situation.

  b Use the tree diagram to determine the chance that:

    i both will boot up

    ii Stephano has no choice but to use his desktop computer.

a D = desktop computer boots up L = laptop boots up

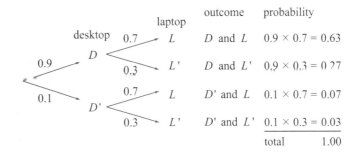

	outcome	probability
	D and L	$0.9 \times 0.7 = 0.63$
	D and L'	$0.9 \times 0.3 = 0.27$
	D' and L	$0.1 \times 0.7 = 0.07$
	D' and L'	$0.1 \times 0.3 = 0.03$
	total	1.00

b   **i**   P(both boot up)   **ii**   P(desktop boots up but laptop does not)

$= \text{P}(D \text{ and } L)$ $= \text{P}(D \text{ and } L')$

$= 0.9 \times 0.7$ $= 0.9 \times 0.3$

$= 0.63$ $= 0.27$

Example 11 ◀⟩ **Self Tutor**

Bag A contains 4 red jelly beans and 1 yellow jelly bean. Bag B contains 2 red and 3 yellow jelly beans. A bag is randomly selected by tossing a coin, and one jelly bean is removed from it. Determine the probability that it is yellow.

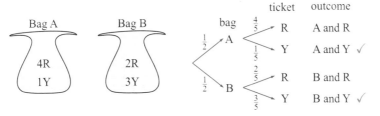

To get a yellow we take either the first branch ticked **or** the second one ticked. We **add** the probabilities for these outcomes.

P(yellow) = P(A and Y) + P(B and Y)

$\phantom{\text{P(yellow)}} = \frac{1}{2} \times \frac{1}{5} + \frac{1}{2} \times \frac{3}{5}$ {branches marked ✓}

$\phantom{\text{P(yellow)}} = \frac{4}{10}$

$\phantom{\text{P(yellow)}} = \frac{2}{5}$

EXERCISE 11F

1 Suppose this spinner is spun twice:

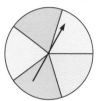

a Copy and complete the branches on the tree diagram shown.

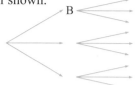

b What is the probability that blue appears on both spins?

c What is the probability that green appears on both spins?

d What is the probability that different colours appear on both spins?

e What is the probability that blue appears on *either* spin?

2 In a particular board game there are nine tiles: five are green and the remainder are brown. The tiles start face down on the table so they all look the same.

a If a player is required to pick a tile at random, determine the probability that it is:

  i green   **ii** brown.

b Suppose a player has to pick two tiles in a row, replacing the first and shuffling them before the second is selected. Copy and complete the tree diagram illustrating the possible outcomes.

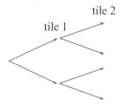

c Using **b**, determine the probability that:

  i both tiles are green

  ii both tiles are brown

  iii tile 1 is brown and tile 2 is green

  iv one tile is brown and the other is green.

3 The probability of the race track being muddy next week is estimated to be $\frac{1}{4}$. If it is muddy, Rising Tide will start favourite with probability $\frac{2}{5}$ of winning. If it is dry he has a 1 in 20 chance of winning.

a Display the sample space of possible results on a tree diagram.

b Determine the probability that Rising Tide will win next week.

4 Machine A cans 60% of the fruit at a factory. Machine B cans the rest. Machine A spoils 3% of its product, while Machine B spoils 4%. Determine the probability that the next can inspected at this factory will be spoiled.

5 Can A contains 2 blue and 3 red blocks and Can B contains 5 blue and 1 red block. A can is chosen at random (by the flip of a coin) and one block is taken at random from it. Determine the probability that the block is red.

6

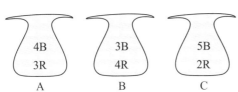

4B	3B	5B
3R	4R	2R
A	B	C

Three bags contain different numbers of blue and red tickets. A bag is selected using a die which has three A faces, two B faces, and one C face.

One ticket is selected randomly from the chosen bag. Determine the probability that it is: **a**   blue   **b**   red.

G · SAMPLING WITH AND WITHOUT REPLACEMENT

Sampling is the process of selecting one object from a large group and inspecting it for some particular feature. The object is then either **put back** (sampling **with replacement**) or **put to one side** (sampling **without replacement**).

Sometimes the inspection process makes it impossible to return the object to the large group. Such processes include:

- Is the chocolate hard- or soft-centred? Bite it or squeeze it to see.
- Does the egg contain one or two yolks? Break it open and see.
- Is the object correctly made? Pull it apart to see.

The sampling process is used for quality control in industrial processes.

Example 12   ◄» **Self Tutor**

A bin contains 4 blue and 5 green marbles. A marble is selected from this bin and its colour is noted. It is then *replaced*. A second marble is then drawn and its colour is noted. Determine the probability that:

a   both are blue   **b**   the first is blue and the second is green

c   there is one of each colour.

Tree diagram:

B = blue
G = green

		outcome	probability
1st marble	2nd marble		
B	$\frac{4}{9}$ → B	B and B	$\frac{4}{9} \times \frac{4}{9} = \frac{16}{81}$
$\frac{4}{9}$	$\frac{5}{9}$ → G	B and G	$\frac{4}{9} \times \frac{5}{9} = \frac{20}{81}$
G	$\frac{4}{9}$ → B	G and B	$\frac{5}{9} \times \frac{4}{9} = \frac{20}{81}$
$\frac{5}{9}$	$\frac{5}{9}$ → G	G and G	$\frac{5}{9} \times \frac{5}{9} = \frac{25}{81}$
		total	1

a   P(both blue)

$= \frac{4}{9} \times \frac{4}{9}$

$= \frac{16}{81}$

b   P(first is B and second is G)

$= \frac{4}{9} \times \frac{5}{9}$

$= \frac{20}{81}$

c   P(one of each colour)

$= $ P(B then G or G then B)

$= $ P(B then G) + P(G then B)

$= \frac{4}{9} \times \frac{5}{9} + \frac{5}{9} \times \frac{4}{9}$

$= \frac{40}{81}$

Example 13   ◀ﻬ **Self Tutor**

Sylke has bad luck with the weather when she takes her summer holidays.
She estimates that it rains 60% of the time and it is cold 70% of the time.

  a Draw a tree diagram to illustrate this situation.
  b Use the tree diagram to determine the chance that for Sylke's holidays:
    i it is cold and raining   **ii** it is fine and cold.

a C = the weather is cold
     R = it is raining

	temperature	rain	outcome	probability
		0.6 → R	C and R	$0.7 \times 0.6 = 0.42$
0.7 → C		0.4 → R'	C and R'	$0.7 \times 0.4 = 0.28$
0.3 → C'		0.6 → R	C' and R	$0.3 \times 0.6 = 0.18$
		0.4 → R'	C' and R'	$0.3 \times 0.4 = 0.12$
			total	1.00

b **i**   P(it is cold and raining)   **ii**   P(it is fine and cold)
        $= P(C$ and $R)$ $= P(R'$ and $C)$
        $= 0.7 \times 0.6$ $= 0.4 \times 0.7$
        $= 0.42$ $= 0.28$

EXERCISE 11G

1 A box contains 6 red and 3 yellow tickets. Two tickets are drawn at random (the first being *replaced* before the second is drawn). Draw a tree diagram to represent the sample space and use it to determine the probability that:

  a both are red   **b** both are yellow

  c the first is red and the second is yellow **d** one is red and the other is yellow.

2 7 tickets numbered 1, 2, 3, 4, 5, 6 and 7 are placed in a hat. Two of the tickets are taken from the hat at random *without replacement*. Determine the probability that:

  a both are odd   **b** both are even

  c the first is even and the second is odd   **d** one is even and the other is odd.

3 Jessica has a bag of 9 acid drops which are all identical in shape. 5 are raspberry flavoured and 4 are orange flavoured. She selects one acid drop at random, eats it, and then takes another, also at random. Determine the probability that:

  a both acid drops were orange flavoured

  b both acid drops were raspberry flavoured

  c the first was raspberry and the second was orange

  d the first was orange and the second was raspberry.

Add your answers to **a**, **b**, **c** and **d**. Explain why the answer must be 1.

4 A cook selects an egg at random from a carton containing 7 ordinary eggs and 5 double-yolk eggs. She cracks the egg into a bowl and sees whether it has two yolks or not. She then selects another egg at random from the carton and checks it.

Let S represent "a single yolk egg" and D represent "a double yolk egg".

   a Draw a tree diagram to illustrate this sampling process.

   b What is the probability that both eggs had two yolks?

   c What is the probability that both eggs had only one yolk?

5  Freda selects a chocolate at random from a box containing 8 hard-centred and 11 soft-centred chocolates. She bites it to see whether it is hard-centred or not. She then selects another chocolate at random from the box and checks it.

Let H represent "a hard-centred chocolate" and S represent "a soft-centred chocolate".

   a Draw a tree diagram to illustrate this sampling process.

   b What is the probability that both chocolates have hard centres?

   c What is the probability that both chocolates have soft centres?

6 A sporting club runs a raffle in which 200 tickets are sold. There are two winning tickets which are drawn at random, in succession, without replacement. If Adam bought 8 tickets in the raffle, determine the probability that he:

   a wins first prize   **b** does not win first prize

   c wins second prize *given that* he did not win first prize.

H   MUTUALLY EXCLUSIVE AND NON-MUTUALLY EXCLUSIVE EVENTS

Suppose we select a card at random from a normal pack of 52 playing cards. Consider carefully these events:

Event X: the card is a heart   *Event Y:* the card is an ace   *Event Z:* the card is a 7

Notice that:

- *X* and *Y* have a common outcome: the Ace of hearts
- *X* and *Z* have a common outcome: the 7 of hearts
- *Y* and *Z* do not have a common outcome.

When considering a situation like this:

- if two events have no common outcomes we say they are **mutually exclusive** or **disjoint**
- if two events have common outcomes they are **not mutually exclusive**.

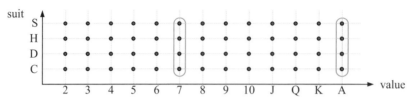

Notice that: P(ace **or** seven) $= \frac{8}{52}$ and   P(ace) + P(seven) $= \frac{4}{52} + \frac{4}{52} = \frac{8}{52}$

So,   if two events A and B are **mutually exclusive** then
$$P(A \textbf{ or } B) = P(A) + P(B)$$

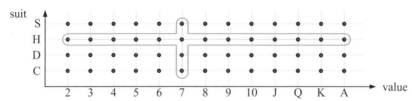

Notice that: P(heart **or** seven) $= \frac{16}{52}$ and   P(heart) + P(seven) $= \frac{13}{52} + \frac{4}{52} = \frac{17}{52}$.

Actually,   P(heart **or** seven) = P(heart) + P(seven) − P(heart **and** seven).

So,   if two events A and B are **not mutually exclusive** then
$$P(A \textbf{ or } B) = P(A) + P(B) - P(A \textbf{ and } B).$$

EXERCISE 11H

1   An ordinary die with faces 1, 2, 3, 4, 5 and 6 is rolled once. Consider these events:

A: getting a 1 B: getting a 3
C: getting an odd number D: getting an even number
E: getting a prime number F: getting a result greater than 3.

  a   List all possible pairs of events which are mutually exclusive.

  b   Find: i   P(B or D)   ii   P(D or E)   iii   P(A or E)
             iv   P(B or E)   v   P(C or D)   vi   P(A or B or F).

2   A coin and an ordinary die are tossed simultaneously.

  a   Draw a grid showing the 12 possible outcomes.

  b   Find the probabilites of getting: i   a head and a 5   ii   a head or a 5.

  c   Check that: P(H or 5) = P(H) + P(5) − P(H **and** 5).

3   Two ordinary dice are rolled.

  a   Draw a grid showing the 36 possible outcomes.

  b   Find the probability of getting: i   a 3 and a 4   ii   a 3 or a 4.

  c   Check that: P(3 or 4) = P(3) + P(4) − P(3 **and** 4).

VENN DIAGRAMS AND CONDITIONAL PROBABILITY

As we observed earlier in the chapter, Venn diagrams are useful for answering certain types of probability questions.

Example 14 ◄)) Self Tutor

In a class of 30 students, 19 play sport, 8 play the piano, and 3 both play sport and the piano. Display this information on a Venn diagram and hence determine the probability that a randomly selected class member plays:

a both sport and the piano

b at least one of sport and the piano

c sport, but not the piano

d exactly one of sport and the piano

e neither sport nor the piano

f the piano if it is known that the student plays sport.

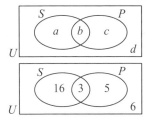

Let S represent the event of 'playing sport', and P represent the event of 'playing the piano'.

Now $a + b = 19$ {as 19 play sport}

$b + c = 8$ {as 8 play the piano}

$b = 3$ {as 3 play both}

$a + b + c + d = 30$ {as there are 30 in the class}

$\therefore \ b = 3, \quad a = 16, \quad c = 5, \quad d = 6.$

a P(S and P)

$= \frac{3}{30}$ or $\frac{1}{10}$

b P(at least one of S and P)

$= \frac{16+3+5}{30}$

$= \frac{24}{30}$ (or $\frac{4}{5}$)

c P(S but not P)

$= \frac{16}{30}$

$= \frac{8}{15}$

d P(exactly one of S and P)

$= \frac{16+5}{30}$

$= \frac{7}{10}$

e P(neither S nor P)

$= \frac{6}{30}$

$= \frac{1}{5}$

f P(P given S)

$= \frac{3}{16+3}$

$= \frac{3}{19}$

EXERCISE 11I.1

1 In a class of 35 students, 18 swim, 14 play tennis, and 8 do neither of these sports. A student is randomly chosen from the class. Determine the probability that the student:

a plays tennis

b does not swim

c does at least one of the sports

d does exactly one of the sports

e swims, but does not play tennis.

2 On a hot day a group of 50 people at the beach were asked why they had come to the beach. 27 had come to swim, 19 had come to surf, and 3 had come to do both. If one person was chosen at random, determine the probability that he or she had come:

   a to surf but not swim   **b** neither to surf nor swim

   c to swim but not surf.

3 From the Venn diagram, $P(A) = \dfrac{a+b}{a+b+c+d}$.

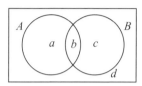

   a Use the Venn diagram to find:

      i $P(B)$ **ii** $P(A \text{ and } B)$ **iii** $P(A \text{ or } B)$
      iv $P(A) + P(B) - P(A \text{ and } B)$.

   b What is the connection between $P(A \text{ or } B)$ and $P(A) + P(B) - P(A \text{ and } B)$?

UNION AND INTERSECTION

In **Chapter 1** we defined the **union** and **intersection** of sets.

The **union** of two events A and B is denoted $A \cup B$.   It includes all outcomes that are in A **or** B.

The **intersection** of two events A and B is denoted $A \cap B$.   It includes all outcomes that are in both A **and** B.

In question **3** of the previous exercise we proved that:

      for two events A and B, $P(A \cup B) = P(A) + P(B) - P(A \cap B)$.

This is known as the **addition law of probability**, and can be written as

      P(**either** A **or** B) = P(A) + P(B) − P(**both** A **and** B).

Example 15   🔊 **Self Tutor**

If $P(B) = 0.4$, $P(A \cup B) = 0.7$
and $P(A \cap B) = 0.2$,   find $P(A)$.

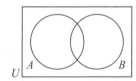

$P(A \cup B) = P(A) + P(B) - P(A \cap B)$
$\therefore \quad 0.7 = P(A) + 0.4 - 0.2$
$\therefore \quad P(A) = 0.5$

or

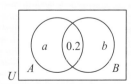

Using a Venn diagram with the probabilities on it,

      $b + 0.2 = 0.4 \quad \therefore \quad b = 0.2$
    $a + 0.2 + 0.2 = 0.7$
        $\therefore \quad a = 0.3$
    $\therefore \quad P(A) = 0.3 + 0.2 = 0.5$

MUTUALLY EXCLUSIVE OR DISJOINT EVENTS

In **Chapter 1** we defined mutually exclusive sets.

If A and B are **mutually exclusive** events then $P(A \cap B) = 0$
and so the addition law becomes

$$P(A \cup B) = P(A) + P(B).$$

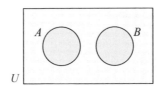

Mutually exclusive events have
no common outcomes.

In a Venn diagram for mutually exclusive events, the circles for the events do not overlap.

Example 16   ◄⑴ **Self Tutor**

A piece of fruit is randomly selected from a basket containing 8 apples and 12 oranges. The event A represents selecting an apple, and O represents selecting an orange.

a   Are A and O mutually exclusive?

b   Find   i $P(A)$ ii $P(O)$ iii $P(A \cap O)$ iv $P(A \cup O)$.

---

a   A piece of fruit cannot be an apple *and* an orange.
∴ A and O are mutually exclusive.

b   i $P(A) = \frac{8}{20} = \frac{2}{5}$ ii $P(O) = \frac{12}{20} = \frac{3}{5}$

   iii $P(A \cap O) = 0$ iv $P(A \cup O) = \frac{20}{20} = 1$

CONDITIONAL PROBABILITY

If we have two events A and B, then

$A \mid B$ is used to represent that 'A occurs knowing that B has occurred'.

$A \mid B$ is often read as 'A given B'.

Example 17   ◄⑴ **Self Tutor**

In a group of 25 students, 15 like chocolate milk (M) and 17 like iced coffee (C). Two students like neither and 9 students like both. One student is randomly selected from the class. What is the probability that the student:

a   likes chocolate milk

b   likes chocolate milk given that he or she likes iced coffee?

The Venn diagram of the situation is shown.

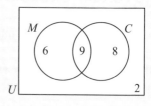

a 15 of the 25 students like chocolate milk.

∴   P(chocolate milk) $= \frac{15}{25}$

b Of the 17 who like iced coffee, 9 like chocolate milk.

∴   P(chocolate milk | iced coffee) $= \frac{9}{17}$

If A and B are events then

$$P(A \mid B) = \frac{P(A \cap B)}{P(B)}.$$

Proof:

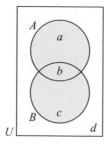

$P(A \mid B)$

$= \dfrac{b}{b + c}$ {Venn diagram}

$= \dfrac{b \div (a + b + c + d)}{(b + c) \div (a + b + c + d)}$

$= \dfrac{P(A \cap B)}{P(B)}$

It follows that $P(A \cap B) = P(A \mid B) \, P(B)$ or $P(A \cap B) = P(B \mid A) \, P(A).$

Example 18   ◀） **Self Tutor**

In a library group of 50 readers, 36 like science fiction, 20 like detective stories, and 12 dislike both.

If a reader is randomly selected, find the probability that he or she:

a likes science fiction and detective stories

b likes at least one of science fiction and detective stories

c likes science fiction given that he or she likes detective stories

d dislikes detective stories given that he or she likes science fiction.

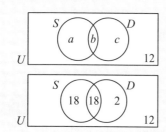

S represents readers who like science fiction.
D represents readers who like detective stories.

We are given that $a + b = 36$

$b + c = 20$

$a + b + c = 38$

∴ $c = 38 - 36$ and so $b = 18$

$= 2$ and $a = 18$

a P(likes both) $= \frac{18}{50} = \frac{9}{25}$ **b** P(likes at least one) $= \frac{38}{50} = \frac{19}{25}$

c $P(S \mid D) = \frac{18}{20} = \frac{9}{10}$ **d** $P(D' \mid S) = \frac{18}{36} = \frac{1}{2}$

Example 19   ◀)) **Self Tutor**

Jar A contains 2 pink and 5 green tickets. Jar B contains 4 pink and 3 green tickets. A die with five faces marked A and one face marked B is rolled and used to select jar A or B. A ticket is then selected from this jar. Determine the probability that:

  a   the ticket is pink   b   the ticket was chosen from B given it is pink.

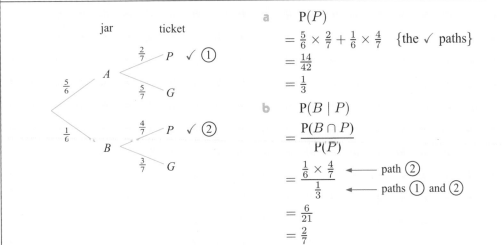

a $P(P)$

$= \frac{5}{6} \times \frac{2}{7} + \frac{1}{6} \times \frac{4}{7}$ {the ✓ paths}

$= \frac{14}{42}$

$= \frac{1}{3}$

b $P(B \mid P)$

$= \frac{P(B \cap P)}{P(P)}$

$= \dfrac{\frac{1}{6} \times \frac{4}{7}}{\frac{1}{3}}$ ◀── path ②, paths ① and ②

$= \frac{6}{21}$

$= \frac{2}{7}$

EXERCISE 11I.2

1   50 students went on a 'thrill seekers' holiday. 40 went white-water rafting, 21 went paragliding, and each student did at least one of these activities.

  a   From a Venn diagram, find how many students did both activities.

  b   If a student from this group is randomly selected, find the probability that he or she:

    i   went white-water rafting but not paragliding

    ii   went paragliding given that he or she went white-water rafting.

2   In a class of 25 students, 19 have fair hair, 15 have blue eyes, and 22 have fair hair, blue eyes or both. A child is selected at random. Determine the probability that the child has:

  a   fair hair and blue eyes   b   neither fair hair nor blue eyes

  c   fair hair but not blue eyes   d   blue eyes given that the child has fair hair.

3

28 students go tramping. 23 get sunburn, 8 get blisters, and 5 get both sunburn and blisters. Determine the probability that a randomly selected student:

  a   did not get blisters

  b   either got blisters or sunburn

  c   neither got blisters nor sunburn

  d   got blisters, given that the student was sunburnt

  e   was sunburnt, given that the student did not get blisters.

4 An examination in French has two parts: aural and written. When 30 students sit for the examination, 25 pass aural, 26 pass written, and 3 fail both parts. Determine the probability that a student who:

    a passed aural also passed written
    b passed aural, failed written.

5 In a small country there are 3 supermarkets: P, Q and R. 60% of the population shop at P, 36% shop at Q, 34% shop at R, 18% shop at P and Q, 15% shop at P and R, 4% shop at Q and R, and 2% shop at all 3 supermarkets. A person is selected at random. Determine the probability that the person shops at:

    a none of the supermarkets
    b at least one of the supermarkets
    c exactly one of the supermarkets
    d either P or Q
    e P, given that the person shops at at least one supermarket
    f R, given that the person shops at either P or Q or both.

6 Marius has 2 bags of peaches. Bag A has 4 ripe and 2 unripe peaches, and bag B has 5 ripe and 1 unripe peaches. Ingrid selects a bag by tossing a coin, and takes a peach from that bag.

    a Determine the probability that the peach is ripe.
    b Given that the peach is ripe, what is the probability it came from B?

7 When Sophia goes to the local shopping centre from Monday to Thursday, the probability that she finds a car park is 95%. When she goes on Friday or Saturday, the probability of finding a car park is 70%. Assuming that she is equally likely to shop on any day from Monday to Saturday, determine the probability that:

    a she finds a car park
    b it is Saturday, given that she finds a car park.

8 On a given day, Claude's car has an 80% chance of starting first time and André's car has a 70% chance of the same. Given that at least one of the cars has started first time, what is the chance that André's car started first time?

WHAT ARE YOUR SURVIVAL PROSPECTS?

LINKS
click here

Areas of interaction:
Community service/Health and social education

REVIEW SET 11A

1 Donna kept records of the number of clients she interviewed over a period of consecutive days.

    a For how many days did the survey last?
    b Estimate Donna's chances of interviewing:
       i no clients on a day
       ii four or more clients on a day
       iii less than three clients on a day.

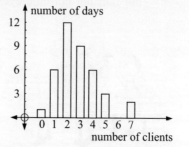

2 Illustrate on a 2-dimensional grid the possible outcomes when a coin and a pentagonal spinner with sides labelled A, B, C, D and E are tossed and spun simultaneously.

3 What is meant by saying that two events are "independent"?

4 Use a tree diagram to illustrate the sample space for the possible four-child families. Hence determine the probability that a randomly chosen four-child family:

    a is all boys   **b** has exactly two boys   **c** has more girls than boys.

5 In a shooting competition, Louise has 80% chance of hitting her target and Kayo has 90% chance of hitting her target. If they both have a single shot, determine the probability that:

    a both hit their targets   **b** neither hits her target
    c at least one hits her target   **d** only Kayo hits her target.

6 Two fair six-sided dice are rolled simultaneously. Determine the probability that the result is a 'double', i.e., both dice show the same number.

7 A bag contains 4 green and 3 red marbles. Two marbles are randomly selected from the bag, the first being replaced before the second is drawn. Determine the probability that:

    a both are green   **b** they are different in colour.

8 A circle is divided into 5 sectors with equal angles at the centre. It is made into a spinner, and the sectors are numbered 1, 2, 3, 4, and 5. A coin is tossed and the spinner is spun.

    a Use a 2-dimensional grid to show the sample space.

    b What is the chance of getting: **i** a head and a 5 **ii** a head or a 5?

9 Bag X contains three white and two red marbles. Bag Y contains one white and three red marbles. A bag is randomly chosen and two marbles are drawn from it. Illustrate the given information on a tree diagram and hence determine the probability of drawing two marbles of the same colour.

10 At a local girls school, 65% of the students play netball, 60% play tennis, and 20% play neither sport. Display this information on a Venn diagram, and hence determine the likelihood that a randomly chosen student plays:

    a netball   **b** netball but not tennis
    c at least one of these two sports   **d** exactly one of these two sports
    e tennis, given that she plays netball.

REVIEW SET 11B

1 Pierre conducted a survey to determine the ages of people walking through a shopping mall. The results are shown in the table alongside. Estimate, to 3 decimal places, the probability that the next person Pierre meets in the shopping mall is:

Age	Frequency
0 - 19	22
20 - 39	43
40 - 59	39
60+	14

    a between 20 and 39 years of age

    b less than 40 years of age   **c** at least 20 years of age.

2 **a** List the sample space of possible results when a tetrahedral die with four faces labelled A, B, C and D is rolled and a 20-cent coin is tossed simultaneously.

b Use a tree diagram to illustrate the sample spaces for the following:

    i Bags A, B and C contain green or yellow tickets. A bag is selected and then a ticket taken from it.

    ii Martina and Justine play tennis. The first to win three sets wins the match.

3 When a box of drawing pins was dropped onto the floor, it was observed that 49 pins landed on their backs and 32 landed on their sides. Estimate, to 2 decimal places, the probability of a drawing pin landing:

back   side

    a on its back   **b** on its side.

4 The letters A, B, C, D, ... N are put in a hat.

    a Determine the probability of drawing a vowel (A, E, I, O or U) if one of the letters is chosen at random.

    b If two letters are drawn without replacement, copy and complete the following tree diagram including all probabilities:

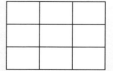

    c Use your tree diagram to determine the probability of drawing:

        i a vowel and a consonant

        ii at least one vowel.

5 A farmer fences his rectangular property into 9 rectangular paddocks as shown alongside.

If a paddock is selected at random, what is the probability that it has:

    a no fences on the boundary of the property

    b one fence on the boundary of the property

    c two fences on the boundary of the property?

6 If $P(A) = \frac{7}{12}$, find $P(A')$.

7 Bag X contains 3 black and 2 red marbles. Bag Y contains 4 black and 1 red marble. A bag is selected at random and then two marbles are selected without replacement. Determine the probability that:

    a both marbles are red   **b** two black marbles are picked from Bag Y.

8 Two dice are rolled simultaneously. Illustrate this information on a 2-dimensional grid. Determine the probability of getting:

    a a double 5   **b** at least one 4

    c a sum greater than 9   **d** a sum of 7 or 11.

9 A class consists of 25 students. 15 have blue eyes, 9 have fair hair, and 3 have both blue eyes and fair hair. Represent this information on a Venn diagram.

Hence find the probability that a randomly selected student from the class:

    a has neither blue eyes nor fair hair   **b** has blue eyes, but not fair hair

    c has fair hair given that he or she has blue eyes

    d does not have fair hair given that he or she does not have blue eyes.

Chapter 12

Algebraic fractions

Contents:

Fractions which involve unknowns are called **algebraic fractions**.

Algebraic fractions occur in many areas of mathematics. We have already seen them in problems involving similar triangles.

A   SIMPLIFYING ALGEBRAIC FRACTIONS

CANCELLATION

We have observed previously that number fractions can be simplified by cancelling common factors.

For example, $\frac{12}{28} = \frac{\overset{1}{\cancel{4}} \times 3}{\underset{1}{\cancel{4}} \times 7} = \frac{3}{7}$ where the common factor 4 was cancelled.

The same principle can be applied to algebraic fractions:

> If the numerator and denominator of an algebraic fraction are both written in factored form and common factors are found, we can simplify by **cancelling the common factors**.

For example,

$$\frac{4ab}{2a} = \frac{2 \times \overset{1}{\cancel{2}} \times \overset{1}{\cancel{a}} \times b}{\underset{1}{\cancel{2}} \times \underset{1}{\cancel{a}}}$$ {fully factorised}

$$= \frac{2b}{1}$$ {after cancellation}

$$= 2b$$

For algebraic fractions, check both numerator and denominator to see if they can be expressed as the product of factors, then look for common factors which can be cancelled.

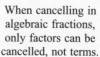

When cancelling in algebraic fractions, only factors can be cancelled, not terms.

ILLEGAL CANCELLATION

Take care with fractions such as $\dfrac{a+3}{3}$.

The expression in the numerator, $a + 3$, **cannot be** written as the product of factors other than $1 \times (a + 3)$. a and 3 are *terms* of the expression, not factors.

A typical **error** in **illegal cancellation** is: $\dfrac{a + \overset{1}{\cancel{3}}}{\underset{1}{\cancel{3}}} = \dfrac{a+1}{1} = a + 1.$

You can check that this cancellation of terms is incorrect by substituting a value for a.

For example, if $a = 3$,   LHS $= \dfrac{a+3}{3} = \dfrac{3+3}{3} = 2,$

whereas   RHS $= a + 1 = 4.$

Example 1 ◄⅁ **Self Tutor**

Simplify: **a** $\dfrac{2x^2}{4x}$ **b** $\dfrac{6xy}{3x^3}$ **c** $\dfrac{x+y}{x}$

a $\dfrac{2x^2}{4x}$

$= \dfrac{\overset{1}{\cancel{2}} \times \overset{1}{\cancel{x}} \times x}{\underset{2}{\cancel{4}} \times \underset{1}{\cancel{x}}}$

$= \dfrac{x}{2}$

b $\dfrac{6xy}{3x^3}$

$= \dfrac{\overset{2}{\cancel{6}} \times \overset{1}{\cancel{x}} \times y}{\underset{1}{\cancel{3}} \times \underset{1}{\cancel{x}} \times x \times x}$

$= \dfrac{2y}{x^2}$

c $\dfrac{x+y}{x}$

cannot be simplified as $x+y$ is a sum, not a product.

Example 2 ◄⅁ **Self Tutor**

Simplify: **a** $\dfrac{(x+3)(x-2)}{4(x+3)}$ **b** $\dfrac{2(x+3)^2}{x+3}$

a $\dfrac{\cancel{(x+3)}^{1}(x-2)}{4\cancel{(x+3)}_{1}}$

$= \dfrac{x-2}{4}$

b $\dfrac{2(x+3)^2}{x+3}$

$= \dfrac{2\cancel{(x+3)}^{1}(x+3)}{\cancel{(x+3)}_{1}}$

$= 2(x+3)$

In these examples $(x+3)$ is the common factor.

EXERCISE 12A.1

1 Simplify if possible:

  a $\dfrac{6a}{3}$ **b** $\dfrac{10b}{5}$ **c** $\dfrac{3}{6x}$ **d** $\dfrac{8t}{t}$ **e** $\dfrac{t+2}{t}$

  f $\dfrac{8a^2}{4a}$ **g** $\dfrac{2b}{4b^2}$ **h** $\dfrac{2x^2}{x^2}$ **i** $\dfrac{4a}{12a^3}$ **j** $\dfrac{4x^2}{8x}$

  k $\dfrac{t^2+8}{t}$ **l** $\dfrac{a^2b}{ab^2}$ **m** $\dfrac{a+b}{a-c}$ **n** $\dfrac{15x^2y^3}{3xy^4}$ **o** $\dfrac{8abc^2}{4bc}$

  p $\dfrac{(2a)^2}{a}$ **q** $\dfrac{(2a)^2}{4a^2}$ **r** $\dfrac{(3a^2)^2}{3a}$ **s** $\dfrac{(3a^2)^2}{9a^2}$ **t** $\dfrac{(3a^2)^2}{18a^3}$

2 Split the following expressions into two parts and simplify if possible.

For example, $\dfrac{x+9}{x} = \dfrac{x}{x} + \dfrac{9}{x} = 1 + \dfrac{9}{x}$.

  a $\dfrac{x+3}{3}$ **b** $\dfrac{4a+1}{2}$ **c** $\dfrac{a+b}{c}$ **d** $\dfrac{a+2b}{b}$

  e $\dfrac{2a+4}{2}$ **f** $\dfrac{3a+6b}{3}$ **g** $\dfrac{4m+8n}{4}$ **h** $\dfrac{4m+8n}{2m}$

3 Which of the expressions in **2** produced a simplified answer and which did not? Explain why this is so.

4 Simplify:

a $\dfrac{3(x+2)}{3}$

b $\dfrac{4(x-1)}{2}$

c $\dfrac{7(b+2)}{14}$

d $\dfrac{2(n+5)}{12}$

e $\dfrac{10}{5(x+2)}$

f $\dfrac{15}{5(3-a)}$

g $\dfrac{6(x+2)}{(x+2)}$

h $\dfrac{x-4}{2(x-4)}$

i $\dfrac{2(x+2)}{x(x+2)}$

j $\dfrac{x(x-5)^2}{3(x-5)}$

k $\dfrac{(x+2)(x+3)}{2(x+2)^2}$

l $\dfrac{(x+2)(x+5)}{5(x+5)}$

m $\dfrac{(x+2)(x-1)}{(x-1)(x+3)}$

n $\dfrac{(x+5)(2x-1)}{3(2x-1)}$

o $\dfrac{(x+6)^2}{3(x+6)}$

p $\dfrac{x^2(x+2)}{x(x+2)(x-1)}$

q $\dfrac{(x+2)^2(x+1)}{4(x+2)}$

r $\dfrac{(x+2)^2(x-1)^2}{(x-1)^2x^2}$

FACTORISATION AND SIMPLIFICATION

It is often necessary to factorise either the numerator or denominator before simplification can be done.

Example 3   ◀)) **Self Tutor**

Simplify: **a** $\dfrac{4a+8}{4}$ **b** $\dfrac{3}{3a-6b}$

a
$$\dfrac{4a+8}{4}$$
$$=\dfrac{{}^1\cancel{4}(a+2)}{\cancel{4}\,^1}$$
$$=\dfrac{(a+2)}{1}$$
$$=a+2$$

b
$$\dfrac{3}{3a-6b}$$
$$=\dfrac{\cancel{3}\,^1}{{}_1\cancel{3}(a-2b)}$$
$$=\dfrac{1}{a-2b}$$

Example 4   ◀)) **Self Tutor**

Simplify: **a** $\dfrac{ab-ac}{b-c}$ **b** $\dfrac{2x^2-4x}{4x-8}$

a
$$\dfrac{ab-ac}{b-c}$$
$$=\dfrac{a\cancel{(b-c)}\,^1}{\cancel{b-c}\,_1}$$
$$=\dfrac{a}{1}$$
$$=a$$

b
$$\dfrac{2x^2-4x}{4x-8}$$
$$=\dfrac{{}^1\cancel{2}x\cancel{(x-2)}\,^1}{{}_2\cancel{4}\cancel{(x-2)}\,_1}$$
$$=\dfrac{x}{2}$$

$$b - a = -1(a - b)$$ is a useful rule for converting $b - a$ into $a - b$. It can sometimes allow us to cancel common factors.

Example 5 ◄) Self Tutor

Simplify: a $\dfrac{3a - 3b}{b - a}$ b $\dfrac{ab^2 - ab}{1 - b}$

a $\dfrac{3a - 3b}{b - a}$

$= \dfrac{3(a - b)^{\,1}}{-1(a - b)^{\,1}}$

$= -3$

b $\dfrac{ab^2 - ab}{1 - b}$

$= \dfrac{ab(b - 1)^{\,1}}{-1(b - 1)^{\,1}}$

$= -ab$

Example 6 ◄) Self Tutor

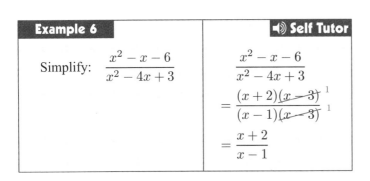

Simplify: $\dfrac{x^2 - x - 6}{x^2 - 4x + 3}$

$\dfrac{x^2 - x - 6}{x^2 - 4x + 3}$

$= \dfrac{(x + 2)(x - 3)^{\,1}}{(x - 1)(x - 3)^{\,1}}$

$= \dfrac{x + 2}{x - 1}$

Don't forget to expand your factorisations to check them.

EXERCISE 12A.2

1 Simplify by cancelling common factors:

a $\dfrac{6}{2(x + 2)}$ b $\dfrac{2x + 6}{2}$ c $\dfrac{3x + 12}{3}$ d $\dfrac{3x + 6}{6}$

e $\dfrac{5x + 20}{10}$ f $\dfrac{3a + 12}{9}$ g $\dfrac{xy + xz}{x}$ h $\dfrac{xy + xz}{z + y}$

i $\dfrac{ab + bc}{ab - bc}$ j $\dfrac{3x - 12}{6(x - 4)^2}$ k $\dfrac{(x + 3)^2}{6x + 18}$ l $\dfrac{2(x - y)^2}{6(x - y)}$

2 Simplify:

a $\dfrac{4x + 8}{2x + 4}$ b $\dfrac{mx + nx}{2x}$ c $\dfrac{mx + nx}{m + n}$ d $\dfrac{x + y}{mx + my}$

e $\dfrac{2x + 4}{2}$ f $\dfrac{x^2 + 2x}{x}$ g $\dfrac{x^2 + 2x}{x + 2}$ h $\dfrac{x}{bx + cx}$

i $\dfrac{3x^2 + 6x}{x + 2}$ j $\dfrac{2x^2 + 6x}{2x}$ k $\dfrac{2x^2 + 6x}{x + 3}$ l $\dfrac{ax^2 + bx}{ax + b}$

3 Simplify, if possible:

a $\dfrac{2a - 2b}{b - a}$
b $\dfrac{3a - 3b}{6b - 6a}$
c $\dfrac{a - b}{b - a}$
d $\dfrac{a + b}{a - b}$

e $\dfrac{x - 2y}{4y - 2x}$
f $\dfrac{3m - 6n}{2n - m}$
g $\dfrac{3x - 3}{x - x^2}$
h $\dfrac{xy^2 - xy}{3 - 3y}$

i $\dfrac{6x^2 - 3x}{1 - 2x}$
j $\dfrac{4x + 6}{4}$
k $\dfrac{12x - 6}{2x - x^2}$
l $\dfrac{x^2 - 4}{x - 2}$

m $\dfrac{x^2 - 4}{x + 2}$
n $\dfrac{x^2 - 4}{2 - x}$
o $\dfrac{x + 3}{x^2 - 9}$
p $\dfrac{m^2 - n^2}{m + n}$

q $\dfrac{m^2 - n^2}{n - m}$
r $\dfrac{3x + 6}{4 - x^2}$
s $\dfrac{16 - x^2}{x^2 - 4x}$
t $\dfrac{x^2 - 4}{4 - x^2}$

u $\dfrac{5x^2 - 5y^2}{10xy - 10y^2}$
v $\dfrac{2d^2 - 2a^2}{a^2 - ad}$
w $\dfrac{4x^2 - 8x}{x^2 - 4}$
x $\dfrac{3x^2 - 6x}{4 - x^2}$

4 Simplify:

a $\dfrac{x^2 - x}{x^2 - 1}$
b $\dfrac{x^2 + 2x + 1}{x^2 + 3x + 2}$
c $\dfrac{x^2 - 4x + 4}{2x^2 - 4x}$

d $\dfrac{x^2 + 4x + 3}{x^2 + 5x + 4}$
e $\dfrac{x^2 - 4}{x^2 - 3x - 10}$
f $\dfrac{x^2 + 7x + 12}{2x^2 + 6x}$

g $\dfrac{x^2 + 4x - 5}{2x^2 + 6x - 20}$
h $\dfrac{x^2 + 6x + 9}{x^2 + 3x}$
i $\dfrac{2x^2 - 7x - 4}{x^2 - 2x - 8}$

j $\dfrac{3x^2 + 5x - 2}{3x^2 - 4x + 1}$
k $\dfrac{2x^2 - 3x - 20}{x^2 - x - 12}$
l $\dfrac{8x^2 + 14x + 3}{2x^2 - x - 6}$

B   MULTIPLYING AND DIVIDING ALGEBRAIC FRACTIONS

The rules for multiplying and dividing algebraic fractions are identical to those used with numerical fractions. These are:

To **multiply** two or more fractions, we multiply the numerators to form the new numerator, and we multiply the denominators to form the new denominator.

$$\frac{a}{b} \times \frac{c}{d} = \frac{a \times c}{b \times d} = \frac{ac}{bd}$$

To **divide** by a fraction we multiply by its reciprocal.

$$\frac{a}{b} \div \frac{c}{d} = \frac{a}{b} \times \frac{d}{c} = \frac{ad}{bc}$$

MULTIPLICATION

Step 1:   Multiply numerators and multiply denominators.

Step 2:   Separate the factors.

Step 3:   Cancel any common factors.

Step 4:   Write in simplest form.

For example, $\dfrac{n^2}{3} \times \dfrac{6}{n} = \dfrac{n^2 \times 6}{3 \times n}$ {Step 1}

$$= \dfrac{n \times \cancel{n}^1 \times 2 \times \cancel{3}^1}{\cancel{3}_1 \times \cancel{n}_1} \qquad \{Steps\ 2\ and\ 3\}$$

$$= \dfrac{2n}{1}$$

$$= 2n \qquad\qquad \{Step\ 4\}$$

Example 7   ◄)) **Self Tutor**

Simplify: a $\dfrac{4}{d} \times \dfrac{d}{8}$ b $\dfrac{5}{g} \times g^3$

a $\dfrac{4}{d} \times \dfrac{d}{8} = \dfrac{\cancel{4}^1 \times \cancel{d}^1}{\cancel{d}_1 \times \cancel{8}_2}$

$\qquad = \tfrac{1}{2}$

b $\dfrac{5}{g} \times g^3 = \dfrac{5}{g} \times \dfrac{g^3}{1}$

$\qquad = \dfrac{5 \times \cancel{g}^1 \times g \times g}{\cancel{g}_1}$

$\qquad = \dfrac{5g^2}{1}$

$\qquad = 5g^2$

DIVISION

Step 1: To divide by a fraction, multiply by its reciprocal.

Step 2: Multiply numerators and multiply denominators.

Step 3: Cancel any common factors.

Step 4: Write in simplest form.

For example,

$$\dfrac{m}{2} \div \dfrac{n}{6} = \dfrac{m}{2} \times \dfrac{6}{n} \qquad \{Step\ 1\}$$

$$= \dfrac{m \times 6}{2 \times n} \qquad \{Step\ 2\}$$

$$= \dfrac{m \times \cancel{6}^3}{\cancel{2}_1 \times n} \qquad \{Step\ 3\}$$

$$= \dfrac{3m}{n} \qquad\qquad \{Step\ 4\}$$

Example 8   ◄)) **Self Tutor**

Simplify: a $\dfrac{6}{x} \div \dfrac{2}{x^2}$ b $\dfrac{8}{p} \div 2$

a $\dfrac{6}{x} \div \dfrac{2}{x^2} = \dfrac{6}{x} \times \dfrac{x^2}{2}$

$\qquad = \dfrac{3 \times \cancel{2}^1 \times \cancel{x}^1 \times x}{\cancel{x}_1 \times \cancel{2}_1}$

$\qquad = 3x$

b $\dfrac{8}{p} \div 2 = \dfrac{8}{p} \times \dfrac{1}{2}$

$\qquad = \dfrac{\cancel{8}^4 \times 1}{p \times \cancel{2}_1}$

$\qquad = \dfrac{4}{p}$

EXERCISE 12B

1   Simplify:

a $\dfrac{a}{2} \times \dfrac{b}{3}$

b $\dfrac{x}{4} \times \dfrac{2}{x}$

c $\dfrac{c}{4} \times \dfrac{2}{c}$

d $\dfrac{a}{2} \times \dfrac{a}{3}$

e $\dfrac{a}{b} \times \dfrac{x}{y}$

f $\dfrac{x}{y} \times \dfrac{y}{x}$

g $\dfrac{x}{3} \times x$

h $\dfrac{x}{4} \times \dfrac{8}{y}$

i $\dfrac{n}{2} \times \dfrac{1}{n^2}$

j $\dfrac{6}{p} \times \dfrac{p}{2}$

k $\dfrac{m}{x} \times \dfrac{x}{n}$

l $x \times \dfrac{2}{x}$

m $\dfrac{5}{t} \times t^2$

n $\left(\dfrac{x}{y}\right)^2$

o $\left(\dfrac{4}{d}\right)^2$

p $\dfrac{a}{b} \times \dfrac{b}{c} \times \dfrac{c}{a}$

2   Simplify:

a $\dfrac{x}{3} \div \dfrac{x}{2}$

b $\dfrac{3}{y} \div \dfrac{6}{y}$

c $3 \div \dfrac{1}{x}$

d $6 \div \dfrac{2}{y}$

e $\dfrac{3}{p} \div \dfrac{1}{p}$

f $\dfrac{c}{n} \div n$

g $d \div \dfrac{5}{d}$

h $x \div \dfrac{x}{3}$

i $1 \div \dfrac{a}{b}$

j $\dfrac{3}{d} \div 2$

k $\dfrac{4}{x} \div \dfrac{x^2}{2}$

l $\dfrac{4}{x} \div \dfrac{8}{x^2}$

m $a \div \dfrac{a^2}{3}$

n $\dfrac{x}{y} \div \dfrac{x^2}{y}$

o $\dfrac{5}{a} \div \dfrac{a}{2}$

p $\dfrac{a^2}{5} \div \dfrac{a}{3}$

C   ADDING AND SUBTRACTING ALGEBRAIC FRACTIONS

The rules for addition and subtraction of algebraic fractions are identical to those used with numerical fractions.

To **add** two or more fractions we obtain the *lowest common denominator* and then add the resulting numerators.

$$\dfrac{a}{c} + \dfrac{b}{c} = \dfrac{a+b}{c}$$

To **subtract** two or more fractions we obtain the *lowest common denominator* and then subtract the resulting numerators.

$$\dfrac{a}{c} - \dfrac{d}{c} = \dfrac{a-d}{c}$$

To find the lowest common denominator, we look for the **lowest common multiple of the denominators**.

For example,   when adding $\frac{3}{4} + \frac{2}{3}$,   the lowest common denominator is 12,

when adding $\frac{2}{3} + \frac{1}{6}$,   the lowest common denominator is 6.

The same method is used when there are variables in the denominator.

For example,   when adding $\dfrac{4}{x} + \dfrac{5}{y}$,   the lowest common denominator is xy,

when adding $\dfrac{4}{x} + \dfrac{3}{2x}$,   the lowest common denominator is $2x$,

when adding $\dfrac{1}{3a} + \dfrac{2}{5b}$,   the lowest common denominator is $15ab$.

To find $\dfrac{x}{2} + \dfrac{3x}{5}$ we find the LCD and then proceed in the same manner as for ordinary fractions.

The LCM of 2 and 5 is 10, so the LCD is 10.

$$\therefore \quad \frac{x}{2} + \frac{3x}{5} = \frac{x \times 5}{2 \times 5} + \frac{3x \times 2}{5 \times 2}$$
$$= \frac{5x}{10} + \frac{6x}{10}$$
$$= \frac{11x}{10}$$

Example 9 | ◀) Self Tutor

Simplify: **a** $\dfrac{x}{3} + \dfrac{5x}{6}$ **b** $\dfrac{3b}{4} - \dfrac{2b}{3}$

a $\dfrac{x}{3} + \dfrac{5x}{6}$

$= \dfrac{x \times 2}{3 \times 2} + \dfrac{5x}{6}$ {LCD $= 6$}

$= \dfrac{2x}{6} + \dfrac{5x}{6}$

$= \dfrac{2x + 5x}{6}$

$= \dfrac{7x}{6}$

b $\dfrac{3b}{4} - \dfrac{2b}{3}$

$= \dfrac{3b \times 3}{4 \times 3} - \dfrac{2b \times 4}{3 \times 4}$ {LCD $= 12$}

$= \dfrac{9b}{12} - \dfrac{8b}{12}$

$= \dfrac{b}{12}$

Example 10 | ◀) Self Tutor

Simplify: **a** $\dfrac{2}{a} + \dfrac{3}{c}$ **b** $\dfrac{7}{x} - \dfrac{5}{2x}$

a $\dfrac{2}{a} + \dfrac{3}{c}$

$= \dfrac{2 \times c}{a \times c} + \dfrac{3 \times a}{c \times a}$ {LCD $= ac$}

$= \dfrac{2c}{ac} + \dfrac{3a}{ac}$

$= \dfrac{2c + 3a}{ac}$

b $\dfrac{7}{x} - \dfrac{5}{2x}$

$= \dfrac{7 \times 2}{x \times 2} - \dfrac{5}{2x}$ {LCD $= 2x$}

$= \dfrac{14}{2x} - \dfrac{5}{2x}$

$= \dfrac{9}{2x}$

Example 11　　　　　　　　　　　　　　　　　◀) **Self Tutor**

Simplify:　　**a** $\dfrac{b}{3} + 1$　　　　　　　　　　**b** $\dfrac{a}{4} - a$

a $\dfrac{b}{3} + 1 = \dfrac{b}{3} + \dfrac{3}{3}$

$\phantom{\textbf{a}\quad \dfrac{b}{3} + 1} = \dfrac{b+3}{3}$

b $\dfrac{a}{4} - a = \dfrac{a}{4} - \dfrac{a \times 4}{1 \times 4}$

$\phantom{\textbf{b}\quad \dfrac{a}{4} - a} = \dfrac{a}{4} - \dfrac{4a}{4}$

$\phantom{\textbf{b}\quad \dfrac{a}{4} - a} = \dfrac{-3a}{4} \ \text{ or } \ -\dfrac{3a}{4}$

EXERCISE 12C

1 Simplify by writing as a single fraction:

a $\dfrac{x}{2} + \dfrac{x}{5}$　　　**b** $\dfrac{x}{3} - \dfrac{x}{6}$　　　**c** $\dfrac{x}{4} + \dfrac{3x}{5}$　　　**d** $\dfrac{x}{2} - \dfrac{x}{5}$

e $\dfrac{2t}{3} - \dfrac{7t}{12}$　　**f** $\dfrac{11n}{21} - \dfrac{n}{7}$　　**g** $\dfrac{a}{2} + \dfrac{a}{3}$　　　**h** $\dfrac{a}{2} + \dfrac{b}{4}$

i $\dfrac{n}{3} + \dfrac{2n}{15}$　　**j** $\dfrac{5g}{6} - \dfrac{g}{3}$　　　**k** $\dfrac{4s}{5} - \dfrac{2s}{3}$　　**l** $a - \dfrac{3a}{5}$

m $\dfrac{x}{3} + \dfrac{x}{2} + \dfrac{x}{6}$　**n** $\dfrac{y}{2} + \dfrac{y}{4} - \dfrac{y}{3}$　**o** $\dfrac{z}{4} + \dfrac{z}{6} - \dfrac{z}{3}$　**p** $2q - \dfrac{q}{3} + \dfrac{2q}{7}$

2 Simplify:

a $\dfrac{3}{a} + \dfrac{2}{b}$　　　**b** $\dfrac{4}{a} + \dfrac{3}{d}$　　　**c** $\dfrac{5}{a} - \dfrac{3}{b}$　　　**d** $\dfrac{3a}{m} - \dfrac{2a}{m}$

e $\dfrac{a}{y} + \dfrac{b}{3y}$　　**f** $\dfrac{4}{a} - \dfrac{5}{2a}$　　**g** $\dfrac{3}{a} - \dfrac{2}{ab}$　　**h** $\dfrac{c}{a} + \dfrac{b}{d}$

i $\dfrac{4}{b} + \dfrac{a}{b}$　　　**j** $\dfrac{2}{a} - \dfrac{c}{d}$　　　**k** $\dfrac{5}{x} + \dfrac{x}{3}$　　　**l** $\dfrac{p}{6} - \dfrac{2}{d}$

m $\dfrac{m}{3} + \dfrac{n}{m}$　　**n** $\dfrac{2m}{p} - \dfrac{m}{n}$　　**o** $\dfrac{3b}{5} + \dfrac{b}{4}$　　**p** $\dfrac{5b}{3} - \dfrac{3b}{5}$

3 Simplify:

a $\dfrac{x}{3} + 2$　　　**b** $\dfrac{m}{2} - 1$　　　**c** $\dfrac{a}{3} + a$　　　**d** $\dfrac{b}{5} - 2$

e $\dfrac{x}{6} - 3$　　　**f** $3 + \dfrac{x}{4}$　　　**g** $5 - \dfrac{x}{6}$　　　**h** $2 + \dfrac{3}{x}$

i $6 - \dfrac{3}{x}$　　　**j** $b + \dfrac{3}{b}$　　　**k** $\dfrac{5}{x} + x$　　　**l** $\dfrac{y}{6} - 2y$

4 Simplify:

a $\dfrac{x}{3} + \dfrac{3x}{5}$　　**b** $\dfrac{3x}{5} - \dfrac{2x}{7}$　　**c** $\dfrac{5}{a} + \dfrac{1}{2a}$　　**d** $\dfrac{6}{y} - \dfrac{3}{4y}$

e $\dfrac{3}{b} + \dfrac{4}{c}$　　**f** $\dfrac{5}{4a} - \dfrac{6}{b}$　　**g** $\dfrac{x}{10} + 3$　　　**h** $4 - \dfrac{x}{3}$

MORE COMPLICATED FRACTIONS

Addition and subtraction of more complicated algebraic fractions can be made relatively straightforward if we adopt a consistent approach.

For example: $\dfrac{x+2}{3} + \dfrac{5-2x}{2} = \dfrac{2}{2}\left(\dfrac{x+2}{3}\right) + \dfrac{3}{3}\left(\dfrac{5-2x}{2}\right)$ {achieves LCD of 6}

$$= \dfrac{2(x+2)}{6} + \dfrac{3(5-2x)}{6} \qquad \text{\{simplify each fraction\}}$$

We can then write the expression as a single fraction and simplify the numerator.

Example 12   ◀⑴ **Self Tutor**

Write as a single fraction: a $\dfrac{x}{12} + \dfrac{x-1}{4}$ b $\dfrac{x-1}{3} - \dfrac{x+2}{7}$

a $\dfrac{x}{12} + \dfrac{x-1}{4}$

$= \dfrac{x}{12} + \dfrac{3}{3}\left(\dfrac{x-1}{4}\right)$

$= \dfrac{x + 3(x-1)}{12}$

$= \dfrac{x + 3x - 3}{12}$

$= \dfrac{4x - 3}{12}$

b $\dfrac{x-1}{3} - \dfrac{x+2}{7}$

$= \dfrac{7}{7}\left(\dfrac{x-1}{3}\right) - \dfrac{3}{3}\left(\dfrac{x+2}{7}\right)$

$= \dfrac{7(x-1)}{21} - \dfrac{3(x+2)}{21}$

$= \dfrac{7(x-1) - 3(x+2)}{21}$

$= \dfrac{7x - 7 - 3x - 6}{21}$

$= \dfrac{4x - 13}{21}$

Example 13   ◀⑴ **Self Tutor**

Write as a single fraction: a $\dfrac{2}{x} + \dfrac{1}{x+2}$ b $\dfrac{5}{x+2} - \dfrac{1}{x-1}$

a $\dfrac{2}{x} + \dfrac{1}{x+2}$

$= \dfrac{2}{x}\left(\dfrac{x+2}{x+2}\right) + \left(\dfrac{1}{x+2}\right)\dfrac{x}{x}$

    {LCD $= x(x+2)$}

$= \dfrac{2(x+2) + x}{x(x+2)}$

$= \dfrac{2x + 4 + x}{x(x+2)}$

$= \dfrac{3x + 4}{x(x+2)}$

b $\dfrac{5}{x+2} - \dfrac{1}{x-1}$

$= \left(\dfrac{5}{x+2}\right)\left(\dfrac{x-1}{x-1}\right) - \left(\dfrac{1}{x-1}\right)\left(\dfrac{x+2}{x+2}\right)$

    {LCD $= (x+2)(x-1)$}

$= \dfrac{5(x-1) - 1(x+2)}{(x+2)(x-1)}$

$= \dfrac{5x - 5 - x - 2}{(x+2)(x-1)}$

$= \dfrac{4x - 7}{(x+2)(x-1)}$

EXERCISE 12D.1

1 Write as a single fraction:

a $\dfrac{x}{4} + \dfrac{x-1}{5}$

b $\dfrac{2x+5}{3} + \dfrac{x}{6}$

c $\dfrac{x}{7} + \dfrac{2x-1}{6}$

d $\dfrac{a+b}{2} + \dfrac{b-a}{3}$

e $\dfrac{x-1}{4} + \dfrac{2x-1}{5}$

f $\dfrac{x+1}{2} + \dfrac{2-x}{7}$

g $\dfrac{x}{5} - \dfrac{x-3}{6}$

h $\dfrac{x-1}{6} - \dfrac{x}{7}$

i $\dfrac{x}{10} - \dfrac{2x-1}{5}$

j $\dfrac{x}{6} - \dfrac{1-x}{12}$

k $\dfrac{x-1}{3} - \dfrac{x-2}{5}$

l $\dfrac{2x+1}{3} - \dfrac{1-3x}{8}$

2 Write as a single fraction:

a $\dfrac{2}{x+1} + \dfrac{3}{x-2}$

b $\dfrac{5}{x+1} + \dfrac{7}{x+2}$

c $\dfrac{5}{x-1} - \dfrac{4}{x+2}$

d $\dfrac{2}{x+2} - \dfrac{4}{2x+1}$

e $\dfrac{3}{x-1} + \dfrac{4}{x+4}$

f $\dfrac{7}{1-x} - \dfrac{8}{x+2}$

g $\dfrac{1}{x+1} + \dfrac{3}{x}$

h $\dfrac{5}{x} - \dfrac{2}{x+3}$

i $\dfrac{x}{x+2} + \dfrac{3}{x-4}$

j $2 + \dfrac{4}{x-3}$

k $\dfrac{3x}{x+2} - 1$

l $\dfrac{x}{x+3} + \dfrac{x-1}{x+2}$

m $\dfrac{2}{x(x+1)} + \dfrac{1}{x+1}$

n $\dfrac{1}{x-1} - \dfrac{1}{x} + \dfrac{1}{x+1}$

o $\dfrac{2}{x+1} - \dfrac{1}{x-1} + \dfrac{3}{x+2}$

p $\dfrac{x}{x-1} - \dfrac{1}{x} + \dfrac{x}{x+1}$

PROPERTIES OF ALGEBRAIC FRACTIONS

Writing expressions as a single fraction can help us to find when the expression is zero.

However, we need to be careful when we cancel common factors, as we can sometimes lose values when an expression is undefined.

Example 14   ◀》 **Self Tutor**

Write as a single fraction: **a** $\dfrac{3}{(x+2)(x-1)} + \dfrac{x}{x-1}$ **b** $\dfrac{-3}{(x+2)(x-1)} + \dfrac{x}{x-1}$

a
$$\dfrac{3}{(x+2)(x-1)} + \dfrac{x}{x-1}$$
$$= \dfrac{3}{(x+2)(x-1)} + \left(\dfrac{x}{x-1}\right)\left(\dfrac{x+2}{x+2}\right) \quad \{\text{LCD} = (x+2)(x-1)\}$$
$$= \dfrac{3 + x(x+2)}{(x+2)(x-1)}$$
$$= \dfrac{x^2 + 2x + 3}{(x+2)(x-1)} \quad \text{which we cannot simplify further.}$$

b $\dfrac{-3}{(x+2)(x-1)} + \dfrac{x}{x-1}$

$= \dfrac{-3}{(x+2)(x-1)} + \left(\dfrac{x}{x-1}\right)\left(\dfrac{x+2}{x+2}\right)$ $\{\text{LCD} = (x+2)(x-1)\}$

$= \dfrac{-3 + x(x+2)}{(x+2)(x-1)}$

$= \dfrac{x^2 + 2x - 3}{(x+2)(x-1)}$

$= \dfrac{(x+3)\cancel{(x-1)}^{\,1}}{(x+2)\cancel{(x-1)}^{\,1}}$

$= \dfrac{x+3}{x+2}$

> The expression is zero when $x = -3$. The expression is undefined when $x = -2$ and also when $x = 1$. We can see this from the original expression.

EXERCISE 12D.2

1   Write as a single fraction:

a $\dfrac{2}{x(x+1)} + \dfrac{1}{x+1}$ b $\dfrac{2}{x(x+1)} + \dfrac{x}{x+1}$ c $\dfrac{2x}{x-3} + \dfrac{4}{(x+2)(x-3)}$

d $\dfrac{2x}{x-3} - \dfrac{30}{(x+2)(x-3)}$ e $\dfrac{3}{(x-2)(x+3)} + \dfrac{x}{x+3}$ f $\dfrac{x}{x+3} - \dfrac{15}{(x-2)(x+3)}$

g $\dfrac{2x}{x+4} - \dfrac{40}{(x-1)(x+4)}$ h $\dfrac{x+5}{x-2} - \dfrac{63}{(x-2)(x+7)}$

2   a   Write $\dfrac{2}{(x+2)(x-3)} + \dfrac{2x}{x-3}$ as a single fraction.

   b   Hence, find x when $\dfrac{2}{(x+2)(x-3)} + \dfrac{2x}{x-3}$ is   i   undefined   ii   zero.

3   Simplify: a $\dfrac{\frac{x}{x-2} - 3}{x-3}$ b $\dfrac{\frac{3x}{x+4} - 1}{x-2}$ c $\dfrac{\frac{x^2}{x+2} - 1}{x+1}$

   d $\dfrac{\frac{x^2}{2-x} + 9}{x-3}$ e $\dfrac{\frac{1}{x^2} - \frac{1}{4}}{x-2}$ f $\dfrac{\frac{x-3}{x^2} - \frac{1}{16}}{x-4}$

REVIEW SET 12A

1   Simplify:

a $\dfrac{6x^2}{2x}$ b $6 \times \dfrac{n}{2}$ c $\dfrac{x}{2} \div 3$ d $\dfrac{8x}{(2x)^2}$

2   Simplify, if possible:

a $\dfrac{8}{4(c+3)}$ b $\dfrac{3x+8}{4}$ c $\dfrac{4x+8}{4}$ d $\dfrac{x(x+1)}{3(x+1)(x+2)}$

3   Write as a single fraction:

a $\dfrac{2x}{3} + \dfrac{3x}{5}$ b $\dfrac{2x}{3} \times \dfrac{3x}{5}$ c $\dfrac{2x}{3} \div \dfrac{3x}{5}$ d $\dfrac{2x}{3} - \dfrac{3x}{5}$

4 Simplify by factorisation:

a $\dfrac{4x+8}{x+2}$

b $\dfrac{5-10x}{2x-1}$

c $\dfrac{4x^2+6x}{2x+3}$

5 Write as a single fraction:

a $\dfrac{x+3}{4}+\dfrac{2x-2}{3}$

b $\dfrac{x-1}{7}-\dfrac{1-2x}{2}$

c $\dfrac{2}{x+2}+\dfrac{1}{x}$

6 Simplify by factorisation:

a $\dfrac{8-2x}{x^2-16}$

b $\dfrac{x^2+7x+12}{x^2+4x}$

c $\dfrac{2x^2-3x-2}{3x^2-4x-4}$

7 **a** Write $\dfrac{3x}{x-4}-\dfrac{60}{(x+1)(x-4)}$ as a single fraction.

  b Hence, find x when $\dfrac{3x}{x-4}-\dfrac{60}{(x+1)(x-4)}$ is **i** undefined **ii** zero.

REVIEW SET 12B

1 Simplify:

a $\dfrac{4a}{6a}$

b $\dfrac{x}{3}\times 6$

c $3\div\dfrac{1}{n}$

d $\dfrac{12x^2}{6x}$

2 Simplify, if possible:

a $\dfrac{3x+15}{5}$

b $\dfrac{3x+15}{3}$

c $\dfrac{2(a+4)}{(a+4)^2}$

d $\dfrac{abc}{2ac(b-a)}$

3 Write as a single fraction:

a $\dfrac{3x}{4}+2x$

b $\dfrac{3x}{4}-2x$

c $\dfrac{3x}{4}\times 2x$

d $\dfrac{3x}{4}\div 2x$

4 Simplify by factorisation:

a $\dfrac{3-x}{x-3}$

b $\dfrac{5x+10}{2x+4}$

c $\dfrac{3x^2-9x}{ax-3a}$

5 Write as a single fraction:

a $\dfrac{x}{5}+\dfrac{2x-1}{3}$

b $\dfrac{x}{6}-\dfrac{1+2x}{2}$

c $\dfrac{3}{2x}-\dfrac{1}{x+2}$

6 Simplify by factorisation:

a $\dfrac{2x^2-8}{x+2}$

b $\dfrac{x^2-5x-14}{x^2-4}$

c $\dfrac{3x^2-5x-2}{4x^2-7x-2}$

7 **a** Write $\dfrac{2x}{x+5}-\dfrac{70}{(x+5)(x-2)}$ as a single fraction.

  b Hence, find x when $\dfrac{2x}{x+5}-\dfrac{70}{(x+5)(x-2)}$ is **i** zero **ii** undefined.

8 Simplify: **a** $\dfrac{\frac{3x+7}{x-1}-13}{x-2}$ **b** $\dfrac{\frac{x^2}{3-x}-\frac{1}{2}}{x-1}$.

Chapter **13**

Formulae

Contents:

A **formula** is an equation which connects two or more variables.

For example, the formula $s = \dfrac{d}{t}$ relates the three variable quantities speed (s), distance travelled (d), and time taken (t).

The plural of formula is **formulae** or **formulas**.

We usually write formulae with one variable on its own on the left hand side. The other variable(s) and constants are written on the right hand side.

The variable on its own is called the **subject** of the formula.

 A   # FORMULA SUBSTITUTION

If a formula contains two or more variables and we know the value of all but one of them, we can **substitute** the known values into the formula and hence find the value of the unknown variable.

> *Step 1:*   Write down the formula.
> *Step 2:*   State the values of the known variables.
> *Step 3:*   Substitute into the formula to form a one variable equation.
> *Step 4:*   Solve the equation for the unknown variable.

Example 1   ◀) **Self Tutor**

When a stone is dropped from a cliff into the sea, the total distance fallen, D metres, is given by the formula $D = \frac{1}{2}gt^2$ where t is the time of fall in seconds and g is the gravitational constant of 9.8 m s^{-2}. Find:

a the distance fallen after 4 seconds

b the time (to the nearest $\frac{1}{100}$th second) taken for the stone to fall 200 metres.

---

a $D = \frac{1}{2}gt^2$ where $g = 9.8$ and $t = 4$

∴ $D = \frac{1}{2} \times 9.8 \times 4^2$ *Calculator:*

  $= 78.4$ $0.5 \boxed{\times} 9.8 \boxed{\times} 4 \boxed{x^2}$ $\boxed{\text{ENTER}}$

∴   the stone has fallen 78.4 metres.

b $D = \frac{1}{2}gt^2$ where $D = 200$ and $g = 9.8$

∴ $\frac{1}{2} \times 9.8 \times t^2 = 200$

∴ $4.9t^2 = 200$

∴ $t^2 = \dfrac{200}{4.9}$

∴ $t = \pm\sqrt{\dfrac{200}{4.9}}$ *Calculator:*

∴ $t \approx 6.39$ {as $t > 0$} $\boxed{\sqrt{}}$ 200 $\boxed{\div}$ 4.9 $\boxed{)}$ $\boxed{\text{ENTER}}$

∴   the time taken is about 6.39 seconds.

EXERCISE 13A

1   The formula for finding the circumference C of a circle with radius r is $C = 2\pi r$. Find:

   a   the circumference of a circle of radius 4.2 cm

   b   the radius of a circle with circumference 112 cm

   c   the diameter of a circle with circumference 400 metres.

2    When a stone is dropped from the top of a cliff, the total distance fallen is given by the formula $D = \frac{1}{2}gt^2$ where D is the distance in metres and t is the time taken in seconds. Given that $g = 9.8 \text{ m s}^{-2}$,   find:

   a   the total distance fallen in the first 2 seconds of fall

   b   the height of the cliff, to the nearest metre, if the stone takes 4.8 seconds to hit the ground.

3   When a car travels a distance d kilometres in time t hours, the average speed for the journey is given by the formula $s = \dfrac{d}{t} \text{ km h}^{-1}$.   Find:

   a   the average speed of a car which travels 250 km in $3\frac{1}{2}$ hours

   b   the distance travelled by a car in $2\frac{3}{4}$ hours if its average speed is 80 km h^{-1}

   c   the time taken, to the nearest minute, for a car to travel 790 km at an average speed of 95 km h^{-1}.

4   A circle's area A is given by $A = \pi r^2$ where r is the length of its radius. Find:

   a   the area of a circle of radius 6.4 cm

   b   the radius of a circular swimming pool which has an area of 160 m^2.

5   A cylinder of radius r and height h has volume given by $V = \pi r^2 h$.   Find:

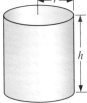

   a   the volume of a cylindrical tin can of radius 8 cm and height 21.2 cm

   b   the height of a cylinder of radius 6 cm and volume 120 cm^3

   c   the radius, in mm, of a copper pipe of volume 470 cm^3 and length 6 m.

6   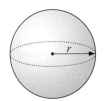 The formula for calculating the total surface area A of a sphere of radius r is $A = 4\pi r^2$. Find:

   a   the total surface area of a sphere of radius 7.5 cm

   b   the radius, in cm, of a spherical balloon which has a surface area of 2 m^2.

7   A sphere of radius r has volume given by $V = \frac{4}{3}\pi r^3$.   Find:

   a   the volume of a sphere of radius 2.37 m

   b   the radius of a sphere that has volume 2500 cm^3.

8 The formula $D = 3.56\sqrt{h}$ km gives the approximate distance to the horizon which can be seen by a person with eye level h metres above sea level. Find:

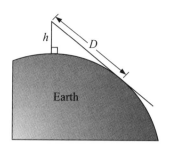

a the distance to the horizon when a person's eye level is 20 m above sea level

b how far above sea level a person's eye must be for the person to be able to see for 25 km.

9

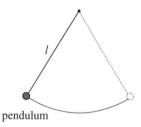

point of support

l

pendulum

The *period* or time taken for one complete swing of a simple pendulum is given approximately by $T = \frac{1}{5}\sqrt{l}$ seconds, where l is the length of the pendulum in cm. Find:

a the time for one complete swing of the pendulum if its length is 45 cm

b the length of a pendulum which has a period of 1.8 seconds.

INVESTIGATION   PIZZA PRICING

Luigi's Pizza Parlour has a 'Seafood Special' pizza advertised this week.

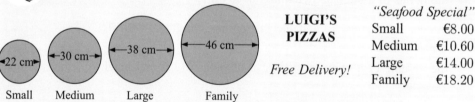

←22 cm→	←30 cm→	←38 cm→	←46 cm→
Small	Medium	Large	Family

LUIGI'S PIZZAS

Free Delivery!

"Seafood Special"
Small	€8.00
Medium	€10.60
Large	€14.00
Family	€18.20

Sasha, Enrico and Bianca decide to find Luigi's formula for determining his price €P for each size pizza. Letting r cm be the radius of a pizza, the formulae they worked out were:

Sasha: $P = \dfrac{17r - 27}{20}$ Enrico: $P = \sqrt{\dfrac{33r - 235}{2}}$ Bianca: $P = 5 + \dfrac{r^2}{40}$.

What to do:

1 Investigate the suitability of each formula.

2 Luigi is introducing a Party size pizza of diameter 54 cm. What do you think his price will be?

B   FORMULA REARRANGEMENT

In the formula $D = xt + p$, D is expressed in terms of the other variables, x, t and p. We therefore say that D is the **subject** of the formula.

We can rearrange formulae to make one of the other variables the subject. However, we must do this carefully to ensure the formulae are still true.

> We **rearrange** formulae using the same processes which we use to solve equations. Anything we do to one side we must also do to the other.

Example 2   ◄) Self Tutor

Make y the subject of $2x + 3y = 12$.

$$2x + 3y = 12$$
$$\therefore \quad 2x + 3y - 2x = 12 - 2x \qquad \{-2x \text{ from both sides}\}$$
$$\therefore \quad 3y = 12 - 2x$$
$$\therefore \quad \frac{3y}{3} = \frac{12 - 2x}{3} \qquad \{\div \text{ both sides by } 3\}$$
$$\therefore \quad y = \frac{12}{3} - \frac{2x}{3} = 4 - \tfrac{2}{3}x$$

Example 3   ◄) Self Tutor

Make y the subject of $x = 5 - cy$.

$$x = 5 - cy$$
$$\therefore \quad x + cy = 5 - cy + cy \qquad \{+cy \text{ to both sides}\}$$
$$\therefore \quad x + cy = 5$$
$$\therefore \quad x + cy - x = 5 - x \qquad \{-x \text{ from both sides}\}$$
$$\therefore \quad cy = 5 - x$$
$$\therefore \quad \frac{cy}{c} = \frac{5 - x}{c} \qquad \{\div \text{ both sides by } c\}$$
$$\therefore \quad y = \frac{5 - x}{c}$$

Example 4   ◄) Self Tutor

Make z the subject of $c = \dfrac{m}{z}$.

$$c = \frac{m}{z}$$
$$\therefore \quad c \times z = \frac{m}{z} \times z \qquad \{\times \text{ both sides by } z\}$$
$$\therefore \quad cz = m$$
$$\therefore \quad \frac{cz}{c} = \frac{m}{c} \qquad \{\div \text{ both sides by } c\}$$
$$\therefore \quad z = \frac{m}{c}$$

EXERCISE 13B.1

1 Make y the subject of:

a $2x+5y=10$ **b** $3x+4y=20$ **c** $2x-y=8$

d $2x+7y=14$ **e** $5x+2y=20$ **f** $2x-3y=-12$

2 Make x the subject of:

a $p+x=r$ **b** $xy=z$ **c** $3x+a=d$

d $5x+2y=d$ **e** $ax+by=p$ **f** $y=mx+c$

g $2+tx=s$ **h** $p+qx=m$ **i** $6=a+bx$

3 Make y the subject of:

a $mx-y=c$ **b** $c-2y=p$ **c** $a-3y=t$

d $n-ky=5$ **e** $a-by=n$ **f** $p=a-ny$

4 Make z the subject of:

a $az=\frac{b}{c}$ **b** $\frac{a}{z}=d$ **c** $\frac{3}{d}=\frac{2}{z}$

d $\frac{z}{2}=\frac{a}{z}$ **e** $\frac{b}{z}=\frac{z}{n}$ **f** $\frac{m}{z}=\frac{z}{a-b}$

5 Make:

a a the subject of $F=ma$ **b** r the subject of $C=2\pi r$

c d the subject of $V=ldh$ **d** K the subject of $A=\frac{b}{K}$

e h the subject of $A=\frac{bh}{2}$ **f** T the subject of $I=\frac{PRT}{100}$

REARRANGEMENT AND SUBSTITUTION

In the previous section on formula substitution, the variables were replaced by numbers and then the equation was solved. However, often we need to substitute several values for the unknowns and solve the equation for each case. In this situation it is quicker to **rearrange** the formula **before substituting**.

Example 5 **Self Tutor**

The circumference of a circle is given by $C=2\pi r$, where r is the circle's radius. Rearrange this formula to make r the subject, and hence find the radius when the circumference is: **a** 10 cm **b** 20 cm **c** 50 cm.

$2\pi r=C$, so $r=\frac{C}{2\pi}$.

a When $C=10$, $r=\frac{10}{2\pi}\approx 1.59$ $\therefore$ the radius is about 1.59 cm.

b When $C=20$, $r=\frac{20}{2\pi}\approx 3.18$ $\therefore$ the radius is about 3.18 cm.

c When $C=50$, $r=\frac{50}{2\pi}\approx 7.96$ $\therefore$ the radius is about 7.96 cm.

EXERCISE 13B.2

1   The equation of a straight line is $5x + 3y = 18$.

Rearrange this formula into the form $y = mx + c$.

Hence, state the value of: **a**   the slope m **b**   the y-intercept c.

2   **a**   Make a the subject of the formula $K = \dfrac{d^2}{2ab}$.

b   Find the value of a when:

i $K = 112$, $d = 24$, $b = 2$ **ii** $K = 400$, $d = 72$, $b = 0.4$.

3   When a car travels a distance d kilometres in time t hours, the average speed s for the journey is given by the formula $s = \dfrac{d}{t}$ km h^{-1}.

a   Make d the subject of the formula. Hence find the distance travelled by a car if:

i   the average speed is 60 km h^{-1} and the time travelled is 3 hours

ii   the average speed is 80 km h^{-1} and the time travelled is $1\frac{1}{2}$ hours

iii   the average speed is 95 km h^{-1} and the time travelled is 1 h 20 min.

b   Make t the subject of the formula. Hence find the time required for a car to travel:

i   180 km at an average speed of 60 km h^{-1}

ii   140 km at an average speed of 35 km h^{-1}

iii   220 km at an average speed of 100 km h^{-1}.

4   The simple interest $\$I$ paid on an investment of $\$C$ is determined by the annual rate of interest r (as a decimal) and the duration of the investment, n years. The interest is given by the formula $I = C \times r \times n$.

a   Make n the subject of the formula.

b   **i**   Find the time required to generate \$1050 interest on an investment of \$6400 at an interest rate of 8% per annum.

ii   Find the time required for an investment of \$1000 to double at an interest rate of 10% per annum.

 FORMULA CONSTRUCTION

Formulae are often constructed by the generalisation of numerical observations. To construct a formula, we can reduce the problem to a specific numerical situation to understand it, and then generalise the result.

For example,   the perimeter of the rectangle is given by

$$P = 3 + 6 + 3 + 6 \text{ metres}$$
$$\therefore \quad P = (2 \times 3) + (2 \times 6) \text{ metres}$$
$$\therefore \quad P \text{ is double the width plus double the length.}$$

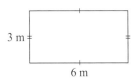

Thus, in general, $P = 2a + 2b$

or $P = 2(a + b)$.

Example 6   ◀) **Self Tutor**

Write the formula for the total cost RM C of a taxi trip given a fixed charge of:
- **a** RM 3 and RM 0.55 per km for 12 km
- **b** RM 3 and RM 0.55 per km for k km   **c** RM 3 and RM d per km for k km
- **d** RM F and RM d per km for k km

a $C = 3 + (0.55 \times 12)$	**b** $C = 3 + (0.55 \times k)$
	$\therefore$ $C = 3 + 0.55k$
c $C = 3 + d \times k$	**d** $C = F + dk$
$\therefore$ $C = 3 + dk$	

Example 7   ◀) **Self Tutor**

Write a formula for the amount $A in a person's bank account if initially the balance was:
- **a** $5000, and $200 was withdrawn each week for 10 weeks
- **b** $5000, and $200 was withdrawn each week for w weeks
- **c** $5000, and x was withdrawn each week for w weeks
- **d** $B, and x was withdrawn each week for w weeks.

a $A = 5000 - 200 \times 10$	**b** $A = 5000 - 200 \times w$
	$\therefore$ $A = 5000 - 200w$
c $A = 5000 - x \times w$	**d** $A = B - x \times w$
$\therefore$ $A = 5000 - xw$	$\therefore$ $A = B - xw$

EXERCISE 13C

1 Write a formula for the amount €A in a new savings account given monthly deposits of:
- **a** €200 over 17 months   **b** €200 over m months   **c** €D over m months

2 Write a formula for the amount $A in a bank account if the initial balance was:
- **a** $2000, and then $150 was deposited each week for 8 weeks
- **b** $2000, and then $150 was deposited each week for w weeks
- **c** $2000, and then d was deposited each week for w weeks
- **d** $P, and then d was deposited each week for w weeks.

3 Write a formula for the total cost £C of hiring a plumber given a fixed call out fee of:
- **a** £40 plus £60 per hour for 5 hours of work
- **b** £40 plus £60 per hour for t hours of work
- **c** £40 plus £x per hour for t hours of work
- **d** £F plus £x per hour for t hours of work.

4 Write a formula for the amount €A in Leon's wallet if initially he had:

    a €200, and he bought 8 presents costing €5 each

    b €200, and he bought x presents costing €5 each

    c €200, and he bought x presents costing €b each

    d €P, and he bought x presents costing €b each.

5 Write a formula for the capacity, C litres, of a tank if initially the tank held:

    a 5000 litres, and 10 litres per minute for 200 minutes ran out through a tap

    b 5000 litres, and r litres per minute for 200 minutes ran out through a tap

    c 5000 litres, and r litres per minute for m minutes ran out through a tap

    d L litres, and r litres per minute for m minutes ran out through the tap.

6 The volume of an object of uniform cross-section is given by

$$V = \text{area of end} \times \text{length}.$$

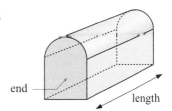

Find formulae for the volume V of the following objects using the above rule:

    a   **b**   **c**

 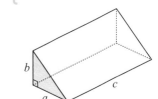

7 The total **surface area** A of a solid can be found by adding the areas of each of its faces and curved surfaces. Find, giving reasons for your answer, a formula for the total surface area of:

    a   **b**   **c**

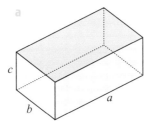 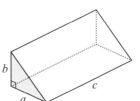 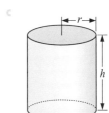

8 Show that the volume of concrete used to make a cylindrical pipe of outside radius R, inside radius r, and length l, is given by

$$V = \pi l (R + r)(R - r).$$

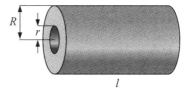

D   FORMULAE BY INDUCTION

Induction is the method of determining a formula for a general situation by first looking at the simplest cases where $n = 1, 2, 3, 4, \ldots$

Consider the set of even numbers: 2, 4, 6, 8, 10, 12, ...

Notice that: $2 = 2 \times 1$ is the 1st even number

$4 = 2 \times 2$ is the 2nd even number

$6 = 2 \times 3$ is the 3rd even number

$8 = 2 \times 4$ is the 4th even number, and so on.

We see from this pattern that   the 10th   even number is 2×10,   which is 20

and   the 37th   even number is 2×37,   which is 74.

We **generalise** by saying that: the nth   even number is $2 \times n$,   which is $2n$.

Example 8   ◀)) **Self Tutor**

Examine the following figures made from matches:

1st: ☐   can be constructed from 4 matches.

2nd: ☐☐   can be constructed from 7 matches.

3rd: ☐☐☐   can be constructed from 10 matches.

Find the number of matches M required to make the:

a   8th figure   b nth figure.

---

a   1st $4 = 1 + 1 \times 3$ $| + \sqsupset$

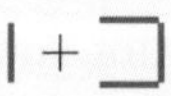

2nd $7 = 1 + 2 \times 3$ $| + \sqsupset + \sqsupset$

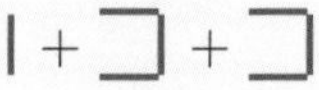

3rd $10 = 1 + 3 \times 3$ $| + \sqsupset + \sqsupset + \sqsupset$

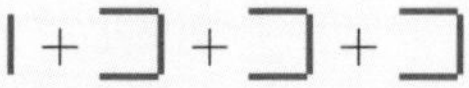

⋮

8th $M = 1 + 8 \times 3 = 25$ matches

b $M = 1 + n \times 3$ {continuing the pattern}

∴ $M = 1 + 3n$ matches

EXERCISE 13D

1   Consider the matchstick pattern: △,   △▽,   △▽△ , ...

Find the number of matchsticks M required to make the:

a   1st, 2nd and 3rd figures   b   4th and 5th figures

c   10th figure   d nth figure.

2 Consider the pattern:
$$2 + 4 = 6 = 2 \times 3$$
$$2 + 4 + 6 = 12 = 3 \times 4$$
$$2 + 4 + 6 + 8 = 20 = 4 \times 5$$

  a Continue the pattern for 3 more cases.

  b Use **a** to predict a formula for $2 + 4 + 6 + 8 + \ldots\ldots + 2n$.

  c Use **b** to predict a formula for $1 + 2 + 3 + 4 + \ldots\ldots + n$.

  d What is the sum of the first 200 positive integers?

3 For the following matchstick pattern, find the number of matches M required to make the:

  a 4th and 5th figures   **b** 20th figure   **c** nth figure.

4 Consider the pattern:
$$1 = 1 = 1^2$$
$$1 + 3 = 4 = 2^2$$
$$1 + 3 + 5 = 9 = 3^2$$

  a Continue the pattern for 3 more cases.

  b Predict the value of $1 + 3 + 5 + 7 + 9 + \ldots\ldots + 99$.

  c The 1st odd number is 1.
    The 2nd odd number is 3.
    The 3rd odd number is 5.
    What is the nth odd number?

  d Write down an expression for the sum of the first n odd numbers starting $1 + 3 + 5 + \ldots\ldots$

  e Write down a formula for adding the first n odd numbers using **d** and your discoveries in **a** and **b**.

5 For the following matchstick pattern, find the number of matches M required to make the:

  a 8th figure   **b** nth figure.

6 Consider the pattern:
$$S_1 = \frac{1}{1 \times 2}, \quad S_2 = \frac{1}{1 \times 2} + \frac{1}{2 \times 3}, \quad S_3 = \frac{1}{1 \times 2} + \frac{1}{2 \times 3} + \frac{1}{3 \times 4}, \quad \ldots\ldots$$

  a Find the values of S_1, S_2, S_3, and S_4.

  b Write down the value of: **i** S_{10} **ii** S_n.

7 Consider the pattern: $S_1 = 1^2$, $S_2 = 1^2 + 2^2$, $S_3 = 1^2 + 2^2 + 3^2$, ...

  a Check that the formula $S_n = \dfrac{n(n+1)(2n+1)}{6}$ is correct for $n = 1, 2, 3$ and 4.

  b Assuming the formula in **a** is always true, find the sum of $1^2 + 2^2 + 3^2 + 4^2 + 5^2 + \ldots\ldots + 100^2$, which is the sum of the squares of the first one hundred integers.

8 Consider the pattern: $N_1 = 1^3$, $N_2 = 1^3 + 2^3$, $N_3 = 1^3 + 2^3 + 3^3$, ...

  a Verify that the formula $N_n = \dfrac{n^2(n+1)^2}{4}$ is correct for $n = 1, 2, 3$, and 4.

  b Use the above formula to find the sum of $1^3 + 2^3 + 3^3 + 4^3 + ... + 50^3$,   which is the sum of the first 50 perfect cubes.

  c Find the sum: $2^3 + 4^3 + 6^3 + 8^3 + ... + 100^3$.

E   MORE DIFFICULT REARRANGEMENTS

Example 9   ◀)) Self Tutor

Make x the subject of $ax + 3 = bx + d$.

$$ax + 3 = bx + d$$
$$\therefore \quad ax + 3 - bx - 3 = bx + d - bx - 3 \qquad \text{\{subtract } bx \text{ and 3 from both sides\}}$$
$$\therefore \quad ax - bx = d - 3 \qquad \text{\{write terms containing } x \text{ on LHS\}}$$
$$\therefore \quad x(a - b) = d - 3 \qquad \text{\{} x \text{ is a common factor on LHS\}}$$
$$\therefore \quad \frac{x(a - b)}{(a - b)} = \frac{d - 3}{(a - b)} \qquad \text{\{divide both sides by } (a - b)\text{\}}$$
$$\therefore \quad x = \frac{d - 3}{a - b}$$

Example 10   ◀)) Self Tutor

Make t the subject of $s = \frac{1}{2}gt^2$ where $t > 0$.

$$\tfrac{1}{2}gt^2 = s \qquad \text{\{rewrite with } t^2 \text{ on LHS\}}$$
$$\therefore \quad gt^2 = 2s \qquad \text{\{multiply both sides by 2\}}$$
$$\therefore \quad t^2 = \frac{2s}{g} \qquad \text{\{divide both sides by } g\text{\}}$$
$$\therefore \quad t = \sqrt{\frac{2s}{g}} \qquad \text{\{as } t > 0\text{\}}$$

Example 11   ◀)) Self Tutor

Make x the subject of $T = \dfrac{a}{\sqrt{x}}$.

$$T = \frac{a}{\sqrt{x}}$$
$$\therefore \quad T^2 = \left(\frac{a}{\sqrt{x}}\right)^2 \qquad \text{\{square both sides\}}$$
$$\therefore \quad T^2 = \frac{a^2}{x}$$
$$\therefore \quad T^2 x = a^2 \qquad \text{\{multiply both sides by } x\text{\}}$$
$$\therefore \quad x = \frac{a^2}{T^2} \qquad \text{\{divide both sides by } T^2\text{\}}$$

Example 12 ◀) **Self Tutor**

Make x the subject of $T = \dfrac{a}{x-b}$.

$$T = \dfrac{a}{x-b}$$

$\therefore \quad T(x-b) = a$ {multiply both sides by $(x-b)$}

$\therefore \quad Tx - Tb = a$

$\therefore \quad Tx = a + Tb$ {write term containing x on LHS}

$\therefore \quad x = \dfrac{a+Tb}{T}$ {divide both sides by T}

Example 13 ◀) **Self Tutor**

Make x the subject of $y = \dfrac{3x+2}{x-1}$.

$$y = \dfrac{3x+2}{x-1}$$

$\therefore \quad y(x-1) = 3x+2$ {multiply both sides by $(x-1)$}

$\therefore \quad xy - y = 3x + 2$

$\therefore \quad xy - 3x = y + 2$ {write terms containing x on LHS}

$\therefore \quad x(y-3) = y + 2$ {x is a common factor}

$\therefore \quad x = \dfrac{y+2}{y-3}$

EXERCISE 13E

1 Make x the subject of:

  a $3x + a = bx + c$ **b** $ax = c - bx$ **c** $mx + a = nx - 2$

  d $8x + a = -bx$ **e** $a - x = b - cx$ **f** $rx + d = e - sx$

2 Make:

  a r the subject of $A = \pi r^2$, $r > 0$ **b** x the subject of $N = \dfrac{x^5}{a}$

  c r the subject of $V = \frac{4}{3}\pi r^3$ **d** x the subject of $D = \dfrac{n}{x^3}$

  e x the subject of $y = 4x^2 - 7$ **f** Q the subject of $P^2 = Q^2 + R^2$

3 Make:

  a a the subject of $d = \dfrac{\sqrt{a}}{n}$ **b** l the subject of $T = \frac{1}{5}\sqrt{l}$

  c a the subject of $c = \sqrt{a^2 - b^2}$ **d** d the subject of $\dfrac{k}{a} = \dfrac{5}{\sqrt{d}}$

    e l the subject of $T = 2\pi\sqrt{\dfrac{l}{g}}$ **f** b the subject of $A = 4\sqrt{\dfrac{a}{b}}$

4 Make:

    a a the subject of $P = 2(a + b)$ **b** h the subject of $A = \pi r^2 + 2\pi rh$

    c r the subject of $I = \dfrac{E}{R + r}$ **d** q the subject of $A = \dfrac{B}{p - q}$

    e x the subject of $A = \dfrac{3}{2x + y}$

    f y the subject of $M = \dfrac{4}{x^2 + y^2},\;\; y > 0$

5 Make x the subject of:

    a $y = \dfrac{x}{x + 1}$ **b** $y = \dfrac{x - 3}{x + 2}$ **c** $y = \dfrac{3x - 1}{x + 3}$

    d $y = \dfrac{5x - 2}{x - 1}$ **e** $y = \dfrac{4x - 1}{2 - x}$ **f** $y = \dfrac{3x + 7}{3 - 2x}$

    g $y = 1 + \dfrac{2}{x - 3}$ **h** $y = -2 + \dfrac{5}{x + 4}$ **i** $y = -3 - \dfrac{6}{x - 2}$

6 The formula for determining the volume V of a sphere of radius r is $V = \frac{4}{3}\pi r^3$.

    a Make r the subject of the formula.

    b Find the radius of a sphere which has volume:

        i 40 cm^3 **ii** 1 000 000 cm^3.

7 The distance S travelled by an object accelerating from a stationary position is given by the formula $S = \frac{1}{2}at^2$ cm where a is the acceleration in cm s^{-2} and t is the time in seconds.

    a Make t the subject of the formula, assuming $t > 0$.

    b Find the time taken for an object which starts at rest and accelerates at 8 cm s^{-2} to travel a distance of:

        i 40 cm   **ii** 10 m.

8 According to Einstein's theory of relativity, the mass of a particle is given by the formula $m = \dfrac{m_0}{\sqrt{1 - \left(\dfrac{v}{c}\right)^2}}$ where m_0 is the mass of the particle at rest,

                                                      v is the speed of the particle, and

                                                      c is the speed of light.

    a Make v the subject of the formula.

    b Find the speed necessary to increase the mass of a particle to three times its rest mass, i.e., so that $m = 3m_0$. Give the value for v as a fraction of c.

    c A cyclotron increased the mass of an electron to $30m_0$. At what speed was the electron travelling, given that $c \approx 3 \times 10^8$ m s^{-1}?

LINKS
click here

HOW MUCH DO WE HAVE LEFT?

Areas of interaction:
Human ingenuity

REVIEW SET 13A

1 The formula for the density D of a substance with mass M and volume V is $D = \dfrac{M}{V}$.

    a Find the density of lead if 350 g of lead occupies 30.7 cm^3.

    b Find the mass of a lump of uranium with density 18.97 g cm^{-3} and volume 2 cm^3.

    c Find the volume of a piece of pine timber with mass 6 kg and density 0.65 g cm^{-3}

2 The period of a pendulum (the time for one complete swing) is approximately given by $T = \frac{1}{5}\sqrt{l}$ seconds, where l is the length of the pendulum in cm. Find:

    a the period if the pendulum has length 74 cm

    b the length of the pendulum if its period is 2.5 seconds.

3 Make x the subject of the formula: **a** $mx + c = y$ **b** $ax = \dfrac{2}{x}$.

4   **a** Write a formula for the volume of water V in a trough if it is empty initially, then:

      i six 8-litre buckets of water are poured into it

      ii n 8-litre buckets of water are poured into it

      iii n l-litre buckets of water are poured into it.

    b Write a formula for the volume of water V in a trough that initially contained 25 litres if n buckets of water, each containing l litres, are poured into it.

5 For the following matchstick pattern, find the number of matches M required to make the: **a** 10th figure   **b** nth figure.

6 Make p the subject of the formula: **a** $r = \dfrac{p+q}{3}$ **b** $y = \sqrt{p^3 + 3}$.

7 Make x the subject of the formula $y = \dfrac{2x - 3}{x - 2}$.

8   **a** Consider the sequence of consecutive odd numbers, 1, 3, 5, 7, ...
Write down:

      i the next three terms   **ii** a formula for the nth term

    b Consider the pattern: $T_1 = \dfrac{1}{1 \times 3}$, $T_2 = \dfrac{1}{3 \times 5}$, $T_3 = \dfrac{1}{5 \times 7}$, ...

    Write down an expression for: **i** T_4, T_5, T_6 **ii** T_{20} **iii** T_n.

REVIEW SET 13B

1 The volume of a cylinder is given by the formula $V = \pi r^2 h$, where r is its radius and h is its height. Find:

a the volume, in cm^3, of a cylinder of height 23 cm and base radius 10 cm

b the height of a cylinder of base radius 12 m and volume 426.4 m^3.

2 Make x the subject of the formula: **a** $y = 3q - 2x$ **b** $3y = \dfrac{4}{x}$

3 Write a formula for the total cost $£C$ of packing parcels of books for dispatch if there is a charge of:

a £2 per parcel plus £1.20 for one book

b £2 per parcel plus £1.20 per book for 5 books

c £p per parcel plus £1.20 per book for b books

d £p per parcel plus £x per book for b books.

4 The equation of a straight line is $2x - 3y = 4$.
Rearrange this formula into the form $y = mx + c$.
Hence, state the value of the   **a** slope m **b** y-intercept c.

5 For the following matchstick pattern, find the number of matches M required to make the:

a 8th figure   **b** nth figure.

6 Make y the subject of the formula $\dfrac{x}{2} = \dfrac{4}{\sqrt{y}}$.

7 The formula for calculating the surface area A of a sphere of radius r is $A = 4\pi r^2$.

a Make r the subject of the formula.

b Find the radius of a sphere whose surface area is 1.5 m^2.

8 Make b the subject of the formula $\dfrac{1}{a} = \dfrac{1}{b} + \dfrac{1}{c}$.

Chapter 14

Relations, functions and sequences

Contents:

OPENING PROBLEM

A piece of paper measures 30 cm by 21 cm. If squares of equal size are cut from its corners, the shape remaining can be formed into an open box.

Things to think about:

1 If 3 cm squares are removed, what is the box's
   a height   **b** length   **c** width   **d** capacity?

2 If 5 cm squares are removed, what is the box's
   a height   **b** length   **c** width   **d** capacity?

3 Does the capacity of the box depend on the size of the squares removed?

4 Is there a formula which allows us to connect the capacity of the box with the side length x cm of the cut out squares?

5 If such a formula exists, how can it be used to answer questions like:
   "What size squares should be removed to create the box of maximum capacity?"

A | RELATIONS AND FUNCTIONS

Sue-Ellen wants to send a parcel to a friend. The cost of posting the parcel a fixed distance will depend on its weight. So, cost is the *dependent* variable and weight is the *independent* variable.

The table alongside shows the costs of posting parcels of various weights from Sue-Ellen to her friend.

For example, the table shows that it will cost $8.00 to post a parcel weighing at least 2 kg but less than 5 kg. It will therefore cost $8.00 to post a parcel weighing 2 kg or 3.6 kg or 4.955 kg.

We can illustrate the postal charges on a graph.

Postal Charges	
Weight w kg	Cost $\$C$
1 kg $\leqslant w <$ 2 kg	$5.00
2 kg $\leqslant w <$ 5 kg	$8.00
5 kg $\leqslant w <$ 10 kg	$12.00
10 kg $\leqslant w <$ 15 kg	$16.00
15 kg $\leqslant w \leqslant$ 20 kg	$20.00

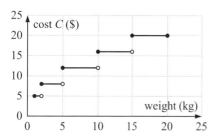

An end point that is included has a filled in circle.

An end point that is not included has an open circle.

We can say that there is a *relationship* between the variables weight and cost, so the table of costs is an example of a **relation**.

A relation may be a finite number of ordered pairs, for example   {(2, 8), (3, 8), (4, 8), (5, 12)},   or an infinite number of ordered pairs such as the relation between the variables weight and cost in the postal charges example above.

The table of postal charges shows weights of parcels of 1 kg up to and including 20 kg, so we can write $1 \leqslant w \leqslant 20$. This set of possible values of the independent variable is called the **domain** of the relation, so in this case the domain is $\{w \mid 1 \leqslant w \leqslant 20\}$.

The costs for posting the parcels are $5, $8, $12, $16 and $20. This set of possible values of the dependent variable is called the **range** of the relation, so in this case the range is $\{5, 8, 12, 16, 20\}$.

We will now look at relations and functions more formally.

RELATIONS

A **relation** is any set of points on the Cartesian plane.

The following are examples of relations:

(1) The set of 8 points represented by the dots is a relation.

There is no equation connecting the variables x and y in this case.

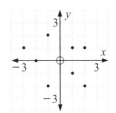

(2) The set of all points on and within the illustrated square is a relation.

It could be specified by
$\{(x, y) \mid -1 \leqslant x \leqslant 0, \quad 0 \leqslant y \leqslant 1\}$

(3) The set of all points on this parabola is a relation. It can be specified by an equation connecting all points (x, y) lying on the curve
$y = -x^2 + 6x - 5.$

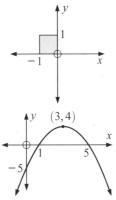

DOMAIN AND RANGE

The **domain** of a relation is the set of possible values that x may have.
The **range** of a relation is the set of possible values that y may have.

The domain and range of a relation are often described using **interval notation**.

For example, consider the line segment from $(1, 3)$ to $(5, -2)$:

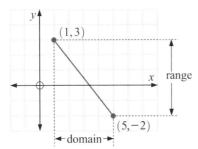

The domain consists of all real x such that $1 \leqslant x \leqslant 5$ and we write this as

$$\{x \mid 1 \leqslant x \leqslant 5\}.$$

the set of all $\quad$ such that

The range is $\{y \mid -2 \leqslant y \leqslant 3\}$.

For numbers *between* a and b we write $a < x < b$.

For numbers '*outside*' a and b we write $x < a$ or $x > b$.

would be written as $a \leqslant x < b$.

A filled in circle indicates the inclusion of the end point.
An open circle indicates the non-inclusion of that point.

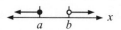

In **(1)** on the previous page, the domain is $\{-3, -2, -1, 1, 2\}$
and the range is $\{-2, -1, 0, 1, 2\}$.

In **(2)**,   the domain is $\{x \mid -1 \leqslant x \leqslant 0\}$ and the range is $\{y \mid 0 \leqslant y \leqslant 1\}$.

In **(3)**,   the domain is $\{x \mid x \in \mathbb{R}\}$ as x can take any real value, and
the range is $\{y \mid y \leqslant 4\}$ as the greatest value of y is 4 and y
values could be very large and negative.

Further examples are:

(4) All values of $x < 2$ are possible.
$\therefore$ the domain is $\{x \mid x < 2\}$.
All values of $y > -1$ are possible.
$\therefore$ the range is $\{y \mid y > -1\}$.

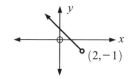

(5) x can take any value.
$\therefore$ the domain is $\{x \mid x \in \mathbb{R}\}$.
y cannot be < -2
$\therefore$ range is $\{y \mid y \geqslant -2\}$.

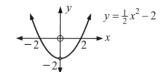

(6) x can take all values except $x = 0$.
$\therefore$ the domain is $\{x \mid x \neq 0\}$.
y can take all values except $y = 0$.
$\therefore$ the range is $\{y \mid y \neq 0\}$.

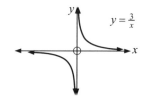

Example 1   ◀) **Self Tutor**

For each of the following graphs, state the domain and range:

a 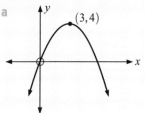   b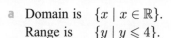

$\mathbb{R}$ represents the set of all real numbers, or all numbers on the number line.

a Domain is $\{x \mid x \in \mathbb{R}\}$.
   Range is $\{y \mid y \leqslant 4\}$.

b Domain is $\{x \mid x \geqslant -4\}$.
   Range is $\{y \mid y \geqslant -4\}$.

EXERCISE 14A

1 State the domain and range of these relations:

a $\{(-1, 5), (-2, 3), (0, 4), (-3, 8), (6, -1), (-2, 3)\}$

b $\{(5, 4), (-3, 4), (4, 3), (2, 4), (-1, 3), (0, 3), (7, 4)\}$.

2 For each of the following graphs, find the domain and range:

a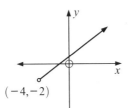

b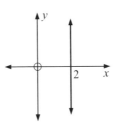

c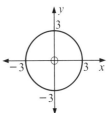

d

e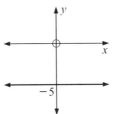

f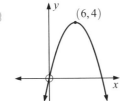

g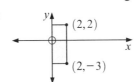

h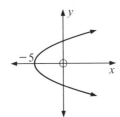

i

3 State the domain and range of:

a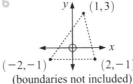

b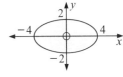

(boundaries not included)

c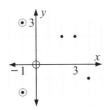

B FUNCTIONS

A **function** is a relation in which no two different ordered pairs have the same first member.

So, $\{(-1, 3), (2, 2), (-1, -2), (3, 2), (4, -1)\}$ is not a function.

different ordered pairs
with same first member.

GEOMETRIC TEST FOR FUNCTIONS: "VERTICAL LINE TEST"

If we draw all possible vertical lines on the graph of a relation:

- the relation is a function if each line cuts the graph no more than once
- the relation is *not* a function if *any* line cuts the graph more than once.

Example 2	◀) **Self Tutor**

Which of these relations are functions?

a 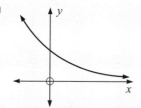 b 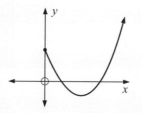 c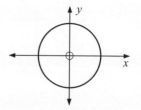

a Every vertical line we could draw cuts the graph only once.
∴ we have a function.

b Every vertical line we could draw cuts the graph at most once.
∴ we have a function.

c This vertical line cuts the graph twice. So, the relation is not a function.

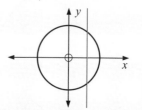

EXERCISE 14B

1 Which of the following sets of ordered pairs are functions? Give reasons for your answers.

a (1, 1), (2, 2), (3, 3), (4, 4)
b (−1, 2), (−3, 2), (3, 2), (1, 2)
c (2, 5), (−1, 4), (−3, 7), (2, −3)
d (3, −2), (3, 0), (3, 2), (3, 4)
e (−7, 0), (−5, 0), (−3, 0), (−1, 0)
f (0, 5), (0, 1), (2, 1), (2, −5)

2 Use the vertical line test to determine which of the following relations are functions:

a 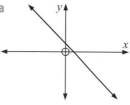 b 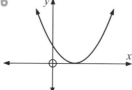 c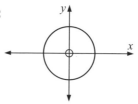

d 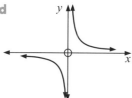 e 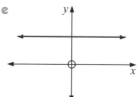 f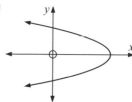

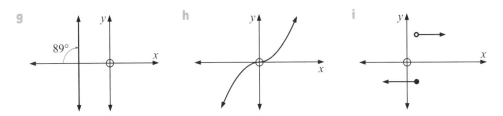

g 89°

h

i

3 Will the graph of a straight line always be a function? Give evidence.

C FUNCTION NOTATION

We sometimes use a 'function machine' to illustrate how functions behave.

For example:

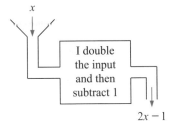

I double the input and then subtract 1

$2x - 1$

So, if 3 is fed into the machine, $2(3) - 1 = 5$ comes out.

The above 'machine' has been programmed to perform a particular function.

If f is used to represent that particular function we can write:

f is the function that will convert x into $2x - 1$.

So, f would convert 2 into $2(2) - 1 = 3$ and
-4 into $2(-4) - 1 = -9$.

This function can be written as: $f : x \mapsto 2x - 1$

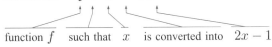

function f such that x is converted into $2x - 1$

Another way to write this function is: $f(x) = 2x - 1$

If $f(x)$ is the value of y for a given value of x, then $y = f(x)$.

Notice that for $f(x) = 2x - 1$, $f(2) = 2(2) - 1 = 3$ and
$f(-4) = 2(-4) - 1 = -9$.

Consequently, $f(2) = 3$ indicates that the point $(2, 3)$ lies on the graph of the function.

Likewise, $f(-4) = -9$ indicates that the point $(-4, -9)$ also lies on the graph.

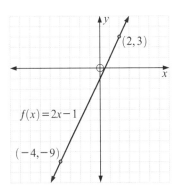

$f(x) = 2x - 1$

$(2, 3)$

$(-4, -9)$

Note: • $f(x)$ is read as "f of x" and is the value of the function at any value of x.

  • f is the function which converts x into $f(x)$,   i.e., $f : x \mapsto f(x)$.

  • $f(x)$ is sometimes called the **image** of x.

Example 3 ◀⑨ **Self Tutor**

If $f : x \mapsto 3x^2 - 4x$,   find the value of: **a** $f(2)$ **b** $f(-5)$

$f(x) = 3x^2 - 4x$

a $f(2) = 3(2)^2 - 4(2)$ {replacing x by (2)}
    $= 3 \times 4 - 8$
    $= 4$

b $f(-5) = 3(-5)^2 - 4(-5)$ {replacing x by (-5)}
    $= 3(25) + 20$
    $= 95$

Example 4 ◀⑨ **Self Tutor**

If $f(x) = 4 - 3x - x^2$,   find in simplest form: **a** $f(-x)$ **b** $f(x+2)$

a $f(-x) = 4 - 3(-x) - (-x)^2$ {replacing x by $(-x)$}
    $= 4 + 3x - x^2$

b $f(x+2) = 4 - 3(x+2) - (x+2)^2$ {replacing x by $(x+2)$}
    $= 4 - 3x - 6 - [x^2 + 4x + 4]$
    $= -2 - 3x - x^2 - 4x - 4$
    $= -x^2 - 7x - 6$

EXERCISE 14C.1

1 If $f : x \mapsto 2x + 3$,   find the value of:

  a $f(0)$ **b** $f(2)$ **c** $f(-1)$ **d** $f(-5)$ **e** $f(-\frac{1}{2})$

2 If $g : x \mapsto x + \dfrac{2}{x}$,   find the value of:

  a $g(1)$ **b** $g(4)$ **c** $g(-1)$ **d** $g(-4)$ **e** $g(-\frac{1}{2})$

3 If $f : x \mapsto 2x^2 - 3x + 2$,   find the value of:

  a $f(0)$ **b** $f(3)$ **c** $f(-3)$ **d** $f(-7)$ **e** $f(\frac{1}{2})$

4 If $f(x) = 5 - 2x$,   find in simplest form:

  a $f(a)$ **b** $f(-a)$ **c** $f(a+1)$ **d** $f(x-3)$ **e** $f(2x)$

5 If $P(x) = x^2 + 4x - 3$, find in simplest form:

    a $P(x + 2)$ **b** $P(1 - x)$ **c** $P(-x)$ **d** $P(x^2)$ **e** $P(x^2 + 1)$

6 If $R(x) = \dfrac{2x - 3}{x + 2}$:   **a** evaluate **i** $R(0)$ **ii** $R(1)$ **iii** $R(-\frac{1}{2})$

    b find a value of x where $R(x)$ does not exist

    c find $R(x - 2)$ in simplest form

    d find x if $R(x) = -5$.

7 If the value of a car t years after purchase is given by $V(t) = 28\,000 - 4000t$ dollars:

    a find $V(4)$ and state what this value means

    b find t when $V(t) = 8000$ and explain what this represents

    c find the original purchase price of the car.

THE DOMAIN OF A FUNCTION

To find the domain of a function, we need to consider what values of the variable make the function undefined.

For example, notice that for:

- $f(x) = \sqrt{x}$, the domain is $\{x \mid x \geqslant 0,\ x \in \mathbb{R}\}$ since $\sqrt{x}$ has meaning only when $x \geqslant 0$.

- $f(x) = \dfrac{1}{\sqrt{x - 1}}$, the domain is $\{x \mid x > 1,\ x \in \mathbb{R}\}$ since, when $x - 1 = 0$ we are 'dividing by zero', and when $x - 1 < 0$, $\sqrt{x - 1}$ is undefined as we can't find the square root of a negative in the real number system.

EXERCISE 14C.2

1 Find the domain of the following:

    a $f(x) = \sqrt{x - 2}$ **b** $f(x) = \sqrt{3 - x}$ **c** $f(x) = \sqrt{x} + \sqrt{2 - x}$

    d $f(x) = \dfrac{1}{\sqrt{x}}$ **e** $f(x) = \dfrac{1}{\sqrt{x}} + \dfrac{1}{\sqrt{x + 2}}$ **f** $f(x) = \dfrac{1}{x\sqrt{4 - x}}$

GRAPHING PACKAGE

2 Check each of your answers to **1** using the graphing package.

INVESTIGATION 1   **FLUID FILLING FUNCTIONS**

When water is added to a container, the depth of water is given by a function of time. If the water is added at a *constant rate*, the volume of water added is directly proportional to the time taken to add it.

DEMO

So, for a container with a uniform cross-section, the graph of depth against time is a straight line, or *linear*. We can see this in the following depth-time graph:

The question arises:
'How does the shape of the container affect the appearance of the graph?'

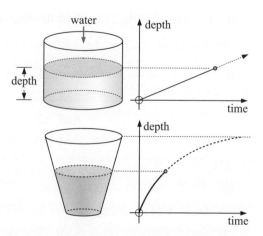

For example, consider the graph shown for a vase of conical shape.

What to do:

1   For each of the following containers, draw a depth-time graph as water is added at a constant rate.

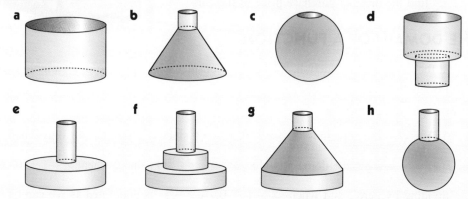

2   Use the water filling demonstration to check your answers to question **1**.

D   COMPOSITE FUNCTIONS

Sometimes functions are built up in two or more stages.

For example, consider the function $F(x) = \sqrt{2x - 3}$.

If we let $g(x) = 2x - 3$ then $F(x) = \sqrt{g(x)}$.

If we then let $f(x) = \sqrt{x}$ then $F(x) = f(g(x))$.

So, $F(x) = \sqrt{2x - 3}$ is *composed* of $f(x) = \sqrt{x}$ and $g(x) = 2x - 3$.

Notice that $g(f(x)) = g(\sqrt{x})$
$$= 2\sqrt{x} - 3, \quad \text{so in general} \quad f(g(x)) \neq g(f(x)).$$

Given $f : x \mapsto f(x)$ and $g : x \mapsto g(x)$,   the **composite function** of f and g will convert x into $f(g(x))$.

Example 5　　　　　　　　　　　　　　　　　　◀)) **Self Tutor**

If $f(x) = 3x + 2$ and $g(x) = x^2 + 4$, find in simplest form:

　a $f(g(x))$ 　　　　　b $g(f(x))$ 　　　　　c $f(f(x))$

a 　$f(g(x))$
$= f(x^2 + 4)$
$= 3(x^2 + 4) + 2$
$= 3x^2 + 12 + 2$
$= 3x^2 + 14$

b 　$g(f(x))$
$= g(3x + 2)$
$= (3x + 2)^2 + 4$
$= 9x^2 + 12x + 4 + 4$
$= 9x^2 + 12x + 8$

c 　$f(f(x))$
$= f(3x + 2)$
$= 3(3x + 2) + 2$
$= 9x + 6 + 2$
$= 9x + 8$

To find $f(g(x))$ we look at the f function, and whenever we see x we replace it by $g(x)$ within brackets.

EXERCISE 14D

1 If $f(x) = 3x - 4$ and $g(x) = 2 - x$, find in simplest form:

　a $f(g(x))$ 　　　b $g(f(x))$ 　　　c $f(f(x))$ 　　　d $g(g(x))$

2 If $f(x) = \sqrt{x}$ and $g(x) = 4x - 3$, find in simplest form:

　a $f(g(x))$ 　　　b $g(f(x))$ 　　　c $f(f(x))$ 　　　d $g(g(x))$

3 Find an f and a g function such that:

　a $f(g(x)) = \sqrt{x - 3}$ 　　　b $f(g(x)) = (x + 5)^3$ 　　　c $f(g(x)) = \dfrac{5}{x + 7}$

　d $g(f(x)) = \dfrac{1}{\sqrt{3 - 4x}}$ 　　　e $g(f(x)) = 3^{x^2}$ 　　　f $g(f(x)) = \left(\dfrac{x + 1}{x - 1}\right)^2$

4 If $f(x) = 3x + 1$ and $g(x) = x^2 + 2x$, find x when $f(g(x)) = 10$.

5 If $f(x) = 2x + 1$ and $g(f(x)) = 4x^2 + 4x + 3$, find $g(x)$.

6 If $g(x) = 1 - 3x$ and $f(g(x)) = 9x^2 - 6x - 2$, find $f(x)$.

E　　　　**TRANSFORMING** $y = f(x)$

In **Chapter 7** on transformation geometry we observed that under a translation with vector $\begin{pmatrix} h \\ k \end{pmatrix}$ the equation of an image is found by replacing x by $(x - h)$ and y by $(y - k)$.

For example, $y = 2x^2$ under $\begin{pmatrix} h \\ k \end{pmatrix}$ becomes $y - k = 2(x - h)^2$.

In general, $y = f(x)$ under $\begin{pmatrix} h \\ k \end{pmatrix}$ becomes $y - k = f(x - h)$.

The following table shows the effect of different transformations on $y = f(x)$:

Transformation	Transformation equations	Rearranged equations	$y = f(x)$ becomes
Translation $\begin{pmatrix} h \\ k \end{pmatrix}$	$\begin{cases} x' = x + h \\ y' = y + k \end{cases}$	$\begin{cases} x = x' - h \\ y = y' - k \end{cases}$	$y - k = f(x - h)$
Reflection in:			
• the x-axis	$\begin{cases} x' = x \\ y' = -y \end{cases}$	$\begin{cases} x = x' \\ y = -y' \end{cases}$	$-y = f(x)$ or $y = -f(x)$
• the y-axis	$\begin{cases} x' = -x \\ y' = y \end{cases}$	$\begin{cases} x = -x' \\ y = y' \end{cases}$	$y = f(-x)$
• the line $y = x$	$\begin{cases} x' = y \\ y' = x \end{cases}$	$\begin{cases} x = y' \\ y = x' \end{cases}$	$x = f(y)$
Dilation:			
• factor k	$\begin{cases} x' = kx \\ y' = ky \end{cases}$	$\begin{cases} x = \dfrac{x'}{k} \\ y = \dfrac{y'}{k} \end{cases}$	$\dfrac{y}{k} = f\left(\dfrac{x}{k}\right)$ or $y = kf\left(\dfrac{x}{k}\right)$
• vertical, factor k	$\begin{cases} x' = x \\ y' = ky \end{cases}$	$\begin{cases} x = x' \\ y = \dfrac{y'}{k} \end{cases}$	$\dfrac{y}{k} = f(x)$ or $y = kf(x)$
• horizontal, factor k	$\begin{cases} x' = kx \\ y' = y \end{cases}$	$\begin{cases} x = \dfrac{x'}{k} \\ y = y' \end{cases}$	$y = f\left(\dfrac{x}{k}\right)$

We see that if y can be written as a function of x then the image of $y = f(x)$ can be found using the listed transformations.

Example 6   ◀ঠ **Self Tutor**

Find the image equation of:

 a $y = x^3$ under a reflection in the line $y = x$

 b $y = 4x - 1$ under a horizontal dilation with factor 2.

---

 a $y = f(x) = x^3$
    under a reflection in $y = x$
    becomes
    $$x = f(y) = y^3$$
    $$\therefore \quad y = \sqrt[3]{x}$$

 b $y = f(x) = 4x - 1$
    under a horizontal dilation with
    factor 2 becomes
    $$y = f\left(\tfrac{x}{2}\right) = 4\left(\tfrac{x}{2}\right) - 1$$
    $$\therefore \quad y = 2x - 1$$

EXERCISE 14E

1 Find the image equation of:

   a $y = -3x^2$ under a translation of $\begin{pmatrix} 5 \\ -2 \end{pmatrix}$

   b $y = \sqrt{x}$ under a reflection in the x-axis

   c $y = 4x + 2$ under a vertical dilation with factor $\frac{1}{2}$

   d $y = 3 - 5x$ under a reflection in the line $y = x$

   e $y = x^2 - 3x + 1$ under a horizontal dilation with factor $\frac{1}{2}$

   f $y = x^2 + x$ under a reflection in the y-axis.

2 If $f(x) = x^2$,   find and graph:

   a $y = f(-x)$ **b** $y = -f(x)$ **c** $y = f(3x)$ **d** $y = 2f(x)$.

   In each case state the transformation that has occurred from $y = f(x)$.

3 The graph of $y = f(x)$ is given below. Without finding image equations as in question **1**, sketch each of the following on the same set of axes:

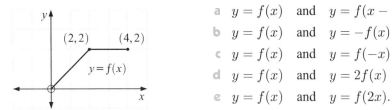

   a $y = f(x)$ and $y = f(x - 1) - 2$

   b $y = f(x)$ and $y = -f(x)$

   c $y = f(x)$ and $y = f(-x)$

   d $y = f(x)$ and $y = 2f(x)$

   e $y = f(x)$ and $y = f(2x)$.

F   INVERSE FUNCTIONS

INVESTIGATION 2   INVERSE FUNCTIONS

In this investigation we explore the concept of an inverse function. We will see how it relates to composite functions and also to one of the transformations studied in the previous section.

What to do:

1 Consider $f(x) = 3x + 2$ which has graph $y = 3x + 2$.

   a Interchange x and y and then make y the subject of this new equation.

   b Let $g(x)$ be the new function in **a**. Hence show that $f(3) = 11$ and $g(11) = 3$.

   c From **b** notice that $g(11) = g(f(3)) = 3$.   Show that $f(g(3)) = 3$ also.

   d Prove that $f(g(x)) = x$ and $g(f(x)) = x$ for f and g above.

   e $f(x)$ and $g(x)$ are said to be **inverse** functions, and $g(x)$, the inverse function of $f(x)$, is often written as $f^{-1}(x)$.

     Find $f^{-1}(x)$ for $f(x) = 3 - 4x$ using the above method, and check that $f(f^{-1}(x)) = f^{-1}(f(x)) = x$.

2   **a** Draw the graph of $f(x)$ and $f^{-1}(x)$ for $f(x) = 3x + 2$ on the same set of axes and also draw the graph of $y = x$.

   b Draw the graph of $f(x)$ and $f^{-1}(x)$ for $f(x) = 3 - 4x$ on the same set of axes and also draw the graph of $y = x$.

   c What do you notice from **a** and **b**?

INVERSE FUNCTIONS

The **inverse function** $f^{-1}(x)$ of the function $y = f(x)$ is the reflection of $y = f(x)$ in the line $y = x$.

$f^{-1}(x)$ has the property that $f(f^{-1}(x)) = f^{-1}(f(x)) = x.$

$f^{-1}(x)$ can be found algebraically by interchanging x and y and then making y the subject of the resulting formula. The new y is $f^{-1}(x)$.

Example 7   ◀) **Self Tutor**

Consider $f(x) = \frac{1}{2}x - 1.$

 a Find $f^{-1}(x)$.   **b** Check that $f(f^{-1}(x)) = f^{-1}(f(x)) = x.$
 c Sketch $y = f(x)$, $y = f^{-1}(x)$ and $y = x$ on the same axes.

---

a $y = \frac{1}{2}x - 1$ has inverse function $x = \frac{1}{2}y - 1$ {interchanging x and y}

$$\therefore \quad 2x = y - 2$$
$$\therefore \quad y = 2x + 2$$
$$\therefore \quad f^{-1}(x) = 2x + 2$$

b $\begin{aligned} f(f^{-1}(x)) &= f(2x + 2) \\ &= \frac{1}{2}(2x + 2) - 1 \\ &= x + 1 - 1 \\ &= x \end{aligned}$ $\begin{aligned} f^{-1}(f(x)) &= 2f(x) + 2 \\ &= 2(\frac{1}{2}x - 1) + 2 \\ &= x - 2 + 2 \\ &= x \end{aligned}$

c

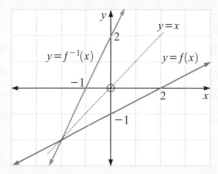

$y = f^{-1}(x)$ is a reflection of $y = f(x)$ in the line $y = x$.

EXERCISE 14F

1 For each of the following functions:
    i find $f^{-1}(x)$ **ii** sketch $y = f(x)$, $y = f^{-1}(x)$ and $y = x$ on the same axes.

    a $f(x) = 2x + 5$ **b** $f(x) = \dfrac{3 - 2x}{4}$ **c** $f(x) = x + 3$

2 Copy the following graphs and draw the graph of each inverse function:

  a 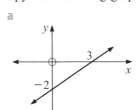   **b** 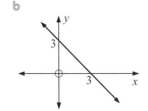   **c**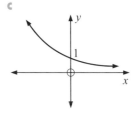

3 If $f(x) = 2x + 7$, find:

    a $f^{-1}(x)$ **b** $f(f^{-1}(x))$ **c** $f^{-1}(f(x))$

4 If $f(x) = \dfrac{2x + 1}{x + 3}$, find:

    a $f^{-1}(x)$ **b** $f(f^{-1}(x))$ **c** $f^{-1}(f(x))$

5   **a** Sketch the graph of $y = x^2$ and reflect it in the line $y = x$.
    b Does $f(x) = x^2$ have an inverse function?
    c Does $f(x) = x^2$, $x \geqslant 0$ have an inverse function?

6 The **horizontal line test** says that *'for a function to have an inverse function, no horizontal line can cut it more than once'*.

    a Explain why this is a valid test for the existence of an inverse function.
    b Which of the following have an inverse function?

    i 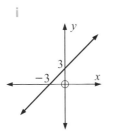   **ii** 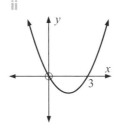   **iii** 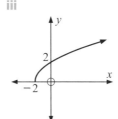   **iv**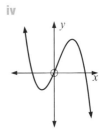

7   **a** Explain why $y = x^2 - 2x + 5$ is a function but does not have an inverse function.
    b Explain why $y = x^2 - 2x + 5$, $x \geqslant 1$ has an inverse function.
    c Show that the inverse function of **b** is $f^{-1}(x) = 1 + \sqrt{x - 4}$.
       Hint: Swap x and y then use the quadratic formula to solve for y in terms of x.

G THE MODULUS FUNCTION

What to do:

1 Suppose $y = x$ if $x \geqslant 0$ and $y = -x$ if $x < 0$.
   Find y for $x = 5, 7, \frac{1}{2}, 0, -2, -8,$ and -10.

2 Draw the graph of $y = \begin{cases} x & \text{if } x \geqslant 0 \\ -x & \text{if } x < 0 \end{cases}$ using the results of **1**.

3 Consider $M(x) = \sqrt{x^2}$ where x^2 must be found before finding the square root.
   Find the values of $M(5), M(7), M(\frac{1}{2}), M(0), M(-2), M(-8)$ and $M(-10)$.

4 What conclusions can be made from **1** and **3**?

MODULUS

The **modulus** or **absolute value** of a real number is its size, ignoring its sign.
We denote the modulus of x by $|x|$.

For example,   the modulus or absolute value of 7 is 7,   and
           the modulus or absolute value of -7 is also 7.

GEOMETRIC DEFINITION OF MODULUS

$|x|$ is the distance of x from 0 on the number line.
Because the modulus is a distance, it cannot be negative.

If $x > 0$:   If $x < 0$:

For example:

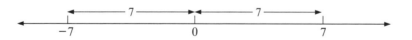

ALGEBRAIC DEFINITION OF MODULUS

From **Investigation 3**, $|x| = \begin{cases} x & \text{if } x \geqslant 0 \\ -x & \text{if } x < 0 \end{cases}$ or $|x| = \sqrt{x^2}$

$y = |x|$ has graph:

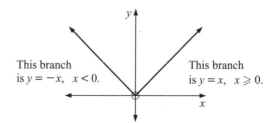

This branch
is $y = -x$, $x < 0$.

This branch
is $y = x$, $x \geqslant 0$.

Example 8 ◀)) **Self Tutor**

If $a = -7$ and $b = 3$ find: **a** $|a + b|$ **b** $|ab|$

a $|a + b|$
$= |-7 + 3|$
$= |-4|$
$= 4$

b $|ab|$
$= |-7 \times 3|$
$= |-21|$
$= 21$

> Perform all operations inside the modulus signs before actually finding the modulus.

Example 9 ◀)) **Self Tutor**

Draw the graph of $f(x) = x + 2|x|$.

If $x > 0$,
$f(x) = x + 2(x) = 3x$

If $x < 0$,
$f(x) = x + 2(-x) = -x$

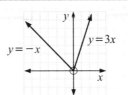

EXERCISE 14G.1

1 If $x = -4$, find the value of:

a $|x + 6|$ **b** $|x - 6|$ **c** $|2x + 3|$ **d** $|7 - x|$

e $|x - 7|$ **f** $|x^2 - 6x|$ **g** $|6x - x^2|$ **h** $\dfrac{|x|}{x + 2}$

2 a Find the value of a^2 and $|a|^2$ if a is:

    i 3   **ii** 0   **iii** -2 **iv** 9   **v** -9 **vi** -20

    b What do you conclude from the results in **a**?

3 a Copy and complete:

    b What can you conclude from the results in **a**?

a	b	$|ab|$	$|a|\,|b|$	$\left|\dfrac{a}{b}\right|$	$\dfrac{|a|}{|b|}$
12	3				
12	-3				
-12	3				
-12	-3				

4 In **Investigation 3** we discovered that $|x| = \sqrt{x^2}$. Using this we find $|x|^2 = x^2$.

Consequently $|x - 2|^2 = (x - 2)^2$.

Prove the following properties of modulus for all real numbers a and b:

    a $|ab| = |a|\,|b|$ **b** $|a - b| = |b - a|$ **c** $\left|\dfrac{a}{b}\right| = \dfrac{|a|}{|b|}$ provided $b \neq 0$.

Hint: In **a**, $(\text{LHS})^2 = |ab|^2 = a^2 b^2$. In **b**, $|a - b| = |-(b - a)|$.

5 **a** Copy and complete:

b What can you conclude from the results in **a**?

a	b	$\lvert a+b \rvert$	$\lvert a \rvert + \lvert b \rvert$	$\lvert a-b \rvert$	$\lvert a \rvert - \lvert b \rvert$
2	5				
2	-5				
-2	5				
-2	-5				

6 On the same set of axes, graph the following pairs of modulus functions. Clearly state the transformation which maps the first function on to the second.

   a $y = \lvert x \rvert$ and $y = \lvert x - 2 \rvert$ **b** $y = \lvert x \rvert$ and $y = \lvert x + 2 \rvert$

   c $y = \lvert x \rvert$ and $y = 2\lvert x \rvert$ **d** $y = \lvert x \rvert$ and $y = -\lvert x \rvert$

   e $y = \lvert x \rvert$ and $y = \lvert x \rvert + 2$ **f** $y = \lvert x \rvert$ and $y = \lvert x - 1 \rvert + 3$

GRAPHING PACKAGE

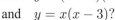

7 By replacing $\lvert x \rvert$ with x for $x \geqslant 0$ and $(-x)$ for $x < 0$ write the following functions without the modulus sign and hence graph each function:

   a $y = -\lvert x \rvert$ **b** $y = \lvert x \rvert + x$ **c** $y = \dfrac{\lvert x \rvert}{x}$ **d** $y = x - 2\lvert x \rvert$

8 Use technology to graph:

   a $y = \lvert (x-2)(x-4) \rvert$ **b** $y = \lvert x(x-3) \rvert$

GRAPHING PACKAGE

   How are these functions related to $y = (x-2)(x-4)$

   and $y = x(x-3)$?

SUMMARY OF MODULUS PROPERTIES

- $\lvert x \rvert$ is never negative, i.e., $\lvert x \rvert \geqslant 0$ for all x
- $\lvert x \rvert^2 = x^2$ for all x
- $\lvert xy \rvert = \lvert x \rvert \lvert y \rvert$ for all x and y
- $\left\lvert \dfrac{x}{y} \right\rvert = \dfrac{\lvert x \rvert}{\lvert y \rvert}$ for all x and y, $y \neq 0$
- $\lvert a-b \rvert = \lvert b-a \rvert$ for all a and b.

MODULUS EQUATIONS

It is clear that $\lvert x \rvert = 2$ has two solutions $x = 2$ and $x = -2$.

In general, **if $\lvert x \rvert = a$ where $a > 0$, then $x = \pm a$.**

Proof: If $\lvert x \rvert = a$

                then $\lvert x \rvert^2 = a^2$

                $\therefore \quad x^2 = a^2$

            $\therefore \quad x^2 - a^2 = 0$

        $\therefore \quad (x+a)(x-a) = 0$

                $\therefore \quad x = \pm a$

We use this rule to solve modulus equations.

Example 10
◄)) **Self Tutor**

Solve for x: **a** $|2x + 5| = 1$ **b** $|2x + 5| = -2$

a $|2x + 5| = 1$

$\therefore \quad 2x + 5 = \pm 1$

$\therefore \quad 2x = 1 - 5 \quad$ or $\quad -1 - 5$

$\therefore \quad 2x = -4 \quad$ or $\quad -6$

$\therefore \quad x = -2 \quad$ or $\quad -3$

b $|2x + 5| = -2$

has no solution as the LHS is never negative.

EXERCISE 14G.2

1 Solve for x:

a $|x| - 5$

b $|x| = -6$

c $|x| = 0$

d $|x + 1| = 4$

e $|4 - x| = 5$

f $|x + 6| = -3$

g $|3x - 5| = 2$

h $|3 - 2x| = 4$

i $|12 - 7x| = 5$

j $\left| \dfrac{2x}{x + 1} \right| = 5$

k $\left| \dfrac{2x - 1}{x + 3} \right| = 2$

l $\left| \dfrac{x + 4}{1 - 2x} \right| = \frac{3}{4}$

2 Use technology to graph:

a $y = |3 - 2x|$ and $y = 4$ and hence check your answer to **1h**

b $y = \left| \dfrac{2x - 1}{x + 3} \right|$ and $y = 2$ and hence check your answer to **1k**.

GRAPHING
PACKAGE

H   WHERE FUNCTIONS MEET

Consider the graphs of a quadratic function and a linear function on the same set of axes.

Notice that we could have:

  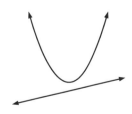

cutting	**touching**	**missing**
(2 points of intersection)	(1 point of intersection)	(no points of intersection)

If the graphs meet, the coordinates of the point(s) of intersection can be found by solving the two equations *simultaneously*.

Example 11   ◀) **Self Tutor**

Find the coordinates of the points of intersection of the graphs with equations
$y = x^2 - x + 3$ and $y = 2x + 7$.

The graphs meet when $x^2 - x + 3 = 2x + 7$

$$\therefore \quad x^2 - 3x - 4 = 0$$
$$\therefore \quad (x + 1)(x - 4) = 0$$
$$\therefore \quad x = -1 \text{ or } 4$$

Substituting into $y = 2x + 7$,   when $x = -1$, $y = 2(-1) + 7 = 5$
when $x = 4$, $y = 2(4) + 7 = 15$

$\therefore$ the graphs meet at $(-1, 5)$ and $(4, 15)$.

EXERCISE 14H

1 Find the coordinates of the point(s) of intersection of the graphs with equations:

a $y = x^2 + 2x - 1$ and $y = x + 5$ **b** $y = \dfrac{2}{x}$ and $y = x - 1$

c $y = 3x^2 + 4x - 1$ and $y = x^2 - 3x - 4$ **d** $y = \dfrac{1}{x}$ and $y = 5x - 4$

2 Use a **graphing package** or a **graphics calculator** to find the coordinates of the points of intersection (to two decimal places) of the graphs with equations:

a $y = x^2 + 3x + 1$ and $y = 2x + 2$

b $y = x^2 - 5x + 2$ and $y = \dfrac{3}{x}$

c $y = -x^2 - 2x + 5$ and $y = x^2 + 7$

d $y = x^2 - 1$ and $y = x^3$.

GRAPHING
PACKAGE

I   NUMBER SEQUENCES

Consider the illustrated pattern of circles:

The first layer has just one blue ball.
The second layer has three pink balls.
The third layer has five black balls.
The fourth layer has seven green balls.

If we let u_n represent the number of balls in the nth layer then $u_1 = 1$, $u_2 = 3$, $u_3 = 5$,   and $u_4 = 7$.

The pattern could be continued forever, generating the **sequence** of numbers:
1, 3, 5, 7, 9, 11, 13, 15, 17, ...

The string of dots indicates that the pattern continues forever.

A **sequence** is a function whose domain is the set of all positive integers
1, 2, 3, 4, 5, ...

The sequence for the pattern of balls can be specified:

- **using words** — "The set of all odd numbers starting with 1."
- **using an explicit formula** — $u_n = 2n + 1$ generates all terms.
  u_n is called the **nth term** or the **general term**.
- **using a recursive formula** — $u_1 = 1$ and $u_{n+1} = u_n + 2$ for all $n \geqslant 1$
  Check: $u_1 = 1$
  $u_2 = u_1 + 2 = 1 + 2 = 3$ ✓
  $u_3 = u_2 + 2 = 3 + 2 = 5$ ✓

ARITHMETIC SEQUENCES

An **arithmetic sequence** is a sequence in which each term differs from the previous one by the same fixed number. We call this number the **common difference**.

For example: 1, 5, 9, 13, 17, ... is arithmetic as $5 - 1 = 9 - 5 = 13 - 9 = 17 - 13$, etc.

Likewise, 42, 37, 32, 27, ... is arithmetic as $37 - 42 = 32 - 37 = 27 - 32$, etc.

Notice in the sequence 1, 5, 9, 13, 17, ... that $u_1 = 1$
$$u_2 = 1 + 4 \qquad = 1 + 1(4)$$
$$u_3 = 1 + 4 + 4 \qquad = 1 + 2(4)$$
$$u_4 = 1 + 4 + 4 + 4 = 1 + 3(4), \quad \text{etc.}$$

This suggests that: If u_n is arithmetic then the nth term is $\boldsymbol{u_n = u_1 + (n - 1)d}$

where u_1 is the first term and d is the constant **common difference**.

Example 12 ◀) Self Tutor

Consider the sequence 3, 9, 15, 21, 27, ...

a Show that the sequence is arithmetic.
b Find the formula for the general term u_n.
c Find the 100th term of the sequence.
d Is i 489 ii 1592 a member of the sequence?

---

a $9 - 3 = 6$, $15 - 9 = 6$, $21 - 15 = 6$, $27 - 21 = 6$
So, assuming that the pattern continues, consecutive terms differ by 6.
∴ the sequence is arithmetic with $u_1 = 3$ and $d = 6$.
b $u_n = u_1 + (n - 1)d$ ∴ $u_n = 3 + 6(n - 1)$ i.e., $u_n = 6n - 3$
c If $n = 100$, $u_{100} = 6(100) - 3 = 597$.

d **i** Let $u_n = 489$

$\therefore$ $6n - 3 = 489$

$\therefore$ $6n = 492$

$\therefore$ $n = 82$

$\therefore$ 489 is a term of the sequence.
In fact it is the 82nd term.

ii Let $u_n = 1592$

$\therefore$ $6n - 3 = 1592$

$\therefore$ $6n = 1595$

$\therefore$ $n = 265\frac{5}{6}$

which is not possible as n is an integer.

$\therefore$ 1592 cannot be a term.

Example 13
🔊 Self Tutor

Find k given that $k + 5$, -1 and $2k - 1$ are consecutive terms of an arithmetic sequence, and hence find the terms.

Since the terms are consecutive,

$$-1 - (k + 5) = (2k - 1) - (-1) \qquad \text{\{equating common differences\}}$$

$\therefore$ $-1 - k - 5 = 2k - 1 + 1$

$\therefore$ $-k - 6 = 2k$

$\therefore$ $-6 = 3k$

$\therefore$ $k = -2$

$\therefore$ the terms are $3, -1, -5$.

Example 14
🔊 Self Tutor

Find the general term u_n for an arithmetic sequence given that $u_3 = 4$ and $u_7 = -24$.

$$u_7 - u_3 = (u_1 + 6d) - (u_1 + 2d)$$
$$= u_1 + 6d - u_1 - 2d$$
$$= 4d$$

But $u_7 - u_3 = -24 - 4 = -28$

$\therefore$ $4d = -28$

$\therefore$ $d = -7$

Now $u_n = u_1 + (n - 1)d$

$\therefore$ $u_3 = u_1 + (2)(-7)$

$\therefore$ $4 = u_1 - 14$

$\therefore$ $u_1 = 18$

$\therefore$ $u_n = 18 + (n - 1)(-7)$

$\therefore$ $u_n = 18 - 7n + 7$

$\therefore$ $u_n = 25 - 7n$

Check:

$u_3 = 25 - 7(3)$
$\quad = 25 - 21$
$\quad = 4$ ✓

$u_7 = 25 - 7(7)$
$\quad = 25 - 49$
$\quad = -24$ ✓

EXERCISE 14I.1

1   Consider the sequence   4, 11, 18, 25, 32, ...
    a   Show that the sequence is arithmetic.   b   Find the formula for its general term.
    c   Find its 30th term.   d   Is 340 a member?
    e   Is 738 a member?

2   Consider the sequence   67, 63, 59, 55, ...
    a   Show that the sequence is arithmetic.   b   Find the formula for its general term.
    c   Find its 60th term.   d   Is -143 a member?
    e   Is 85 a member?

3   An arithmetic sequence is defined by $u_n = 11n - 7$.
    a   Find u_1 and d.   b   Find the 37th term.
    c   What is the least term of the sequence which is greater than 250?

4   A sequence is defined by $u_n = \dfrac{21 - 4n}{2}$.
    a   Prove that the sequence is arithmetic.   b   Find u_1 and d.   c   Find u_{55}.
    d   For what values of n are the terms of the sequence less than -300?

5   Find k given the consecutive arithmetic terms:
    a   31, k, 13   b k, 8, $k + 11$ c $k + 2$, $2k + 3$, 17

6   Find the general term u_n for an arithmetic sequence given that:
    a $u_4 = 37$ and $u_{10} = 67$ b $u_5 = -10$ and $u_{12} = -38$
    c   the fourth term is -4 and the fifteenth term is 29
    d   the tenth and sixth terms are -16 and -13 respectively.

7   Consider the finite arithmetic sequence   3, $2\frac{1}{2}$, 2, ..., -6.
    a   Find u_1 and d.   b   How many terms does the sequence have?

8   An arithmetic sequence starts 17, 24, 31, 38, ... What is the first term of the sequence to exceed 40 000?

GEOMETRIC SEQUENCES

A sequence is **geometric** if each term can be obtained from the previous one by multiplying by the same non-zero constant.

For example: 2, 6, 18, 54, ...   is a geometric sequence as

$$2 \times 3 = 6 \quad \text{and} \quad 6 \times 3 = 18 \quad \text{and} \quad 18 \times 3 = 54.$$

Notice that $u_2 = u_1 \times 3$
    and $u_3 = u_2 \times 3 = u_1 \times 3 \ \times 3 = u_1 \times 3^2$,
          $u_4 = u_3 \times 3 = u_1 \times 3^2 \times 3 = u_1 \times 3^3$,
          $u_5 = u_4 \times 3 = u_1 \times 3^3 \times 3 = u_1 \times 3^4$.

This suggests the following **algebraic definition**:

> If u_n is geometric then $u_n = u_1 \times r^{n-1}$ for all positive integers n.
> u_1 is the **first term** and r is a **constant** called the **common ratio**.

Notice:
- r is called the common ratio because $\dfrac{u_{n+1}}{u_n} = r$ for all n.
- $2, 6, 18, 54, ...$ is geometric with $r = 3$.
- $2, -6, 18, -54, ...$ is geometric with $r = -3$.

Example 15   ◀) **Self Tutor**

For the sequence $16, 8, 4, 2, 1, ...$
  a Show that the sequence is geometric.   b Find the general term u_n.
  c Hence, find the 10th term as a fraction.

a $\dfrac{8}{16} = \dfrac{1}{2}$, $\dfrac{4}{8} = \dfrac{1}{2}$, $\dfrac{2}{4} = \dfrac{1}{2}$, $\dfrac{1}{2} = \dfrac{1}{2}$

So, assuming the pattern continues, consecutive terms have a common ratio of $\dfrac{1}{2}$.

$\therefore$ the sequence is geometric with $u_1 = 16$ and $r = \dfrac{1}{2}$.

b $u_n = u_1 r^{n-1}$ $\therefore$ $u_n = 16 \times \left(\dfrac{1}{2}\right)^{n-1}$ or $u_n = 2^4 \times (2^{-1})^{n-1}$
$= 2^4 \times 2^{-n+1}$
$= 2^{4+(-n+1)}$
$= 2^{5-n}$

c $u_{10} = 16 \times \left(\dfrac{1}{2}\right)^9 = \dfrac{2^4}{2^9} = \dfrac{1}{2^5} = \dfrac{1}{32}$

Example 16   ◀) **Self Tutor**

$k - 1$, $k + 2$ and $3k$ are consecutive terms of a geometric sequence. Find k.

Equating common ratios gives $\qquad \dfrac{3k}{k+2} = \dfrac{k+2}{k-1}$

$\therefore$ $3k(k-1) = (k+2)^2$

$\therefore$ $3k^2 - 3k = k^2 + 4k + 4$

$\therefore$ $2k^2 - 7k - 4 = 0$

$\therefore$ $(k-4)(2k+1) = 0$

$\therefore$ $k = 4$ or $-\dfrac{1}{2}$

Check: If $k = 4$, the terms are: $3, 6, 12.$ ✓ $\{r = 2\}$
If $k = -\dfrac{1}{2}$, the terms are: $-\dfrac{3}{2}, \dfrac{3}{2}, -\dfrac{3}{2}.$ ✓ $\{r = -1\}$

Example 17 🔊 **Self Tutor**

A geometric sequence has $u_2 = -5$ and $u_5 = 40$. Find its general term.

$$u_2 = u_1 r = -5 \quad \ldots\ldots (1) \quad \{\text{using } u_n = u_1 r^{n-1} \text{ with } n = 2\}$$

$$\text{and} \quad u_5 = u_1 r^4 = 40 \quad \ldots\ldots (2) \quad \{\text{using } u_n = u_1 r^{n-1} \text{ with } n = 5\}$$

$$\text{So,} \quad \frac{u_1 r^4}{u_1 r} = \frac{40}{-5} \quad \{(2) \div (1)\}$$

$$\therefore \quad r^3 = -8$$

$$\therefore \quad r = \sqrt[3]{-8}$$

$$\therefore \quad r = -2$$

$$\text{and so in (1)} \quad u_1(-2) = -5$$

$$\therefore \quad u_1 = \tfrac{5}{2}$$

$$\text{Thus} \quad u_n = \tfrac{5}{2} \times (-2)^{n-1}$$

EXERCISE 14I.2

1 For the geometric sequence with first two terms given, find b and c:

    a $3, 6, b, c, \ldots$
    b $8, 2, b, c, \ldots$
    c $15, -5, b, c, \ldots$

2   **a** Show that the sequence $1, 3, 9, 27, \ldots$ is geometric.

    b Find u_n and hence find the 10th term.

3   **a** Show that the sequence $40, -20, 10, -5, \ldots$ is geometric.

    b Find u_n and hence find the 12th term as a fraction.

4 Show that the sequence $16, -4, 1, -0.25, \ldots$ is geometric and hence find the 8th term as a decimal.

5 Find the general term of the geometric sequence: $3, 3\sqrt{2}, 6, 6\sqrt{2}, \ldots$

6 Find k given that the following are consecutive terms of a geometric sequence:

    a $k, 2, 6$
    b $4, 6, k$
    c $k, 2\sqrt{2}, k^2$

    d $3, k, 27$
    e $k, 3k, 10k + 7$
    f $k, k + 4, 8k + 2$

7 Find the general term u_n of the geometric sequence which has:

    a $u_3 = 16$ and $u_8 = 512$
    b $u_3 = 32$ and $u_6 = -4$

    c $u_7 = 24$ and $u_{15} = 384$
    d $u_3 = 3$ and $u_9 = \tfrac{3}{8}$.

8 A geometric sequence has general term u_n with $u_3 = 12$ and $u_7 = \tfrac{3}{4}$. Find u_{12}.

9 u_n is the general term of a geometric sequence.

    a If $u_2 = -2\tfrac{1}{2}$ and $u_5 = \tfrac{5}{16}$, find u_{10}.

    b If $u_3 = 7$ and $u_8 = -7$, find u_{88}.

    c If $u_3 = 18$ and $u_5 = 162$, find u_{11}.

J | RECURRENCE RELATIONSHIPS

Perhaps the most famous example of a recurrence relationship is that which generates the **Fibonacci sequence**:

1, 1, 2, 3, 5, 8, 13, 21, 34, 55, ...

The pattern starts with two 1s, and after this each term is obtained by adding the two terms preceding it:

$1 + 1 = 2$
$1 + 2 = 3$
$2 + 3 = 5$
$3 + 5 = 8$
$\vdots$

Leonardo Fibonacci

We can hence write down a **recurrence relationship**:

$u_1 = u_2 = 1$ and $u_{n+2} = u_{n+1} + u_n$ for $n = 1, 2, 3, 4, 5, 6, 7, \ldots\ldots$

Check: If $n = 1$, $u_3 = u_2 + u_1 = 1 + 1 = 2$ ✓
    If $n = 2$, $u_4 = u_3 + u_2 = 2 + 1 = 3$ ✓
    If $n = 3$, $u_5 = u_4 + u_3 = 3 + 2 = 5$ ✓

Leonardo Fibonacci (1170-1250) noticed that the sequence   1, 1, 2, 3, 5, 8, ...   occurred frequently in the natural world.

For example, he noticed that flowers of particular species have the same number of petals and that these numbers are all members of the Fibonacci sequence.

3 petals	lily, iris
5 petals	buttercup
8 petals	delphinium
13 petals	cineraria
21 petals	aster
34 petals	pyrethrum

Fibonacci also observed the number sequence in:

- the number of leaves arranged about the stem in plants
- the seed patterns of the sunflower
- the seed pattern on the pine cone.

The recurrence relationship is very useful for dealing with the Fibonacci sequence because its explicit formula is very complicated. In fact, it is:

$$u_n = \frac{1}{\sqrt{5}} \left[\left(\frac{1 + \sqrt{5}}{2} \right)^n - \left(\frac{1 - \sqrt{5}}{2} \right)^n \right] \quad \text{for} \quad n = 1, 2, 3, 4, 5, \ldots\ldots$$

ARITHMETIC SEQUENCES

The sequence   4, 7, 10, 13, ...   can be generated using $u_n = 3n + 1$ or by using the recurrence relationship:

$$\text{“}u_1 = 4 \quad \text{and} \quad u_{n+1} = u_n + 3 \quad \text{where } n \text{ is a positive integer”.}$$

This is easily seen as $u_1 = 4$ and $u_2 = u_1 + 3 = 4 + 3 \ = 7$

and $u_3 = u_2 + 3 = 7 + 3 \ = 10$

and $u_4 = u_3 + 3 = 10 + 3 = 13$ etc.

In general,   if $\boldsymbol{u_n = u_1 + (n-1)d}$ where u_1 and d are constants

then $\boldsymbol{u_{n+1} = u_n + d}$.

GEOMETRIC SEQUENCES

The sequence   3, 6, 12, 24, ...   can be generated using the general term formula $u_n = 3 \times 2^{n-1}$ where n is a positive integer.

However, the same sequence can be generated using the recurrence relationship:

$$\text{“}u_1 = 3 \quad \text{and} \quad u_{n+1} = 2u_n \quad \text{where } n \text{ is a positive integer”.}$$

We have $u_1 = 3$

and $u_2 = 2u_1 = 2 \times 3 = 6$ $\{$letting $n = 1\}$

and $u_3 = 2u_2 = 2 \times 6 = 12$ $\{$letting $n = 2\}$

etc.

In general,   if $\boldsymbol{u_n = u_1 r^{n-1}}$ where u_1 and r are constants

then $\boldsymbol{u_{n+1} = r u_n}$.

Example 18	◄》 **Self Tutor**

Find the next three members of the sequence given by:

a $u_1 = 7$ and $u_{n+1} = u_n - 2$ b $u_1 = 24$ and $u_{n+1} = \frac{1}{2}u_n$

a   If $n = 1$, $u_2 = u_1 - 2$

$= 7 - 2$

$= 5$

If $n = 2$, $u_3 = u_2 - 2$

$= 5 - 2$

$= 3$

If $n = 3$, $u_4 = u_3 - 2$

$= 3 - 2$

$= 1$

b   If $n = 1$, $u_2 = \frac{1}{2}u_1$

$= \frac{1}{2} \times 24$

$= 12$

If $n = 2$, $u_3 = \frac{1}{2}u_2$

$= \frac{1}{2} \times 12$

$= 6$

If $n = 3$, $u_4 = \frac{1}{2}u_3$

$= \frac{1}{2} \times 6$

$= 3$

Example 19   ◀)) **Self Tutor**

Find the explicit formula for u_n if:

   a $u_{n+1} = u_n + 7$ and $u_1 = 5$ **b** $u_{n+1} = 0.4u_n$ and $u_1 = 100$

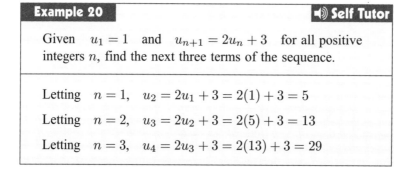

a We identify this sequence as arithmetic   Now $u_n = u_1 + (n-1)d$
    with $d = 7$. $\therefore$ $u_n = 5 + (n-1)7$
                                          $\therefore$ $u_n = 7n - 2$

b We identify this sequence as geometric   Now $u_n = u_1 r^{n-1}$
    with $r = 0.4$. $\therefore$ $u_n = 100 \times (0.4)^{n-1}$

Sequences do not have to be arithmetic or geometric.

For example, the Fibonacci sequence is neither arithmetic nor geometric.

Example 20   ◀)) **Self Tutor**

Given $u_1 = 1$ and $u_{n+1} = 2u_n + 3$ for all positive integers n, find the next three terms of the sequence.

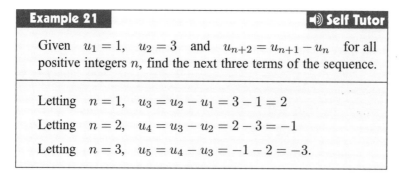

Letting $n = 1$, $u_2 = 2u_1 + 3 = 2(1) + 3 = 5$

Letting $n = 2$, $u_3 = 2u_2 + 3 = 2(5) + 3 = 13$

Letting $n = 3$, $u_4 = 2u_3 + 3 = 2(13) + 3 = 29$

The Fibonacci sequence is also an example of a recurrence relationship that relates any term to the previous *two* terms.

Example 21   ◀)) **Self Tutor**

Given $u_1 = 1$, $u_2 = 3$ and $u_{n+2} = u_{n+1} - u_n$ for all positive integers n, find the next three terms of the sequence.

Letting $n = 1$, $u_3 = u_2 - u_1 = 3 - 1 = 2$

Letting $n = 2$, $u_4 = u_3 - u_2 = 2 - 3 = -1$

Letting $n = 3$, $u_5 = u_4 - u_3 = -1 - 2 = -3$.

EXERCISE 14J

1   Find the next *three* members of the sequence defined by:

   a $u_1 = 2$ and $u_{n+1} = u_n + 3$ **b** $u_1 = 11.7$ and $u_{n+1} = u_n - 2.1$

   c $u_1 = 1268$ and $u_{n+1} = u_n + 23.9$ **d** $u_1 = 4$ and $u_{n+1} = 3u_n$

   e $u_1 = 1000$ and $u_{n+1} = \frac{1}{10}u_n$ **f** $u_1 = 128$ and $u_{n+1} = -\frac{1}{2}u_n$.

2 Find the explicit formula for u_n if:

  a $u_1 = 41$ and $u_{n+1} = u_n + 5$ **b** $u_1 = 11.8$ and $u_{n+1} = u_n - 1.7$

  c $u_1 = 12$ and $u_{n+1} = \frac{1}{3}u_n$ **d** $u_1 = 36$ and $u_{n+1} = -\frac{1}{2}u_n$.

3 Find the next three members of the sequence defined by:

  a $u_1 = 1$ and $u_{n+1} = 2u_n - 1$ **b** $u_{n+1} = 3 - u_n$ and $u_1 = 2$

  c $u_{n+1} = \frac{1}{3}u_n - 1$ and $u_1 = 3$ **d** $u_{n+1} = u_n^2 - 1$ and $u_1 = 1$.

4 Find the next four terms of the sequence defined by:

  a $u_1 = 1$, $u_2 = 0$ and $u_{n+2} = u_{n+1} - u_n$

  b $u_1 = u_2 = 1$ and $u_{n+2} = 2u_{n+1} + 3u_n$.

FIBONACCI

LINKS
click here

Areas of interaction:
Human ingenuity

INVESTIGATION 4   SEQUENCES IN FINANCE

Arithmetic and **geometric sequences** are observed in many financial calculations.

What to do:

1 $1000 is invested at a **simple** interest rate of 7% per year with the interest paid at the end of each year.

After 1 year, its value is 1000×1.07 {to increase by 7% we multiply by 107%}

After 2 years, its value is 1000×1.14 {an increase of 14% on the original}

  a Find the value of the investment at the end of:

     i 3 years   **ii** 4 years   **iii** 5 years.

  b Do the amounts form an arithmetic or geometric sequence or neither of these? Give reasons for your answer.

  c Give an explicit formula for finding any term u_n of the sequence being generated.

  d Give a recursive formula for the sequence.

2 $6000 is invested at a fixed rate of 7% p.a. **compound** interest over a lengthy period. Interest is paid at the end of each year.

After 1 year, its value is 6000×1.07

After 2 years, its value is   ($6000 \times 1.07) \times 1.07 = \$6000 \times (1.07)^2$

  a Explain why the amount after 3 years is given by $6000 \times (1.07)^3$.

  b Write down, in the same form, the amount after:

     i 4 years   **ii** 5 years   **iii** 6 years.

c Do the amounts at the end of each year form an arithmetic or geometric sequence or neither of these? Give reasons for your answer.

d Give an explicit formula for finding any term u_n of the sequence being generated.

e Give a recursive formula for the sequence.

3 A photocopier originally cost \$12 000 and it depreciates in value (loses value) by 20% each year.

   a Find its value at the end of:

      i one year   **ii** two years   **iii** three years.

   b Do the resulting annual values form an arithmetic or geometric sequence?

   c If the answer to **b** is yes, find:

      i an explicit formula for finding its value at the end of the nth year

      ii a recursive formula for the value.

REVIEW SET 14A

1 For the following graphs, determine:

   i the range and domain   **ii** whether the relation is a function.

a

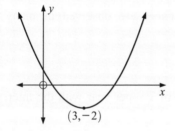

b

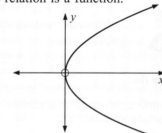

c

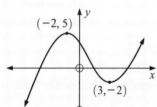

d

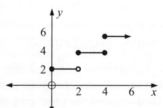

2 If $f(x) = 3x - x^2$, find: **a** $f(2)$ **b** $f(-1)$ **c** $f(\frac{1}{2})$.

3 If $g(x) = x^2 - 3x$, find in simplest form: **a** $g(-x)$ **b** $g(x + 2)$.

4 If $f(x) = 5 - 2x$ and $g(x) = x^2 + 2x$ find:

   a $f(g(x))$ **b** x when $g(x) = 20$ **c** $f^{-1}(x)$ in the form $ax + b$.

5 Consider $f(x) = |2x - 4|$.

   a Sketch the graph of the function $f(x)$.

   b Find the solutions of $|2x - 4| = 5$ from the graph in **a**.

   c Check your answer to **b** by solving the equation algebraically.

6 Consider the sequence $-6, -2, 2, 6, \ldots\ldots$

    a Show that the sequence is arithmetic.

    b Find a formula for the general term u_n.

    c Find the 100th term of the sequence.

    d Find the largest term that is less than 500.

7 Find the general term u_n of the geometric sequence with $u_4 = 24$ and $u_7 = -192$.

8 Find the next three members of the sequence with $u_1 = 2$ and $u_{n+1} = 2u_n + 4$.

9 Find the coordinates of the points of intersection of the graphs with equations $y = x^2 + 4x - 2$ and $y = 2x + 1$.

10   **a** Find the image of $y = 2x^2$ under:

      i a translation of $\begin{pmatrix} -1 \\ 3 \end{pmatrix}$ **ii** a vertical dilation with factor 3.

    b On the same set of axes, draw the graphs of $f(x) = 3 - x^2$, $y = f(-x)$ and $y = 2f(x)$.

REVIEW SET 14B

1 For the following graphs, determine:

    i the range and domain   **ii** whether the relation is a function.

  a

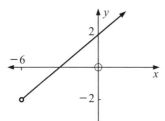

  b

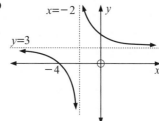

  c

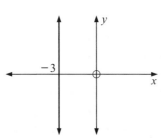

  d

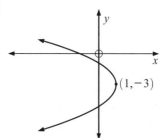

2 If $f(x) = 5x - x^2$, find in simplest form:

    a $f(-3)$ **b** $f(-x)$ **c** $f(x + 1)$

3 If $g(x) = x^2 - 1$ and $h(x) = 3x + 2$ find:

    a $g(h(x))$ **b** $h(g(x))$ **c** $h^{-1}(x)$ in the form $ax + b$.

4 Consider $f(x) = |3 - 4x|$.

   a Sketch the graph of $y = f(x)$.

   b Find the solutions of $|3 - 4x| = 7$ from the graph in **a**.

   c Check your answer to **b** algebraically.

5 Find the general term u_n for an arithmetic sequence given that the third term is 24 and the 11th term is -36.

6 Show that the sequence $64, -32, 16, -8, 4, \ldots\ldots$ is geometric, and hence find the 16th term as a fraction.

7 $2k + 7$, $1 - k$ and $k - 7$ are consecutive terms of a geometric sequence. Find k and hence find the three terms given.

8 Find an explicit formula for u_n if:

   a $u_{n+1} = u_n - 3$ and $u_1 = 7$

   b $u_1 = 24$ and $u_{n+1} = -\frac{2}{3}u_n$.

9 Find the coordinates of the points of intersection of the graphs with equations $y = \dfrac{3}{x}$ and $y = 2x - 1$.

10 **a** Find the image of $y = \dfrac{5}{x}$ under:

   i a reflection in the x-axis

   ii a dilation with factor $\frac{3}{4}$.

   b On the same set of axes, graph $f(x) = 2x + 1$, $y = 2f(x)$ and $y = f(2x)$.

Chapter 15

Vectors

Contents:

OPENING PROBLEM

Ian can swim in a swimming pool at a speed of 2 km h^{-1}. However, today he needs to swim directly across a river in which the water is flowing at a constant speed of 5 km h^{-1} to his right.

Things to think about:

- What effect does the current in the river have on the speed and direction in which Ian swims?
- How can we accurately find the speed and direction that Ian will travel if he tries to swim directly across the river?
- In what direction must Ian face so that he swims directly across the river?

VECTORS AND SCALARS

To solve questions like those in the **Opening Problem**, we need to examine the **size** or **magnitude** of the quantities under consideration as well as the **direction** in which they are acting.

To achieve this we use quantities called **vectors** which have both size or magnitude and also direction.

> Quantities which only have magnitude are called **scalars**.
>
> Quantities which have both magnitude and direction are called **vectors**.

For example, **velocity** is a vector since it deals with speed (a scalar) in a particular direction.

Other examples of vector quantities are: acceleration, force, displacement, and momentum.

A DIRECTED LINE SEGMENT REPRESENTATION

Consider a bus which is travelling at 100 km h^{-1} in a south east direction.

A good way of representing this situation is to use an arrow on a scale diagram.

The **length of the arrow** represents the size or magnitude of the velocity and the **arrowhead** shows the direction of travel.

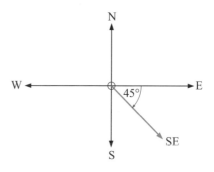

Scale: 1 cm represents 50 km h^{-1}

Consider the vector represented by the line segment from O to A.

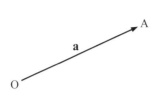

- This **vector** could be represented by

$$\overrightarrow{OA} \quad \text{or} \quad \mathbf{a} \quad \text{or} \quad \overrightarrow{a}.$$

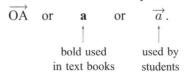

- The **magnitude** or **length** could be represented by

$$|\overrightarrow{OA}| \quad \text{or} \quad OA \quad \text{or} \quad |\mathbf{a}| \quad \text{or} \quad |\overrightarrow{a}|.$$

For  we say that $\overrightarrow{AB}$ is the vector which **emanates** from A and **terminates** at B, and that $\overrightarrow{AB}$ is the **position vector** of B relative to A.

Example 1 ◀⑴ **Self Tutor**

On a scale diagram, sketch the vector which represents a velocity of 15 ms^{-1} in a westerly direction.

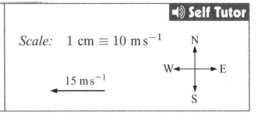

Example 2 ◀⑴ **Self Tutor**

Draw a scaled arrow diagram representing 40 ms^{-1} on a bearing $075°$.

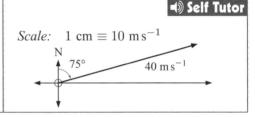

EXERCISE 15A

1 Using a scale of 1 cm represents 10 units, sketch a vector to represent:

   a 40 kmh^{-1} in a SW direction

   b 35 ms^{-1} in a northerly direction

   c a displacement of 25 m in a direction $120°$

   d an aeroplane taking off at an angle of $12°$ to the runway with a speed of 60 ms^{-1}.

2 If ⟶ represents a force of 45 Newtons due east, draw a directed line segment representing a force of:

   a 75 N due west

   b 60 N south west.

3 Draw a scaled arrow diagram representing the following vectors:

   a a velocity of 60 kmh^{-1} in a NE direction

   b a momentum of 45 $kgms^{-1}$ in the direction $250°$

   c a displacement of 25 km in the direction $055°$

   d an aeroplane taking off at an angle of $10°$ to the runway at a speed of 90 kmh^{-1}.

B   VECTOR EQUALITY

Two vectors are **equal** if they have the same magnitude *and* direction.

If arrows are used to represent vectors, then equal vectors are **parallel** and **equal in length**.

This means that equal vector arrows are translations of one another.

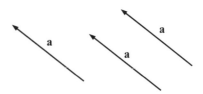

THE ZERO VECTOR

The **zero vector**, **0** is a vector of length 0.
It is the only vector with no direction.

NEGATIVE VECTORS

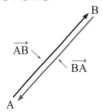

Notice that $\overrightarrow{AB}$ and $\overrightarrow{BA}$ have the same length but opposite directions.

We say that $\overrightarrow{BA}$ is *the negative of* $\overrightarrow{AB}$ and write $\overrightarrow{BA} = -\overrightarrow{AB}$.

Given the vector **a** shown, we can draw the vector $-\mathbf{a}$.

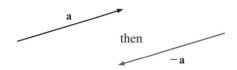

a and $-\mathbf{a}$ are parallel, equal in length, but opposite in direction.

Example 3   ◀) **Self Tutor**

ABCD is a parallelogram in which $\overrightarrow{AB} = \mathbf{a}$
and $\overrightarrow{BC} = \mathbf{b}$.

Find vector expressions for:

  a $\overrightarrow{BA}$ b $\overrightarrow{CB}$ c $\overrightarrow{AD}$ d $\overrightarrow{CD}$

  a $\overrightarrow{BA} = -\mathbf{a}$ {the negative vector of $\overrightarrow{AB}$}

  b $\overrightarrow{CB} = -\mathbf{b}$ {the negative vector of $\overrightarrow{BC}$}

  c $\overrightarrow{AD} = \mathbf{b}$ {parallel to and the same length as $\overrightarrow{BC}$}

  d $\overrightarrow{CD} = -\mathbf{a}$ {parallel to and the same length as $\overrightarrow{BA}$}

EXERCISE 15B

1 State the vectors which are:

   a equal in magnitude

   b parallel

   c in the same direction

   d equal

   e negatives of one another.

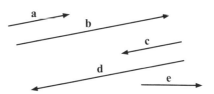

2 The figure alongside consists of two isosceles triangles with [PQ] ∥ [SR] and $\overrightarrow{PQ} = \mathbf{p}$, $\overrightarrow{PS} = \mathbf{q}$. Which of the following statements are true?

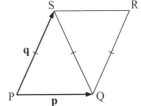

   a $\overrightarrow{RS} = \mathbf{p}$ **b** $\overrightarrow{QR} = \mathbf{q}$ **c** $\overrightarrow{QS} = \mathbf{q}$

   d QS = PS   **e** $\overrightarrow{PS} = -\overrightarrow{RQ}$

C   VECTOR ADDITION

We have already been operating with vectors without realising it.

Bearing problems are an example of this. The vectors in this case are **displacements**.

A typical problem could be:

"A girl runs from A in a northerly direction for 3 km and then in a westerly direction for 2 km to B. How far is she from her starting point and in what direction?"

We can use trigonometry and Pythagoras' theorem to answer such problems as we need to find θ and x.

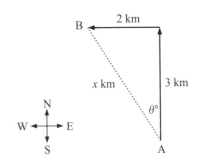

DISPLACEMENT VECTORS

Suppose we have three towns A, B and C.

A trip from A to B followed by a trip from B to C is equivalent to a trip from A to C.

This can be expressed in a vector form as the sum $\overrightarrow{AB} + \overrightarrow{BC} = \overrightarrow{AC}$ where the + sign could mean 'followed by'.

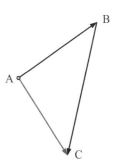

VECTOR ADDITION

After considering displacements in diagrams like those above, we can now define vector addition geometrically:

To add **a** and **b**:   *Step 1:*   Draw **a**.

Step 2:   At the arrowhead end of **a**, draw **b**.

Step 3:   Join the beginning of **a** to the arrowhead end of **b**. This is vector   **a + b**.

So, given    we have   a+b

COMPUTER DEMO

Example 4   ◀) Self Tutor

Find a single vector which is equal to:

a $\overrightarrow{AB} + \overrightarrow{BE}$

b $\overrightarrow{DC} + \overrightarrow{CA} + \overrightarrow{AE}$

c $\overrightarrow{CB} + \overrightarrow{BD} + \overrightarrow{DC}$

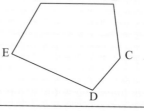

a $\overrightarrow{AB} + \overrightarrow{BE} = \overrightarrow{AE}$ {as shown}

b $\overrightarrow{DC} + \overrightarrow{CA} + \overrightarrow{AE} = \overrightarrow{DE}$

c $\overrightarrow{CB} + \overrightarrow{BD} + \overrightarrow{DC} = \overrightarrow{CC} = \mathbf{0}$ {zero vector}

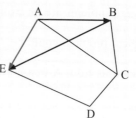

THE ZERO VECTOR

Having defined vector addition, we are now able to state that:

The **zero vector**, **0** is a vector of length 0.

For any vector **a**: $\mathbf{a} + \mathbf{0} = \mathbf{0} + \mathbf{a} = \mathbf{a}$

$\mathbf{a} + (-\mathbf{a}) = (-\mathbf{a}) + \mathbf{a} = \mathbf{0}$

When we write the zero vector by hand, we usually write $\overrightarrow{0}$.

Example 5   ◀) Self Tutor

Jason walks for 3.8 km in the direction 110° and then 2.7 km in the direction 020°.

Find his displacement from his starting position.

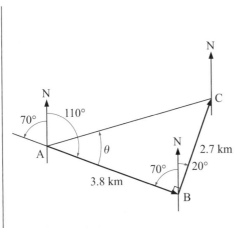

ABC is $70^o + 20^o = 90^o$

Using Pythagoras' theorem:

$$AC^2 = 3.8^2 + 2.7^2$$
$$\therefore \quad AC = \sqrt{3.8^2 + 2.7^2}$$
$$\therefore \quad AC \approx 4.66 \text{ km}$$

Using the tangent ratio, $\tan\theta = \dfrac{2.7}{3.8}$

$$\therefore \quad \theta = \tan^{-1}\left(\dfrac{2.7}{3.8}\right)$$
$$\therefore \quad \theta \approx 35.4^o$$

Now $110^o - 35.4^o \approx 74.6^o$

So, Jason is 4.66 km from his starting point on a bearing of 074.6^o.

Example 6
◀) **Self Tutor**

Sonya can swim at 3 km h^{-1} in calm water. She swims in a river where the current is 1 km h^{-1} in an easterly direction. Find Sonya's resultant velocity if she swims:

  a with the current   b against the current

  c northwards, across the river.

Scale: 1 cm ≡ 1 km h^{-1}

The velocity vector of the river is

  a Sonya's velocity vector is

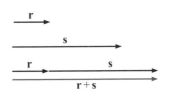

The net result is **r** + **s**.

    ∴ Sonya swims at 4 km h^{-1} in the direction of the current.

  b Sonya's velocity vector is

The net result is **r** + **s**.

    ∴ Sonya swims at 2 km h^{-1} against the current.

  c

Sonya's velocity vector is   and the net result is **r** + **s**.

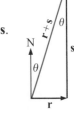

$$\therefore \quad |\mathbf{r}+\mathbf{s}| = \sqrt{10} \approx 3.16$$
$\tan\theta = \frac{1}{3}$ so $\theta = \tan^{-1}(\frac{1}{3}) \approx 18.4^o$

    ∴ Sonya swims at about 3.16 km h^{-1} in the direction 018.4^o.

EXERCISE 15C

1 Copy the given vectors **p** and **q** and hence show how to find   **p** + **q**:

a

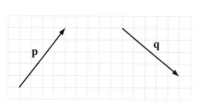

b

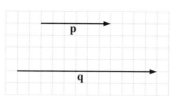

c

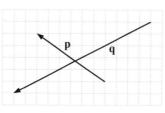

d

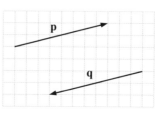

e

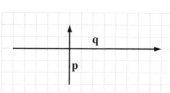

f

2 Find a single vector which is equal to:

a $\overrightarrow{QR} + \overrightarrow{RS}$ b $\overrightarrow{PQ} + \overrightarrow{QR}$

c $\overrightarrow{PS} + \overrightarrow{SR} + \overrightarrow{RQ}$ d $\overrightarrow{PR} + \overrightarrow{RQ} + \overrightarrow{QS}$

3 a Use vector diagrams to find i **p** + **q**   ii **q** + **p**   given that

   p is   and **q** is

   b For any two vectors **p** and **q**, is **p** + **q** = **q** + **p**?

4 Paolo rides for 20 km in the direction $310°$ and then for 15 km in the direction $040°$. Find Paolo's displacement from his starting point.

5 Gina drives along a straight highway for 4.2 km in a north-westerly direction and then along another road for 5.3 km in a north-easterly direction. Find her displacement from her starting position.

6 Consider an aeroplane trying to fly at 500 km h^{-1} due north. Find the actual speed and direction of the aeroplane if a gale of 100 km h^{-1} is blowing:

   a from the south   b from the north   c from the west.

7 If a vessel is trying to travel east at 10 km h^{-1}, what will be its actual speed and direction if there is a current of 10 km h^{-1}:

   a from the east   b from the west   c from the south?

8   An aircraft flying at 400 km h^{-1} aiming due east encounters a 60 km h^{-1} wind from the north. Find the actual speed and direction of the aircraft.

9   A ship travelling at 23 knots on a course 124° encounters a current of 4 knots in the direction 214°. Find the actual speed and direction of the ship.

 # VECTOR SUBTRACTION

VECTOR SUBTRACTION

To subtract one vector from another, we simply **add its negative**, i.e., $\mathbf{a} - \mathbf{b} = \mathbf{a} + (-\mathbf{b})$.

For example:

for  and then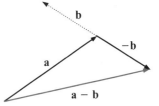

Example 7   ◀) **Self Tutor**

Given and

find $\mathbf{s} - \mathbf{t}$.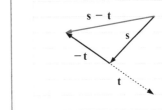

Example 8   ◀) **Self Tutor**

For points P, Q, R and S, simplify the following vector expressions:

a $\overrightarrow{QR} - \overrightarrow{SR}$ b $\overrightarrow{QR} - \overrightarrow{SR} - \overrightarrow{PS}$

a $\overrightarrow{QR} - \overrightarrow{SR}$
  $= \overrightarrow{QR} + \overrightarrow{RS}$ {as $\overrightarrow{RS} = -\overrightarrow{SR}$}
  $= \overrightarrow{QS}$

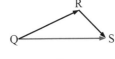

b $\overrightarrow{QR} - \overrightarrow{SR} - \overrightarrow{PS}$
  $= \overrightarrow{QR} + \overrightarrow{RS} + \overrightarrow{SP}$
  $= \overrightarrow{QP}$

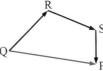

Example 9   ◀)) **Self Tutor**

Xiang Zhu is about to fire an arrow at a target. In
still conditions, the arrow would travel at 18 m s^{-1}.
Today, however, there is a wind of 6 m s^{-1} blowing
from the left directly across the arrow's path.

  a In what direction should Zhu fire the arrow?

  b What will be its actual speed?

Suppose Zhu is at Z and the target is at T. Let **a** be the arrow's velocity in still conditions,
w be the velocity of the wind, and **x** be the vector $\overrightarrow{ZT}$.

Now $\qquad\qquad$ $\mathbf{a} + \mathbf{w} = \mathbf{x}$

$\qquad \therefore \quad \mathbf{a} + \mathbf{w} - \mathbf{w} = \mathbf{x} - \mathbf{w}$

$\qquad\qquad \therefore \quad \mathbf{a} = \mathbf{x} - \mathbf{w}$

a Now $|\mathbf{a}| = 18$ m s^{-1} and $|\mathbf{w}| = 6$ m s^{-1}

$\qquad \therefore \quad \sin\theta = \frac{6}{18} = \frac{1}{3}$

$\qquad \therefore \quad \theta = \sin^{-1}\left(\frac{1}{3}\right) \approx 19.47^{o}$

$\qquad \therefore$ Zhu should fire about 19.5^{o} to the left of the target.

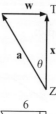

b By Pythagoras' theorem, $|\mathbf{x}|^2 + 6^2 = 18^2$

$\qquad \therefore \quad |\mathbf{x}| = \sqrt{18^2 - 6^2} \approx 16.97$ m s^{-1}

$\qquad \therefore$ the arrow will travel at about 17.0 m s^{-1}.

EXERCISE 15D

1 For the following vectors **p** and **q**, show how to construct **p** − **q**:

a 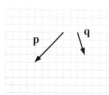   **b** 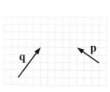   **c**

d 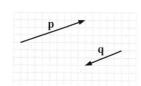   **e** 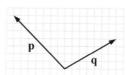   **f**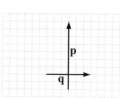

2 For points P, Q, R and S, simplify the following vector expressions:

  a $\overrightarrow{QR} + \overrightarrow{RS}$ $\qquad\qquad$ **b** $\overrightarrow{PS} - \overrightarrow{RS}$ $\qquad\qquad$ **c** $\overrightarrow{RS} + \overrightarrow{SR}$

  d $\overrightarrow{RS} + \overrightarrow{SP} + \overrightarrow{PQ}$ $\qquad$ **e** $\overrightarrow{QP} - \overrightarrow{RP} + \overrightarrow{RS}$ $\qquad$ **f** $\overrightarrow{RS} - \overrightarrow{PS} - \overrightarrow{QP}$

3 An aeroplane needs to fly due north at a speed of 500 km h^{-1}. However, it is affected
by a 40 km h^{-1} wind blowing constantly from the west. What direction must it head
towards and at what speed?

4 A motorboat wishes to travel NW towards a safe haven before an electrical storm arrives. In still water the boat can travel at 30 km h^{-1}. However, a strong current is flowing at 10 km h^{-1} from the north east.

   a In what direction must the boat head?

   b At what speed will the boat be travelling?

E ▌ VECTORS IN COMPONENT FORM

So far we have examined vectors from their geometric representation.

We have used arrows where:

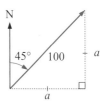

- the **length** of the arrow represents size or magnitude
- the **arrowhead** indicates direction.

Consider a car travelling at 100 km h^{-1} in a NE direction.

The velocity vector could be represented by using the x and y-steps which are necessary to go from the start to the finish.

$$a^2 + a^2 = 100^2$$
$$\therefore \quad 2a^2 = 10\,000$$
$$\therefore \quad a^2 = 5000$$
$$\therefore \quad a \approx 70.7$$

In this case the **column vector** $\begin{pmatrix} 70.7 \\ 70.7 \end{pmatrix}$ gives the x and y-steps.

y-component x-component $\begin{pmatrix} x \\ y \end{pmatrix}$ is the **component form** of a vector.

For example,   given $\begin{pmatrix} -1 \\ 2 \end{pmatrix}$ we could draw

where -1 is the horizontal step
and 2 is the vertical step.

VECTORS BETWEEN TWO POINTS

The position vector of point $A(a_1, a_2)$ relative to the origin $O(0, 0)$ is $\overrightarrow{OA} = \begin{pmatrix} x\text{-step} \\ y\text{-step} \end{pmatrix} = \begin{pmatrix} a_1 \\ a_2 \end{pmatrix}$.

Likewise,

the position vector of $B(b_1, b_2)$ relative to $A(a_1, a_2)$

is $\overrightarrow{AB} = \begin{pmatrix} x\text{-step} \\ y\text{-step} \end{pmatrix} = \begin{pmatrix} b_1 - a_1 \\ b_2 - a_2 \end{pmatrix}$.

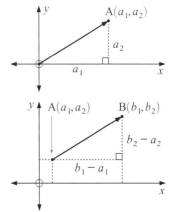

This result could also be found using:

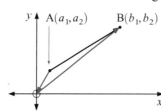

$$\overrightarrow{AB} = \overrightarrow{AO} + \overrightarrow{OB}$$
$$= -\overrightarrow{OA} + \overrightarrow{OB}$$
$$= -\begin{pmatrix} a_1 \\ a_2 \end{pmatrix} + \begin{pmatrix} b_1 \\ b_2 \end{pmatrix}$$
$$= \begin{pmatrix} b_1 - a_1 \\ b_2 - a_2 \end{pmatrix}$$

Example 10   ◉ Self Tutor

If A is at $(2, -3)$ and B at $(4, 2)$ find   **a** $\overrightarrow{AB}$ **b** $\overrightarrow{BA}$

a $\overrightarrow{AB} = \begin{pmatrix} 4-2 \\ 2--3 \end{pmatrix} = \begin{pmatrix} 2 \\ 5 \end{pmatrix}$ **b** $\overrightarrow{BA} = \begin{pmatrix} 2-4 \\ -3-2 \end{pmatrix} = \begin{pmatrix} -2 \\ -5 \end{pmatrix}$

From this example we notice that $\overrightarrow{BA} = -\overrightarrow{AB}$.

VECTOR EQUALITY

Vectors are equal if and only if their x-components are equal *and* their y-components are equal.

i.e., $\begin{pmatrix} p \\ q \end{pmatrix} = \begin{pmatrix} r \\ s \end{pmatrix}$ if and only if $p = r$ *and* $q = s$.

Example 11   ◉ Self Tutor

A car travels at a speed of 20 m s^{-1} in the direction $125°$.
Write this as a vector in component form.

Sketch:

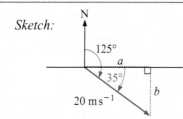

$\cos 35° = \dfrac{a}{20}$,   so $a = 20 \times \cos 35° \approx 16.4$

$\sin 35° = \dfrac{b}{20}$,   so $b = 20 \times \sin 35° \approx 11.5$

$\therefore$ the vector is $\begin{pmatrix} a \\ -b \end{pmatrix} \approx \begin{pmatrix} 16.4 \\ -11.5 \end{pmatrix}$

EXERCISE 15E.1

1 Draw arrow diagrams to represent the vectors:

    a $\begin{pmatrix} 4 \\ 2 \end{pmatrix}$ **b** $\begin{pmatrix} 0 \\ 3 \end{pmatrix}$ **c** $\begin{pmatrix} -2 \\ 5 \end{pmatrix}$ **d** $\begin{pmatrix} 3 \\ 4 \end{pmatrix}$

2 Write the illustrated vectors in component form:

    a   **b**   **c**

d    e    f

3   If A is at $(3, 4)$, B is at $(-1, 2)$, and C is at $(2, -1)$, find:

     a $\overrightarrow{OA}$ b $\overrightarrow{AB}$ c $\overrightarrow{CO}$ d $\overrightarrow{BC}$ e $\overrightarrow{CA}$

4   Draw an arrow diagram representing the following vectors and hence write them as ordered pairs:

     a   a velocity of 60 m s^{-1} in the direction 120°

     b   a displacement of 15 km in the direction 221°

     c   an aeroplane on the runway takes off at an angle of 9° and a speed of 160 km h^{-1}.

VECTOR ADDITION

Consider adding vectors $\mathbf{a} = \begin{pmatrix} a_1 \\ a_2 \end{pmatrix}$ and $\mathbf{b} = \begin{pmatrix} b_1 \\ b_2 \end{pmatrix}$.

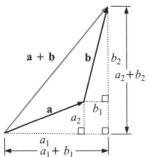

Notice that the

horizontal step for $\mathbf{a} + \mathbf{b}$ is $a_1 + b_1$ and the

            vertical step for $\mathbf{a} + \mathbf{b}$ is $a_2 + b_2$.

if $\mathbf{a} = \begin{pmatrix} a_1 \\ a_2 \end{pmatrix}$ and $\mathbf{b} = \begin{pmatrix} b_1 \\ b_2 \end{pmatrix}$ then $\mathbf{a} + \mathbf{b} = \begin{pmatrix} a_1 + b_1 \\ a_2 + b_2 \end{pmatrix}$.

Example 12   ◀)) **Self Tutor**

If $\mathbf{a} = \begin{pmatrix} 2 \\ 5 \end{pmatrix}$ and $\mathbf{b} = \begin{pmatrix} 1 \\ -3 \end{pmatrix}$

find $\mathbf{a} + \mathbf{b}$.

Check your answer graphically.

$$\mathbf{a} + \mathbf{b} = \begin{pmatrix} 2 \\ 5 \end{pmatrix} + \begin{pmatrix} 1 \\ -3 \end{pmatrix} = \begin{pmatrix} 3 \\ 2 \end{pmatrix}$$

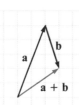

Start at the non-arrow end and move horizontally then vertically to the arrow end.

NEGATIVE VECTORS

Consider the vector $\mathbf{a} = \begin{pmatrix} 5 \\ 2 \end{pmatrix}$.

Notice that $-\mathbf{a} = \begin{pmatrix} -5 \\ -2 \end{pmatrix}$.

In general,   if $\mathbf{a} = \begin{pmatrix} a_1 \\ a_2 \end{pmatrix}$ then $-\mathbf{a} = \begin{pmatrix} -a_1 \\ -a_2 \end{pmatrix}$.

ZERO VECTOR

The zero vector is $\mathbf{0} = \begin{pmatrix} 0 \\ 0 \end{pmatrix}$.

For any vector $\mathbf{a}$: $\mathbf{a} + \mathbf{0} = \mathbf{0} + \mathbf{a} = \mathbf{0}$.
$\mathbf{a} + (-\mathbf{a}) = (-\mathbf{a}) + \mathbf{a} = \mathbf{0}$.

VECTOR SUBTRACTION

To subtract one vector from another, we simply **add its negative**,   i.e., $\mathbf{a} - \mathbf{b} = \mathbf{a} + (-\mathbf{b})$.

Notice that, if $\mathbf{a} = \begin{pmatrix} a_1 \\ a_2 \end{pmatrix}$ and $\mathbf{b} = \begin{pmatrix} b_1 \\ b_2 \end{pmatrix}$ then $\mathbf{a} - \mathbf{b} = \mathbf{a} + (-\mathbf{b})$

$$= \begin{pmatrix} a_1 \\ a_2 \end{pmatrix} + \begin{pmatrix} -b_1 \\ -b_2 \end{pmatrix}$$

$$= \begin{pmatrix} a_1 - b_1 \\ a_2 - b_2 \end{pmatrix}$$

If $\mathbf{a} = \begin{pmatrix} a_1 \\ a_2 \end{pmatrix}$ and $\mathbf{b} = \begin{pmatrix} b_1 \\ b_2 \end{pmatrix}$ then $\mathbf{a} - \mathbf{b} = \begin{pmatrix} a_1 - b_1 \\ a_2 - b_2 \end{pmatrix}$.

Example 13   ◀) **Self Tutor**

Given $\mathbf{p} = \begin{pmatrix} 3 \\ -2 \end{pmatrix}$ and $\mathbf{q} = \begin{pmatrix} 1 \\ 4 \end{pmatrix}$ find: **a** $\mathbf{p} - \mathbf{q}$ **b** $\mathbf{q} - \mathbf{p}$

a $\mathbf{p} - \mathbf{q} = \begin{pmatrix} 3 \\ -2 \end{pmatrix} - \begin{pmatrix} 1 \\ 4 \end{pmatrix}$ **b** $\mathbf{q} - \mathbf{p} = \begin{pmatrix} 1 \\ 4 \end{pmatrix} - \begin{pmatrix} 3 \\ -2 \end{pmatrix}$

$= \begin{pmatrix} 2 \\ -6 \end{pmatrix}$ $= \begin{pmatrix} -2 \\ 6 \end{pmatrix}$

THE LENGTH OF A VECTOR

By the theorem of Pythagoras,

the **length** of $\mathbf{a} = \begin{pmatrix} a_1 \\ a_2 \end{pmatrix}$ is $|\mathbf{a}| = \sqrt{a_1{}^2 + a_2{}^2}$.

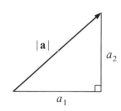

For example,

- the length of $\begin{pmatrix} 5 \\ 2 \end{pmatrix}$ is $\sqrt{5^2 + 2^2} = \sqrt{25 + 4} = \sqrt{29}$ units

- the length of $\begin{pmatrix} -4 \\ 3 \end{pmatrix}$ is $\sqrt{(-4)^2 + 3^2} = \sqrt{16 + 9} = 5$ units

EXERCISE 15E.2

1 If $\mathbf{a} = \begin{pmatrix} 2 \\ -3 \end{pmatrix}$, $\mathbf{b} = \begin{pmatrix} 3 \\ -1 \end{pmatrix}$, $\mathbf{c} = \begin{pmatrix} -2 \\ -3 \end{pmatrix}$ find:

    a $\mathbf{a} + \mathbf{b}$ b $\mathbf{b} + \mathbf{a}$ c $\mathbf{b} + \mathbf{c}$ d $\mathbf{c} + \mathbf{b}$

    e $\mathbf{a} + \mathbf{c}$ f $\mathbf{c} + \mathbf{a}$ g $\mathbf{a} + \mathbf{a}$ h $\mathbf{b} + \mathbf{a} + \mathbf{c}$

2 Given $\mathbf{p} = \begin{pmatrix} -1 \\ 3 \end{pmatrix}$, $\mathbf{q} = \begin{pmatrix} -2 \\ -3 \end{pmatrix}$ and $\mathbf{r} = \begin{pmatrix} 3 \\ -4 \end{pmatrix}$ find:

    a $\mathbf{p} - \mathbf{q}$ b $\mathbf{q} - \mathbf{r}$ c $\mathbf{p} + \mathbf{q} - \mathbf{r}$

    d $\mathbf{p} - \mathbf{q} - \mathbf{r}$ e $\mathbf{q} - \mathbf{r} - \mathbf{p}$ f $\mathbf{r} + \mathbf{q} - \mathbf{p}$

3   a Given $\overrightarrow{AB} = \begin{pmatrix} 1 \\ 4 \end{pmatrix}$ and $\overrightarrow{AC} = \begin{pmatrix} -2 \\ 1 \end{pmatrix}$, find $\overrightarrow{BC}$.

    b Given $\overrightarrow{AB} = \begin{pmatrix} -3 \\ 2 \end{pmatrix}$, $\overrightarrow{BD} = \begin{pmatrix} 0 \\ 4 \end{pmatrix}$ and $\overrightarrow{CD} = \begin{pmatrix} 1 \\ -3 \end{pmatrix}$, find $\overrightarrow{AC}$.

4 Find the length of these vectors:

    a $\begin{pmatrix} 1 \\ 4 \end{pmatrix}$ b $\begin{pmatrix} 6 \\ 0 \end{pmatrix}$ c $\begin{pmatrix} 3 \\ -2 \end{pmatrix}$ d $\begin{pmatrix} -1 \\ -5 \end{pmatrix}$ e $\begin{pmatrix} -4 \\ 2 \end{pmatrix}$ f $\begin{pmatrix} -6 \\ -1 \end{pmatrix}$

5 For the following pairs of points, find: i $\overrightarrow{AB}$ ii the distance AB.

    a A(3, 5) and B(1, 2)   b A(−2, 1) and B(3, −1)

    c A(3, 4) and B(0, 0)   d A(11, −5) and B(−1, 0)

F   SCALAR MULTIPLICATION

Numbers such as 1 and −2 are called *scalars* because they have size but no direction.

$\mathbf{a}$ and $-2\mathbf{a}$ are examples of multiplying a vector by a scalar.

$2\mathbf{a}$ is the short way of writing $\mathbf{a} + \mathbf{a}$ and $-2\mathbf{a} = (-\mathbf{a}) + (-\mathbf{a})$

For   we have   and

So, $2\mathbf{a}$ has the same direction as $\mathbf{a}$ and is twice as long as $\mathbf{a}$, and

     $-2\mathbf{a}$ is in the opposite direction to $\mathbf{a}$ and is twice as long as $\mathbf{a}$.

Example 14   ◀) **Self Tutor**

For $\mathbf{r} = \begin{pmatrix} 3 \\ 2 \end{pmatrix}$ and $\mathbf{s} = \begin{pmatrix} 2 \\ -2 \end{pmatrix}$, find **a** $2\mathbf{r} + \mathbf{s}$ **b** $\mathbf{r} - 2\mathbf{s}$ geometrically.

a

b

So, $2\mathbf{r} + \mathbf{s} = \begin{pmatrix} 8 \\ 2 \end{pmatrix}$.   So, $\mathbf{r} - 2\mathbf{s} = \begin{pmatrix} -1 \\ 6 \end{pmatrix}$.

In component form,   if k is a scalar then $k \begin{pmatrix} a \\ b \end{pmatrix} = \begin{pmatrix} ka \\ kb \end{pmatrix}$

i.e., each component is multiplied by k.

We can now check the results of **Example 14** algebraically:

In **a**, $2\mathbf{r} + \mathbf{s} = 2 \begin{pmatrix} 3 \\ 2 \end{pmatrix} + \begin{pmatrix} 2 \\ -2 \end{pmatrix}$ and in **b**, $\mathbf{r} - 2\mathbf{s} = \begin{pmatrix} 3 \\ 2 \end{pmatrix} - 2 \begin{pmatrix} 2 \\ -2 \end{pmatrix}$

$$= \begin{pmatrix} 6 \\ 4 \end{pmatrix} + \begin{pmatrix} 2 \\ -2 \end{pmatrix} \qquad\qquad = \begin{pmatrix} 3 \\ 2 \end{pmatrix} - \begin{pmatrix} 4 \\ -4 \end{pmatrix}$$

$$= \begin{pmatrix} 8 \\ 2 \end{pmatrix} \qquad\qquad\qquad = \begin{pmatrix} -1 \\ 6 \end{pmatrix}$$

Example 15   ◀) **Self Tutor**

Draw sketches of any two vectors $\mathbf{p}$ and $\mathbf{q}$ such that: **a** $\mathbf{p} = 2\mathbf{q}$ **b** $\mathbf{p} = -\frac{1}{2}\mathbf{q}$.

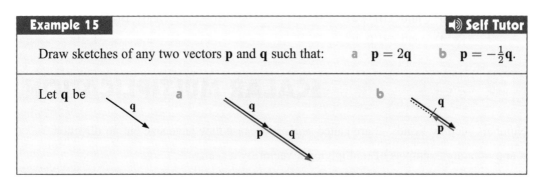

EXERCISE 15F

1 For $\mathbf{r} = \begin{pmatrix} 2 \\ 3 \end{pmatrix}$ and $\mathbf{s} = \begin{pmatrix} 4 \\ -2 \end{pmatrix}$, find geometrically:

   a $2\mathbf{r}$ **b** $-3\mathbf{s}$ **c** $\frac{1}{2}\mathbf{r}$ **d** $\mathbf{r} - 2\mathbf{s}$

   e $3\mathbf{r} + \mathbf{s}$ **f** $2\mathbf{r} - 3\mathbf{s}$ **g** $\frac{1}{2}\mathbf{s} + \mathbf{r}$ **h** $\frac{1}{2}(2\mathbf{r} + \mathbf{s})$

2 Check your answers to **1** using component form arithmetic.

3 Draw sketches of any two vectors $\mathbf{p}$ and $\mathbf{q}$ such that:

    a $\mathbf{p} = \mathbf{q}$ **b** $\mathbf{p} = -\mathbf{q}$ **c** $\mathbf{p} = 3\mathbf{q}$ **d** $\mathbf{p} = \frac{3}{4}\mathbf{q}$ **e** $\mathbf{p} = -\frac{3}{2}\mathbf{q}$

4 If $\mathbf{a}$ is any vector, prove that $|k\mathbf{a}| = |k|\,|\mathbf{a}|$.
Hint: Write $\mathbf{a}$ in component form.

G   VECTOR EQUATIONS

When solving vector equations we use the same methods as for ordinary equations in algebra. However, we cannot *divide* both sides of a vector equation by a scalar. Instead, we multiply both sides by its reciprocal.

For example, if $3\mathbf{x} = \mathbf{a}$, then $\mathbf{x} = \frac{1}{3}\mathbf{a}$ and *not* $\dfrac{\mathbf{a}}{3}$.

So,   if $k\mathbf{x} = \mathbf{a}$ then $\mathbf{x} = \dfrac{1}{k}\mathbf{a}$.

Proof: If $k\mathbf{x} = \mathbf{a}$ then

$$\frac{1}{k}(k\mathbf{x}) = \frac{1}{k}\mathbf{a}$$

$$\therefore \quad 1\mathbf{x} = \frac{1}{k}\mathbf{a}$$

$$\therefore \quad \mathbf{x} = \frac{1}{k}\mathbf{a}$$

Example 16   ◀⑨ **Self Tutor**

Make $\mathbf{x}$ the subject of: **a** $2\mathbf{x} - \mathbf{r} = \mathbf{p}$ **b** $\mathbf{n} - 3\mathbf{x} = \mathbf{m}$.

a $2\mathbf{x} - \mathbf{r} = \mathbf{p}$

   $\therefore \quad 2\mathbf{x} - \mathbf{r} + \mathbf{r} = \mathbf{p} + \mathbf{r}$ {adding $\mathbf{r}$ to both sides}

     $\therefore \quad 2\mathbf{x} + \mathbf{0} = \mathbf{p} + \mathbf{r}$

       $\therefore \quad 2\mathbf{x} = \mathbf{p} + \mathbf{r}$

         $\therefore \quad \mathbf{x} = \frac{1}{2}(\mathbf{p} + \mathbf{r})$

b $\mathbf{n} - 3\mathbf{x} = \mathbf{m}$

   $\therefore \quad \mathbf{n} - 3\mathbf{x} - \mathbf{n} = \mathbf{m} - \mathbf{n}$

     $\therefore \quad -3\mathbf{x} = \mathbf{m} - \mathbf{n}$

       $\therefore \quad 3\mathbf{x} = \mathbf{n} - \mathbf{m}$

         $\therefore \quad \mathbf{x} = \frac{1}{3}(\mathbf{n} - \mathbf{m})$

EXERCISE 15G

1 Showing all steps, make **x** the subject of:

a $4\mathbf{x} = \mathbf{p}$

b $-3\mathbf{x} = \mathbf{q}$

c $\frac{1}{2}\mathbf{x} = \mathbf{p}$

d $-\frac{2}{3}\mathbf{x} = \mathbf{r}$

e $2\mathbf{x} + \mathbf{p} = \mathbf{q}$

f $4\mathbf{p} - 3\mathbf{x} = \mathbf{q}$

g $\mathbf{p} - \mathbf{x} = \mathbf{q} + 2\mathbf{x}$

h $3\mathbf{m} - \frac{1}{2}\mathbf{x} = \mathbf{n}$

i $2\mathbf{d} + \frac{1}{3}\mathbf{x} = \mathbf{e}$

2 Let $\mathbf{r} = \begin{pmatrix} 2 \\ -1 \end{pmatrix}$ and $\mathbf{s} = \begin{pmatrix} 3 \\ 2 \end{pmatrix}$. Find **y** if:

a $3\mathbf{y} = \mathbf{s}$

b $\frac{1}{3}\mathbf{y} = \mathbf{r}$

c $\mathbf{s} + 2\mathbf{y} = \mathbf{r}$

d $4\mathbf{s} - 2\mathbf{y} = \mathbf{r}$

3 Let $\mathbf{p} = \begin{pmatrix} 4 \\ 2 \end{pmatrix}$ and $\mathbf{q} = \begin{pmatrix} -1 \\ -3 \end{pmatrix}$. Find **x** if:

a $\frac{1}{2}\mathbf{x} = \mathbf{p}$

b $\mathbf{q} + 2\mathbf{x} = \mathbf{p}$

c $3\mathbf{p} - \frac{1}{2}\mathbf{x} = \mathbf{q}$

d $2\mathbf{x} - \mathbf{p} = \mathbf{q} + \mathbf{x}$

e $3\mathbf{x} + \mathbf{q} = \mathbf{p} - \mathbf{x}$

f $\mathbf{x} + 2\mathbf{p} = \mathbf{q} - 3\mathbf{x}$

H   PARALLELISM OF VECTORS

Two vectors are **parallel** if one is a scalar multiple of the other.

Conversely,   if two vectors are parallel then one vector is a scalar multiple of the other.

If **a** is parallel to **b** then we write   **a** ∥ **b**.

Thus,   • if **a** = k**b** for some non-zero scalar k, then   **a** ∥ **b**

          • if **a** ∥ **b**   there exists a non-zero scalar k such that   **a** = k**b**.

Notice that $\mathbf{a} = \begin{pmatrix} 6 \\ 3 \end{pmatrix}$ and $\mathbf{b} = \begin{pmatrix} 2 \\ 1 \end{pmatrix}$ are such that   **a** = 3**b**.

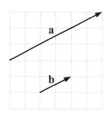

We can see that   **a** ∥ **b**.

Notice also that $|\mathbf{a}| = \sqrt{36 + 9}$
$$= \sqrt{45}$$
$$= 3\sqrt{5}$$
$$= 3\,|\mathbf{b}|.$$

Consider the vector $k\mathbf{a}$ which is parallel to **a**.

In general:

• If $k > 0$ then $k\mathbf{a}$ has the same direction as **a**.

• If $k < 0$ then $k\mathbf{a}$ has the opposite direction to **a**.

• $|k\mathbf{a}| = |k|\,|\mathbf{a}|$ i.e.,   the length of $k\mathbf{a}$ is the **modulus** of k times the length of **a**.

Example 17   ◀ŷ **Self Tutor**

What two facts can be deduced about **p** and **q** if:

    a $\mathbf{p} = 5\mathbf{q}$ **b** $\mathbf{q} = -\frac{3}{4}\mathbf{p}$?

---

  a $\mathbf{p} = 5\mathbf{q}$

    $\therefore$ **p** is parallel to **q** and $|\mathbf{p}| = |5|\,|\mathbf{q}| = 5\,|\mathbf{q}|$

    $\therefore$ **p** is 5 times longer than **q**, and they have the same direction.

  b $\mathbf{q} = -\frac{3}{4}\mathbf{p}$

    $\therefore$ **q** is parallel to **p** and $|\mathbf{q}| = \left|-\frac{3}{4}\right|\,|\mathbf{p}| = \frac{3}{4}\,|\mathbf{p}|$

    $\therefore$ **q** is $\frac{3}{4}$ as long as **p**, but has the opposite direction.

EXERCISE 15H

1 What two facts can be deduced if:

    a $\mathbf{p} = 2\mathbf{q}$ **b** $\mathbf{p} = \frac{1}{2}\mathbf{q}$ **c** $\mathbf{p} = -3\mathbf{q}$ **d** $\mathbf{p} = -\frac{1}{3}\mathbf{q}$?

2 $\begin{pmatrix} 5 \\ 2 \end{pmatrix}$ and $\begin{pmatrix} k \\ -4 \end{pmatrix}$ are parallel. Find k.

3 Find the scalar t given that

    a $\begin{pmatrix} 3 \\ 2 \end{pmatrix}$ and $\begin{pmatrix} 9 \\ t \end{pmatrix}$ are parallel   **b** $\begin{pmatrix} -4 \\ 1 \end{pmatrix}$ and $\begin{pmatrix} t \\ -5 \end{pmatrix}$ are parallel.

4 If $\begin{pmatrix} 3 \\ a \end{pmatrix}$ and $\begin{pmatrix} 5a + 2 \\ 8 \end{pmatrix}$ are parallel, find a.

5 Use vector methods only to show that P$(-2, 5)$, Q$(3, 1)$, R$(2, -1)$ and S$(-3, 3)$, form the vertices of a parallelogram.

6 Use vector methods to find the remaining vertex of parallelogram ABCD:

> Vertices are always listed in order, so PQRS is
>
> either
>
>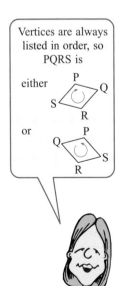
>
> or

  a

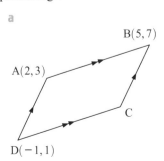

  b

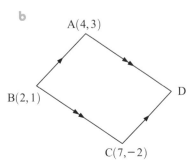

THE SCALAR PRODUCT OF TWO VECTORS

Consider the two vectors $\mathbf{a} = \begin{pmatrix} a_1 \\ a_2 \end{pmatrix}$ and $\mathbf{b} = \begin{pmatrix} b_1 \\ b_2 \end{pmatrix}$ shown which make an angle of θ between them.

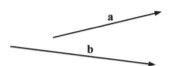

We can translate either of the vectors so that they both emanate from the same point.

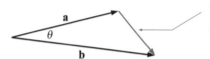

This vector is $-\mathbf{a} + \mathbf{b} = \mathbf{b} - \mathbf{a}$ and has length $|\mathbf{b} - \mathbf{a}|$.

Using the cosine rule, $\quad |\mathbf{b} - \mathbf{a}|^2 = |\mathbf{a}|^2 + |\mathbf{b}|^2 - 2\,|\mathbf{a}|\,|\mathbf{b}|\cos\theta$

$$\text{But} \quad \mathbf{b} - \mathbf{a} = \begin{pmatrix} b_1 \\ b_2 \end{pmatrix} - \begin{pmatrix} a_1 \\ a_2 \end{pmatrix} = \begin{pmatrix} b_1 - a_1 \\ b_2 - a_2 \end{pmatrix}$$

$$\therefore \quad (b_1 - a_1)^2 + (b_2 - a_2)^2 = a_1^2 + a_2^2 + b_1^2 + b_2^2 - 2\,|\mathbf{a}|\,|\mathbf{b}|\cos\theta$$

$$\therefore \quad b_1^2 - 2a_1 b_1 + a_1^2 + b_2^2 - 2a_2 b_2 + a_2^2 = a_1^2 + a_2^2 + b_1^2 + b_2^2 - 2\,|\mathbf{a}|\,|\mathbf{b}|\cos\theta$$

$$\therefore \quad 2\,|\mathbf{a}|\,|\mathbf{b}|\cos\theta = 2a_1 b_1 + 2a_2 b_2$$

$$\therefore \quad |\mathbf{a}|\,|\mathbf{b}|\cos\theta = a_1 b_1 + a_2 b_2$$

We notice that if $\mathbf{a}$ and $\mathbf{b}$ are perpendicular then $\theta = 90^\circ$. In this case $\cos\theta = 0$ and so $a_1 b_1 + a_2 b_2 = 0$.

So, with a test for perpendicularity foremost in our minds, we define the following **scalar product** or **dot product** for vectors $\mathbf{a}$ and $\mathbf{b}$.

If two vectors $\mathbf{a} = \begin{pmatrix} a_1 \\ a_2 \end{pmatrix}$ and $\mathbf{b} = \begin{pmatrix} b_1 \\ b_2 \end{pmatrix}$ make an angle of θ between them then $\mathbf{a} \bullet \mathbf{b} = a_1 b_1 + a_2 b_2 = |\mathbf{a}|\,|\mathbf{b}|\cos\theta$ is their **scalar** or **dot product**.

$a_1 b_1 + a_2 b_2$ is called the **algebraic form** of scalar product.

$|\mathbf{a}|\,|\mathbf{b}|\cos\theta$ is called the **geometric form** of scalar product.

We can now write down a test for whether two vectors are perpendicular:

$$\mathbf{a} \text{ is perpendicular to } \mathbf{b} \text{ if } \mathbf{a} \bullet \mathbf{b} = \mathbf{0}.$$

If $\mathbf{a}$ is perpendicular to $\mathbf{b}$ we write $\mathbf{a} \perp \mathbf{b}$.

Example 18   ◀) **Self Tutor**

For the vectors $\mathbf{p} = \begin{pmatrix} 3 \\ 1 \end{pmatrix}$ and $\mathbf{q} = \begin{pmatrix} 2 \\ -1 \end{pmatrix}$ find:

a $\mathbf{p} \bullet \mathbf{q}$

b   the angle between $\mathbf{p}$ and $\mathbf{q}$.

a $\mathbf{p} \bullet \mathbf{q}$

$= \begin{pmatrix} 3 \\ 1 \end{pmatrix} \bullet \begin{pmatrix} 2 \\ -1 \end{pmatrix}$

$= 6 + -1$

$= 5$

b $\mathbf{p} \bullet \mathbf{q} = |\mathbf{p}|\,|\mathbf{q}| \cos\theta$

$\therefore \quad 5 = \sqrt{9+1}\sqrt{4+1} \cos\theta$

$\therefore \quad 5 = \sqrt{10}\sqrt{5} \cos\theta$

$\therefore \quad 5 = 5\sqrt{2} \cos\theta$

$\therefore \quad \frac{1}{\sqrt{2}} = \cos\theta$

$\therefore \quad \theta = 45^{o}$

Example 19   ◀) **Self Tutor**

If the two vectors $\mathbf{a} = \begin{pmatrix} 2 \\ -5 \end{pmatrix}$ and $\mathbf{b} = \begin{pmatrix} t \\ -3 \end{pmatrix}$ are perpendicular, find t.

As $\mathbf{a} \perp \mathbf{b}$, $\mathbf{a} \bullet \mathbf{b} = 0$

$\therefore \quad \begin{pmatrix} 2 \\ -5 \end{pmatrix} \bullet \begin{pmatrix} t \\ -3 \end{pmatrix} = 0$

$\therefore \quad 2t + 15 = 0$

$\therefore \quad t = -\frac{15}{2}$

Example 20   ◀) **Self Tutor**

Find the measure of angle $A\widehat{C}B$ for $A(3, -1)$, $B(2, 0)$ and $C(-1, 4)$.

We draw both vectors so they emanate from C.

$\overrightarrow{CA} = \begin{pmatrix} 4 \\ -5 \end{pmatrix}$ and $\overrightarrow{CB} = \begin{pmatrix} 3 \\ -4 \end{pmatrix}$

Now $\overrightarrow{CA} \bullet \overrightarrow{CB} = |\overrightarrow{CA}|\,|\overrightarrow{CB}| \cos\theta$

$\therefore \quad 12 + 20 = \sqrt{16+25}\sqrt{9+16} \cos\theta$

$\therefore \quad 32 = \sqrt{41} \times 5 \cos\theta$

$\therefore \quad \cos\theta = \dfrac{32}{5\sqrt{41}}$

$\therefore \quad \theta = \cos^{-1}\left(\dfrac{32}{5\sqrt{41}}\right) \approx 1.79^{o}$

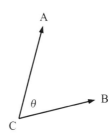

So, the measure of angle $A\widehat{C}B$ is about 1.79^{o}.

EXERCISE 15I.1

1 For the vectors **p** and **q**, find: **i** **p** • **q**   **ii** the angle between **p** and **q**.

a $\mathbf{p} = \begin{pmatrix} 1 \\ 3 \end{pmatrix}$, $\mathbf{q} = \begin{pmatrix} 2 \\ 1 \end{pmatrix}$

b $\mathbf{p} = \begin{pmatrix} 2 \\ 4 \end{pmatrix}$, $\mathbf{q} = \begin{pmatrix} 1 \\ 2 \end{pmatrix}$

c $\mathbf{p} = \begin{pmatrix} 2 \\ -4 \end{pmatrix}$, $\mathbf{q} = \begin{pmatrix} 2 \\ 1 \end{pmatrix}$

d $\mathbf{p} = \begin{pmatrix} -1 \\ 4 \end{pmatrix}$, $\mathbf{q} = \begin{pmatrix} 3 \\ 2 \end{pmatrix}$

e $\mathbf{p} = \begin{pmatrix} 3 \\ 4 \end{pmatrix}$, $\mathbf{q} = \begin{pmatrix} -5 \\ 12 \end{pmatrix}$

f $\mathbf{p} = \begin{pmatrix} 1 \\ -4 \end{pmatrix}$, $\mathbf{q} = \begin{pmatrix} -3 \\ 2 \end{pmatrix}$

2 Find t if:

a $\begin{pmatrix} t \\ 3 \end{pmatrix}$ is perpendicular to $\begin{pmatrix} 1 \\ -2 \end{pmatrix}$

b $\begin{pmatrix} -2 \\ t \end{pmatrix}$ is perpendicular to $\begin{pmatrix} 6 \\ t \end{pmatrix}$

c $\begin{pmatrix} t+2 \\ t \end{pmatrix}$ is perpendicular to $\begin{pmatrix} -4 \\ 3 \end{pmatrix}$

d $\begin{pmatrix} 2 \\ t^2 \end{pmatrix}$ is perpendicular to $\begin{pmatrix} t+4 \\ -3 \end{pmatrix}$.

3 Given the points   A(3, 2), B(−1, 3) and C(k, −4),   find k if $\widehat{ABC}$ is a right angle.

4 Find the measure of:

a $\widehat{ABC}$ for   A(−1, −2),   B(2, 4)   and   C(3, −1)

b $\widehat{BAC}$ for   A(4, 1),   B(3, −3)   and   C(−1, 6)

c $\widehat{PQR}$ for   R(2, 2),   P(−1, 5)   and   Q(3, −4)

d $\widehat{KML}$ for   K(4, 2),   L(3, 7)   and   M(5, −1).

5 Find the measure of all angles of triangle PQR for:

a P(−2, 4),   Q(3, −1)   and   R(1, 0)   **b** P(4, 1),   Q(−1, 3)   and   R(2, −1).

THE ANGLE BETWEEN TWO LINES

We have seen previously that the gradient of a line can be written as $\dfrac{y\text{-step}}{x\text{-step}}$.

So, if the gradient of a line is given by some fraction $\dfrac{a}{b}$, then the line has direction vector $\begin{pmatrix} b \\ a \end{pmatrix}$.

In the case of lines which continue infinitely in both directions, we agree to talk about the *acute* angle between them.

We therefore use the formula $\cos \theta = \dfrac{|\mathbf{a} \bullet \mathbf{b}|}{|\mathbf{a}| \, |\mathbf{b}|}$

where **a** and **b** are the direction vectors of the given lines l_1 and l_2 respectively.

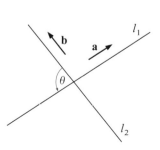

Example 21 ◄)) **Self Tutor**

Find the measure of the acute angle between the lines with equations $2x + y = 5$ and $2x - 3y = 18$.

$2x + y = 5$ has gradient $-\frac{2}{1}$ and $\therefore$ has direction vector $\mathbf{a} = \begin{pmatrix} 1 \\ -2 \end{pmatrix}$.

$2x - 3y = 18$ has gradient $\frac{2}{3}$ and $\therefore$ has direction vector $\mathbf{b} = \begin{pmatrix} 3 \\ 2 \end{pmatrix}$.

If the angle between the lines is θ, then

$$\cos \theta = \frac{|\mathbf{a} \bullet \mathbf{b}|}{|\mathbf{a}| \, |\mathbf{b}|} = \frac{|(1 \times 3) + (-2 \times 2)|}{\sqrt{1+4}\sqrt{9+4}}$$

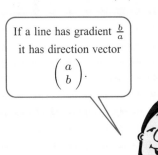

If a line has gradient $\frac{b}{a}$ it has direction vector $\begin{pmatrix} a \\ b \end{pmatrix}$.

$$= \frac{|-1|}{\sqrt{5}\sqrt{13}} = \frac{1}{\sqrt{65}}$$

$$\therefore \quad \theta = \cos^{-1}\left(\tfrac{1}{\sqrt{65}}\right) \approx 82.9^{o}$$

$\therefore$ the acute angle is about 82.9^{o}.

EXERCISE 15I.2

1 Find a direction vector for the line:

    a $y = x - 2$ **b** $y = -2x + 1$ **c** $3x - y = 7$ **d** $2x + 3y = 4$

2 Find the measure of the acute angle between the lines with equations:

    a $x + y = 5$ and $x + 2y = 6$ **b** $y = x + 3$ and $y = 1 - 4x$

    c $x + 2y = 1$ and $3x + y = 8$ **d** $y = 2x + 1$ and $x - 4y = 4$.

PROPERTIES OF THE SCALAR PRODUCT

For any vectors $\mathbf{a}$, $\mathbf{b}$, $\mathbf{c}$ and $\mathbf{d}$:

   ► $\mathbf{a} \bullet \mathbf{b} = \mathbf{b} \bullet \mathbf{a}$

   ► $\mathbf{a} \bullet \mathbf{a} = |\mathbf{a}|^2$

   ► $\mathbf{a} \bullet (\mathbf{b} + \mathbf{c}) = \mathbf{a} \bullet \mathbf{b} + \mathbf{a} \bullet \mathbf{c}$

   ► $(\mathbf{a} + \mathbf{b}) \bullet (\mathbf{c} + \mathbf{d}) = \mathbf{a} \bullet \mathbf{c} + \mathbf{a} \bullet \mathbf{d} + \mathbf{b} \bullet \mathbf{c} + \mathbf{b} \bullet \mathbf{d}$

We can prove these properties by using general vectors.

For example, let $\mathbf{a} = \begin{pmatrix} a_1 \\ a_2 \end{pmatrix}$, $\mathbf{b} = \begin{pmatrix} b_1 \\ b_2 \end{pmatrix}$ and $\mathbf{c} = \begin{pmatrix} c_1 \\ c_2 \end{pmatrix}$

$$\therefore \quad \mathbf{a} \bullet (\mathbf{b} + \mathbf{c}) = \begin{pmatrix} a_1 \\ a_2 \end{pmatrix} \bullet \begin{pmatrix} b_1 + c_1 \\ b_2 + c_2 \end{pmatrix} = a_1(b_1 + c_1) + a_2(b_2 + c_2)$$

$$= a_1 b_1 + a_1 c_1 + a_2 b_2 + a_2 c_2$$

$$= (a_1 b_1 + a_2 b_2) + (a_1 c_1 + a_2 c_2)$$

$$= \mathbf{a} \bullet \mathbf{b} + \mathbf{a} \bullet \mathbf{c}$$

EXERCISE 15I.3

1 Prove that $\mathbf{a} \bullet \mathbf{b} = \mathbf{b} \bullet \mathbf{a}$ for any two vectors $\mathbf{a}$ and $\mathbf{b}$.

2 Prove that $\mathbf{a} \bullet \mathbf{a} = |\mathbf{a}|^2$ for any vector $\mathbf{a}$.

3 Prove that $(\mathbf{a} + \mathbf{b}) \bullet (\mathbf{c} + \mathbf{d}) = \mathbf{a} \bullet \mathbf{c} + \mathbf{a} \bullet \mathbf{d} + \mathbf{b} \bullet \mathbf{c} + \mathbf{b} \bullet \mathbf{d}$ for any vectors $\mathbf{a}$, $\mathbf{b}$, $\mathbf{c}$ and $\mathbf{d}$.

J   VECTOR PROOF (EXTENSION)

We can use vectors to prove important geometrical facts. The use of vectors in such proofs provides us with an alternative to using deductive or coordinate arguments. In fact, vector proofs are often easier.

USEFUL TOOLS IN VECTOR PROOF

- If $\mathbf{a} = k\mathbf{b}$ where k is a scalar then $\mathbf{a}$ and $\mathbf{b}$ are parallel and $|\mathbf{a}| = |k|\,|\mathbf{b}|$.

- If M is the midpoint of [AB] then $\overrightarrow{OM} = \frac{1}{2}\mathbf{a} + \frac{1}{2}\mathbf{b}$.

    Proof: $\overrightarrow{OM} = \overrightarrow{OA} + \overrightarrow{AM}$

    $= \overrightarrow{OA} + \frac{1}{2}\overrightarrow{AB}$

    $= \mathbf{a} + \frac{1}{2}(-\mathbf{a} + \mathbf{b})$

    $= \mathbf{a} - \frac{1}{2}\mathbf{a} + \frac{1}{2}\mathbf{b}$

    $= \frac{1}{2}\mathbf{a} + \frac{1}{2}\mathbf{b}$

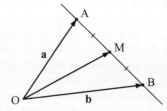

- $\mathbf{a}$ is perpendicular to $\mathbf{b}$ if $\mathbf{a} \bullet \mathbf{b} = 0$.
- Properties of scalar product (see above).

Example 22   ◀) **Self Tutor**

Use vector geometry to prove the 'midpoint theorem':
The line joining the midpoints of two sides of a triangle is parallel to the third side and half its length.

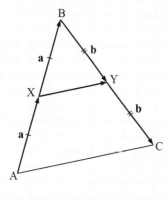

In triangle ABC, X and Y are the midpoints of [AB] and [BC] respectively.

So,   let $\overrightarrow{AX} = \overrightarrow{XB} = \mathbf{a}$

and $\overrightarrow{BY} = \overrightarrow{YC} = \mathbf{b}$.

Now $\overrightarrow{XY} = \overrightarrow{XB} + \overrightarrow{BY} = \mathbf{a} + \mathbf{b}$

and $\overrightarrow{AC} = \overrightarrow{AB} + \overrightarrow{BC} = 2\mathbf{a} + 2\mathbf{b}$

$\therefore \quad \overrightarrow{XY} = \frac{1}{2}(\overrightarrow{AC})$

Thus   [XY] $\parallel$ [AC]   and   XY $= \frac{1}{2}$(AC)

So,   [XY] is parallel to [AC] and half its length.

Example 23   ◀◢ **Self Tutor**

Use vector geometry to prove that: *The angle in a semi-circle is a right angle.*

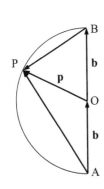

Let $\overrightarrow{OP} = \mathbf{p}$ and $\overrightarrow{AO} = \overrightarrow{OB} = \mathbf{b}$ {radii in same direction}

$\therefore\quad \overrightarrow{AP} = \mathbf{b} + \mathbf{p}$ and $\overrightarrow{BP} = -\mathbf{b} + \mathbf{p}$

$\therefore\quad \overrightarrow{AP} \bullet \overrightarrow{BP} = (\mathbf{b} + \mathbf{p}) \bullet (-\mathbf{b} + \mathbf{p})$

$\qquad = -\mathbf{b} \bullet \mathbf{b} + \mathbf{b} \bullet \mathbf{p} - \mathbf{p} \bullet \mathbf{b} + \mathbf{p} \bullet \mathbf{p}$

$\qquad = -|\mathbf{b}|^2 + |\mathbf{p}|^2$ $\{\mathbf{b} \bullet \mathbf{p} = \mathbf{p} \bullet \mathbf{b}$ and $\mathbf{b} \bullet \mathbf{b} = |\mathbf{b}|^2\}$

$\qquad = -|\mathbf{p}|^2 + |\mathbf{p}|^2$ {as $|\mathbf{b}| = |\mathbf{p}|$}

$\qquad = 0$

$\therefore\quad \overrightarrow{AP}$ is perpendicular to $\overrightarrow{BP}$

$\therefore\quad A\widehat{P}B$ is a right angle regardless of P's position.

EXERCISE 15J

1 Prove that: *If a pair of opposite sides of a quadrilateral are parallel and*
        equal in length, then the quadrilateral is a parallelogram.

Hint: Consider

Let $\overrightarrow{AB} = \overrightarrow{DC} = \mathbf{r}$ and $\overrightarrow{AD} = \mathbf{s}$.
Then find $\overrightarrow{BC} = \overrightarrow{BA} + \overrightarrow{AD} + \overrightarrow{DC}$
in terms of $\mathbf{r}$ and $\mathbf{s}$.

2 Prove that: *The diagonals of a parallelogram bisect each other.*

Hint: Consider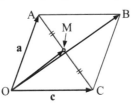

Assume that M is the midpoint of
[AC], then find $\overrightarrow{OB}$ and $\overrightarrow{OM}$ in
terms of $\mathbf{a}$ and $\mathbf{c}$.

3 ABCD is a quadrilateral in which
    BP = PD   and   AP = PC.
    Let $\overrightarrow{AP} = \mathbf{r}$ and $\overrightarrow{PB} = \mathbf{s}$.

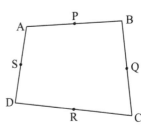

  a Find, in terms of $\mathbf{r}$ and $\mathbf{s}$:

   i $\overrightarrow{PC}$ and $\overrightarrow{DP}$ **ii** $\overrightarrow{AB}$ and $\overrightarrow{DC}$.

  b What is the significance of the answers to **a ii**?

  c Copy and complete: *If the diagonals of a quadrilateral bisect each other .....*

4 P, Q, R and S are the midpoints of [AB], [BC], [CD]
    and [DA] respectively.

    Let $\overrightarrow{AP} = \mathbf{p}, \overrightarrow{BQ} = \mathbf{q}, \overrightarrow{CR} = \mathbf{r}$.

    Hence find vector expressions, in terms of $\mathbf{p}$, $\mathbf{q}$, and $\mathbf{r}$,

    for: **a** $\overrightarrow{AD}$ **b** $\overrightarrow{AS}$ **c** $\overrightarrow{PQ}$ **d** $\overrightarrow{SR}$.

    What can be deduced from **c** and **d**?

5 OABC is a parallelogram and M is the midpoint of [OC]. T lies on [AM] such that AT : TM = 2 : 1.

    a Prove that O, T and B are collinear.   **b** Find the ratio in which T divides [OB].

6 Prove that: *The line joining the apex to the midpoint of the base of an isosceles triangle is perpendicular to the base.*

    Hint: Use the figure:

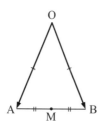

Let $\overrightarrow{OA} = \mathbf{a}$ and $\overrightarrow{OB} = \mathbf{b}$.

Find $\overrightarrow{OM}$ and $\overrightarrow{AB}$ in terms of $\mathbf{a}$ and $\mathbf{b}$, then find $\overrightarrow{OM} \bullet \overrightarrow{AB}$.

7 Prove that: *The diagonals of a rhombus are perpendicular.*

    Hint:

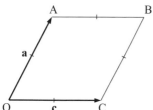

You may assume that a rhombus is a parallelogram.

Find $\overrightarrow{AC}$ and $\overrightarrow{OB}$ in terms of $\mathbf{a}$ and $\mathbf{c}$.

8 Triangle OAB is equilateral. [BP] is parallel to [OA] and a half of its length. [PQ] is parallel to [BA] and a quarter of its length.

    If $\overrightarrow{OA} = \mathbf{r}$ and $\overrightarrow{OB} = \mathbf{s}$:

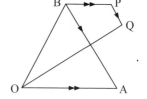

    a find vector expressions for $\overrightarrow{AB}$ and $\overrightarrow{OQ}$ in terms of $\mathbf{r}$ and $\mathbf{s}$

    b prove that [AB] is perpendicular to [OQ].

9 It is known that $|\mathbf{c} + \mathbf{d}| = |\mathbf{c} - \mathbf{d}|$ for two vectors $\mathbf{c}$ and $\mathbf{d}$. Prove that $\mathbf{c}$ and $\mathbf{d}$ are perpendicular:

    a using vector algebra   **Hint:** $|\mathbf{c} + \mathbf{d}|^2 = (\mathbf{c} + \mathbf{d}) \bullet (\mathbf{c} + \mathbf{d})$

    b using a vector diagram.

REVIEW SET 15A

1 Using a scale of 1 cm represents 10 units, sketch a vector to represent:

    a an aeroplane landing at an angle of $8°$ to the runway with a speed of 60 m s^{-1}

    b a displacement of 45 m in the direction $060°$.

2 For the following vectors **p**, **q** and **r**, show how to construct:

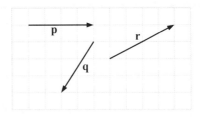

   a   **p** + **r**   **b**   **r** − **q** − **p**

3

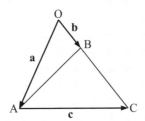

In the figure alongside, $\overrightarrow{OA} = \mathbf{a}$, $\overrightarrow{OB} = \mathbf{b}$, and $\overrightarrow{AC} = \mathbf{c}$.

Find, in terms of **a**, **b** and **c**:

   a $\overrightarrow{CA}$ **b** $\overrightarrow{AB}$ **c** $\overrightarrow{OC}$ **d** $\overrightarrow{BC}$

4 For points A, B, C and D, simplify the following vector expressions:

   a $\overrightarrow{AB} + \overrightarrow{BD}$ **b** $\overrightarrow{BC} - \overrightarrow{DC}$ **c** $\overrightarrow{AB} - \overrightarrow{CB} + \overrightarrow{CD} - \overrightarrow{AD}$

5 A yacht is moving at 10 km h^{-1} in a south easterly direction and encounters a 3 km h^{-1} current from the north. Find the actual speed and direction of the yacht.

6 What can be deduced about vectors **a** and **b** if $\mathbf{a} = \tfrac{1}{3}\mathbf{b}$?

7 If $\mathbf{p} = \begin{pmatrix} 4 \\ 3 \end{pmatrix}$, $\mathbf{q} = \begin{pmatrix} 3 \\ -5 \end{pmatrix}$ and $\mathbf{r} = \begin{pmatrix} 0 \\ -4 \end{pmatrix}$, find:

   a $2\mathbf{p} + \mathbf{q}$ **b** $\mathbf{p} - \mathbf{q} - \mathbf{r}$ **c** the length of **q**

8 Make **x** the subject of:

   a $3\mathbf{x} = \mathbf{a}$ **b** $\mathbf{a} - 2\mathbf{x} = \mathbf{c}$

9 Find the scalar k if $\begin{pmatrix} 2 \\ -3 \end{pmatrix}$ and $\begin{pmatrix} k \\ 6 \end{pmatrix}$ are:

   a parallel   **b** perpendicular.

10 Use vectors to find the remaining vertex of:

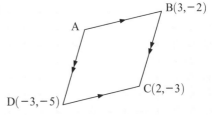

11 For the vectors $\mathbf{p} = \begin{pmatrix} 1 \\ 2 \end{pmatrix}$ and $\mathbf{q} = \begin{pmatrix} 3 \\ -2 \end{pmatrix}$ find:

   a $\mathbf{p} \bullet \mathbf{q}$ **b** the angle between **p** and **q**.

12 Find the measure of $\widehat{CBA}$ for A(1, 2), B(−2, 3) and C(0, −4).

REVIEW SET 15B

1 What can be said about vectors **p** and **q** if:

   a $|\mathbf{p}| = |\mathbf{q}|$ **b** $\mathbf{p} = 2\mathbf{q}$?

2 How are $\overrightarrow{AB}$ and $\overrightarrow{BA}$ related?

3 A pilot wishes to fly his aeroplane due east at a speed of 200 km h^{-1}. However, he is hampered by a wind blowing constantly at 40 km h^{-1} from the south.

   a In what direction must he head?

   b What would be his speed in still conditions?

4 Given   **a** ↗   and   ↘ **b**   illustrate $\mathbf{a} - \mathbf{b}$.

5 For $\mathbf{m} = \begin{pmatrix} 3 \\ -1 \end{pmatrix}$ and $\mathbf{n} = \begin{pmatrix} 2 \\ 4 \end{pmatrix}$ find:

   a $\mathbf{m} - 2\mathbf{n}$ **b** $|\mathbf{m} + \mathbf{n}|$.

6 Find t if $\begin{pmatrix} 2 \\ t \end{pmatrix}$ and $\begin{pmatrix} -3 \\ 4 \end{pmatrix}$ are:

   a perpendicular   **b** parallel.

7 Make **x** the subject of: **a** $\mathbf{n} = \frac{1}{2}\mathbf{x}$ **b** $\mathbf{a} - \mathbf{x} = \mathbf{b} + 2\mathbf{x}$.

8 For $A(-1, 1)$ and $B(2, -3)$ find:

   a $\overrightarrow{AB}$ **b** the distance AB.

9 Find the measure of the angle between $\mathbf{a} = \begin{pmatrix} 1 \\ 1 \end{pmatrix}$ and $\mathbf{b} = \begin{pmatrix} 1 \\ -2 \end{pmatrix}$.

10 For $P(1, 4)$, $Q(-2, 5)$ and $R(-1, -2)$, find the measure of $Q\widehat{R}P$.

11 In the given figure, $\overrightarrow{AB} = \mathbf{p}$ and $\overrightarrow{BC} = \mathbf{q}$. $\overrightarrow{DC}$ is parallel to $\overrightarrow{AB}$ and twice its length. Find, in terms of **p** and **q**:

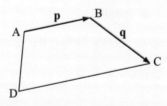

   a $\overrightarrow{DC}$ **b** $\overrightarrow{AC}$ **c** $\overrightarrow{AD}$.

12 Find the measure of the acute angle between the lines with equations $x + y = 8$ and $2x - 3y = 10$.

Chapter 16

Exponential functions and logarithms

Contents:

OPENING PROBLEM

In 1995, Australian scientists started testing the rabbit calicivirus on Wardang Island in an attempt to eradicate rabbits. The island was relatively isolated and overrun by rabbits and it thus provided an excellent test site. The disease was found to be highly contagious and the introduction of the virus had a dramatic impact on the island's rabbit population.

Scientists monitored rabbit numbers over a series of weeks and found that the number of rabbits R could be predicted by the formula

$R = 8000 \times (0.837)^t$ where t is the number of weeks after the calicivirus was released.

Consider the following questions:

1 If we let $t = 0$ weeks, how many rabbits were on the island?

2 If we let $t = 3\frac{1}{2}$ weeks, we get $R = 8000 \times (0.837)^{3.5}$. Discuss 'to the power of 3.5'.

3 How long would it take to reduce the rabbit numbers to 80?

4 Will all rabbits ever be eradicated?

5 What would the graph of rabbit numbers plotted against the time after the release of the virus look like?

INDEX NOTATION

We often deal with numbers that are repeatedly multiplied together, such as $5 \times 5 \times 5$.   We can use **indices** or **exponents** to conveniently represent such expressions.

Using **index notation** we would represent $5 \times 5 \times 5$ as 5^3,   which reads "5 to the power 3". We say that 5 is the **base** and 3 is the **index** or **exponent**.

> If n is a positive integer, then a^n is the product of n factors of a.
>
> $$a^n = \underbrace{a \times a \times a \times a \times \dots \dots \times a}_{n \text{ factors}}$$

A   INDEX LAWS

In previous years we have seen the following **index laws**. These laws are true for all positive bases a and b and all integer indices m and n.

- $a^m \times a^n = a^{m+n}$ To **multiply** numbers with the same base, keep the base and **add** the indices.

- $\dfrac{a^m}{a^n} = a^{m-n}$ To **divide** numbers with the same base, keep the base and **subtract** the indices.

- $(a^m)^n = a^{m \times n}$ When raising a power to a power, keep the base and **multiply** the indices.

- $(ab)^n = a^n b^n$ The power of a product is the product of the powers.

- $\left(\dfrac{a}{b}\right)^n = \dfrac{a^n}{b^n}$ The power of a quotient is the quotient of the powers.

- $a^0 = 1, \quad a \neq 0$ Any non-zero number raised to the power of zero is 1.

- $a^{-n} = \dfrac{1}{a^n}$ and $\dfrac{1}{a^{-n}} = a^n$ and in particular $a^{-1} = \dfrac{1}{a}$.

Example 1   🔊 Self Tutor

Express in simplest form with a prime number base:

a $\quad 9^4$
b $\quad 4 \times 2^p$
c $\quad \dfrac{3^x}{9^y}$
d $\quad 25^{x-1}$

---

a $\quad 9^4$

$\quad = (3^2)^4$

$\quad = 3^{2 \times 4}$

$\quad = 3^8$

b $\quad 4 \times 2^p$

$\quad = 2^2 \times 2^p$

$\quad = 2^{2+p}$

c $\quad \dfrac{3^x}{9^y}$

$\quad = \dfrac{3^x}{(3^2)^y}$

$\quad = \dfrac{3^x}{3^{2y}}$

$\quad = 3^{x-2y}$

d $\quad 25^{x-1}$

$\quad = (5^2)^{x-1}$

$\quad = 5^{2(x-1)}$

$\quad = 5^{2x-2}$

Example 2   🔊 Self Tutor

Remove the brackets of: a $\quad (2x)^3$ b $\quad \left(\dfrac{3c}{b}\right)^4$

---

a $\quad (2x)^3$

$\quad = 2^3 \times x^3$

$\quad = 8x^3$

b $\quad \left(\dfrac{3c}{b}\right)^4$

$\quad = \dfrac{3^4 \times c^4}{b^4}$

$\quad = \dfrac{81c^4}{b^4}$

Remember that each factor within the brackets has to be raised to the power outside them.

Example 3   🔊 Self Tutor

Simplify, giving answers in simplest rational form:

a $\quad 7^0$ b $\quad 3^{-2}$ c $\quad 3^0 - 3^{-1}$ d $\quad \left(\tfrac{5}{3}\right)^{-2}$

---

a $\quad 7^0 = 1$

b $\quad 3^{-2} = \dfrac{1}{3^2} = \tfrac{1}{9}$

c $\quad 3^0 - 3^{-1} = 1 - \tfrac{1}{3} = \tfrac{2}{3}$

d $\quad \left(\tfrac{5}{3}\right)^{-2} = \left(\tfrac{3}{5}\right)^2 = \tfrac{9}{25}$

Notice that

$$\left(\frac{a}{b}\right)^{-2} = \left(\frac{b}{a}\right)^{2}$$

EXERCISE 16A

1   Simplify using $a^m \times a^n = a^{m+n}$:

   a $3^2 \times 3^5$ b $4^3 \times 4^2$ c $x^6 \times x^3$ d $x^9 \times x$

   e $y^5 \times y^4$ f $x^5 \times x^n$ g $y^m \times y^2$ h $t^3 \times t^4 \times t^5$

2   Simplify using $\dfrac{a^m}{a^n} = a^{m-n}$:

   a $\dfrac{3^6}{3^2}$ b $\dfrac{7^9}{7^5}$ c $8^4 \div 8^3$ d $\dfrac{x^7}{x^3}$

   e $\dfrac{y^9}{y^4}$ f $\dfrac{t^6}{t^x}$ g $\dfrac{p^n}{p^2}$ h $t^{3m} \div t$

3   Simplify using $(a^m)^n = a^{mn}$:

   a $(5^3)^2$ b $(3^4)^5$ c $(2^3)^6$ d $(t^4)^3$

   e $(x^2)^7$ f $(y^3)^m$ g $(m^a)^5$ h $(a^{3m})^4$

4   Express in simplest form with a prime number base:

   a 4 b 16 c 27 d 4^2

   e 25^2 f $2^t \times 8$ g $3^a \div 3$ h $2^n \times 4^n$

   i $\dfrac{9}{3^x}$ j $\dfrac{5^{n+2}}{5^{n-2}}$ k $(3^4)^{a+1}$ l $3^x \times 3^{4-x}$

   m $\dfrac{4^a}{2^b}$ n $\dfrac{8^x}{16^y}$ o $\dfrac{5^{1+x}}{5^{x-1}}$ p $\dfrac{3^a \times 9^a}{27^{a+2}}$

5   Remove the brackets of:

   a $(xy)^2$ b $(ab)^3$ c $(rs)^4$ d $(xyz)^2$

   e $(2a)^3$ f $(3b)^3$ g $(5a)^4$ h $(3xy)^3$

   i $(10xy)^5$ j $\left(\dfrac{p}{q}\right)^2$ k $\left(\dfrac{m}{n}\right)^3$ l $\left(\dfrac{2a}{b}\right)^4$

6   Simplify the following expressions using one or more of the index laws:

   a $\dfrac{x^4}{x}$ b $4b^2 \times 2b^3$ c $\dfrac{a^6 b^3}{a^4 b}$

   d $\dfrac{18x^6}{3x^3}$ e $\dfrac{5x^3 y^2}{15xy}$ f $\dfrac{24t^6 r^4}{15t^6 r^2}$

   g $3pq^3 \times 5p^5$ h $\dfrac{x^{12}}{(x^3)^2}$ i $\dfrac{t^6 \times t^4}{(t^2)^3}$

7   Simplify, giving answers in simplest rational form:

   a 3^0 b 6^{-1} c 4^{-1} d 5^0

   e 3^2 f 3^{-2} g 5^3 h 5^{-3}

   i 7^2 j 7^{-2} k 10^3 l 10^{-3}

8 Simplify, giving answers in simplest rational form:

a $\left(\frac{1}{2}\right)^0$

b $\dfrac{5^4}{5^4}$

c $2t^0$

d $(2t)^0$

e 7^0

f 3×4^0

g $\dfrac{5^3}{5^5}$

h $\dfrac{2^6}{2^{10}}$

i $\left(\frac{1}{4}\right)^{-1}$

j $\left(\frac{3}{8}\right)^{-1}$

k $\left(\frac{2}{3}\right)^{-1}$

l $\left(\frac{1}{5}\right)^{-1}$

m $2^0 + 2^1$

n $5^0 - 5^{-1}$

o $3^0 + 3^1 - 3^{-1}$

p $\left(\frac{1}{3}\right)^{-2}$

q $\left(\frac{2}{3}\right)^{-3}$

r $\left(1\frac{1}{2}\right)^{-3}$

s $\left(\frac{4}{5}\right)^{-2}$

t $\left(2\frac{1}{2}\right)^{-2}$

9 Write the following without brackets or negative indices:

a $(3b)^{-1}$

b $3b^{-1}$

c $7a^{-1}$

d $(7a)^{-1}$

e $\left(\dfrac{1}{t}\right)^{-2}$

f $(4t)^{-2}$

g $(5t)^{-2}$

h $(5t^{-2})^{-1}$

i xy^{-1}

j $(xy)^{-1}$

k xy^{-3}

l $(xy)^{-3}$

m $(3pq)^{-1}$

n $3(pq)^{-1}$

o $3pq^{-1}$

p $\dfrac{(xy)^3}{y^{-2}}$

10 Find the smaller of 2^{125} and 3^{75} without a calculator.
Hint: $2^{125} = (2^5)^{25}$

B   RATIONAL (FRACTIONAL) INDICES

The index laws we used in the previous section can also be applied to rational indices, or indices which are written as a fraction.

In previous years we have established that: $a^{\frac{1}{2}} = \sqrt{a}$ and $a^{\frac{1}{3}} = \sqrt[3]{a}.$

In general, $a^{\frac{1}{n}} = \sqrt[n]{a}$ where $\sqrt[n]{a}$ is called the 'nth root of a'.

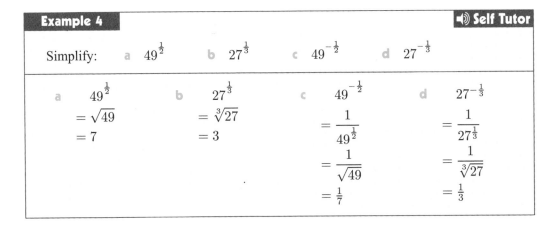

INVESTIGATION 1   **RATIONAL INDICES**

This investigation will help you discover the meaning of numbers raised to rational indices of the form $\dfrac{m}{n}$ where $m, n \in \mathbb{Z}$.

For example, what does $8^{\frac{2}{3}}$ mean?

What to do:

1 Use the graphing package to draw the graphs of $y = 8^x$ and $x = \frac{2}{3}$ on the same set of axes.

Find the value of $8^{\frac{2}{3}}$ by locating the intersection of the two graphs.   **GRAPHING PACKAGE**

2 Use the rule $(a^m)^n$ to simplify $\left(8^2\right)^{\frac{1}{3}}$ and $\left(8^{\frac{1}{3}}\right)^2$.

3 Simplify $\left(8^2\right)^{\frac{1}{3}} = \sqrt[3]{8^2} = \ldots\ldots$

Simplify $\left(8^{\frac{1}{3}}\right)^2 = \left(\sqrt[3]{8}\right)^2 = \ldots\ldots$

4 Use **3** to write $a^{\frac{m}{n}}$ in two different forms.

From the investigation you should have discovered that $a^{\frac{m}{n}} = \sqrt[n]{a^m}$ or $\left(\sqrt[n]{a}\right)^m$.

In practice we seldom use these laws, but they do help to give meaning to rational indices.

EXERCISE 16B

1 Evaluate the following without using a calculator:

    a $4^{\frac{1}{2}}$ **b** $4^{-\frac{1}{2}}$ **c** $16^{\frac{1}{2}}$ **d** $16^{-\frac{1}{2}}$

    e $25^{\frac{1}{2}}$ **f** $25^{-\frac{1}{2}}$ **g** $8^{\frac{1}{3}}$ **h** $8^{-\frac{1}{3}}$

    i $64^{\frac{1}{3}}$ **j** $64^{-\frac{1}{3}}$ **k** $32^{\frac{1}{5}}$ **l** $32^{-\frac{1}{5}}$

    m $125^{\frac{1}{3}}$ **n** $(-125)^{\frac{1}{3}}$ **o** $(-1)^{\frac{1}{2}}$ **p** $(-1)^{\frac{1}{3}}$

2 Write the following in index form:

    a $\sqrt{10}$ **b** $\dfrac{1}{\sqrt{10}}$ **c** $\sqrt[3]{15}$ **d** $\dfrac{1}{\sqrt[3]{15}}$

    e $\sqrt[4]{19}$ **f** $\dfrac{1}{\sqrt[4]{19}}$ **g** $\sqrt[5]{13}$ **h** $\dfrac{1}{\sqrt[5]{13}}$

3 Use your calculator to evaluate, correct to 4 significant figures where necessary:

    a $\sqrt[3]{64}$ **b** $\sqrt[4]{81}$ **c** $\sqrt[5]{1024}$ **d** $\sqrt[3]{200}$

    e $\sqrt[4]{400}$ **f** $\sqrt[5]{1000}$ **g** $\sqrt[7]{128}$ **h** $\sqrt[3]{10.83}$

4 Without using a calculator, find the value of the following:

    a $8^{\frac{4}{3}}$ **b** $8^{-\frac{2}{3}}$ **c** $4^{\frac{3}{2}}$ **d** $4^{-\frac{3}{2}}$ **e** $27^{\frac{2}{3}}$ **f** $27^{-\frac{2}{3}}$

    g $32^{\frac{2}{5}}$ **h** $32^{-\frac{3}{5}}$ **i** $64^{\frac{5}{6}}$ **j** $125^{-\frac{2}{3}}$ **k** $81^{\frac{3}{4}}$ **l** $81^{-\frac{3}{4}}$

C   EXPONENTIAL FUNCTIONS

An **exponential function** is a function in which the variable occurs as part of the index or exponent.

The simplest exponential functions have the form $f(x) = a^x$ where a is a positive constant, $a \neq 1$.

For example, graphs of the exponential functions
$f(x) = 2^x$ and $g(x) = (\frac{1}{2})^x = 2^{-x}$
are shown alongside.

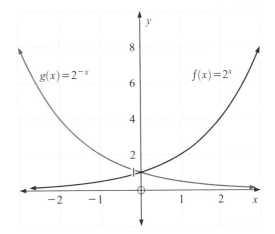

All graphs of the form $f(x) = a^x$ where a is a positive constant, $a \neq 1$:

- have a **horizontal asymptote** $y = 0$ (the x-axis)
- pass through (0, 1) since $f(0) = a^0 = 1$.

Example 5   ◄❱ **Self Tutor**

For the function $f(x) = 3 - 2^{-x}$, find: a $f(0)$ b $f(3)$ c $f(-2)$

a $f(0) = 3 - 2^0$	b $f(3) = 3 - 2^{-3}$	c $f(-2) = 3 - 2^{-(-2)}$
$= 3 - 1$	$= 3 - \frac{1}{8}$	$= 3 - 2^2$
$= 2$	$= 2\frac{7}{8}$	$= 3 - 4$
		$= -1$

EXERCISE 16C

1 If $f(x) = 3^x + 2$, find the value of: a $f(0)$ b $f(2)$ c $f(-1)$

2 If $f(x) = 5^{-x} - 3$, find the value of: a $f(0)$ b $f(1)$ c $f(-2)$

3 If $g(x) = 3^{x-2}$, find the value of: a $g(0)$ b $g(4)$ c $g(-1)$

4 a Complete the table of values shown for the function $f(x) = 3^x$.

x	-3	-2	-1	0	1	2	3
y							

    b Use the table of values in a to graph $y = f(x)$.

    c On the same set of axes and without a table of values, graph:

       i $y = -f(x)$ ii $y = f(-x)$ iii $y = f(2x)$ iv $y = 2f(x)$.

5   **a**   Click on the icon to obtain a printable graph of $y = 2^x$.

Use the graph to estimate, to one decimal place, the value of:

GRAPH OF
$y = 2^x$

    i $2^{0.7}$ **ii** $2^{1.8}$ **iii** $2^{-0.5}$.

  b   Check your estimates in **a** using the $\boxed{\wedge}$ key on your calculator.

  c   Use the graph to estimate, correct to one decimal place, the solution of the equation:

    i $2^x = 5$ **ii** $2^x = 1.5$ **iii** $2^x = -1$.

6   Find the image of:

  a $y = 2^x$ under the translation $\begin{pmatrix} -1 \\ 3 \end{pmatrix}$

  b $y = 3^x$ under the translation $\begin{pmatrix} 2 \\ -4 \end{pmatrix}$

  c $y = 2^{-x}$ under:

    i   a reflection in the x-axis   **ii**   a reflection in the y-axis

    iii   a reflection in the line $y = x$.

  d $y = 3^x$ under:

    i   a vertical dilation with factor 2   **ii**   a horizontal dilation with factor $\frac{1}{3}$.

7   Explain why $(-2)^x$ is undefined for some real numbers x.

INVESTIGATION 2   SOLVING EXPONENTIAL EQUATIONS GRAPHICALLY

Consider the exponential equation $3^x = 6$.

Since $3^1 = 3$ and $3^2 = 9$,   the solution for x must lie between 1 and 2.

A **graphics calculator** can be used to solve this equation by drawing the graphs of $y = 3^x$ and $y = 6$ and finding their **point of intersection**. To find out how to do this, consult the instructions on pages **21** to **24**.

Alternatively, click on the icon to obtain a graphing package.

GRAPHING PACKAGE

What to do:

1   Draw the graph of $y = 3^x$.

2   Estimate x when $y = 6$. On your calculator you can do this using **trace**.

3   Draw the graph of $y = 6$ on the same set of axes.

4   Check your estimate in **2** by finding the coordinates of the point of intersection of the graphs.

5   Solve for x, correct to 3 decimal places:

    a $3^x = 10$ **b** $3^x = 30$ **c** $3^x = 100$

    d $2^x = 12$ **e** $5^x = 40$ **f** $7^x = 42$

If using a calculator you may have to change the viewing window scales.

GROWTH AND DECAY

In this section we will examine situations where quantities are either increasing or decreasing exponentially. These situations are known as **growth** and **decay**, and occur frequently in the world around us.

For example, under favourable conditions the populations of animals and bacteria will grow exponentially. Radioactive substances and items that depreciate usually decay exponentially.

GROWTH

Under favourable conditions, a population of rabbits will grow exponentially.

Suppose the population is given by $P = 100 \times 2^t$ where t is the time in months.

We can use this relationship to answer questions about the rabbit population. For example, to find the population after $6\frac{1}{2}$ months, we substitute $t = 6.5$ and find

$$P = 100 \times 2^{6.5}$$
$$\approx 9051 \text{ rabbits.} \quad \{100 \boxed{\times} 2 \boxed{\wedge} 6.5 \boxed{\text{ENTER}} \}$$

Clearly, the population cannot continue to grow exponentially in the long term because eventually the rabbits will run out of food. Nevertheless, an exponential model is valuable and accurate in the short term.

Example 6 ◆) **Self Tutor**

During a locust plague, the area of land eaten is given by $A = 8000 \times 2^{0.5n}$ hectares where n is the number of weeks after the initial observation.

  a Find the size of the area initially eaten.

  b Find the size of the area eaten after: i 4 weeks   ii 7 weeks.

  c Use a and b to draw a sketch graph of A against n.

---

  a Initially, $n = 0$ $\therefore$ $A = 8000 \times 2^0$
$$\therefore A = 8000 \text{ hectares}$$

  b i When $n = 4$,
$$A = 8000 \times 2^{0.5 \times 4}$$
$$= 8000 \times 2^2$$
$$= 32\,000 \text{ ha}$$

    ii When $n = 7$,
$$A = 8000 \times 2^{0.5 \times 7}$$
$$= 8000 \times 2^{3.5}$$
$$\approx 90\,500 \text{ ha} \quad (3 \text{ s.f.})$$

EXERCISE 16D

1 A local zoo starts a breeding program to ensure the survival of a species of mongoose. From a previous program, the expected population in n years' time is given by $P = 40 \times 2^{0.2n}$.

    a What is the initial population purchased by the zoo?

    b What is the expected population after:

        i 3 years   ii 10 years   iii 30 years?

    c Sketch the graph of P against n using only a and b.

2 In Tasmania a reserve is set aside for the breeding of echidnas. The expected population size after t years is given by $P = 50 \times 2^{\frac{t}{3}}$.

    a What is the initial breeding colony size?

    b Find the expected colony size after:

        i 3 years   ii 9 years   iii 20 years.

    c Graph the population as t increases using only a and b above.

3 In Uganda, the number of breeding females of an endangered population of gorillas is G_0. Biologists predict that the number of breeding females G in n years' time will, if left alone by man, grow according to $G = G_0 \times 5^{0.07n}$.

    a If initially 28 breeding females are in the colony, find G_0.

    b Find G when i $n = 3$ years   ii $n = 10$ years   iii $n = 30$ years

    c Sketch the graph of G against n using a and b only.

DECAY

When the value of a variable decreases exponentially over time, we call it **decay**.

Examples of decay include: • cooling of a cup of tea or coffee

                      • radioactive decay

                      • the drop in current when an electrical appliance is turned off.

Example 7   ◀》 **Self Tutor**

The current I flowing through the electric circuit in a fan, t milliseconds after it is switched off, is given by $I = 320 \times 2^{-0.5t}$ milliamps.

    a Find the initial current in the circuit.

    b Find the current after i 4   ii 10   iii 20 milliseconds.

    c Sketch the graph of I against t using a and b only.

    a When $t = 0$, $I = 320 \times 2^{-0.5 \times 0}$

                        $= 320$ milliamps

b   **i**   When $t = 4$,
$$I = 320 \times 2^{-0.5 \times 4}$$
$$= 320 \times 2^{-2}$$
$$= 320 \times \tfrac{1}{4}$$
$$= 80 \text{ milliamps}$$

ii   When $t = 10$,
$$I = 320 \times 2^{-0.5 \times 10}$$
$$= 320 \times 2^{-5}$$
$$= 320 \times \tfrac{1}{32}$$
$$= 10 \text{ milliamps}$$

iii When $t = 20$,
$$I = 320 \times 2^{-0.5 \times 20}$$
$$= 320 \times 2^{-10}$$
$$= 320 \times \tfrac{1}{1024}$$
$$= \tfrac{5}{16} \text{ milliamps}$$

c

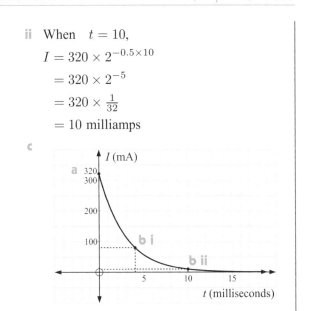

4   The weight of radioactive material in an ore sample after t years is given by
$W = 2.3 \times 2^{-0.06t}$ grams.

   a   Find the initial weight.

   b   Find the weight after   **i**   20 years   **ii**   200 years   **iii**   2000 years.

   c   Sketch the graph of W against t using **a** and **b** only.

   d   What is the percentage loss in weight from $t = 0$ to $t = 20$?

5   Boiling water is placed in a refrigerator and after t minutes its temperature is given by
$T = 100 \times 2^{-\frac{t}{4}}$ °C.

   a   Find the inital temperature of the water.

   b   Find the water temperature after   **i**   2 minutes   **ii**   10 minutes   **iii**   1 hour.

   c   Graph T against t using **a** and **b** only.

E   COMPOUND INTEREST

If you bank $1000, you are in effect lending the money to the bank. The bank in turn uses your money to lend to other people. The bank pays you interest to encourage your custom, and they charge interest to borrowers at a higher rate; this is how the bank makes money.

When you place money in the bank, the bank now owes you money, and we call this amount your **balance**. This balance is the **principal** on which the bank will pay you interest. After a period of time, the interest is automatically added to your account. When this happens, the next lot of interest will be calculated on the higher balance. This creates a **compounding** effect on the interest as you are getting **interest on interest**.

Consider an investment of $1000 with interest of 6% p.a. paid each year and compounded.

After year	Interest paid	Account balance
0	-	$1000.00
1	6% of $1000.00 = $60.00	$1000.00 + $60.00 = $1060.00
2	6% of $1060.00 = $63.60	$1060.00 + $63.60 = $1123.60
3	6% of $1123.60 = $67.42	$1123.60 + $67.42 = $1191.02

Notice the increasing amount of interest each year.

Each year, the account balance becomes $(100\% + 6\%)$ or 106% of its previous value.

$$\therefore \quad \text{the value after 3 years} = \$1000 \times 1.06 \times 1.06 \times 1.06$$
$$= \$1000 \times (1.06)^3$$
$$= \$1191.02$$

This suggests that if the money is left in your account for n years, it will amount to $\$1000 \times (1.06)^n$.

The **annual multiplier** is $(1 + i)$ where i is the annual interest rate expressed as a decimal.

These observations lead to the **compound growth formula**:

$$\boldsymbol{F_v = P_v(1 + i)^n} \quad \text{where} \quad F_v \text{ is the \textbf{future value}}$$
$$P_v \text{ is the \textbf{present value} or amount initially invested}$$
$$i \text{ is the \textbf{annual interest rate} as a decimal}$$
$$n \text{ is the \textbf{number of years of investment}.}$$

Example 8 ◀) **Self Tutor**

a What will $5000 invested at 8% p.a. compound interest amount to after 2 years?

b How much interest is earned?

Interest earned is $F_v - P_v$

a		b	
	$F_v = P_v(1 + i)^n$		Interest earned
$\therefore$	$F_v = 5000 \times (1 + 0.08)^2$		$= \$5832 - \$5000$
	$= 5000 \times (1.08)^2$		$= \$832$
	$= \$5832$		

FINDING THE PRINCIPAL

Example 9 ◀) **Self Tutor**

If I am able to invest at 8.5% p.a. compounding annually, how much should I invest now to achieve a maturing value of $10 000 in 4 years' time?

$$F_v = P_v(1+i)^n$$
$$\therefore \quad 10\,000 = P_v \times (1+0.085)^4 \quad \{\text{as } 8.5\% = 0.085\}$$
$$\therefore \quad 10\,000 = P_v \times (1.085)^4$$
$$\therefore \quad \frac{10\,000}{(1.085)^4} = P_v \qquad \{\text{dividing by } (1.085)^4\}$$
$$\therefore \quad 7215.74 = P_v \qquad \{\textit{Calculator:} \quad 10\,000 \boxed{\div} \; 1.085 \boxed{\wedge} \; 4 \boxed{\text{ENTER}} \}$$
$$\therefore \quad \text{I should invest} \quad \$7215.74 \quad \text{now.}$$

FINDING THE RATE OF INTEREST

The compound interest formula can also be used to find the annual rate of increase for investments.

Example 10   ◀⦂ **Self Tutor**

If I bought a bottle of wine for $550 and 5 years later it was valued at $1550, at what annual rate has my investment increased? Give your answer correct to two decimal places.

$$P_v(1+i)^n = F_v$$
$$\therefore \quad 550 \times (1+i)^5 = 1550$$
$$\therefore \quad (1+i)^5 = \frac{1550}{550} \qquad \{\text{dividing by } 550\}$$
$$\therefore \quad 1+i = \sqrt[5]{\frac{1550}{550}} \qquad \{\text{finding the fifth root of both sides}\}$$
$$\therefore \quad i = \sqrt[5]{\frac{1550}{550}} - 1 \qquad \{\text{subtracting 1 from both sides}\}$$
$$\therefore \quad i \approx 0.2303$$

$\{\textit{Calculator:} \quad \boxed{(} \; 1550 \boxed{\div} \; 550 \boxed{)} \; \boxed{\wedge} \; \boxed{(} \; 1 \boxed{\div} \; 5 \boxed{)} \; \boxed{-} \; 1 \boxed{\text{ENTER}} \}$

$\therefore \quad$ the investment increased by $\approx 23.03\%$ p.a.

EXERCISE 16E

1 Copy and complete the table to find the future value when €8000 is invested at 5% p.a. compound interest:

After year	Interest paid	Future value
0	-	€8000
1	5% of €8000 = €400	
2		
3		

2 **a** What will an investment of £40 000 at 10% p.a. compounding yearly amount to after 3 years?

 b What part of this is interest?

3 How much compound interest is earned by investing ¥ 50 000 at 8% p.a. compounding yearly, if the investment is over a 2 year period?

4 How much money must be invested now if you require $20 000 for a holiday in 4 years' time and the money can be invested at a fixed rate of 7.5% p.a. compounding annually?

5 What initial investment is required to produce a maturing amount of 15 000 euros in 60 months' time given that a fixed rate of 5.5% p.a. compounding annually is guaranteed?

6 Ken bought a valuable coin for €2000 and three years later sold it for €3500. Find the yearly rate of increase for this investment.

7 A block of land was purchased for $150 000 and 4 years later was sold for $270 000. Find the annual rate of increase for this investment.

8 The local council valued your house at £146 000 and 5 years later they valued it at £213 000. Find the annual rate of increase for the valuation of your house.

DEPRECIATION

Depreciation describes how goods diminish in value over time.

Motor cars, office furniture, computers, and many other items decrease in value as they age. We call this process **depreciation**.

Things usually depreciate because they become damaged and imperfect through use and time, or because their technology becomes superseded.

The following table shows how a computer bought for $1500 depreciates by 20% each year. Items are depreciated on their **reduced balance** each year. This creates a compounding effect similar to what we saw with interest in the previous section.

Age (years)	Depreciation	Value
0	-	$1500.00
1	20% of $1500.00 = $300.00	$1500.00 − $300.00 = $1200.00
2	20% of $1200.00 = $240.00	$1200.00 − $240.00 = $ 960.00
3	20% of $960.00 = $192.00	$960.00 − $192.00 = $ 768.00

At the end of each year, the computer is only worth $(100\% - 20\%) = 80\%$ of its previous value. Thus, we multiply by 0.8.

Its value after 1 year is $V_1 = \$1500 \times 0.8,$

after 2 years is $V_2 = V_1 \times 0.8 = \$1500 \times (0.8)^2,$

and after 3 years is $V_3 = V_2 \times 0.8 = \$1500 \times (0.8)^3.$

Depreciation is an example of exponential decay!

This suggests that after n years, the value will be $V_n = \$1500 \times (0.8)^n.$

The **depreciation formula** is:

$$F_v = P_v(1 - i)^n \qquad \text{where}$$

F_v is the **future value** after n time periods

P_v is the **original purchase price** or **present value**

i is the **depreciation rate per period** as a decimal

n is the **number** of periods.

Example 11   ◀) **Self Tutor**

A photocopier was purchased for \$18 500.

a Given that photocopiers generally depreciate at 15% per year, find its value after 5 years.

b By how much has it lost value?

a $P_v = 18\,500$ Now $F_v = P_v(1 - i)^n$

$\quad i = 0.15$ $\therefore \quad F_v = 18\,500(1 - 0.15)^5$

$\quad n = 5$ $\quad\quad = 18\,500(0.85)^5$

$\quad\quad\quad\quad\quad\quad\quad \approx \$8208.55$

b Depreciation $= \$18\,500 - \$8208.55 = \$10\,291.45$

Depreciation is $P_v - F_v$

EXERCISE 16F

1 A car was purchased for \$32 500, and its value depreciated annually by 16%. Find its value after 10 years.

2 A motorbike was purchased for £8495 in July 2004 and depreciated at 12% each year.

a Copy and complete the following table:

Number of years owned	Depreciation or annual loss in value	Value after n years
0	-	£8495
1	£1019.40	£7475.60
2		
3		
4		

b The motorbike is used for a delivery service, and so the depreciation each year can be claimed as a tax deduction. How much can be 'claimed' during the 4th year?

c Find the value of the motorbike at the end of the 8th year.

d What is the significance of $F_9 - F_{10}$?

3 a If I buy a car for \$38 500 and keep it for 3 years, what will its value be at the end of that period given an annual depreciation rate of 20%?

b By how much will it have depreciated?

4 A cabin cruiser was bought for €120 000 in April 1998 and was sold for €45 000 in April 2006. At what average annual rate of depreciation did the boat lose its value?

5 A small jet aeroplane was purchased for 3.4 million dollars in January 1998 and sold for 2.35 million dollars in July 2005. What was its average annual rate of depreciation over this period?

G   EXPONENTIAL EQUATIONS

An **exponential equation** is an equation in which the unknown occurs as part of the index or exponent.

For example: $2^x = 8$ and $30 \times 3^x = 7$ are both exponential equations.
If $2^x = 8$,   then $2^x = 2^3$.   Thus $x = 3$ is a solution, and it is in fact the only solution.

> If $a^x = a^k$,   then $x = k$.
>
> If the base numbers are the same, we can **equate indices**.

Example 12   ◀) Self Tutor

Solve for x: **a** $2^x = 32$ **b** $3^{x-2} = \frac{1}{9}$

If we can make the base numbers the same then we can equate the indices.

a $2^x = 32$	**b** $3^{x-2} = \frac{1}{9}$
$\therefore \quad 2^x = 2^5$	$\therefore \quad 3^{x-2} = 3^{-2}$
$\therefore \quad x = 5$	$\therefore \quad x - 2 = -2$
	$\therefore \quad x = 0$

Example 13   ◀) Self Tutor

Solve for x: **a** $6 \times 3^x = 54$ **b** $4^{x-1} = \left(\frac{1}{2}\right)^{1-3x}$

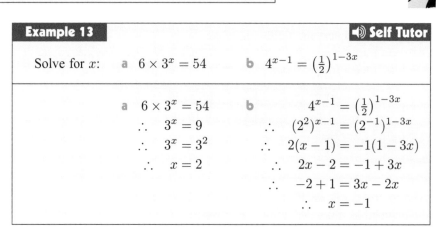

a $6 \times 3^x = 54$
$\therefore \quad 3^x = 9$
$\therefore \quad 3^x = 3^2$
$\therefore \quad x = 2$

b $4^{x-1} = \left(\frac{1}{2}\right)^{1-3x}$
$\therefore \quad (2^2)^{x-1} = (2^{-1})^{1-3x}$
$\therefore \quad 2(x-1) = -1(1-3x)$
$\therefore \quad 2x - 2 = -1 + 3x$
$\therefore \quad -2 + 1 = 3x - 2x$
$\therefore \quad x = -1$

EXERCISE 16G

1 Solve for x:

a $3^x = 3$	**b** $3^x = 9$	**c** $2^x = 8$	**d** $5^x = 1$
e $3^x = \frac{1}{3}$	**f** $5^x = \frac{1}{5}$	**g** $2^x = \frac{1}{16}$	**h** $5^{x+2} = 25$
i $2^{x+2} = \frac{1}{4}$	**j** $3^{x-1} = \frac{1}{27}$	**k** $2^{x-1} = 32$	**l** $3^{1-2x} = \frac{1}{27}$
m $4^{2x+1} = \frac{1}{2}$	**n** $9^{x-3} = 3$	**o** $\left(\frac{1}{2}\right)^{x-1} = 2$	**p** $\left(\frac{1}{3}\right)^{2-x} = 9$

2 Solve for x:

    a $5 \times 2^x = 40$ **b** $6 \times 2^{x+2} = 24$ **c** $3 \times \left(\frac{1}{2}\right)^x = 12$

    d $4 \times 5^x = 500$ **e** $8 \times \left(\frac{1}{2}\right)^x = 1$ **f** $7 \times \left(\frac{1}{3}\right)^x = 63$

    g $2^{2-5x} = 4^x$ **h** $5^{x-1} = \left(\frac{1}{25}\right)^x$ **i** $9^{x-2} = \left(\frac{1}{3}\right)^{3x-1}$

    j $2^x \times 4^{2-x} = 8$ **k** $3^{x+1} \times 9^{-x} = \left(\frac{1}{3}\right)^{x+1}$ **l** $2^{x^2-2x} = 8$

H   EXPANSION AND FACTORISATION

EXPANSION

To expand expressions like $7^x(7^{2x} - 1)$, $(3^x + 1)(3^x - 2)$ and $(2^x + 5)^2$ we can use the same expansion laws as seen previously:

$$a(b + c) = ab + ac$$
$$(a + b)(c + d) = ac + ad + bc + bd$$
$$(a + b)(a - b) = a^2 - b^2$$
$$(a + b)^2 = a^2 + 2ab + b^2$$

Example 14   ◄⦆ **Self Tutor**

Expand and simplify: $5^{-x}(3 \times 5^x - 5^{2x})$

$5^{-x}(3 \times 5^x - 5^{2x})$
$= 3 \times 5^{-x} \times 5^x - 5^{-x} \times 5^{2x}$ { $\times$ each term in the brackets by 5^{-x}}
$= 3 \times 5^{-x+x} - 5^{-x+2x}$
$= 3 \times 5^0 - 5^x$ {adding indices}
$= 3 - 5^x$

Example 15   ◄⦆ **Self Tutor**

Expand and simplify: **a** $(2^x + 3)(2^x + 5)$ **b** $(3^x - 3^{-x})^2$

  a $(2^x + 3)(2^x + 5)$
      $= (2^x)^2 + 5(2^x) + 3(2^x) + 15$ {using FOIL}
      $= 2^{2x} + 8(2^x) + 15$
      $= 4^x + 2^{3+x} + 15$

  b $(3^x + 3^{-x})^2$
      $= (3^x)^2 + 2(3^x)(3^{-x}) + (3^{-x})^2$ $\{(a + b)^2 = a^2 + 2ab + b^2\}$
      $= 3^{2x} + 2(3^0) + 3^{-2x}$
      $= 3^{2x} + 2 + 3^{-2x}$

EXERCISE 16H.1

1 Expand and simplify:

   a $2^x(2^x + 1)$ **b** $3^x(1 - 3^{-x})$ **c** $2^{-x}(2^x + 3)$ **d** $7^{-x}(7^{3x} + 7^x)$

2 Expand and simplify:

   a $(3^x + 1)(3^x + 2)$ **b** $(2^x + 1)(2^x + 5)$ **c** $(5^x - 3)(5^x - 7)$

   d $(2^x + 1)^2$ **e** $(3^x + 2)^2$ **f** $(4^x - 7)^2$

   g $(3^x + 1)^2$ **h** $(3^x - 8)^2$ **i** $(5^x - 3)^2$

   j $(2^x + 5)(2^x\ 5)$ **k** $(7^x + 7^{-x})^2$ **l** $(3 - 2^{-x})^2$

FACTORISATION

We first look for **common factors** and then for other forms such as **perfect squares** and the **difference of two squares**.

Example 16   ◀ッ **Self Tutor**

Factorise: **a** $3^{n+3} + 3^n$ **b** $2^{n+2} + 8$ **c** $5^{3n} + 5^{2n}$

$$
\begin{array}{lll}
\textbf{a} & \quad 3^{n+3} + 3^n & \textbf{b} \quad 2^{n+2} + 8 \\
& = 3^n 3^3 + 3^n & = 2^n 2^2 + 8 \\
& = 3^n(3^3 + 1) & = 4(2^n) + 8 \\
& = 3^n \times 28 & = 4(2^n + 2)
\end{array}
$$

$$
\begin{array}{l}
\textbf{c} \quad 5^{3n} + 5^{2n} \\
= 5^{2n}5^n + 5^{2n} \\
= 5^{2n}(5^n + 1)
\end{array}
$$

Example 17   ◀ッ **Self Tutor**

Factorise: **a** $9^x - 4$ **b** $25^x + 4(5^x) + 4$

$$
\begin{array}{ll}
\textbf{a} \quad 9^x - 4 & \\
= (3^x)^2 - 2^2 & \text{\{difference of two squares\}} \\
= (3^x + 2)(3^x - 2) & \{a^2 - 2^2 = (a + 2)(a - 2)\} \\[2mm]
\textbf{b} \quad 25^x + 4(5^x) + 4 & \\
= (5^x)^2 + 4(5^x) + 4 & \text{\{compare} \quad a^2 + 4a + 4\} \\
= (5^x + 2)^2 & \{a^2 + 4a + 4 = (a + 2)^2\}
\end{array}
$$

Example 18   ◀ッ **Self Tutor**

Factorise: $4^x - 9(2^x) + 20$

$$
\begin{array}{ll}
\quad 4^x - 9(2^x) + 20 & \\
= (2^x)^2 - 9(2^x) + 20 & \text{\{compare} \quad a^2 - 9a + 20\} \\
= (2^x - 4)(2^x - 5) & \{a^2 - 9a + 20 = (a - 4)(a - 5)\}
\end{array}
$$

Example 19   ◀) **Self Tutor**

Simplify: a $\dfrac{2^x + 6^x}{2^x}$ b $\dfrac{3^{n+1} - 3^n}{3^n}$ c $\dfrac{5^{n+2} + 5^n}{13}$

a $\dfrac{2^x + 6^x}{2^x}$

$= \dfrac{2^x + 2^x 3^x}{2^x}$

$= \dfrac{\overset{1}{\cancel{2^x}}(1 + 3^x)}{\underset{1}{\cancel{2^x}}}$

$= 1 + 3^x$

b $\dfrac{3^{n+1} - 3^n}{3^n}$

$= \dfrac{3^n 3^1 - 3^n}{3^n}$

$= \dfrac{\overset{1}{\cancel{3^n}}(3 - 1)}{\underset{1}{\cancel{3^n}}}$

$= 2$

c $\dfrac{5^{n+2} + 5^n}{13}$

$= \dfrac{5^n(5^2 + 1)}{13}$

$= \dfrac{5^n \times \overset{2}{\cancel{26}}}{\underset{1}{\cancel{13}}}$

$= 2 \times 5^n$

Example 20   ◀) **Self Tutor**

Solve for x: $9^x = 7(3^x) + 18$

$9^x = 7(3^x) + 18$

$\therefore \quad (3^2)^x - 7(3^x) - 18 = 0$

$\therefore \quad (3^x)^2 - 7(3^x) - 18 = 0$ {compare $a^2 - 7a - 18 = 0$}

$\therefore \quad (3^x - 9)(3^x + 2) = 0$ {$a^2 - 7a - 18 = (a - 9)(a + 2)$}

$\therefore \quad 3^x = 9 \quad \text{or} \quad 3^x = -2$

$\therefore \quad x = 2$ {as 3^x cannot be negative}

EXERCISE 16H.2

1   Factorise:

   a $3^{2x} + 3^x$ b $2^{n+2} + 2^n$ c $4^n + 4^{3n}$

   d $6^{n+1} - 6$ e $7^{n+2} - 7$ f $3^{n+2} - 9$

   g $5(2^n) + 2^{n+2}$ h $3^{n+2} + 3^{n+1} + 3^n$ i $2^{n+1} + 3(2^n) + 2^{n-1}$

2   Factorise:

   a $4^x - 9$ b $9^x - 25$ c $64 - 9^x$

   d $16 - 25^x$ e $4^x - 9^x$ f $25^x + 6(5^x) + 9$

   g $4^x + 10(2^x) + 25$ h $36^x - 14(6^x) + 49$ i $49^x - 4(7^x) + 4$

3   Factorise:

   a $4^x + 8(2^x) + 15$ b $4^x + 6(2^x) - 7$ c $9^x - 3(3^x) - 10$

   d $9^x - 6(3^x) + 8$ e $25^x + 4(5^x) - 12$ f $64^x + 3(8^x) - 4$

4   Simplify:

   a $\dfrac{3^n + 6^n}{3^n}$ b $\dfrac{4^m + 8^m}{4^m}$ c $\dfrac{4^m + 8^m}{1 + 2^m}$ d $\dfrac{7^b + 21^b}{7^b}$

   e $\dfrac{4^{n+2} - 4^n}{4^n}$ f $\dfrac{4^{n+2} - 4^n}{15}$ g $\dfrac{2^{m+n} - 2^n}{2^n}$ h $\dfrac{3^{n+2} - 3^n}{3^{n+1}}$

   i $\dfrac{2^n + 2^{n+1}}{2^n + 2^{n-1}}$ **j** $\dfrac{3^{m+1} - 3^{m-1}}{3^m + 3^{m+1}}$ **k** $\dfrac{2^{x+y} - 2^y}{2^y}$ **l** $\dfrac{2^{x+y} - 2^y}{2^x - 1}$

5 Solve for x:

   a $9^x + 3 = 4(3^x)$ **b** $4^x - 10(2^x) + 16 = 0$ **c** $4^x + 2^x = 20$

   d $9^x + 3(3^x) + 2 = 0$ **e** $25^x + 4(5^x) = 5$ **f** $25^x = 23(5^x) + 50$

   g $49^x + 7 = 8(7^x)$ **h** $64^x + 8 = 6(8^x)$ **i** $81^x = 8(9^x) + 9$

LOGARITHMS

In many exponential equations it is not possible to easily make the base numbers on both sides the same. For example, if $2^x = 5$ we cannot easily write 5 with a base number of 2.

To overcome this problem, we write both sides with a base of 10, and to do this we use **logarithms**.

> The **logarithm in base 10** of a positive number is its power of 10.
>
> So, any positive number a can be written in base 10 as $a = 10^{\log a}$.

INVESTIGATION 3   LOGARITHMS

The logarithm of any positive number can be evaluated using the ⬛log⬛ key on your calculator. You will need to do this to evaluate the logarithms in this investigation.

What to do:

1 Copy and complete:

Number	Number as a power of 10	log of number
10		
100		
1000		
100 000	10^5	$\log(100\,000) = 5$
0.1		
0.001		

2 Copy and complete:

Number	Number as a power of 10	log of number
$\sqrt{10}$		
$\sqrt[3]{10}$		
$\sqrt{1000}$		
$\dfrac{1}{\sqrt{10}}$		

3 Can you draw any conclusion from your table? For example, you may wish to comment on when a logarithm is positive or negative.

Example 21   ◀) **Self Tutor**

Write the following numbers as powers of 10:

  a 2   b 20

---

  a $2 = 10^{\log 2}$ b $20 = 10^{\log 20}$

      $\approx 10^{0.301\,029\,995}$ $\approx 10^{1.301\,029\,995}$

In **Example 21** above, notice that $\log 20 = \log 2 + 1$.

This is because $20 = 2 \times 10 = 10^{\log 2} \times 10^1 = 10^{1 + \log 2}$.

Example 22   ◀) **Self Tutor**

Solve for x using logarithms, giving answers to 4 significant figures:

  a $2^x = 100$ b $(1.12)^x = 3$

---

  a $2^x = 100$ b $(1.12)^x = 3$

  $\therefore\ (10^{\log 2})^x = 10^2$ $\therefore\ (10^{\log 1.12})^x = 10^{\log 3}$

  $\therefore\ \ x \times \log 2 = 2$ $\therefore\ \ x \times \log 1.12 = \log 3$

      $\therefore\ \ x = \dfrac{2}{\log 2}$ $\therefore\ \ x = \dfrac{\log 3}{\log 1.12}$

      $\therefore\ \ x \approx 6.644$ $\therefore\ \ x \approx 9.694$

  $\{2\ \boxed{\div}\ \boxed{\text{log}}\ 2\ \boxed{)}\ \boxed{\text{ENTER}}\ \}$ $\{\ \boxed{\text{log}}\ 3\ \boxed{)}\ \boxed{\div}\ \boxed{\text{log}}\ 1.12\ \boxed{)}\ \boxed{\text{ENTER}}\ \}$

EXERCISE 16I.1

1 Write the following as powers of 10 using $a = 10^{\log a}$:

    a 8   b 80   c 800   d 80 000

    e 0.03   f 0.003   g 0.3   h 0.000 003

    i 37   j 0.0614   k 26 700   l 0.006 372 1

2 Solve for x using logarithms, giving answers to 4 significant figures:

    a $10^x = 80$ b $10^x = 8000$ c $10^x = 0.025$

    d $10^x = 456.3$ e $10^x = 0.8764$ f $10^x = 0.000\,179\,2$

3 Solve for x using logarithms, giving answers to 4 significant figures:

    a $2^x = 3$ b $2^x = 10$ c $2^x = 400$

    d $2^x = 0.0075$ e $5^x = 1000$ f $6^x = 0.836$

    g $(1.1)^x = 1.86$ h $(1.25)^x = 3$ i $(0.87)^x = 0.001$

    j $(0.7)^x = 0.21$ k $(1.085)^x = 2$ l $(0.997)^x = 0.5$

4 The weight of bacteria in a culture t hours after it has been established is given by $W = 2.5 \times 2^{0.04t}$ grams. After what time will the weight reach:

    a 4 grams   b 15 grams?

5   The population of bees in a hive t hours after it has been discovered is given by
    $P = 5000 \times 2^{0.09t}$.

    After what time will the population reach:

    a   15 000   b   50 000?

LOGARITHM LAWS

The following laws are true for all logarithms:

- $\log(xy) = \log x + \log y$

- $\log \left(\dfrac{x}{y} \right) = \log x - \log y$

- $\log(x^n) = n \log x$

The following are proofs for the logarithm laws in base 10:

Proof: Consider $x = 10^{\log x}$ and $y = 10^{\log y}$.

$$xy = 10^{\log x} 10^{\log y}$$
$$= 10^{\log x + \log y}$$
$$\therefore \ \log(xy) = \log x + \log y$$

$$\frac{x}{y} = \frac{10^{\log x}}{10^{\log y}}$$
$$= 10^{\log x - \log y}$$
$$\therefore \ \log \left(\frac{x}{y} \right) = \log x - \log y$$

$$x^n = (10^{\log x})^n$$
$$= 10^{n \log x}$$
$$\therefore \ \log(x^n) = n \log x$$

Notice that $\log \left(\dfrac{1}{x} \right) = \log x^{-1} = -1 \log x$.   Hence $\log \left(\dfrac{1}{x} \right) = -\log x$.

Also,   since $\log 1 = \log 10^0$, $\log 1 = 0$.

Example 23	◀)) **Self Tutor**

Write as a single logarithm: a $\log 2 + \log 7$ b $\log 6 - \log 3$

a $\log 2 + \log 7$ b $\log 6 - \log 3$
       $= \log(2 \times 7)$ $= \log \left(\frac{6}{3} \right)$
       $= \log 14$ $= \log 2$

Example 24	◀)) **Self Tutor**

Simplify, without using a calculator:

$\dfrac{\log 49}{\log \left(\frac{1}{7} \right)}$

$$\frac{\log 49}{\log \left(\frac{1}{7} \right)} = \frac{\log 7^2}{\log 7^{-1}}$$

$$= \frac{2 \log 7}{-1 \log 7}$$

$$= -2$$

EXERCISE 16I.2

1   Write as a single logarithm in the form $\log k$:

   a $\log 6 + \log 5$ b $\log 10 - \log 2$ c $2 \log 2 + \log 3$

   d $\log 5 - 2 \log 2$ e $\frac{1}{2} \log 4 - \log 2$ f $\log 2 + \log 3 + \log 5$

   g $\log 20 + \log(0.2)$ h $-\log 2 - \log 3$ i $3 \log \left(\frac{1}{8}\right)$

   j $4 \log 2 + 3 \log 5$ k $6 \log 2 - 3 \log 5$ l $1 + \log 2$

   m $1 - \log 2$ n $2 - \log 5$ o $3 + \log 2 + \log 7$

2   Explain why $\log 30 = \log 3 + 1$ and $\log(0.3) = \log 3 - 1$

3   Without using a calculator, simplify:

   a $\dfrac{\log 8}{\log 2}$ b $\dfrac{\log 9}{\log 3}$ c $\dfrac{\log 4}{\log 8}$ d $\dfrac{\log 5}{\log \left(\frac{1}{5}\right)}$

   e $\dfrac{\log(0.5)}{\log 2}$ f $\dfrac{\log 8}{\log(0.25)}$ g $\dfrac{\log 2^b}{\log 8}$ h $\dfrac{\log 4}{\log 2^a}$

4   Without using a calculator, show that:

   a $\log 8 = 3 \log 2$ b $\log 32 = 5 \log 2$ c $\log \left(\frac{1}{7}\right) = -\log 7$

   d $\log \left(\frac{1}{4}\right) = -2 \log 2$ e $\log \sqrt{5} = \frac{1}{2} \log 5$ f $\log \sqrt[3]{2} = \frac{1}{3} \log 2$

   g $\log \left(\frac{1}{\sqrt{3}}\right) = -\frac{1}{2} \log 3$ h $\log 5 = 1 - \log 2$ i $\log 500 = 3 - \log 2$

5   $7^4 = 2401 \approx 2400$

   Show that $\log 7 \approx \frac{3}{4} \log 2 + \frac{1}{4} \log 3 + \frac{1}{2}$.

LOGARITHMIC EQUATIONS

The logarithm laws can be used to help rearrange equations. They are particularly useful when dealing with exponential equations.

Example 25   ◀)) **Self Tutor**

Write the following as logarithmic equations in base 10:

   a $y = a^3 b^2$ b $y = \dfrac{m}{\sqrt{n}}$

---

   a $y = a^3 b^2$ b $y = \dfrac{m}{\sqrt{n}}$

    ∴ $\log y = \log(a^3 b^2)$

    ∴ $\log y = \log a^3 + \log b^2$ ∴ $\log y = \log \left(\dfrac{m}{n^{\frac{1}{2}}}\right)$

    ∴ $\log y = 3 \log a + 2 \log b$ ∴ $\log y = \log m - \log n^{\frac{1}{2}}$

                                                  ∴ $\log y = \log m - \frac{1}{2} \log n$

Example 26   ◀)) **Self Tutor**

Write these equations without logarithms:

  a $\log D = 2x + 1$ **b** $\log N \approx 1.301 - 2x$

a $\log D = 2x + 1$	**b** $\log N \approx 1.301 - 2x$
$\therefore$ $D = 10^{2x+1}$	$\therefore$ $N \approx 10^{1.301 - 2x}$
or $D = (100)^x \times 10$	$\therefore$ $N \approx \dfrac{10^{1.301}}{10^{2x}} \approx \dfrac{20}{10^{2x}}$

Example 27   ◀)) **Self Tutor**

Write these equations without logarithms:

  a $\log C = \log a + 3 \log b$ **b** $\log G = 2 \log d - 1$

a $\log C = \log a + 3 \log b$	**b** $\log G = 2 \log d - 1$
$= \log a + \log b^3$	$= \log d^2 - \log 10^1$
$= \log(ab^3)$	$= \log \left(\dfrac{d^2}{10} \right)$
$\therefore$ $C = ab^3$	$\therefore$ $G = \dfrac{d^2}{10}$

EXERCISE 16I.3

1 Write the following as logarithmic equations in base 10:

  a $y = ab^2$ **b** $y = \dfrac{a^2}{b}$ **c** $y = d\sqrt{p}$ **d** $M = a^2 b^5$

  e $P = \sqrt{ab}$ **f** $Q = \dfrac{\sqrt{m}}{n}$ **g** $R = abc^2$ **h** $T = 5\sqrt{\dfrac{d}{c}}$

2 Write these equations without logarithms:

  a $\log Q = x + 2$ **b** $\log J = 2x - 1$ **c** $\log M = 2 - x$

  d $\log P \approx 0.301 + x$ **e** $\log R \approx x + 1.477$ **f** $\log K = \frac{1}{2}x + 1$

3 Write these equations without logarithms:

  a $\log A = \log B - 2 \log C$ **b** $2 \log p + \log q = \log s$

  c $-\log d + 3 \log m = \log n - 2 \log p$

RESEARCH

Write a one page report on the following topics:

- Who invented logarithms?
- The exponential e.
- Logarithms in bases other than 10, especially in base e.

LOGARITHMS IN OTHER BASES

We notice that if $10^x = b$ then $x = \log_{10} b$ or simply $\log b$.

In general, $a^x = b \iff x = \log_a b$ where the logarithm is in base a.

$\iff$ is read 'if and only if'

| **Example 28** | ◀) **Self Tutor** |

Write an equivalent logarithmic statement for $3^4 = 81$.

$$3^4 = 81$$
$$\therefore \quad \log_3(3^4) = \log_3 81$$
$$\therefore \quad 4\log_3 3 = \log_3 81$$
$$\therefore \quad 4 = \log_3 81 \qquad \{\text{since} \quad \log_3 3 = 1\}$$

EXERCISE 16I.4

1   Write an equivalent logarithmic statement for:

    a $\quad 2^3 = 8$ b $\quad 3^2 = 9$ c $\quad 5^{-1} = \frac{1}{5}$ d $\quad 2^5 = 32$

    e $\quad 7^0 = 1$ f $\quad 3^{-4} = \frac{1}{81}$ g $\quad 2^{-6} = \frac{1}{64}$ h $\quad 2^{\frac{1}{2}} = \sqrt{2}$

2   Write an equivalent exponential statement for:

    a $\quad \log_{10} 1000 = 3$ b $\quad \log_2 16 = 4$ c $\quad \log_3\left(\frac{1}{3}\right) = -1$

    d $\quad \log_4 1 = 0$ e $\quad \log_7\left(\frac{1}{49}\right) = -2$ f $\quad \log_{\frac{1}{7}}\left(\frac{1}{49}\right) = 2$

3   Find:

    a $\quad \log_3 9$ b $\quad \log_2 32$ c $\quad \log_2 \sqrt{2}$ d $\quad \log_4 \sqrt{2}$

    e $\quad \log_3 3\sqrt{3}$ f $\quad \log_6 1$ g $\quad \log_8 8$ h $\quad \log_8\left(\frac{1}{8}\right)$

    i $\quad \log_{\frac{1}{8}}\left(\frac{1}{8}\right)$ j $\quad \log_{\sqrt{2}}\left(\frac{1}{\sqrt{2}}\right)$ k $\quad \log_2\left(\frac{1}{\sqrt{2}}\right)$ l $\quad \log_8\left(\frac{1}{\sqrt{2}}\right)$

4   Solve for x:

    a $\quad \log_2 x = 2$ b $\quad \log_5 x = -2$ c $\quad \log_2(x+2) = 2$ d $\quad \log_5(2x) = -1$

GRAPHS OF LOGARITHMIC FUNCTIONS

Consider $\quad x = 2^y \iff y = \log_2 x$.

We know that $\quad 2^y > 0$ for all y, so the domain of $\quad y = \log_2 x$ is $\quad \{x \mid x > 0, x \in \mathbb{R}\}$

We can hence graph this function from a table of values using positive x:

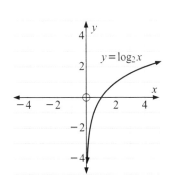

x	$\frac{1}{8}$	$\frac{1}{4}$	$\frac{1}{2}$	1	2	4	8
y	-3	-2	-1	0	1	2	3

Since $y = \log_2 x \iff x = 2^y$, the graph of $y = \log_2 x$ is a reflection of the graph of $y = 2^x$ in the line $y = x$.

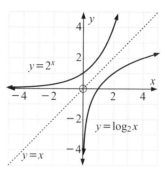

EXERCISE 161.5

1 On the same set of axes, graph $y = 3^x$ and $y = \log_3 x$.

2 On the same set of axes, graph $y = \left(\frac{1}{2}\right)^x$ and $y = \log_{\frac{1}{2}} x$.

3 Use graphical means to solve:

    a $\log_{10} x = x - 1$ **b** $\log_2 x = 2^{-x}$

GRAPHING PACKAGE

4 **a** Graph $y = \log_2 x$ and $y = \dfrac{\log_{10} x}{\log_{10} 2}$ on the same set of axes.

    b What do you notice from **a**?

    c Simplify $\dfrac{\log_{10} 20}{\log_{10} 2}$.

LINKS
click here

EARTHQUAKES

Areas of interaction:
Environments/Human ingenuity

REVIEW SET 16A

1 Simplify:

    a $2a^4 \times a^5$ **b** $\dfrac{a^b}{a^x}$ **c** $(3a^2)^3$

2 Express $\dfrac{4^{n+1}}{2^{2n}}$ in simplest form with a prime number base.

3 Simplify, giving answers in simplest rational form:

    a $3^0 + 3^{-1}$ **b** $\left(\frac{2}{5}\right)^{-2}$ **c** $64^{-\frac{1}{3}}$

4 If $f(x) = 3^x - 1$, find the value of:

    a $f(0)$ **b** $f(3)$ **c** $f(-1)$ **d** $f(-2)$

5 On the same set of axes, without using technology, draw the graphs of $y = 2^x$ and $y = 2^x + 2$.

    a State the y-intercepts and the equations of the horizontal asymptotes.

    b Describe the transformation required to draw the graph of $y = 2^x + 2$ from the graph of $y = 2^x$.

6 The weight of radioactive substance remaining after t years is given by $W = 1000 \times 2^{-0.03t}$ grams. Find:

   a the initial weight

   b the weight after: **i** 10 years   **ii** 100 years   **iii** 1000 years.

   c Graph W against t using **a** and **b** only.

   d How long will it take for the weight to reach 50 grams?

7 A bank offers 7.4% compound interest on amounts greater than £100 000 which are invested for a 5 year period. How much interest would be earned if £120 000 was invested?

8 A new caravan costing $15 000 depreciates at a rate of 16% p.a. What will be its value in 5 years' time?

9 Solve for x without using a calculator: $27^x = 3$

10 Expand and simplify:

   a $2^x(2^x - 2^{-x})$ **b** $(3^x + 2)(3^x - 1)$ **c** $(5^x - 2)^2$

11 Fully factorise:

   a $5^{n+2} - 5^n$ **b** $25 - 16^x$ **c** $4^x - 6(2^x) + 8$

12 Solve for x: $9^x - 2(3^x) - 3 = 0$

13 **a** Write 50 as a power of 10 using $a = 10^{\log a}$.

   b Solve $7^x = 2.32$ using logarithms, giving your answer to 4 significant figures.

14 Without using a calculator, simplify the following:

   a $\log 4 + \log 2$ **b** $\log a^2 - \log a$ **c** $\dfrac{\log 16}{\log 2}$

15 Find x given that $\log_2(x + 1) = -3$.

REVIEW SET 16B

1 Simplify:

   a $3xy^2 \times 5x^2y^3$ **b** $\dfrac{4x^2y}{8xy^3}$ **c** $\dfrac{(2a)^3}{ab^2}$

2 Write in simplest form without negative indices:

   a $(5x)^{-2}$ **b** $\dfrac{3x^2y}{y^{-4}}$ **c** $125^{-\frac{1}{3}}$

3 If $P(x) = 2 \times 3^{-x}$, find the value of:

   a $P(0)$ **b** $P(1)$ **c** $P(2)$ **d** $P(-1)$ **e** $P(-2)$

4 On the same set of axes, without using technology, draw the graphs of $y = 2^x$ and $y = 3 \times 2^x$.

   a State the y-intercepts and the equations of the horizontal asymptotes.

   b Describe the transformation required to draw the graph of $y = 3 \times 2^x$ from the graph of $y = 2^x$.

5 The weight of radioactive substance after t years is given by the formula $W = W_0 \times 3^{-0.003t}$ grams. Find:

   a the initial weight of radioactive substance

   b the percentage of the substance remaining after:

     i 100 years   **ii** 500 years   **iii** 1000 years.

   c Graph W against t using **a** and **b** only.

6 Henri and Michaela wish to have 800 000 euros saved in a superannuation fund in 20 years' time.

   a How much do they need to invest now if the fund earns 9.5% p.a.?

   b How much interest will be generated in this time?

7 A motor vehicle is purchased for \$25 000. What will be its value after a period of 6 years if it depreciates at a rate of $12\frac{1}{2}\%$ p.a.?

8 Find x, without using your calculator: $2^{1-x} = 8$

9 Expand and simplify:

   a $(3^x + 1)^2$ **b** $(5 - 2^x)^2$ **c** $(4^x - 2^{-x})^2$

10 Simplify:

   a $\dfrac{3^{n+1} - 3^n}{3^n}$ **b** $\dfrac{3^{n+1} - 3^n}{2}$ **c** $\dfrac{2^{n+1} + 2^n}{2^n + 2^{n-1}}$

11 Solve for x: $4^x - 9(2^x) + 8 = 0$

12 Solve using logarithms, giving your answer to 4 significant figures: $(0.2)^x = 1.8$

13 Without using a calculator, simplify the following:

   a $\log 8 - \log 2$ **b** $\frac{1}{3} \log 27$ **c** $\dfrac{\log 4}{\log \sqrt{2}}$

14 If $2^a = 3^{a+1}$, show that $a = \dfrac{\log 3}{\log(\frac{2}{3})}$.

Chapter 17

Quadratic functions

Contents:

In this chapter we will consider relationships between variables which are **quadratic** in nature. Such relationships can be described algebraically using **quadratic functions**.

OPENING PROBLEM

A cannonball fired vertically upwards from ground level has height given by the relationship $H = 36t - 3t^2$ metres, where t is the time in seconds after firing.

Consider the following:

1 If we sketch a graph of the height H against the time t after firing, what shape will result?

2 How long would it take for the cannonball to reach its maximum height?

3 What would be the maximum height reached?

4 How long would the person who fired the cannonball have to clear the area?

A   QUADRATIC FUNCTIONS

A **quadratic function** is a relationship between two variables which can be written in the form $y = ax^2 + bx + c$ where x and y are the variables and a, b, and c represent constants with $a \neq 0$.

Using function notation, $y = ax^2 + bx + c$ can be written as $f(x) = ax^2 + bx + c$.

FINDING y GIVEN x

For any value of x, the corresponding value of y can be found by substitution into the function equation.

Example 1	◀) Self Tutor

If $y = 2x^2 + 4x - 5$ find the value of y when: **a** $x = 0$ **b** $x = 3$.

a When $x = 0$,
$$y = 2(0)^2 + 4(0) - 5$$
$$= 0 + 0 - 5$$
$$= -5$$

b When $x = 3$,
$$y = 2(3)^2 + 4(3) - 5$$
$$= 2(9) + 12 - 5$$
$$= 18 + 12 - 5$$
$$= 25$$

FINDING x GIVEN y

When we substitute a value for y, we are left with a quadratic equation which we need to solve for x. Since the equation is quadratic, there may be 0, 1 or 2 possible values for x for any one value of y.

Example 2   ◀) **Self Tutor**

If $y = x^2 - 6x + 8$ find the value(s) of x when: a $y = 15$ b $y = -1$

a If $y = 15$ then
$$x^2 - 6x + 8 = 15$$
$$\therefore \quad x^2 - 6x - 7 = 0$$
$$\therefore \quad (x + 1)(x - 7) = 0$$
$$\therefore \quad x = -1 \quad \text{or} \quad x = 7$$
So, there are 2 solutions.

b If $y = -1$ then
$$x^2 - 6x + 8 = -1$$
$$\therefore \quad x^2 - 6x + 9 = 0$$
$$\therefore \quad (x - 3)^2 = 0$$
$$\therefore \quad x = 3$$
So, there is only one solution.

Example 3   ◀) **Self Tutor**

A stone is thrown into the air. Its height above the ground is given by the function $h(t) = -5t^2 + 30t + 2$ metres   where t is the time in seconds from when the stone is thrown.

  a   How high is the stone above the ground at time $t = 3$ seconds?

  b   From what height above the ground was the stone released?

  c   At what time is the stone's height above the ground 27 m?

a $h(3) = -5(3)^2 + 30(3) + 2$
$$= -45 + 90 + 2$$
$$= 47$$
$\therefore$ the stone is 47 m above the ground.

b The stone was released when $t = 0$ s.
$\therefore \quad h(0) = -5(0)^2 + 30(0) + 2 = 2$
$\therefore$ the stone was released from 2 m above ground level.

c When $h(t) = 27$,
$$-5t^2 + 30t + 2 = 27$$
$$\therefore \quad -5t^2 + 30t - 25 = 0$$
$$\therefore \quad t^2 - 6t + 5 = 0 \qquad \{\text{dividing each term by } -5\}$$
$$\therefore \quad (t - 1)(t - 5) = 0 \qquad \{\text{factorising}\}$$
$$\therefore \quad t = 1 \text{ or } 5$$
$\therefore$ the stone is 27 m above the ground after 1 second and after 5 seconds.

EXERCISE 17A

1 Which of the following are quadratic functions?

  a $y = 2x^2 - 4x + 10$ b $y = 15x - 8$ c $y = -2x^2$

  d $y = \frac{1}{3}x^2 + 6$ e $3y + 2x^2 - 7 = 0$ f $y = 15x^3 + 2x - 16$

2 For each of the following functions, find the value of y for the given value of x:

    a $y = x^2 + 5x - 14$ when $x = 2$ **b** $y = 2x^2 + 9x$ when $x = -5$

    c $y = -2x^2 + 3x - 6$ when $x = 3$ **d** $y = 4x^2 + 7x + 10$ when $x = -2$

3 State whether the following quadratic functions are satisfied by the given ordered pairs:

    a $f(x) = 6x^2 - 10$ $(0, 4)$ **b** $y = 2x^2 - 5x - 3$ $(4, 9)$

    c $y = -4x^2 + 6x$ $(-\frac{1}{2}, -4)$ **d** $y = -7x^2 + 9x + 11$ $(-1, -6)$

    e $f(x) = 3x^2 - 11x + 20$ $(2, -10)$ **f** $f(x) = -3x^2 + x + 6$ $(\frac{1}{3}, 4)$

4 For each of the following quadratic functions, find the value(s) of x for the given value of y:

    a $y = x^2 + 6x + 10$ when $y = 1$ **b** $y = x^2 + 5x + 8$ when $y = 2$

    c $y = x^2 - 5x + 1$ when $y = -3$ **d** $y = 3x^2$ when $y = -3$.

5 Find the value(s) of x for which:

    a $f(x) = 3x^2 - 3x + 6$ takes the value 6

    b $f(x) = x^2 - 2x - 7$ takes the value -4

    c $f(x) = -2x^2 - 13x + 3$ takes the value -4

    d $f(x) = 2x^2 - 10x + 1$ takes the value -11.

6 An object is projected into the air with a velocity of 80 m s^{-1}. Its height after t seconds is given by the function $h(t) = 80t - 5t^2$ metres.

    a Calculate the height after: **i** 1 second   **ii** 3 seconds   **iii** 5 seconds.

    b Calculate the time(s) at which the height is: **i** 140 m   **ii** 0 m.

    c Explain your answers in part **b**.

7 A cake manufacturer finds that the profit from making x cakes per day is given by the function $P(x) = -\frac{1}{2}x^2 + 36x - 40$ dollars.

    a Calculate the profit if: **i** 0 cakes   **ii** 20 cakes   are made per day.

    b How many cakes per day are made if the profit is $270?

B   GRAPHS OF QUADRATIC FUNCTIONS

The graphs of all quadratic functions are **parabolas**. The parabola is one of the *conic sections*.

Conic sections are curves which can be obtained by cutting a cone with a plane. The Ancient Greek mathematicians were fascinated by conic sections.

You may like to find the conic sections for yourself by cutting an icecream cone.

Cutting parallel to the side produces a parabola, as shown in the diagram opposite.

The name parabola comes from the Greek word for **thrown** because when an object is thrown, its path makes a parabolic arc.

There are many other examples of parabolas in every day life. For example, parabolic mirrors are used in car headlights, heaters, radar discs, and radio telescopes because of their special geometric properties.

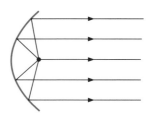

Alongside is a single span parabolic bridge. Other suspension bridges, such as the Golden Gate bridge in San Francisco, also form parabolic curves.

THE SIMPLEST QUADRATIC FUNCTION

The simplest quadratic function is $y = x^2$. Its graph can be drawn from a table of values.

x	-3	-2	-1	0	1	2	3
y	9	4	1	0	1	4	9

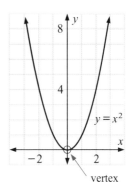

Notice that:

- The curve is a **parabola** and it opens upwards.
- There are no negative y values, i.e., the curve does not go below the x-axis.
- The curve is **symmetrical** about the y-axis because, for example, when $x = -3$, $y = (-3)^2 = 9$ and when $x = 3$, $y = 3^2 = 9$.
- The curve has a **turning point** or **vertex** at $(0, 0)$.

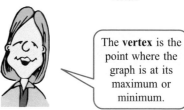

The **vertex** is the point where the graph is at its maximum or minimum.

Example 4 ◀) **Self Tutor**

Draw the graph of $y = x^2 + 2x - 3$ from a table of values from $x = -3$ to $x = 3$.

Consider $f(x) = x^2 + 2x - 3$

Now, $f(-3) = (-3)^2 + 2(-3) - 3$
$\quad\quad\quad = 9 - 6 - 3$
$\quad\quad\quad = 0$

We can do the same for the other values of x.
Tabled values are:

x	-3	-2	-1	0	1	2	3
y	0	-3	-4	-3	0	5	12

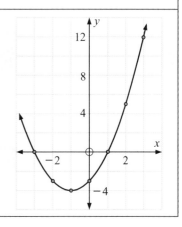

EXERCISE 17B.1

1 From a table of values for $x = -3, -2, -1, 0, 1, 2, 3$ draw the graph of:

   a $y = x^2 - 2x + 8$ **b** $y = -x^2 + 2x + 1$ **c** $y = 2x^2 + 3x$

   d $y = -2x^2 + 4$ **e** $y = x^2 + x + 4$ **f** $y = -x^2 + 4x - 9$

2 Use a **graphing package** or **graphics calculator** to check your graphs in question **1** .

GRAPHING PACKAGE

INVESTIGATION 1   GRAPHS OF QUADRATIC FUNCTIONS

In this investigation we consider different forms of quadratic functions, and how the form of the quadratic affects its graph.

GRAPHING PACKAGE

Part 1: Graphs of the form $y = x^2 + k$ **where k is a constant**

What to do:

1 Using a **graphing package** or **graphics calculator**:

   i graph the two functions on the same set of axes

   ii state the coordinates of the vertex of each function.

   a $y = x^2$ and $y = x^2 + 2$ **b** $y = x^2$ and $y = x^2 - 2$

   c $y = x^2$ and $y = x^2 + 4$ **d** $y = x^2$ and $y = x^2 - 4$

2 What effect does the value of k have on:

   a the position of the graph   **b** the shape of the graph?

3 What transformation is needed to graph $y = x^2 + k$ from $y = x^2$?

Part 2: Graphs of the form $y = (x - h)^2$

What to do:

1 Using a **graphing package** or **graphics calculator**:

   i graph the two functions on the same set of axes

   ii state the coordinates of the vertex of each function.

   a $y = x^2$ and $y = (x - 2)^2$ **b** $y = x^2$ and $y = (x + 2)^2$

   c $y = x^2$ and $y = (x - 4)^2$ **d** $y = x^2$ and $y = (x + 4)^2$

2 What effect does the value of h have on:

   a the position of the graph   **b** the shape of the graph?

3 What transformation is needed to graph $y = (x - h)^2$ from $y = x^2$?

Part 3:   Graphs of the form $y = (x - h)^2 + k$

What to do:

1 *Without the assistance of technology*, sketch the graph of $y = (x - 2)^2 + 3$.
   State the coordinates of the vertex and comment on the shape of the graph.

2 Use a **graphing package** or **graphics calculator** to draw, on the same set of axes,
   the graphs of $y = x^2$ and $y = (x - 2)^2 + 3$.

3 Repeat steps **1** and **2** for $y = (x + 4)^2 - 1$.

4 Copy and complete:
   - The graph of $y = (x - h)^2 + k$ is the same shape as the graph of ......
   - The graph of $y = (x - h)^2 + k$ is a .... of the graph of $y = x^2$
     through a translation of ....

Part 4:   Graphs of the form $y = ax^2, \quad a \neq 0$

What to do:

1 Using a **graphing package** or **graphics calculator**:

      i graph the two functions on the same set of axes
      ii state the coordinates of the vertex of each function.

   a $y = x^2$ and $y = 2x^2$ **b** $y = x^2$ and $y = 4x^2$

   c $y = x^2$ and $y = \frac{1}{2}x^2$ **d** $y = x^2$ and $y = -x^2$

   e $y = x^2$ and $y = -2x^2$ **f** $y = x^2$ and $y = -\frac{1}{2}x^2$

2 These functions are all members of the family $y = ax^2$ where a is the coefficient
   of the x^2 term. What effect does a have on:

   a the position of the graph   **b** the shape of the graph

   c the direction in which the graph opens?

Part 5:   Graphs of the form $y = a(x - h)^2 + k, \quad a \neq 0$

What to do:

1 *Without the assistance of technology*, sketch the graphs of $y = 2x^2$ and
   $y = 2(x - 1)^2 + 3$ on the same set of axes. State the coordinates of the
   vertices and comment on the shape of the two graphs.

2 Use a **graphing package** or **graphics calculator** to check your graphs in step **1**.

3 Repeat steps **1** and **2** for:

   a $y = -x^2$ and $y = -(x + 2)^2 + 3$

   b $y = \frac{1}{2}x^2$ and $y = \frac{1}{2}(x - 2)^2 - 4$

4 Copy and complete:
   - The graph of $y = a(x - h)^2 + k$ has the same shape and opens in the same
     direction as the graph of ......
   - The graph of $y = a(x - h)^2 + k$ is a .... of the graph of $y = ax^2$
     through a translation of ......

From the investigation the following important facts should have been discovered:

- Graphs of the form $y = x^2 + k$ have exactly the same shape as the graph of $y = x^2$. In fact, k is the **vertical translation** factor.

  Every point on the graph of $y = x^2$ is translated $\begin{pmatrix} 0 \\ k \end{pmatrix}$ to give the graph of $y = x^2 + k$.

- Graphs of the form $y = (x-h)^2$ have exactly the same shape as the graph of $y = x^2$. In fact, h is the **horizontal translation** factor.

  Every point on the graph of $y = x^2$ is translated $\begin{pmatrix} h \\ 0 \end{pmatrix}$ to give the graph of $y = (x-h)^2$.

- Graphs of the form $y = (x-h)^2 + k$ have the same shape as the graph of $y = x^2$ and can be obtained from $y = x^2$ by using a **horizontal shift** of h units and a **vertical shift** of k units. This is a **translation** of $\begin{pmatrix} h \\ k \end{pmatrix}$. The **vertex** is at $(h,\ k)$.

- If $a > 0$, $y = ax^2$ opens upwards i.e., $\smile$

  If $a < 0$, $y = ax^2$ opens downwards i.e., $\frown$

  If $a < -1$ or $a > 1$ then $y = ax^2$ is 'thinner' than $y = x^2$.
  If $-1 < a < 1$, $a \neq 0$ then $y = ax^2$ is 'wider' than $y = x^2$.

-

$$a > 0 \quad \smile$$
$$a < 0 \quad \frown$$

$$y = a(x - h)^2 + k$$

$a < -1$ or $a > 1$, thinner than $y = x^2$
$-1 < a < 1$, $a \neq 0$, wider than $y = x^2$

vertical shift of k units:
if $k > 0$ it goes up
if $k < 0$ it goes down

horizontal shift of h units:
if $h > 0$ it goes right
if $h < 0$ it goes left

Example 5   ◀) **Self Tutor**

Sketch $y = x^2$ and $y = x^2 + 3$ on the same set of axes.
Mark the vertex of $y = x^2 + 3$.

We draw $y = x^2$ and translate it 3 units upwards, i.e., $\begin{pmatrix} 0 \\ 3 \end{pmatrix}$.

∴ the vertex is now at $(0,\ 3)$.

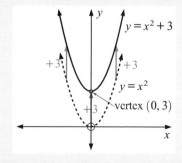

Example 6   ◀) **Self Tutor**

Sketch $y = x^2$ and $y = (x+3)^2$ on the same set of axes.
Mark the vertex of $y = (x+3)^2$.

We draw $y = x^2$ and translate it

3 units to the left,   i.e., $\begin{pmatrix} -3 \\ 0 \end{pmatrix}$.

∴ the vertex is now at $(-3,\, 0)$.

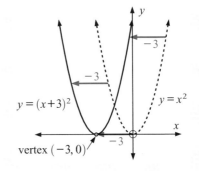

Example 7   ◀) **Self Tutor**

Sketch each of the following functions on the same set of axes as $y = x^2$. In each
case state the coordinates of the vertex.

a $y = (x-2)^2 + 3$

b $y = (x+2)^2 - 5$

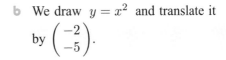

a We draw $y = x^2$ and translate it
   by $\begin{pmatrix} 2 \\ 3 \end{pmatrix}$.

b We draw $y = x^2$ and translate it
   by $\begin{pmatrix} -2 \\ -5 \end{pmatrix}$.

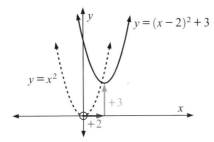

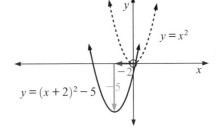

The vertex is at $(2,\, 3)$.

The vertex is at $(-2,\, -5)$.

EXERCISE 17B.2

1 Sketch each of the following functions on the same set of axes as
   $y = x^2$.   Use a separate set of axes for each part, and in each case
   state the coordinates of the vertex.

GRAPHING
PACKAGE

   a $y = x^2 - 3$ b $y = x^2 - 1$ c $y = x^2 + 1$

   d $y = x^2 - 5$ e $y = x^2 + 5$ f $y = x^2 - \frac{1}{2}$

2 Use a **graphics calculator** or **graphing package** to check your graphs in question 1.

3 Sketch each of the following functions on the same set of axes as $y = x^2$. Use a separate set of axes for each part, and in each case state the coordinates of the vertex.

   a $y = (x - 3)^2$ **b** $y = (x + 1)^2$ **c** $y = (x - 1)^2$

   d $y = (x - 5)^2$ **e** $y = (x + 5)^2$ **f** $y = (x - \frac{3}{2})^2$

4 Use a **graphics calculator** or **graphing package** to check your graphs in question **3**.

5 Sketch each of the following functions on the same set of axes as $y = x^2$. Use a separate set of axes for each part, and in each case state the coordinates of the vertex.

   a $y = (x - 1)^2 + 3$ **b** $y = (x - 2)^2 - 1$ **c** $y = (x + 1)^2 + 4$

   d $y = (x + 2)^2 - 3$ **e** $y = (x + 3)^2 - 2$ **f** $y = (x - 3)^2 + 3$

6 Use a **graphics calculator** or **graphing package** to check your graphs in question **5**.

COMPLETING THE SQUARE

We have seen previously how completing the square can be used to solve quadratic equations which do not factorise.

This same process can be used to convert quadratic functions into the form $y = (x - h)^2 + k$, and hence make them easier to graph.

Consider
$$y = x^2 - 4x + 1$$
$$\therefore \quad y = x^2 - 4x + 2^2 + 1 - 2^2$$
$$\therefore \quad y = x^2 - 4x + 2^2 \ - \ 3$$
$$\therefore \quad y = (x - 2)^2 - 3$$

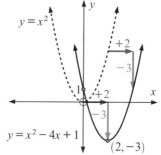

So, the graph of $y = x^2 - 4x + 1$ is the image of the graph of $y = x^2$ under the translation $\begin{pmatrix} 2 \\ -3 \end{pmatrix}$.

Example 8   ◀ᵈ⁾ **Self Tutor**

Write $y = x^2 + 2x + 5$ in the form $y = (x - h)^2 + k$ by completing the square, and hence sketch $y = x^2 + 2x + 5$, stating the coordinates of the vertex.

$$y = x^2 + 2x + 5$$
$$\therefore \quad y = x^2 + 2x + 1^2 + 5 - 1^2$$
$$\therefore \quad y = (x + 1)^2 + 4$$

       ↑   ↑

   shift 1   shift 4
   unit left   units up

The vertex is at $(-1, \ 4)$.

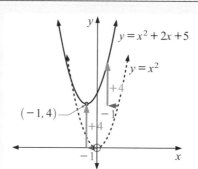

EXERCISE 17B.3

1 Write the following quadratics in the form $y = (x - h)^2 + k$ by completing the square, and hence sketch each function, stating the coordinates of the vertex:

a $y = x^2 + 2x + 4$

b $y = x^2 - 6x + 3$

c $y = x^2 + 4x - 1$

d $y = x^2 - 2x + 5$

e $y = x^2 - 2x$

f $y = x^2 + 5x$

g $y = x^2 + 5x - 3$

h $y = x^2 - 3x + 3$

i $y = x^2 - 5x + 2$

2 Use a **graphing package** or **graphics calculator** to check your graphs in question **1**.

GRAPHING PACKAGE

3 Use a **graphing package** or **graphics calculator** to graph each of the following functions, and *hence* write each function in the form $y = (x - h)^2 + k$:

a $y = x^2 - 2x + 3$

b $y = x^2 - 6x + 1$

c $y = x^2 + 4x + 5$

d $y = x^2 + 2x - 4$

e $y = x^2 - 3x + 1$

f $y = x^2 - 9x$

GRAPHS WHEN THE LEADING COEFFICIENT ≠ 1

Example 9   ◄⏻ **Self Tutor**

Sketch $y = x^2$ on a set of axes and hence sketch:

a $y = 3x^2$

b $y = -3x^2$

---

a $y = 3x^2$ is 'thinner' than $y = x^2$.

b $y = -3x^2$ is the same shape as $y = 3x^2$ but opens downwards.

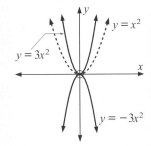

Example 10   ◄⏻ **Self Tutor**

Sketch the graph of $y = -(x - 2)^2 - 3$ from the graph of $y = x^2$ and hence state the coordinates of its vertex.

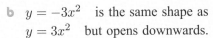

reflect in   horizontal shift   vertical shift
x-axis   2 units right   3 units down

We start with $y = x^2$ and perform the reflection $\mathbf{M}_x$ followed by the translation $\begin{pmatrix} 2 \\ -3 \end{pmatrix}$.

The vertex is at $(2, -3)$.

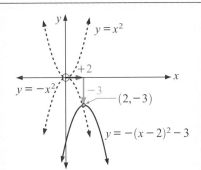

Consider the quadratic function $y = 3(x - 1)^2 + 2$.

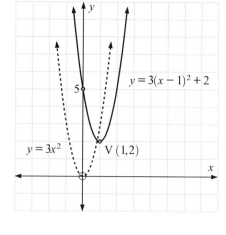

$$y = 3(x - 1)^2 + 2$$

$$a = 3 \qquad h = 1 \qquad k = 2$$

This graph has the same shape as the graph of $y = 3x^2$ but with vertex $(1, 2)$.

On expanding: $y = 3(x - 1)^2 + 2$
$$\therefore \quad y = 3(x^2 - 2x + 1) + 2$$
$$\therefore \quad y = 3x^2 - 6x + 3 + 2$$
$$\therefore \quad y = 3x^2 - 6x + 5$$

From this we can see that:

> the graph of a quadratic of the form $y = ax^2 + bx + c$ has the same shape as the graph of $y = ax^2$.

EXERCISE 17B.4

1   On separate sets of axes sketch $y = x^2$ and each of the following functions. Comment on:

    i the shape of the graph   **ii** the direction in which the graph opens.

  a $y = 5x^2$ **b** $y = -5x^2$ **c** $y = \frac{1}{3}x^2$

  d $y = -\frac{1}{3}x^2$ **e** $y = -4x^2$ **f** $y = \frac{1}{4}x^2$

2   Use a **graphics calculator** or **graphing package** to check your graphs in question **1**.

GRAPHING PACKAGE

3   Sketch the graphs of the following functions without using tables of values and state the coordinates of their vertices:

  a $y = -(x - 1)^2 + 3$ **b** $y = 2x^2 + 4$ **c** $y = -(x - 2)^2 + 4$

  d $y = 3(x + 1)^2 - 4$ **e** $y = \frac{1}{2}(x + 3)^2$ **f** $y = -\frac{1}{2}(x + 3)^2 + 1$

  g $y = -2(x + 4)^2 + 3$ **h** $y = 2(x - 3)^2 + 5$ **i** $y = \frac{1}{2}(x - 2)^2 - 1$

4   Use a **graphics calculator** or **graphing package** to check your graphs in question **3**.

5   For each of the following graphs, find the function they represent in the form $y = a(x - h)^2 + k$.

  a

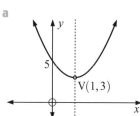

  b

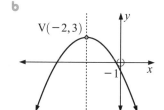

  c

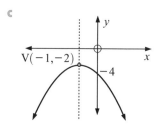

6 Match each quadratic function with its corresponding graph:

a $y = -1(x+1)^2 + 3$ b $y = -2(x-3)^2 + 2$ c $y = x^2 + 2$

d $y = -1(x-1)^2 + 1$ e $y = (x-2)^2 - 2$ f $y = \frac{1}{3}(x+3)^2 - 3$

g $y = -x^2$ h $y = -\frac{1}{2}(x-1)^2 + 1$ i $y = 2(x+2)^2 - 1$

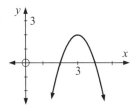
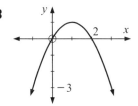
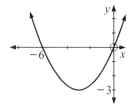

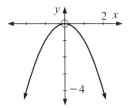
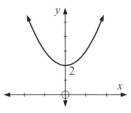
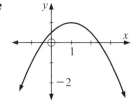

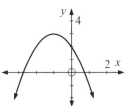
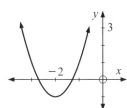
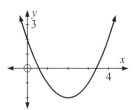

7 Use a **graphing package** or **graphics calculator** to graph each pair of quadratic functions on the same set of axes. Compare the shapes of the two graphs.

a $y = 2x^2$ and $y = 2x^2 - 3x + 1$ b $y = -x^2$ and $y = -x^2 - 6x + 4$

c $y = 3x^2$ and $y = 3x^2 - 5x$ d $y = -2x^2$ and $y = -2x^2 + 5$

C   AXES INTERCEPTS

Given the equation of any curve:

An **x-intercept** is a value of x where the graph meets the x-axis,

A **y-intercept** is a value of y where the graph meets the y-axis.

x-intercepts are found by letting y be 0 in the equation of the curve.

y-intercepts are found by letting x be 0 in the equation of the curve.

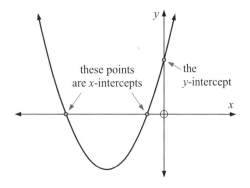

these points are x-intercepts

the y-intercept

INVESTIGATION 2   **AXES INTERCEPTS**

What to do:

1   For the following quadratic functions, use a graphing
    package or graphics calculator to:

GRAPHING
PACKAGE

     i draw the graph   **ii** find the y-intercept

     iii find any x-intercepts

   a $y = x^2 - 3x - 4$ **b** $y = -x^2 + 2x + 8$ **c** $y = 2x^2 - 3x$

   d $y = -2x^2 + 2x - 3$ **e** $y = (x-1)(x-3)$ **f** $y = -(x+2)(x-3)$

   g $y = 3(x+1)(x+4)$ **h** $y = 2(x-2)^2$ **i** $y = -3(x+1)^2$

2   From your observations in question **1**:

   a State the y-intercept of a quadratic function in the form $y = ax^2 + bx + c$.

   b State the x-intercepts of quadratic function in the form $y = a(x-\alpha)(x-\beta)$.

   c What do you notice about the x-intercepts of quadratic functions in the form
     $y = a(x-\alpha)^2$?

THE y-INTERCEPT

You will have noticed that for a quadratic function of the form $y = ax^2 + bx + c$, the
y-intercept is the constant term c. This is because any curve cuts the y-axis when $x = 0$.

For example,   if $y = x^2 - 2x - 3$ and we let $x = 0$

       then $y = 0^2 - 2(0) - 3$

       $\therefore$ $y = -3$ (the constant term)

THE x-INTERCEPTS

You should have noticed that for a quadratic function of the form $y = a(x-\alpha)(x-\beta)$,
the x-intercepts are α and β. This is because any curve cuts the x-axis when $y = 0$.

So, if we substitute $y = 0$ into the function we get $a(x-\alpha)(x-\beta) = 0$

          $\therefore$ $x = \alpha$ or β {by the Null Factor law}

This suggests that x-intercepts are easy to find when the quadratic is in **factorised** form.

Example 11	◀ **Self Tutor**

Find the x-intercepts of:

   a $y = 2(x-3)(x+2)$ **b** $y = -(x-4)^2$

> If a quadratic
> function has only
> one x-intercept then
> its graph must
> **touch** the x-axis.

a   When $y = 0$,

     $2(x-3)(x+2) = 0$

   $\therefore$ $x = 3$ or $x = -2$

   $\therefore$ the x-intercepts are 3
     and -2.

b   When $y = 0$,

     $-(x-4)^2 = 0$

     $\therefore$ $x = 4$

   $\therefore$ the x-intercept is 4.

FACTORISING TO FIND x-INTERCEPTS

> For any quadratic function of the form $y = ax^2 + bx + c$, the x-intercepts can be found by solving the equation $ax^2 + bx + c = 0$.

You will recall from **Chapter 9** that quadratic equations may have *two solutions*, *one solution*, or *no solutions*.

These solutions correspond to the *two x-intercepts*, *one x-intercept*, or *no x-intercepts* found when the graphs of the quadratic functions are drawn.

Example 12	◀)) **Self Tutor**

Find the x-intercept(s) of the quadratic functions:

a $y = x^2 - 6x + 9$ **b** $y = -x^2 - x + 6$

a When $y = 0$,
$$x^2 - 6x + 9 = 0$$
$$\therefore \quad (x-3)^2 = 0$$
$$\therefore \quad x = 3$$
$$\therefore \quad \text{the } x\text{-intercept is } 3.$$

b When $y = 0$,
$$-x^2 - x + 6 = 0$$
$$\therefore \quad x^2 + x - 6 = 0$$
$$\therefore \quad (x+3)(x-2) = 0$$
$$\therefore \quad x = -3 \text{ or } 2$$
$$\therefore \quad \text{the } x\text{-intercepts are } -3 \text{ and } 2.$$

EXERCISE 17C.1

1 For the following functions, state the y-intercept:

   a $y = x^2 + 3x + 3$ **b** $y = x^2 - 5x + 2$ **c** $y = 2x^2 + 7x - 8$

   d $y = 3x^2 - x + 1$ **e** $y = -x^2 + 3x + 6$ **f** $y = -2x^2 + 5 - x$

   g $y = 6 - x - x^2$ **h** $y = 8 + 2x - 3x^2$ **i** $y = 5x - x^2 - 2$

2 For the following functions, find the x-intercepts:

   a $y = (x-3)(x+1)$ **b** $y = -(x-2)(x-4)$ **c** $y = 2(x+3)(x+2)$

   d $y = -3(x-4)(x-5)$ **e** $y = 2(x+3)^2$ **f** $y = -5(x-1)^2$

3 For the following functions find the x-intercepts:

   a $y = x^2 - 9$ **b** $y = 2x^2 - 6$ **c** $y = x^2 + 7x + 10$

   d $y = x^2 + x - 12$ **e** $y = 4x - x^2$ **f** $y = -x^2 - 6x - 8$

   g $y = -2x^2 - 4x - 2$ **h** $y = 4x^2 - 24x + 36$ **i** $y = x^2 - 4x + 1$

   j $y = x^2 + 4x - 3$ **k** $y = x^2 - 6x - 2$ **l** $y = x^2 + 8x + 11$

GRAPHS FROM AXES INTERCEPTS

If we know the x- and y-intercepts of a quadratic function then we can use them to draw its graph.

Example 13   ◀ʲ) **Self Tutor**

Sketch the graphs of the following functions by considering:
    i   the value of a ii   the y-intercept   iii   the x-intercepts.

  a $y = x^2 - 2x - 3$ b $y = -2(x+1)(x-2)$

---

  a $y = x^2 - 2x - 3$
    i   Since $a = 1$, the parabola
      opens upwards   i.e.,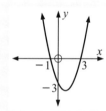
    ii y-intercepts occurs when $x = 0$,
      ∴   the y-intercept is -3
    iii x-intercepts occur when $y = 0$
      ∴ $x^2 - 2x - 3 = 0$
      ∴ $(x-3)(x+1) = 0$
      ∴ $x = 3$ or $x = -1$
      ∴   the x-intercepts are 3 and -1

  b $y = -2(x+1)(x-2)$
    i   Since $a = -2$, the parabola
      opens downwards   i.e.,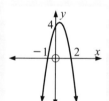
    ii y-intercepts occurs when $x = 0$,
      ∴ $y = -2(0+1)(0-2)$
          $= -2 \times 1 \times -2$
          $= 4$
      ∴   the y-intercept is 4
    iii x-intercepts occur when $y = 0$
      ∴ $-2(x+1)(x-2) = 0$
      ∴ $x = -1$ or $x = 2$
      ∴   the x-intercepts are -1 and 2

Sketch:

Sketch:

Example 14   ◀ʲ) **Self Tutor**

Sketch the graph of $y = 2(x-3)^2$ by considering:
  a   the value of a b   the y-intercept   c   the x-intercepts.

$y = 2(x-3)^2$
  a   Since $a = 2$,   the parabola opens upwards   i.e.,
  b y-intercept occurs when $x = 0$
    ∴ $y = 2(0-3)^2 = 18$
    ∴   the y-intercept is 18
  c x-intercepts occur when $y = 0$
    ∴ $2(x-3)^2 = 0$
      ∴ $x = 3$
  ∴   the x-intercept is 3

There is only one x-intercept, which means the graph
touches the x-axis.

EXERCISE 17C.2

1 Sketch the graph of the quadratic function with:

    a x-intercepts -1 and 1, and y-intercept -1

    b x-intercepts -3 and 1, and y-intercept 2

    c x-intercepts 2 and 5, and y-intercept -4

    d x-intercept 2 and y-intercept 4.

2 Sketch the graphs of the following by considering:

    i the value of a **ii** the y-intercept **iii** the x-intercepts.

    a $y = x^2 - 4x + 4$ **b** $y = (x - 1)(x + 3)$ **c** $y = 2(x + 2)^2$

    d $y = -(x - 2)(x + 1)$ **e** $y = -3(x + 1)^2$ **f** $y = -3(x - 4)(x - 1)$

    g $y = 2(x + 3)(x + 1)$ **h** $y = 2x^2 + 3x + 2$ **i** $y = -2x^2 - 3x + 5$

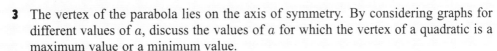

D   AXIS OF SYMMETRY AND VERTEX

We have seen from the previous exercise that the graph of any quadratic function:

- is a **parabola**
- is symmetrical about an **axis of symmetry**
- has a **turning point** or **vertex**.

If the graph has two x-intercepts then the axis of symmetry must be mid-way between them. We will use this property in the following investigation to establish an equation for the axis of symmetry.

INVESTIGATION 3   AXIS OF SYMMETRY AND VERTEX

Consider the quadratic function $y = ax^2 + bx + c$ whose graph cuts the x-axis at A and B. Let the equation of the axis of symmetry be $x = h$.

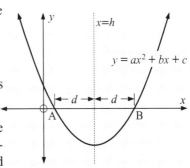

What to do:

1 Use the quadratic formula to find the coordinates of A and B.

2 Since A and B are the same distance d from the axis of symmetry, h must be the average of the x-coordinates of A and B. Use this property to find the axis of symmetry in terms of a, b and c.

3 The vertex of the parabola lies on the axis of symmetry. By considering graphs for different values of a, discuss the values of a for which the vertex of a quadratic is a maximum value or a minimum value.

From the investigation, you should have discovered that:

the equation of the **axis of symmetry** of $y = ax^2 + bx + c$ is $x = \dfrac{-b}{2a}$.

This equation is true for all quadratic functions, not just those with two x-intercepts.

Proof: We know the equation $y = a(x - h)^2 + k$ has vertex (h, k), so its axis of symmetry is $x = h$.

Expanding $y = a(x - h)^2 + k$, we find
$$y = a(x^2 - 2hx + h^2) + k$$
$$\therefore \quad y = ax^2 - 2ahx + [ah^2 + k].$$

Comparing the coefficients of x with those of $y = ax^2 + bx + c$, we find $-2ah = b$.

$\therefore \quad h = \dfrac{-b}{2a}$, and so the axis of symmetry is $x = \dfrac{-b}{2a}$.

Example 15　　　　　　　　　　　　　　　　　　　◀) **Self Tutor**

Find the equation of the axis of symmetry of $y = 2x^2 + 3x + 1$.

$y = 2x^2 + 3x + 1$ has $a = 2$, $b = 3$, $c = 1$

$\therefore$ the axis of symmetry has equation $x = \dfrac{-b}{2a} = \dfrac{-3}{2 \times 2}$ i.e., $x = -\frac{3}{4}$

TURNING POINT (OR VERTEX)

The **turning point** or **vertex** of any parabola is the point at which the function has a

maximum value (for $a < 0$) $\bigcap$ or a **minimum value** (for $a > 0$) $\bigcup$.

As the turning point lies on the axis of symmetry, its x-coordinate will be $x = \dfrac{-b}{2a}$.

The y-coordinate can be found by substituting the value for x into the function.

Example 16　　　　　　　　　　　　　　　　　　　◀) **Self Tutor**

Determine the coordinates of the vertex of $y = 2x^2 + 8x + 3$.

$y = 2x^2 + 8x + 3$ has $a = 2$, $b = 8$, and $c = 3$,

so $\dfrac{-b}{2a} = \dfrac{-8}{2 \times 2} = -2$

$\therefore$ the equation of the axis of symmetry is $x = -2$

When $x = -2$, $y = 2(-2)^2 + 8(-2) + 3 = 8 - 16 + 3 = -5$

$\therefore$ the vertex has coordinates $(-2, -5)$.

> The vertex is called the **maximum turning point** or the **minimum turning point** depending on whether the graph opens downwards or upwards.

Example 17

🔊 **Self Tutor**

For the quadratic function $y = -x^2 + 2x + 3$:

  a find its axes intercepts

  b find the equation of the axis of symmetry

  c find the coordinates of the vertex

  d sketch the function showing all important features.

a When $x = 0$, $y = 3$

  ∴ the y-intercept is 3.

  When $y = 0$, $\quad -x^2 + 2x + 3 = 0$

    ∴ $\quad x^2 - 2x - 3 = 0$

    ∴ $\quad (x - 3)(x + 1) = 0$

      ∴ $\quad x = 3$ or -1

  ∴ the x-intercepts are 3 and -1.

c From **b**, when $x = 1$,

$y = -(1)^2 + 2(1) + 3$

$\quad = -1 + 2 + 3$

$\quad = 4$

∴ the vertex is $(1, 4)$.

b $a = -1$, $b = 2$, $c = 3$

  ∴ $\dfrac{-b}{2a} = \dfrac{-2}{-2} = 1$

  ∴ the axis of symmetry is $x = 1$.

d
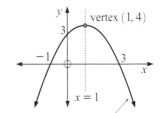

Example 18

🔊 **Self Tutor**

  a Sketch the graph of $y = 2(x - 2)(x + 4)$ using axes intercepts.

  b Find the equation of the axis of symmetry and the coordinates of the vertex.

a $y = 2(x - 2)(x + 4)$

  Since $a = 2$ the parabola opens upwards i.e.,

  When $x = 0$,

  ∴ $y = 2 \times -2 \times 4 = -16$

  ∴ y-intercept is -16.

  When $y = 0$,

    $2(x - 2)(x + 4) = 0$

  ∴ $\quad x = 2$ or $x = -4$

  ∴ the x-intercepts are 2 and -4.

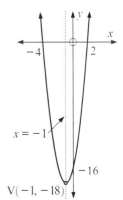

b The axis of symmetry is halfway between the x-intercepts

  ∴ the axis of symmetry is $x = -1$ {-1 is the average of -4 and 2}

  When $x = -1$, $\quad y = 2(-1 - 2)(-1 + 4)$

                   $= 2 \times -3 \times 3$

                   $= -18$

  ∴ the coordinates of the vertex are $(-1, -18)$.

Example 19   ◀) **Self Tutor**

Sketch the parabola which has x-intercepts -2 and 6, and y-intercept 2.
Find the equation of the axis of symmetry.

The axis of symmetry lies half-way
between the x-intercepts.

The average of -2 and 6 is 2, so the
axis of symmetry is $x = 2$.

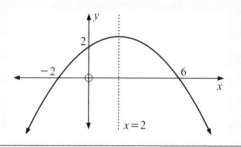

EXERCISE 17D

1 Determine the equation of the axis of symmetry of:

   a $y = x^2 + 4x + 1$ **b** $y = 2x^2 - 6x + 3$ **c** $y = 3x^2 + 4x - 1$

   d $y = -x^2 - 4x + 5$ **e** $y = -2x^2 + 5x + 1$ **f** $y = \frac{1}{2}x^2 - 10x + 2$

   g $y = \frac{1}{3}x^2 + 4x$ **h** $y = 100x - 4x^2$ **i** $y = -\frac{1}{10}x^2 + 30x$

2 Find the turning point or vertex for the following quadratic functions:

   a $y = x^2 - 4x + 2$ **b** $y = x^2 + 2x - 3$ **c** $y = 2x^2 + 4$

   d $y = -3x^2 + 1$ **e** $y = 2x^2 + 8x - 7$ **f** $y = -x^2 - 4x - 9$

   g $y = 2x^2 + 6x - 1$ **h** $y = 2x^2 - 10x + 3$ **i** $y = -\frac{1}{2}x^2 + x - 5$

3 For each of the following quadratic functions find:

      i the axes intercepts   **ii** the equation of the axis of symmetry
     iii the coordinates of the vertex   **iv** and hence sketch the graph.

   a $y = x^2 - 2x - 8$ **b** $y = x^2 + 3x$ **c** $y = 4x - x^2$

   d $y = x^2 + 4x + 4$ **e** $y = x^2 + 3x - 4$ **f** $y = -x^2 + 2x - 1$

   g $y = -x^2 - 6x - 8$ **h** $y = -x^2 + 3x - 2$ **i** $y = 2x^2 + 5x - 3$

   j $y = 2x^2 - 5x - 12$ **k** $y = -3x^2 - 4x + 4$ **l** $y = -\frac{1}{4}x^2 + 5x$

4 For each of the following, find the equation of the axis of symmetry:

   a   **b**   **c**

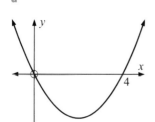
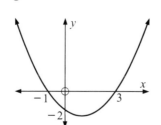
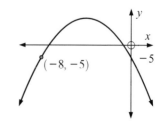

5 For each of the following quadratic functions:

    i sketch the graph using axes intercepts and *hence* find

    ii the equation of the axis of symmetry

    iii the coordinates of the vertex.

  a $y = x^2 + 4x + 4$ b $y = x(x-2)$ c $y = 2(x-2)^2$

  d $y = -(x-1)(x+3)$ e $y = -2(x-1)^2$ f $y = -5(x+2)(x-2)$

  g $y = 2(x+1)(x+4)$ h $y = 2x^2 - 3x - 2$ i $y = -2x^2 - x + 3$

6 For each of the following:

    i sketch the parabola   ii find the equation of the axis of symmetry.

  a x-intercepts 2 and -1, y-intercept -3

  b x-intercepts 3 and -3, y-intercept 6

  c x-intercept -2 (touching), y-intercept 4

  d x-intercept 2 (touching), y-intercept -6

7 Find all x-intercepts of the quadratic function which:

  a cuts the x-axis at 1, and has axis of symmetry $x = 2$

  b cuts the x-axis at -1, and has axis of symmetry $x = -1\frac{1}{2}$

  c touches the x-axis at 2.

E   QUADRATIC OPTIMISATION

If the relationship between two variables is a quadratic function, then its graph will be either

$\bigcup$ or $\bigcap$ and the function will have a minimum or maximum value.

For $y = ax^2 + bx + c$:

- if $a > 0$, the **minimum** value of y occurs at $x = -\dfrac{b}{2a}$

- if $a < 0$, the **maximum** value of y occurs at $x = -\dfrac{b}{2a}$.

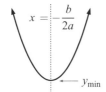

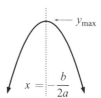

The process of finding the maximum or minimum value of a function is called **optimisation**.

Optimisation is a very useful tool when looking at such issues as:

- maximising profits   • minimising costs   • maximising heights reached.

Example 20   ◀⫲ **Self Tutor**

The height H metres of a rocket t seconds after it is fired vertically upwards is given
by $H(t) = 100t - 5t^2$, $t \geqslant 0$.

   a How long does it take for the rocket to reach its maximum height?

   b What is the maximum height reached by the rocket?

   c How long does it take for the rocket to fall back to earth?

---

  a $H(t) = 100t - 5t^2$

     $\therefore$ $H(t) = -5t^2 + 100t$ where $a = -5$

    The maximum height is reached when $t = \dfrac{-b}{2a} = \dfrac{-100}{2(-5)} = 10$

    $\therefore$ the maximum height is reached after 10 seconds.

  b $H(10) = 100 \times 10 - 5 \times 10^2$

           $= 1000 - 500$

           $= 500$

    $\therefore$ the maximum height reached is 500 m.

  c The rocket falls back to earth when $H(t) = 0$

         $\therefore$ $0 = 100t - 5t^2$

    $\therefore$ $5t^2 - 100t = 0$

    $\therefore$ $5t(t - 20) = 0$ {factorising}

        $\therefore$ $t = 0$ or $t = 20$

    $\therefore$ the rocket falls back to earth after 20 seconds.

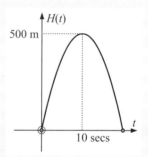

EXERCISE 17E

1 The height H metres of a ball t seconds after it is hit vertically
upwards is given by $H(t) = 40t - 5t^2$.

   a How long does it take for the ball to reach its maximum height?

   b What is the maximum height reached by the ball?

   c How long does it take for the ball to hit the ground?

2 A manufacturer finds that the profit €P from assembling x bicycles per day is given by
$P(x) = -x^2 + 50x - 200$.

   a How many bicycles should be assembled per day to maximise the profit?

   b What is the maximum profit?

   c What is the loss made if no bicycles are assembled in a day? Suggest why this loss
would be made.

3 The driver of a car travelling downhill on a road applied the brakes. The speed s of the
car, t seconds after the brakes were applied, is given by
$s(t) = -6t^2 + 12t + 60$ km h^{-1}.

   a How fast was the car travelling when the driver applied the brakes?

b After how many seconds was the speed of the car 64.5 km h^{-1}? Explain your answer.

c After how many seconds did the car reach its maximum speed?

d What was the maximum speed reached?

4 The hourly profit $\$P$ obtained from operating a fleet of n taxis is given by $P(n) = 120n - 200 - 2n^2$.

   a What number of taxis gives the maximum hourly profit?

   b What is the maximum hourly profit?

   c How much money is lost per hour if no taxis are on the road?

5 The temperature T $^\circ$C in a greenhouse t hours after dusk (7.00 pm) is given by $T(t) = \frac{1}{4}t^2 - 6t + 25$ for $t \leqslant 20$.

   a What is the temperature in the greenhouse at dusk?

   b At what time is the temperature at a minimum?

   c What is the minimum temperature?

6 A vegetable gardener has 40 m of fencing to enclose a rectangular garden plot where one side is an existing brick wall. If the width is x m as shown:

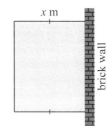

   a show that the area enclosed is given by $A = -2x^2 + 40x$ m^2

   b find x such that the vegetable garden has the maximum possible area

   c find the maximum possible area.

7 Answer the questions posed in the **Opening Problem** on page **414**.

8 Infinitely many rectangles may be inscribed within the triangle shown alongside. One of them is illustrated.

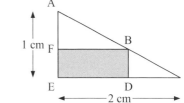

   a Show that triangles ABF and ACE are similar.

   b If EF $= x$ cm, show that BF $= 2(1 - x)$ cm

   c Show that the area of rectangle BDEF is given by $A = -2x^2 + 2x$ cm^2.

   d Find x such that the area of the rectangle is maximised. What is the maximum area?

REVIEW SET 17A

1 If $g(x) = x^2 - 3x - 15$ find:

   a $g(0)$ **b** $g(1)$ **c** x such that $g(x) = 3$.

2 On the same set of axes, sketch $y = x^2$ and the function:

   a $y = 3x^2$ **b** $y = (x - 2)^2 + 1$ **c** $y = -(x + 3)^2 - 2$

3 For $y = -2(x - 1)(x + 3)$ find the:

    a   **i** direction the parabola opens   **ii** y-intercept

        iii x-intercepts   **iv** equation of the axis of symmetry.

    b Sketch a graph of the function showing all of the above features.

4 For $y = x^2 - 2x - 15$ find the:

    a   **i** y-intercept   **ii** x-intercepts

        iii equation of the axis of symmetry   **iv** coordinates of the vertex.

    b Sketch a graph of the function showing all of the above features.

5 A stone was thrown from the top of a cliff 60 metres above sea level. The height of the stone above sea level t seconds after it was released is given by $H(t) = -5t^2 + 20t + 60$ metres.

    a Find the time taken for the stone to reach its maximum height.

    b What was the maximum height above sea level reached by the stone?

    c How long did it take before the stone struck the water?

REVIEW SET 17B

1 If $f(x) = 2x^2 + x - 2$,   find:

    a $f(1)$ **b** $f(-3)$ **c** x such that $f(x) = 4$.

2 On the same set of axes, sketch $y = x^2$ and the function:

    a $y = -\frac{1}{2}x^2$ **b** $y = (x + 2)^2 + 5$ **c** $y = -(x - 1)^2 - 3$

3 For $y = 3(x - 2)^2$ find the:

    a   **i** direction the parabola opens   **ii** y-intercept

        iii x-intercepts   **iv** equation of the axis of symmetry.

    b Sketch a graph of the function showing all of the above features.

4 For $y = -x^2 + 7x - 10$ find the:

    a   **i** y-intercept   **ii** x-intercepts

        iii equation of the axis of symmetry   **iv** coordinates of the vertex.

    b Sketch a graph of the function showing all of the above features.

5 The height of a cannonball t seconds after it is fired into the air is given by $H(t) = -4t^2 + 16t + 9$ metres.

    a Find the time taken for the cannonball to reach its maximum height.

    b What is the maximum height reached by the cannonball?

    c How long will it take for the cannonball to fall back to earth?

6 The graph of $y = a(x - h)^2 + k$ is shown alongside.

    a Find the value of h.

    b Find the values of a and k by solving simultaneous equations.

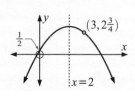

Chapter 18

Advanced trigonometry

Contents:

In this chapter we extend our knowledge of trigonometry in a number of areas. We will consider angles in radian measure, the sine function and how it can be used to model natural phenomena, and we will also learn more trigonometric identities.

OPENING PROBLEM

An aeroplane propeller is painted brown, but with white tips so they can be clearly seen. The propeller rotates anticlockwise when viewed from the front.

Suppose the propeller blades are all 1 m long, and the origin is the centre of the propeller. We label the tip of one blade as point P.

Things to think about:

1 As the propeller rotates, what function describes the height of the point P above the origin?

2 What shape does the graph of this function have?

Click on the icon to watch a demonstration of the propeller's motion. Check your answers with those obtained in the demonstration.

A   RADIAN MEASURE

Instead of using degrees, there is another way of measuring angle size. We can use **radians**, which measure the arc length around a circle from the angle of zero degrees.

Consider the unit circle diagram shown.

As the radius $r = 1$, the circumference of the circle is $2\pi \times 1 = 2\pi$.

So, if arc length is used to measure angle size, then 2π radians $\equiv 360°$.

$$\pi^c \equiv 180°$$ is worth remembering.

In general, we leave off the symbol for radians altogether.

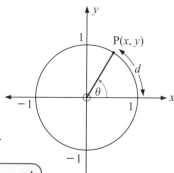

So, $30° \equiv \frac{\pi}{6}$
$45° \equiv \frac{\pi}{4}$
$90° \equiv \frac{\pi}{2}$
$180° \equiv \pi$
$270° \equiv \frac{3\pi}{2}$
        etc.

All angles are measured from the positive x-axis. The anticlockwise direction is positive.

As $\pi^c \equiv 180^o$

$1^c \equiv \left(\frac{180}{\pi}\right)^o \approx 57.3^o$

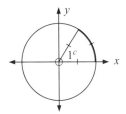

One **radian** is the angle swept out by an arc of length equal to the radius of the circle.

In higher mathematics, only radian measure is used. It is more convenient, and results using radian measure are usually simpler.

For example:

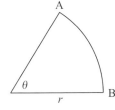

Using degrees,

arc AB $= \left(\frac{\theta}{360}\right) \times 2\pi r.$

Using radians,

arc AB $= r\theta.$

DEGREE-RADIAN CONVERSIONS

The following diagram is useful for converting from one system of measure to the other:

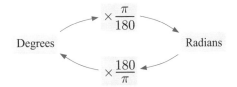

Convert 150° to radians in terms of π.

$150^o \equiv 150 \times \frac{\pi}{180}^c$ or $150^o \equiv 5 \times 30^o$

$\equiv \frac{5\pi}{6}^c$ $\equiv 5 \times \frac{\pi}{6}$

$\equiv \frac{5\pi}{6}$

Convert 131.8^o to radians, correct to 3 significant figures.

$131.8^o \equiv 131.8 \times \frac{\pi}{180}$ radians

≈ 2.30 radians

Convert $\frac{7\pi}{6}$ radians to degrees.

$\frac{7\pi}{6} \equiv \frac{7\overset{1}{\cancel{\pi}}}{\underset{1}{\cancel{6}}} \times \frac{\overset{30^o}{\cancel{180}^o}}{\underset{1}{\cancel{\pi}}}$

$\equiv 210^o$

Example 4   🔊 **Self Tutor**

Convert 1.237 radians to degrees, correct to 3 significant figures.

$$1.237^c \equiv 1.237 \times \frac{180}{\pi} \text{ degrees}$$
$$\approx 70.9^o$$

EXERCISE 18A

1 Using $30^o \equiv \frac{\pi}{6}^c$, convert to radians:

    a 60° **b** 120° **c** 15° **d** 10° **e** 40° **f** 210°

2 Using $45^o \equiv \frac{\pi}{4}^c$, convert to radians:

    a 90° **b** 135° **c** 225° **d** 22.5^o **e** 5° **f** 315°

3 Convert to radians, correct to 3 significant figures.

    a 17.8^o **b** 59.72^o **c** 113.8^o **d** 217.92^o

4 Convert the following radian measures into degrees:

    a $\frac{\pi}{5}$ **b** $\frac{2\pi}{5}$ **c** $\frac{\pi}{18}$ **d** $\frac{5\pi}{18}$ **e** $\frac{\pi}{10}$

    f $\frac{7\pi}{10}$ **g** $\frac{\pi}{9}$ **h** $\frac{5\pi}{9}$ **i** $\frac{\pi}{20}$ **j** $\frac{7\pi}{20}$

    k $\frac{\pi}{8}$ **l** $\frac{3\pi}{8}$ **m** $\frac{7\pi}{3}$ **n** $\frac{11\pi}{6}$ **o** $\frac{15\pi}{4}$

5 Convert the following radian measures into degrees, correct to 3 significant figures.

    a 3^c **b** 12.8^c **c** 0.7892^c **d** 2.155^c

6 Copy and complete:

    a

Degrees	0	45	90	135	180	225	270	315	360
Radians									

    b

Degrees	0	30	60	90	120	150	180	210	240	270	300	330	360
Radians													

7 **a** Show that for θ in radians:

      i the arc length $l = r\theta$

      ii the sector area $A = \frac{1}{2}r^2\theta$.

    b Find the arc length and area of a sector of radius 10 cm and angle 3 radians.

    c If a sector has radius 5 cm and arc length 7 cm, find its area.

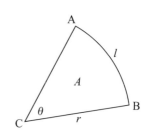

B   TRIGONOMETRIC RATIOS FROM THE UNIT CIRCLE

Consider again the **unit circle** with centre $(0, 0)$ and radius 1 unit.

If $P(x, y)$ moves around the unit circle such that [OP] makes an angle of θ with the positive x-axis then

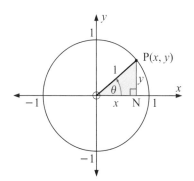

$$\cos \theta = \frac{ON}{OP} = \frac{x}{1} = x \quad \text{and} \quad \sin \theta = \frac{PN}{OP} = \frac{y}{1} = y.$$

So,   P has coordinates $(\cos \theta, \sin \theta)$.

Using Pythagoras, $x^2 + y^2 = 1$ and so $\cos^2 \theta + \sin^2 \theta = 1.$

Notice that $-1 \leqslant x \leqslant 1$ and $-1 \leqslant y \leqslant 1$ for all points on the unit circle, so

$$-1 \leqslant \cos \theta \leqslant 1 \quad \text{and} \quad -1 \leqslant \sin \theta \leqslant 1 \quad \text{for all } \theta.$$

ANGLE MEASUREMENT

For any point P on the unit circle, the angle θ is measured from the positive x-axis.

θ is **positive** for anticlockwise rotations.

θ is **negative** for clockwise rotations.

For example,
$\theta = 210^o$ and $\phi = -150^o$.

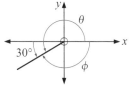

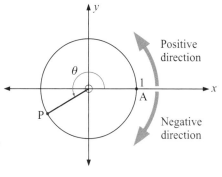

We can use cosine and sine to find the coordinates of any point on the unit circle for any angle measured from the positive x-axis.

For example,

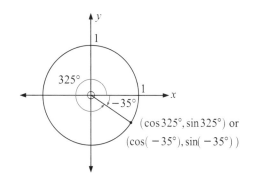

Example 5   ◀)) **Self Tutor**

From a unit circle diagram, find $\cos 270^o$ and $\sin 270^o$.

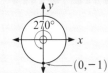

$\cos 270^o = 0$ {the x-coordinate}

$\sin 270^o = -1$ {the y-coordinate}

Example 6   ◀)) **Self Tutor**

Find the possible exact values of $\sin \theta$ when $\cos \theta = \frac{1}{2}$. Illustrate your answers.

$$\cos^2 \theta + \sin^2 \theta = 1$$
$$\therefore \quad \left(\tfrac{1}{2}\right)^2 + \sin^2 \theta = 1$$
$$\therefore \quad \tfrac{1}{4} + \sin^2 \theta = 1$$
$$\therefore \quad \sin^2 \theta = \tfrac{3}{4}$$
$$\therefore \quad \sin \theta = \pm \tfrac{\sqrt{3}}{2}$$

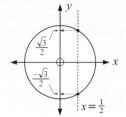

Helpful hint:

We have seen previously how the quadrants of the Cartesian Plane are labelled in anticlockwise order from 1st to 4th.

We can also use a letter to show which trigonometric ratios are positive in each quadrant.

You might like to remember them using

> **A**ll **S**illy **T**urtles **C**rawl.

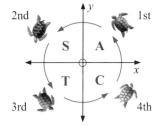

Example 7   ◀)) **Self Tutor**

Find the exact value of $\cos \theta$ if $\sin \theta = \frac{3}{4}$ and $\frac{\pi}{2} < \theta < \pi$.

θ lies in quadrant 2 where $\cos \theta$ is *negative*.

Now $\cos^2 \theta + \sin^2 \theta = 1$

$$\therefore \quad \cos^2 \theta + \left(\tfrac{3}{4}\right)^2 = 1$$
$$\therefore \quad \cos^2 \theta + \tfrac{9}{16} = 1$$
$$\therefore \quad \cos^2 \theta = \tfrac{7}{16}$$
$$\therefore \quad \cos \theta = \pm \tfrac{\sqrt{7}}{4}$$

But $\cos \theta < 0$, so $\cos \theta = -\frac{\sqrt{7}}{4}$.

EXERCISE 18B

1 **a** Write down the exact coordinates of points A, B and C.

   b Use your calculator to give the coordinates of A, B and C correct to 3 significant figures.

2 Give unit circle evidence for why:

   a $\cos 380° = \cos 20°$ **b** $\sin 413° = \sin 53°$

   c $\sin 160° = \sin 20°$ **d** $\cos 160° = -\cos 20°$

3 Use a unit circle diagram to find the values of:

   a $\cos 0°$ and $\sin 0°$
   b $\cos 90°$ and $\sin 90°$

   c $\cos 2\pi$ and $\sin 2\pi$
   d $\cos 450°$ and $\sin 450°$

   e $\cos\left(-\frac{\pi}{2}\right)$ and $\sin\left(-\frac{\pi}{2}\right)$
   f $\cos\left(\frac{7\pi}{2}\right)$ and $\sin\left(\frac{7\pi}{2}\right)$

   g $\cos(-180°)$ and $\sin(-180°)$
   h $\cos\left(\frac{-3\pi}{2}\right)$ and $\sin\left(\frac{-3\pi}{2}\right)$.

4 Find the possible values of $\sin\theta$ when:

   a $\cos\theta = \frac{3}{5}$ **b** $\cos\theta = -\frac{1}{4}$ **c** $\cos\theta = 1$ **d** $\cos\theta = 0$

5 Find the possible values of $\cos\theta$ when:

   a $\sin\theta = \frac{12}{13}$ **b** $\sin\theta = -1$ **c** $\sin\theta = 0$ **d** $\sin\theta = -\frac{3}{5}$

6 The diagram alongside shows the 4 quadrants. They are numbered anticlockwise.

   a Copy and complete:

Quadrant	Degree measure	Radian measure	$\cos\theta$	$\sin\theta$
1	$0 < \theta < 90$	$0 < \theta < \frac{\pi}{2}$	positive	positive
2				
3				
4				

   b In which quadrants are the following true?

   i $\sin\theta$ is negative

   ii $\cos\theta$ is positive

   iii $\cos\theta$ and $\sin\theta$ are both negative

   iv $\cos\theta$ is positive and $\sin\theta$ is negative

> **Remember:**
> All Silly
> Turtles
> Crawl

7 Find the exact value of:

   a $\cos\theta$ if $\sin\theta = \frac{2}{3}$ and $0 < \theta < \frac{\pi}{2}$

   b $\cos\theta$ if $\sin\theta = \frac{4}{5}$ and $\frac{\pi}{2} < \theta < \pi$

   c $\cos\theta$ if $\sin\theta = -\frac{1}{3}$ and $\pi < \theta < \frac{3\pi}{2}$

   d $\cos\theta$ if $\sin\theta = -\frac{5}{13}$ and $\frac{3\pi}{2} < \theta < 2\pi$

   e $\sin\theta$ if $\cos\theta = \frac{3}{5}$ and $0 < \theta < \frac{\pi}{2}$

f $\sin \theta$ if $\cos \theta = \frac{1}{4}$ and $\frac{3\pi}{2} < \theta < 2\pi$

g $\sin \theta$ if $\cos \theta = -\frac{3}{4}$ and $\frac{\pi}{2} < \theta < \pi$

h $\sin \theta$ if $\cos \theta = -\frac{5}{13}$ and $\pi < \theta < \frac{3\pi}{2}$.

C THE MULTIPLES OF 30° AND 45°

MULTIPLES OF 45° OR $\frac{\pi}{4}$

Consider $\theta = 45° \equiv \frac{\pi}{4}$.

Triangle OBP is isosceles as angle OPB measures $45°$ also.

$\therefore$ OB = BP = a, say.

and $a^2 + a^2 = 1^2$ {Pythagoras}

$\therefore$ $2a^2 = 1$

$\therefore$ $a^2 = \frac{1}{2}$

$\therefore$ $a = \frac{1}{\sqrt{2}}$ as $a > 0$

$\therefore$ P is $(\frac{1}{\sqrt{2}}, \frac{1}{\sqrt{2}})$ where $\frac{1}{\sqrt{2}} \approx 0.7$.

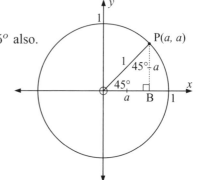

We can now find the coordinates of all points on the unit circle corresponding to multiples of $45°$ by using rotations and reflections.

So, we have:

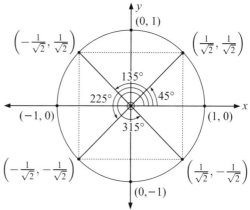

MULTIPLES OF 30° OR $\frac{\pi}{6}$

Consider $\theta = 60° \equiv \frac{\pi}{3}$.

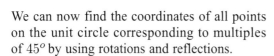

Triangle OAP is isosceles with vertical angle $60°$. The remaining angles are therefore $60°$ and so triangle AOP is equilateral.

The altitude [PN] bisects base [OA], so ON = $\frac{1}{2}$.

If P is $(\frac{1}{2}, k)$, then $(\frac{1}{2})^2 + k^2 = 1$

$\therefore$ $\frac{1}{4} + k^2 = 1$

$\therefore$ $k^2 = \frac{3}{4}$

$\therefore$ $k = \frac{\sqrt{3}}{2}$ {as $k > 0$}

$\therefore$ P is $(\frac{1}{2}, \frac{\sqrt{3}}{2})$ where $\frac{\sqrt{3}}{2} \approx 0.9$.

We can now find the coordinates of all points on the unit circle corresponding to multiples of 30° by using rotations and reflections.

So, we have:

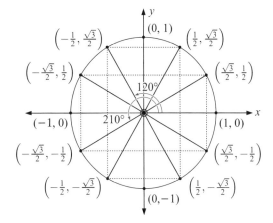

Summary:

- If θ is a **multiple of 90°** or $\frac{\pi}{2}$, the coordinates of the points on the unit circle involve 0 and ± 1.
- If θ is a **multiple of 45°** or $\frac{\pi}{4}$, but not a multiple of 90°, the coordinates involve $\pm\frac{1}{\sqrt{2}}$.
- If θ is a **multiple of 30°** or $\frac{\pi}{6}$, but not a multiple of 90°, the coordinates involve $\pm\frac{1}{2}$ and $\pm\frac{\sqrt{3}}{2}$.

For any angle θ, we can calculate the **tangent** of the angle using the ratio:

$$\tan\theta = \frac{\sin\theta}{\cos\theta}.$$

Example 8 ◀)) **Self Tutor**

Use a unit circle diagram to find $\sin\theta$, $\cos\theta$ and $\tan\theta$ for

a $\theta = \frac{\pi}{3}$　　　　**b** $\theta = \frac{5\pi}{6}$　　　　**c** $\theta = \frac{5\pi}{4}$

a

$\sin\frac{\pi}{3} = \frac{\sqrt{3}}{2}$

$\cos\frac{\pi}{3} = \frac{1}{2}$

$\tan\frac{\pi}{3} = \frac{\frac{\sqrt{3}}{2}}{\frac{1}{2}} = \sqrt{3}$

b

$\sin\frac{5\pi}{6} = \frac{1}{2}$

$\cos\frac{5\pi}{6} = -\frac{\sqrt{3}}{2}$

$\tan\frac{5\pi}{6} = \frac{\frac{1}{2}}{-\frac{\sqrt{3}}{2}} = -\frac{1}{\sqrt{3}}$

c

$\sin\frac{5\pi}{4} = -\frac{1}{\sqrt{2}}$

$\cos\frac{5\pi}{4} = -\frac{1}{\sqrt{2}}$

$\tan\frac{5\pi}{4} = 1$

Example 9   ◀) **Self Tutor**

Use a unit circle diagram to find all angles between $0°$ and $360°$ which have a cosine of $\frac{1}{2}$.

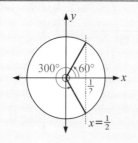

As the cosine is $\frac{1}{2}$, we draw the vertical line $x = \frac{1}{2}$.

Because $\frac{1}{2}$ is involved, we know the required angles are multiples of $30°$.

They are $60°$ and $300°$.

EXERCISE 18C.1

1 Use a unit circle to find $\sin\theta$, $\cos\theta$ and $\tan\theta$ for:

   a $\theta = \frac{\pi}{6}$ **b** $\theta = \frac{\pi}{4}$ **c** $\theta = 0$ **d** $\theta = \frac{3\pi}{4}$

   e $\theta = \frac{\pi}{2}$ **f** $\theta = \frac{2\pi}{3}$ **g** $\theta = \frac{3\pi}{2}$ **h** $\theta = \pi$

   i $\theta = \frac{7\pi}{6}$ **j** $\theta = \frac{4\pi}{3}$ **k** $\theta = \frac{5\pi}{6}$ **l** $\theta = \frac{5\pi}{2}$

   m $\theta = \frac{5\pi}{3}$ **n** $\theta = \frac{7\pi}{4}$ **o** $\theta = \frac{11\pi}{6}$ **p** $\theta = 2\pi$

2 Without using a calculator, find the exact values of:

   a $\sin^2 45°$ **b** $\cos^2\left(\frac{\pi}{3}\right)$ **c** $\tan^2\left(\frac{\pi}{6}\right)$ **d** $\cos^3\left(-\frac{\pi}{6}\right)$

   Check your answers using a calculator.

3 Use a unit circle diagram to find all angles between $0°$ and $360°$ which have:

   a a sine of $\frac{1}{2}$ **b** a cosine of $\frac{\sqrt{3}}{2}$ **c** a sine of $\frac{1}{\sqrt{2}}$

   d a sine of $-\frac{1}{2}$ **e** a sine of $-\frac{1}{\sqrt{2}}$ **f** a cosine of $-\frac{\sqrt{3}}{2}$.

4 Use a unit circle diagram to find all angles between $0°$ and $720°$ which have:

   a a sine of $\frac{\sqrt{3}}{2}$ **b** a cosine of $-\frac{1}{2}$ **c** a cosine of -1.

5 For $0 \leqslant \theta \leqslant 2\pi$, find θ given that:

   a $\sin\theta = \frac{1}{2}$ **b** $\cos\theta = \frac{\sqrt{3}}{2}$ **c** $\sin\theta = -1$ **d** $\cos\theta = 1$

   e $\sin\theta = \frac{1}{\sqrt{2}}$ **f** $\cos\theta = -\frac{1}{\sqrt{2}}$ **g** $\cos^2\theta = 1$ **h** $\sin^2\theta = \frac{1}{2}$

   i $\cos\theta = -\frac{1}{2}$ **j** $\sin\theta = 0$ **k** $\sin\theta = \frac{\sqrt{3}}{2}$ **l** $\cos^2\theta = -1$

6 **a** For $0 \leqslant \theta \leqslant 2\pi$, find θ given that $\sin\theta = \cos\theta$.

     b Find the solutions to $\sin\theta = \cos\theta$ for: **i** $-\pi \leqslant \theta \leqslant \pi$ **ii** $0 \leqslant \theta \leqslant 4\pi$

GRAPHS FROM THE UNIT CIRCLE

The diagram alongside gives the y-coordinates for all points on the unit circle at intervals of $\frac{\pi}{6}$.

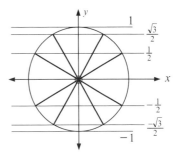

A table for $\sin \theta$ can be constructed from these values:

θ	0	$\frac{\pi}{6}$	$\frac{2\pi}{6}$	$\frac{3\pi}{6}$	$\frac{4\pi}{6}$	$\frac{5\pi}{6}$	π	$\frac{7\pi}{6}$	$\frac{8\pi}{6}$	$\frac{9\pi}{6}$	$\frac{10\pi}{6}$	$\frac{11\pi}{6}$	2π
$\sin \theta$	0	$\frac{1}{2}$	$\frac{\sqrt{3}}{2}$	1	$\frac{\sqrt{3}}{2}$	$\frac{1}{2}$	0	$-\frac{1}{2}$	$-\frac{\sqrt{3}}{2}$	-1	$-\frac{\sqrt{3}}{2}$	$-\frac{1}{2}$	0

Plotting $\sin \theta$ against θ gives:

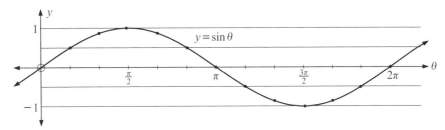

EXERCISE 18C.2

1 a By finding x-coordinates of points on the unit circle, copy and complete:

θ	0	$\frac{\pi}{6}$	$\frac{2\pi}{6}$	$\frac{3\pi}{6}$	$\frac{4\pi}{6}$	$\frac{5\pi}{6}$	π	$\frac{7\pi}{6}$	$\frac{8\pi}{6}$	$\frac{9\pi}{6}$	$\frac{10\pi}{6}$	$\frac{11\pi}{6}$	2π
$\cos \theta$													

b Use **a** to graph $y = \cos \theta$ for $0 \leqslant \theta \leqslant 2\pi$, making sure the graph is fully labelled.

c What is the maximum value of $\cos \theta$ and when does it occur?

d What is the minimum value of $\cos \theta$ and when does it occur?

2 Below is an accurate graph of $y = \sin \theta$. Use the graph to solve the following equations for $0° \leqslant \theta \leqslant 720°$:

a $\sin \theta = 0$ **b** $\sin \theta = \frac{1}{2}$ **c** $\sin \theta = \frac{\sqrt{3}}{2}$ **d** $\sin \theta = -1$

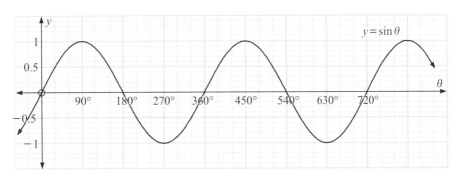

3 Below is an accurate graph of $y = \cos\theta$. Use the graph to solve the following equations for $0° \leqslant \theta \leqslant 720°$:

a $\cos\theta = 1$ **b** $\cos\theta = -\frac{1}{2}$ **c** $\cos\theta = -\frac{1}{\sqrt{2}}$ **d** $\cos\theta = 0$

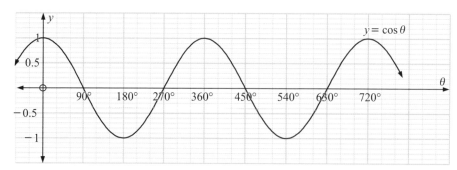

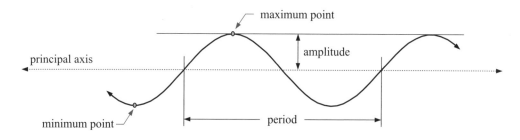

D   GRAPHING TRIGONOMETRIC FUNCTIONS

The sine and cosine functions are called **periodic functions** because they repeat themselves again and again. Before we consider the graphs of these functions in detail, we need to learn appropriate language for describing them.

TERMINOLOGY

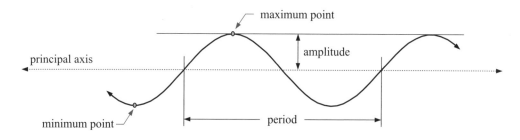

- A **periodic function** is one which repeats itself over and over in a horizontal direction.
- The **period** of a periodic function is the length of one repetition or cycle.
- The graph oscillates about a horizontal line called the **principal axis** or **mean line**.
- A **maximum point** occurs at the top of a crest.
- A **minimum point** occurs at the bottom of a trough.
- The **amplitude** is the vertical distance between a maximum or minimum point and the principal axis.

THE BASIC SINE FUNCTION, $f(x) = \sin x$

Instead of using θ, we now use x to represent the angle variable.

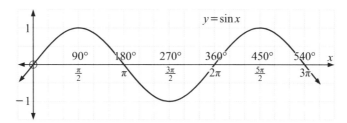

We expect the *period* to be 2π, since our position on the unit circle starts repeating after one full revolution. The *maximum* value is 1 and the *minimum* is -1 as $-1 \leqslant y \leqslant 1$ on the unit circle. The *amplitude* is 1.

GRAPHING PACKAGE

Use the **graphing package** to obtain the graph of $y = \sin x$ and hence check these features.

THE BASIC COSINE FUNCTION, $f(x) = \cos x$

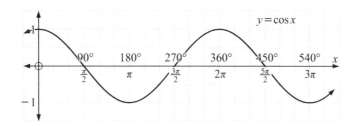

The basic cosine function has the same period, maximum and minimum values, and amplitude as the basic sine function. In fact, it is a **translation** of the basic sine function of $\frac{\pi}{2}$ units to the left.

INVESTIGATION   FAMILIES OF TRIGONOMETRIC FUNCTIONS

In this investigation we consider different transformations of the basic sine function.

GRAPHING PACKAGE

What to do:

1 Use the graphing package to graph on the same set of axes:

    a $y = \sin x$ **b** $y = 2\sin x$ **c** $y = \frac{1}{2}\sin x$

    d $y = -\sin x$ **e** $y = -\frac{1}{3}\sin x$ **f** $y = -\frac{3}{2}\sin x$

2 All of the graphs in **1** have the form $y = A\sin x$.
    Comment on the significance of:

    a the sign of A **b** the size of A, or $|A|$.

3 Use the graphing package to graph on the same set of axes:

    a $y = \sin x$ **b** $y = \sin 2x$ **c** $y = \sin\left(\frac{1}{2}x\right)$ **d** $y = \sin 3x$

4 All of the graphs in **3** have the form $y = \sin Bx$ where $B > 0$.
  a Does B affect the: **i** amplitude   **ii** period?
  b What is the period of $y = \sin Bx$, $B > 0$?

5 Graph the following on the same set of axes:
  a $y = \sin x$ **b** $y = \sin(x - 2)$ **c** $y = \sin(x + 2)$

6 What translation moves $y = \sin x$ to $y = \sin(x - C)$?

7 Graph the following on the same set of axes:
  a $y = \sin x$ **b** $y = \sin x + 2$ **c** $y = \sin x - 2$

8 What translation moves $y = \sin x$ to $y = \sin x + D$?

9 What translation moves $y = \sin x$ to $y = \sin(x - C) + D$?

10 What sequence of transformations map $y = \sin x$ onto $y = A \sin B(x - C) + D$?

Consider the general sine function $y = A \sin B(x - C) + D$

From the investigation you should have observed the following properties:

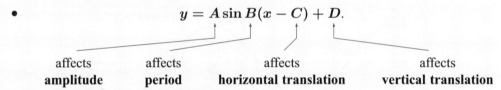

- $$y = A \sin B(x - C) + D.$$

  affects   affects   affects   affects
  amplitude   **period**   **horizontal translation**   **vertical translation**

- the amplitude is $|A|$ and the period is $\frac{2\pi}{B}$ for $B > 0$.

- $y = \sin(x - C) + D$ is obtained from $y = \sin x$ by the translation $\begin{pmatrix} C \\ D \end{pmatrix}$

- $y = A \sin B(x - C) + D$ is obtained from $y = \sin x$ by a vertical dilation of
  factor A and a horizontal dilation of factor $\frac{1}{B}$, followed by the translation $\begin{pmatrix} C \\ D \end{pmatrix}$.

For example:

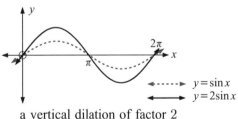

a vertical dilation of factor 2

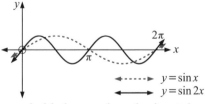

period halves under a horizontal
dilation of factor $\frac{1}{2}$

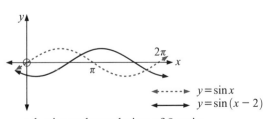

a horizontal translation of 2 units

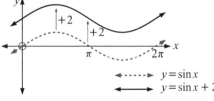

a vertical translation of 2 units

Click on the icon to obtain a demonstration for the general sine function.

DEMO

The properties of the general cosine function $y = A\cos B(x - C) + D$ are the same as those of the general sine function.

EXERCISE 18D

1 Without using technology, sketch for $0 \leqslant x \leqslant 4\pi$:

    a $y = 3\sin x$ **b** $y = \frac{1}{3}\sin x$ **c** $y = -2\sin x$

    d $y = \sin 3x$ **e** $y = \sin\left(\frac{x}{2}\right)$ **f** $y = \sin\left(\frac{x}{3}\right)$

2 Without using technology, sketch for $0 \leqslant x \leqslant 4\pi$:

    a $y = 2\cos x$ **b** $y = \frac{1}{2}\cos x$ **c** $y = -\frac{1}{3}\cos x$

    d $y = \cos 2x$ **e** $y = \cos\left(\frac{x}{2}\right)$ **f** $y = \cos\left(\frac{3x}{2}\right)$

3 Find the period of:

    a $y = \sin 2x$ **b** $y = \sin\left(\frac{x}{3}\right)$ **c** $y = \sin(0.6x)$

    d $y = \sin 4x + 1$ **e** $y = \sin\frac{1}{2}(x - 2)$ **f** $y = \sin 3x - 1$

4 Find the basic sine function with a period of:

    a 5   **b** $\frac{\pi}{5}$

5 Find the period of:

    a $y = \cos 3x$ **b** $y = \cos\left(\frac{x}{4}\right)$ **c** $y = \cos 2(x - 1)$

6 Without using technology, sketch for $0 \leqslant x \leqslant 2\pi$:

    a $y = \sin(x - 1)$ **b** $y = \sin x - 1$ **c** $y = 2\sin\left(x - \frac{\pi}{3}\right)$

    d $y = \cos\left(x - \frac{\pi}{6}\right) + 2$ **e** $y = \sin\left(x + \frac{\pi}{3}\right) - 1\frac{1}{2}$ **f** $y = 2\cos 3x$

    g $y = -\sin x + 1$ **h** $y = 2\cos x - 1$ **i** $y = -\cos 2x + 1$

E   MODELLING WITH SINE FUNCTIONS

We have already seen how the sine and cosine functions are periodic. They can be used to model many situations in the real world that exhibit this behaviour. We call these situations **periodic phenomena**.

Examples of periodic phenomena include:

- average daily temperatures through the seasons
- the depth of water in a harbour varying with the tide
- the number of daylight hours at a particular location.

Consider again the transformation of $y = \sin x$ into $y = A \sin B(x - C) + D$.

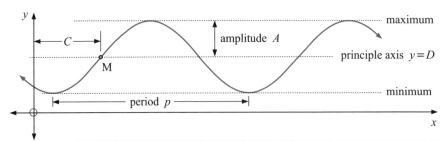

Notice that:

- the amplitude $A = \dfrac{\text{max} - \text{min}}{2}$

- the period $p = \dfrac{2\pi}{B}$, so $B = \dfrac{2\pi}{p}$

- if O is transformed to the point M, then C is the horizontal distance from the y-axis to M.

- $D = \dfrac{\text{max} + \text{min}}{2}$

If we are given real data then we can use these properties to evaluate the coefficients A, B, C and D in the general sine function. We thus obtain a sine model for the data.

MEAN MONTHLY TEMPERATURE

The mean monthly maximum temperatures (°C) for Christchurch, New Zealand, are shown in the following table:

Month	Jan	Feb	Mar	Apr	May	Jun	Jul	Aug	Sep	Oct	Nov	Dec
Temp	21	20	$18\frac{1}{2}$	15	$11\frac{1}{2}$	9	8	9	11	$14\frac{1}{2}$	17	19

The graph over a two year period is:

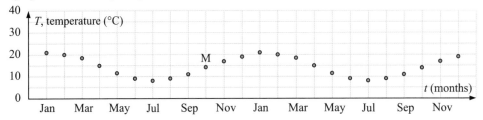

We will attempt to model this data using the general sine function

$$y = A \sin B(x - C) + D$$

or in this case $T = A \sin B(t - C) + D$.

The period is 12 months, so $\dfrac{2\pi}{B} = 12$ and hence $B = \frac{\pi}{6}$.

The amplitude $= \dfrac{\text{max} - \text{min}}{2} = \dfrac{21 - 8}{2} = 6.5$, so $A = 6.5$.

The principal axis is midway between the maximum and minimum values, so $D = \dfrac{\text{max} + \text{min}}{2}$.

So, the model is $T = 6.5 \sin \frac{\pi}{6}(t - C) + 14.5$

Point M(10, 14.5) lies on the principal axis, so $C = 10$.

The model is therefore $T = 6.5 \sin \frac{\pi}{6}(t - 10) + 14.5$, and it is superimposed on the original data as follows:

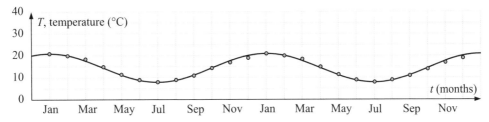

TIDAL MODELS

The tide follows regular patterns of rising and falling due to the combined gravitational effects from the sun and the moon.

The weekend tides in Whitby are shown in the table alongside.

High tide corresponds to 7.2 m and low tide to 3.8 m above a marker point.

	Low	High
Saturday	7:57 am, 8:24 pm	2:29 pm
Sunday	8:41 am, 9:08 pm	2:42 am, 3:20 pm

Plotting these heights with t being the time after midnight before the first low tide, we get:

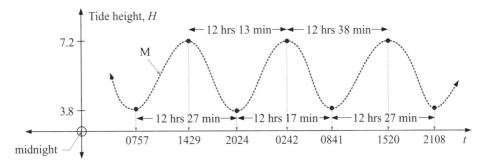

We will attempt to model this periodic data using the general sine function

$$y = A \sin B(x - C) + D,$$

or in this case $H = A \sin B(t - C) + D.$

Since max $= 7.2$ and min $= 3.8$, $D = \dfrac{7.2 + 3.8}{2} = 5.5$

and $A = \dfrac{7.2 - 3.8}{2} = 1.7.$

The graph shows that the 'average' period is about 12 hours 24 min ≈ 12.4 hours.

But the period is $\dfrac{2\pi}{B}$, so $\dfrac{2\pi}{B} \approx 12.4$ and thus $B \approx \dfrac{2\pi}{12.4} \approx 0.507.$

Finally, we suppose M is the midpoint between the first low and first high tides.

Now $\frac{1}{2}(14\!:\!29 \text{ hours} - 7\!:\!57 \text{ hours}) = \frac{1}{2}(6 \text{ hours } 32 \text{ mins}) = 3 \text{ hours } 16 \text{ mins}$

$\therefore$ M is at 7:57 + 3 hours 16 mins = 11:13

$\therefore$ the x-coordinate of M is 11.22

$\therefore$ the model is $H \approx 1.7 \sin 0.507(t - 11.22) + 5.5$ m

EXERCISE 18E

1   The following table shows the mean monthly minimum temperatures ($^{\circ}$C) for a city in Uruguay.

Month	Jan	Feb	Mar	Apr	May	Jun	July	Aug	Sept	Oct	Nov	Dec
Temp	15	16	$14\frac{1}{2}$	12	10	$7\frac{1}{2}$	7	$7\frac{1}{2}$	$8\frac{1}{2}$	$10\frac{1}{2}$	$12\frac{1}{2}$	14

Fit a sine model to this data as a function of time without using technology.

2   The following table shows the mean monthly maximum temperatures ($^{\circ}$C) for Fremantle.

Month	Jan	Feb	Mar	Apr	May	Jun	July	Aug	Sept	Oct	Nov	Dec
Temp	28	28	27	23	21	18	18	17	18	21	23	26

Fit a sine model to this data as a function of time without using technology.

3   Obtain periodic data like that in questions 1 and 2 for the city or region in which you live. Fit a sine model to the data.

4   The tides along the German coast cause the water level to change 8 metres between high tide and low tide. The mean level is 6 metres. If the period between successive high tides is 12 hours and 24 minutes, and high tide is at midnight one day, model the water level as a function of time after that midnight.

5   A harbour experiences a tidal change in water level between 4 metres and 8 metres. The period of successive low tides is about 12 hours and 24 minutes. If a boat has a draught of 5 metres, during what proportion of the day can the boat leave or arrive safely?

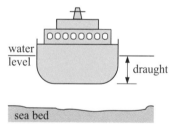

F   TRIGONOMETRIC EQUATIONS

In this section we solve equations involving the trigonometric ratios $\sin \theta$, $\cos \theta$ and $\tan \theta$.

To do this we recognise that:

- if two angles have the same sine they have the same y-coordinate

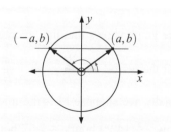

- if two angles have the same cosine they have the same x-coordinate

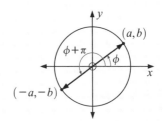

- if two angles have the same tangent they are located $180°$ or π apart.

When solving these problems, it is often useful to begin with a **working angle** in quadrant 1 that is symmetric to the angle in question. To do this we use the **modulus** of the given ratio. You will observe how to use a working angle in the following example.

Example 10　　　　　　　　　　　　　　◀》 **Self Tutor**

Solve on $\quad 0 \leqslant \theta \leqslant 2\pi, \quad$ to 3 decimal places:

a $\sin \theta = \frac{1}{3}$ 　　　**b** $\cos \theta = -0.7516$ 　　　**c** $\tan \theta = -2.179$

a

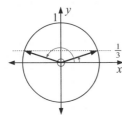

$\sin \theta = \frac{1}{3}$, so the angle is in quadrant 1 or 2.

$\therefore \quad \theta = \sin^{-1}\left(\frac{1}{3}\right) \quad$ or $\quad \pi - \sin^{-1}\left(\frac{1}{3}\right)$

$\therefore \quad \theta \approx 0.3398 \quad$ or $\quad \pi - 0.3398$

$\therefore \quad \theta \approx 0.340 \quad$ or $\quad 2.802$

> Make sure that the mode of your calculator is set to radians.

b

$\cos \theta = -0.7516$, so the angle is in quadrant 2 or 3.

We start by considering a working angle α in the first quadrant.

For this angle,

$\cos \alpha = 0.7516$

$\therefore \quad \alpha = \cos^{-1}(0.7516) \approx 0.7203$

$\therefore \quad \theta \approx \pi - 0.7203 \quad$ or $\quad \pi + 0.7203$

$\therefore \quad \theta \approx 2.421 \quad$ or $\quad 3.862$

c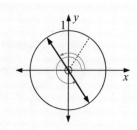

$\tan \theta = -2.179$,   so the angle is in quadrant 2 or 4.

We start by considering a working angle α in the first quadrant. For this angle,

$$\tan \alpha = 2.179$$
$$\therefore \quad \tan \alpha = \tan^{-1}(2.179) \approx 1.1405$$
$$\therefore \quad \theta \approx \pi - 1.1405 \quad \text{or} \quad 2\pi - 1.1405$$
$$\therefore \quad \theta \approx 2.001 \quad \text{or} \quad 5.143$$

Example 11   ◀) **Self Tutor**

Solve for θ where $0 \leqslant \theta \leqslant 2\pi$:

a $2 \sin^2 \theta = \sin \theta$

b $3 \cos^2 \theta = 2 \cos \theta + 1$

a
$$2 \sin^2 \theta = \sin \theta$$
$$\therefore \quad 2 \sin^2 \theta - \sin \theta = 0$$
$$\therefore \quad \sin \theta (2 \sin \theta - 1) = 0$$
$$\therefore \quad \sin \theta = 0 \text{ or } \tfrac{1}{2}$$
$$\therefore \quad \theta = 0, \tfrac{\pi}{6}, \tfrac{5\pi}{6}, \pi \text{ or } 2\pi$$

b
$$3 \cos^2 \theta = 2 \cos \theta + 1$$
$$\therefore \quad 3 \cos^2 \theta - 2 \cos \theta - 1 = 0$$
$$\therefore \quad (3 \cos \theta + 1)(\cos \theta - 1) = 0$$
$$\therefore \quad \cos \theta = -\tfrac{1}{3} \text{ or } 1$$

Using a working angle α with $\cos \alpha = \tfrac{1}{3}$,
$$\alpha \approx 1.231$$
$$\therefore \quad \theta = 0, \quad \pi - 1.231, \quad \pi + 1.231 \quad \text{or} \quad 2\pi$$
$$\therefore \quad \theta \approx 0, \quad 1.911, \quad 4.373 \quad \text{or} \quad 6.283$$

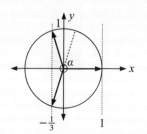

EXERCISE 18F

1 Solve on $0 \leqslant \theta \leqslant 2\pi$, to 3 decimal places:

a $\sin \theta = \tfrac{2}{3}$
b $\sin \theta = \tfrac{3}{5}$
c $\sin \theta = -\tfrac{1}{3}$

d $\sin \theta = 0.781$
e $\sin \theta = -0.4066$
f $\sin \theta = -0.9382$

2 Solve on $0 \leqslant \theta \leqslant 2\pi$, to 3 decimal places:

a $\cos \theta = \tfrac{3}{4}$
b $\cos \theta = -\tfrac{4}{5}$
c $\cos \theta = 0.816$

d $\cos \theta = -0.275$
e $\cos \theta = -0.766$
f $\cos \theta = 2$

3 Solve on $0 \leqslant \theta \leqslant 2\pi$, to 3 decimal places:

a $\tan \theta = \tfrac{1}{3}$
b $\tan \theta = 2.5$
c $\tan \theta = -\tfrac{5}{3}$

d $\tan \theta = -6.734$
e $\tan \theta = 20.67$
f $\tan \theta = -0.3865$

4 Solve on $0 \leqslant \theta \leqslant 2\pi$, to 3 decimal places:

   a $\cos\theta = -\frac{4}{7}$ **b** $\sin\theta = -0.8$ **c** $\tan\theta = -3.251$

   d $\tan\theta = 7.92$ **e** $\cos\theta = 0.8338$ **f** $\sin\theta = 1.6224$

   g $\cos\theta = -0.506$ **h** $\tan\theta = 0.777$ **i** $\sin\theta = -0.1313$

5 Solve on $0 \leqslant \theta \leqslant 2\pi$, to 3 decimal places, where necessary:

   a $2\cos^2\theta = \cos\theta$ **b** $\sin^2\theta = \sin\theta$ **c** $3\sin^2\theta = 1$

   d $4\sin\theta = 5\sin^2\theta$ **e** $\cos^2\theta - 2\cos\theta + 1 = 0$

   f $(\cos\theta + 1)(2\cos\theta + 1) = 0$ **g** $2\sin^2\theta = 3\sin\theta + 5$

   h $5\cos^2\theta = 1 + 4\cos\theta$ **i** $6\cos^2\theta + 5\cos\theta = -1$

 # NEGATIVE AND COMPLEMENTARY ANGLE FORMULAE

NEGATIVE ANGLE FORMULAE

P and P′ have the same x-coordinate, but their y-coordinates are negatives.

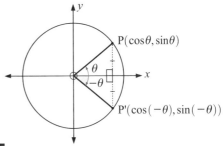

Hence $\cos(-\theta) = \cos\theta$

            $\sin(-\theta) = -\sin\theta$

COMPLEMENTARY ANGLE FORMULAE

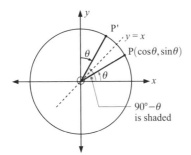

Consider P′ on the unit circle, which corresponds to the angle $(90^o - \theta)$.

∴   P′ is $(\cos(90^o - \theta),\ \sin(90^o - \theta))$ ...... (1)

But P′ is the image of P under a reflection in the line $y = x$.

∴   P′ is $(\sin\theta,\ \cos\theta)$ ...... (2)

Comparing (1) and (2) gives

$$\cos(90^o - \theta) = \sin\theta \qquad\qquad \cos\left(\tfrac{\pi}{2} - \theta\right) = \sin\theta$$
$$\qquad\qquad\qquad\qquad\qquad\text{or}$$
$$\sin(90^o - \theta) = \cos\theta \qquad\qquad \sin\left(\tfrac{\pi}{2} - \theta\right) = \cos\theta$$

Example 12   ◀) **Self Tutor**

Simplify:

   a $5\sin\theta - 2\sin(-\theta)$ **b** $4\cos\theta - \cos(-\theta)$ **c** $4\cos\left(\tfrac{\pi}{2} - \theta\right) - 3\sin\theta$

> **a** $5\sin\theta - 2\sin(-\theta)$
> $= 5\sin\theta - 2[-\sin\theta]$
> $= 5\sin\theta + 2\sin\theta$
> $= 7\sin\theta$
>
> **b** $4\cos\theta - \cos(-\theta)$
> $= 4\cos\theta - [\cos\theta]$
> $= 4\cos\theta - \cos\theta$
> $= 3\cos\theta$
>
> **c** $4\cos(\frac{\pi}{2} - \theta) - 3\sin\theta$
> $= 4\sin\theta - 3\sin\theta$
> $= \sin\theta$

EXERCISE 18G

1 Simplify:

   a $2\sin\theta + \sin(-\theta)$ **b** $3\sin(-\theta) - \sin\theta$ **c** $4\cos\theta + 2\cos(-\theta)$

   d $8\sin\theta - 3\sin(-\theta)$ **e** $\cos^2(-\alpha)$ **f** $\sin^2(-\alpha)$

   g $\cos(-\alpha)\cos\alpha - \sin(-\alpha)\sin\alpha$

2 Prove that $\tan(-\theta) = -\tan\theta$ for all θ.

3 Simplify:

   a $4\cos\theta - 2\sin(90^\circ - \theta)$ **b** $2\cos(-\theta) - 5\sin(90^\circ - \theta)$

   c $3\cos(90^\circ - \theta) - \sin\theta$ **d** $2\sin(-\theta) - 7\cos(\frac{\pi}{2} - \theta)$

   e $6\sin\theta + \cos(\frac{\pi}{2} - \theta)$ **f** $3\sin(\frac{\pi}{2} - \theta) + 4\cos\theta$

4 What is the relationship between $\tan(90^\circ - \theta)$ and $\tan\theta$?

5 Consider the argument: $\sin\theta = \dfrac{b}{c}$ and $\cos(90^\circ - \theta) = \dfrac{b}{c}$

               $\therefore$ $\sin\theta = \cos(90^\circ - \theta)$

   Explain why this 'proof' is not acceptable in general.

H   ADDITION FORMULAE

ADDITION FORMULAE

If A and B are **any** two angles then:

$$\mathbf{\cos(A + B)} = \cos A \cos B - \sin A \sin B$$
$$\mathbf{\cos(A - B)} = \cos A \cos B + \sin A \sin B$$
$$\mathbf{\sin(A + B)} = \sin A \cos B + \cos A \sin B$$
$$\mathbf{\sin(A - B)} = \sin A \cos B - \cos A \sin B$$

and these are known as the **addition formulae**.

Proof:

Consider   P($\cos A$, $\sin A$) and   Q($\cos B$, $\sin B$) as any two points on the unit circle, so angle POQ is $A - B$.

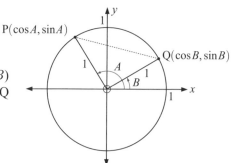

Now $PQ = \sqrt{(\cos A - \cos B)^2 + (\sin A - \sin B)^2}$ {distance formula}

$$\therefore \quad (PQ)^2 = \cos^2 A - 2\cos A \cos B + \cos^2 B + \sin^2 A - 2\sin A \sin B + \sin^2 B$$
$$= \cos^2 A + \sin^2 A + \cos^2 B + \sin^2 B - 2(\cos A \cos B + \sin A \sin B)$$
$$= 1 + 1 - 2(\cos A \cos B + \sin A \sin B)$$
$$= 2 - 2(\cos A \cos B + \sin A \sin B) \quad ...... \ (1)$$

But, by the *cosine rule* in ΔPOQ,

$$(PQ)^2 = 1^2 + 1^2 - 2(1)(1)\cos(A - B)$$
$$= 2 - 2\cos(A - B) \quad ...... \ (2)$$
$$\therefore \quad \cos(A - B) = \cos A \cos B + \sin A \sin B \quad \text{\{comparing (1) and (2)\}}$$

From this formula the other three formulae can be established:

$$\cos(A + B) = \cos(A - (-B))$$
$$= \cos A \cos(-B) + \sin A \sin(-B)$$
$$= \cos A \cos B + \sin A(-\sin B) \quad \{\cos(-\theta) = \cos \theta \ \text{ and } \ \sin(-\theta) = -\sin \theta\}$$
$$= \cos A \cos B - \sin A \sin B$$
$$\sin(A - B) = \cos(\tfrac{\pi}{2} - (A - B))$$
$$= \cos((\tfrac{\pi}{2} - A) + B)$$
$$= \cos(\tfrac{\pi}{2} - A)\cos B - \sin(\tfrac{\pi}{2} - A)\sin B \quad \{\sin(\tfrac{\pi}{2} - \theta) = \cos \theta \ \text{ and }$$
$$= \sin A \cos B - \cos A \sin B \qquad\qquad\qquad \cos(\tfrac{\pi}{2} - \theta) = \sin \theta\}$$
$$\sin(A + B) = \sin(A - (-B))$$
$$= \sin A \cos(-B) - \cos A \sin(-B)$$
$$= \sin A \cos B - \cos A(-\sin B)$$
$$= \sin A \cos B + \cos A \sin B$$

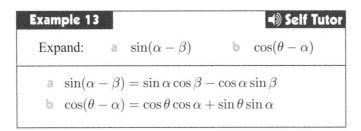

| **Example 13** | ◀ Self Tutor |

Expand: a $\sin(\alpha - \beta)$ b $\cos(\theta - \alpha)$

   a $\sin(\alpha - \beta) = \sin \alpha \cos \beta - \cos \alpha \sin \beta$

   b $\cos(\theta - \alpha) = \cos \theta \cos \alpha + \sin \theta \sin \alpha$

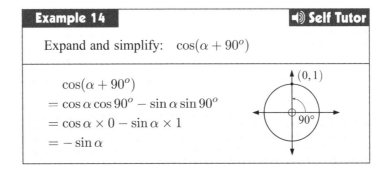

| **Example 14** | ◀ Self Tutor |

Expand and simplify: $\cos(\alpha + 90°)$

$$\cos(\alpha + 90°)$$
$$= \cos \alpha \cos 90° - \sin \alpha \sin 90°$$
$$= \cos \alpha \times 0 - \sin \alpha \times 1$$
$$= -\sin \alpha$$

EXERCISE 18H

1 Expand and simplify:

    a $\sin(B + C)$　　　　**b** $\cos(M - N)$　　　　**c** $\sin(P - Q)$

    d $\cos(\alpha + \theta)$　　　　**e** $\sin(\beta + \alpha)$　　　　**f** $\cos(\alpha - \beta)$

2 Expand and simplify

    a $\sin(90° + \alpha)$　　　　**b** $\cos(270° + \beta)$　　　　**c** $\sin(180° - A)$

    d $\cos(\alpha + \frac{\pi}{2})$　　　　**e** $\sin(\pi + \beta)$　　　　**f** $\cos(\theta - \frac{3\pi}{2})$

    g $\sin(\theta + \frac{\pi}{6})$　　　　**h** $\cos(\frac{\pi}{3} - \alpha)$　　　　**i** $\sin(\theta + \frac{\pi}{4})$

    j $\cos(\frac{\pi}{4} + \phi)$　　　　**k** $\sin(\frac{3\pi}{4} + C)$　　　　**l** $\cos(A - \frac{\pi}{6})$

3 Simplify using the addition formula in reverse:

    a $\cos A \cos B + \sin A \sin B$　　　　**b** $\sin \alpha \cos \beta - \cos \alpha \sin \beta$

    c $\cos M \cos N - \sin M \sin N$　　　　**d** $\sin C \cos D + \cos C \sin D$

    e $2 \sin \alpha \cos \beta - 2 \cos \alpha \sin \beta$　　　　**f** $\sin \alpha \sin \beta - \cos \alpha \cos \beta$

4 The **duplication** or **double angle** formulae are:　$\sin 2A = 2 \sin A \cos A$　and
$$\cos 2A = \cos^2 A - \sin^2 A.$$

    a Prove these two formulae using the addition formulae.

    b If　$\sin \alpha = \frac{3}{5}$　and　$\cos \alpha = -\frac{4}{5}$,　find:　**i** $\sin 2\alpha$　**ii** $\cos 2\alpha$.

5 Use the duplication formulae in question 4 to prove that:

    a $(\sin \alpha + \cos \alpha)^2 = 1 + \sin 2\alpha$　　　　**b** $\cos^4 \theta - \sin^4 \theta = \cos 2\theta$

6 In the given figure, find in terms of m:

    a $\tan \theta$　　　　**b** the length AC

    c $\sin 2\theta$　　　　**d** $\cos 2\theta$.

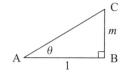

7 Illustrated is a unit circle diagram where $\overrightarrow{OP}$ and $\overrightarrow{OQ}$ make angles of B and A respectively.

    a Find $\overrightarrow{OP}$ and $\overrightarrow{OQ}$.

    b Use the scalar product of two vectors to establish that
$$\cos(A - B) = \cos A \cos B + \sin A \sin B.$$

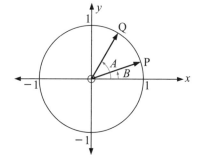

LINKS
click here

IN TUNE WITH TRIGONOMETRY

Areas of interaction:
Human ingenuity

REVIEW SET 18A

1 Convert to radians in terms of π: **a** $75°$ **b** $22\tfrac{1}{2}°$.

2 Convert to degrees: **a** $\tfrac{\pi}{10}$ **b** $\tfrac{7\pi}{9}$

3 Convert 2.78^c to degrees, to 3 significant figures.

4 Find:

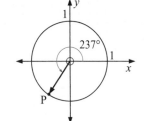

    a the exact coordinates of P

    b the approximate coordinates of P, correct to 3 significant figures.

5 Use a unit circle diagram to find the exact values of:

    a $\sin 315°$ **b** $\cos\left(\tfrac{5\pi}{6}\right)$ **c** $\tan\left(\tfrac{7\pi}{6}\right)$

6 If $\cos\theta = \tfrac{2}{3}$, find the possible values of $\sin\theta$.

7 Find $\cos\theta$ given that $\sin\theta = -\tfrac{2}{\sqrt{5}}$ and $\pi < \theta < \tfrac{3\pi}{2}$.

8 If $\sqrt{2}\cos\theta + 1 = 0$ where $0 \leqslant \theta \leqslant 2\pi$ find:

    a $\cos\theta$ **b** θ in terms of π.

9 On the same set of axes, graph on $0 \leqslant x \leqslant 2\pi$:

    a $y = \sin x$ and $y = 2 + \sin x$

    b $y = \cos x$ and $y = 2\cos 2x$.

10 Solve on $0 \leqslant \theta \leqslant 2\pi$,   correct to 3 decimal places:

    a $\sin\theta = \tfrac{3}{4}$ **b** $\cos\theta = -\tfrac{1}{3}$ **c** $\tan\theta = 2.8$

11 Given $2\cos^2\theta - \cos\theta - 1 = 0$ on $0 \leqslant \theta \leqslant 2\pi$,   find:

    a $\cos\theta$ **b** θ

12 Expand and simplify:

    a $\sin(\pi + \theta)$ **b** $\cos(\tfrac{2\pi}{3} - \theta)$

13 The following table displays the mean minimum monthly temperatures for New York:

Month	Jan	Feb	Mar	Apr	May	Jun	Jul	Aug	Sept	Oct	Nov	Dec
$T\ (°C)$	-3	-2	1	7	12	17	21	20	16	11	6	-1

Fit the sine model to the data without using technology.

14 **a** Find x in simplest form.

    b Use the $\cos(A + B)$ expansion formula to show that $\cos 75° = \dfrac{\sqrt{3}-1}{2\sqrt{2}}$.

    c Using **a** and **b**, find in simplest radical form:

        i $\sin 75°$ **ii** $\tan 75°$

REVIEW SET 18B

1 **a** Convert $105°$ to radians in terms of π.

    b Convert $\frac{7\pi}{18}$ to degrees.

2 Use a unit circle diagram to find the exact value of:

    a $\cos\left(\frac{2\pi}{3}\right)$ **b** $\sin\left(-\frac{\pi}{4}\right)$ **c** $\tan\left(\frac{5\pi}{6}\right)$

3 If $\sin\theta = -\frac{3}{5}$, find the possible values of:

    a $\cos\theta$ **b** $\tan\theta$

4 Find $\sin\theta$ given that $\cos\theta = -\frac{3}{\sqrt{13}}$ and $\pi < \theta < \frac{3\pi}{2}$.

5 Find θ on $0 \leqslant \theta \leqslant 2\pi$ if:

    a $\cos\theta = -\frac{1}{2}$ **b** $\sin\theta = \frac{\sqrt{3}}{2}$

6 On the same set of axes, graph:

    a $y = \sin x$ and $y = \sin(x - 2)$

    b $y = \cos x$ and $y = -\cos 2x$

7 What is the period of $y = 2\sin 3(x - 1)$?

8 Solve on $0 \leqslant \theta \leqslant 2\pi$, correct to 3 decimal places:

    a $\cos\theta = 0.821$ **b** $\sin\theta = 2$ **c** $\tan\theta = -1.738$

9 Expand and simplify:

    a $\sin\left(\theta - \frac{\pi}{4}\right)$ **b** $\sqrt{3}\cos\left(\phi + \frac{\pi}{6}\right)$

10 Simplify $\cos(\alpha + \beta)\cos\beta + \sin(\alpha + \beta)\sin\beta$ in one step.

11 Simplify: $4\sin\left(\frac{\pi}{2} - \theta\right) - 2\cos(-\theta)$

12 Solve for θ on the interval $0 \leqslant \theta \leqslant 2\pi$ if $2\sin^2\theta = \sin\theta + 1$

13 The following data displays the mean maximum monthly temperatures of London, England:

Month	Jan	Feb	Mar	Apr	May	Jun	Jul	Aug	Sept	Oct	Nov	Dec
T (^{o}C)	7	7	11	13	17	20	22	22	19	14	11	8

Fit the sine model to the data without using technology.

14 **a** Use the $\sin(A + B)$ and $\cos(A + B)$ expansion formulae to prove that:

    i $\sin 2\theta = 2\sin\theta\cos\theta$ **ii** $\cos 2\theta = \cos^2\theta - \sin^2\theta$

    b Hence find a formula for $\sin 3\theta$ in terms of $\sin\theta$ only.

    c If $\sin 3\theta = 0$, what are the possible values of $\sin\theta$?

Chapter **19**

Inequalities

Contents:

In this course so far, we have mostly dealt with **equations** in which two expressions are separated by the equality sign $=$.

In this chapter we consider **inequalities** or **inequations** in which two expressions are separated by one of the four inequality signs $<$, $\leqslant$, $>$ or $\geqslant$.

We begin the chapter by considering **sign diagrams** as these are a useful tool for our study of inequalities and they are also used in other areas of mathematics.

OPENING PROBLEM

Consider the inequality $\dfrac{3x + 2}{1 - x} > 4$.

Jon's method of solving this problem was:

$$\text{If}\quad \frac{3x + 2}{1 - x} > 4$$
$$\text{then}\quad 3x + 2 > 4(1 - x)$$
$$\therefore\quad 3x + 2 > 4 - 4x$$
$$\therefore\quad 7x > 2$$
$$\therefore\quad x > \tfrac{2}{7}$$

However, Sarah pointed out that if $x = 5$ then $\dfrac{3x + 2}{1 - x} = \dfrac{17}{-4} = -4\tfrac{1}{4}$, and $-4\tfrac{1}{4}$ is **not** greater than 4.

They concluded that there was something wrong with Jon's method of solution.

A graph also highlighted the error.
It seems that the correct answer
is $\tfrac{2}{7} < x < 1$.

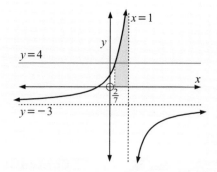

Things to think about:

1 At what step was Jon's method wrong?

2 Can you find an algebraic method which does give the correct answer?

A   SIGN DIAGRAMS

Sometimes we do not need a complete graph of a function, but only wish to know when the function is positive, negative, zero or undefined. A **sign diagram** enables us to do this, and is relatively easy to construct.

A sign diagram consists of:

- a **horizontal line** which is really the x-axis
- **positive** $(+)$ and **negative** $(-)$ signs indicating when the graph is **above** and **below** the x-axis respectively
- **critical values** which are the graph's x-intercepts or where it is undefined.

Consider the graph:

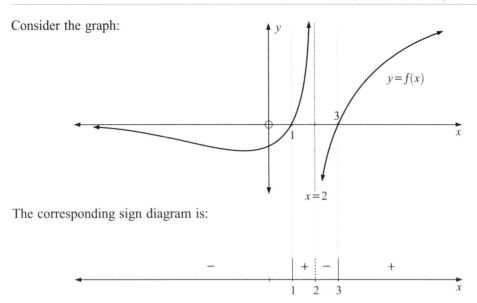

The corresponding sign diagram is:

We use a solid line to indicate a critical value where the function is zero, and a dashed line to indicate where the function is undefined.

Further examples are:

Function	$y = (x + 2)(x - 1)$	$y = -2(x - 1)^2$	$y = \dfrac{4}{x}$
Graph			
Sign diagram			

Notice that:

- A sign change occurs about the critical value for single factors such as $(x + 2)$ and $(x - 1)$,   indicating **cutting** of the x-axis.

- No sign change occurs about the critical value for squared factors such as $(x - 1)^2$, indicating **touching** of the x-axis.

Example 1   ◀》 **Self Tutor**

Draw sign diagrams for: **a** $(x+3)(x-1)$ **b** $2(2x+5)(3-x)$

a $(x+3)(x-1)$ has critical values -3 and 1.

We try any number > 1:
When $x = 10$,
$(x+3)(x-1) = 13 \times 9 > 0$.

The factors are single so the signs alternate.

$\therefore$ the sign diagram is

b $2(2x+5)(3-x)$ has critical values $-\frac{5}{2}$ and 3.

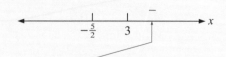

When $x = 10$,
$2(2x+5)(3-x) = 2 \times 25 \times -7 < 0$.

The factors are single so the signs alternate.

$\therefore$ the sign diagram is

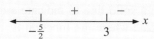

Example 2   ◀》 **Self Tutor**

Draw sign diagrams for: **a** $-(x+3)^2$ **b** $\dfrac{x-1}{2x+1}$

a $-(x+3)^2$ has critical value -3.

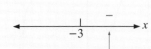

When $x = 10$,
$-(x+3)^2 = -13^2 < 0$.
A squared factor indicates no change of sign about the critical value.

$\therefore$ the sign diagram is

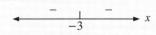

b $\dfrac{x-1}{2x+1}$ is zero when $x = 1$ and undefined when $x = -\frac{1}{2}$.

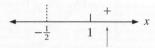

When $x = 10$, $\dfrac{x-1}{2x+1} = \frac{9}{21} > 0$

Since $(x-1)$ and $(2x+1)$ are single factors, the signs alternate.

$\therefore$ the sign diagram is

EXERCISE 19A

1 Draw sign diagrams corresponding to the graphs below:

a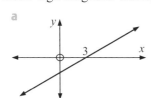

b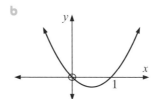

c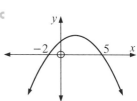

d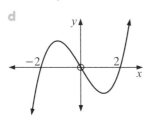

e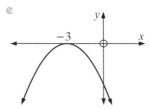

f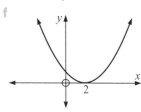

g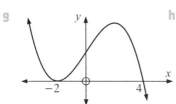

h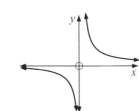

i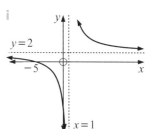

2 Draw sign diagrams for:

a $(x+3)(x-1)$

b $x(x-4)$

c $x(x+5)$

d $-(x+2)(x-3)$

e $(3x-1)(4-x)$

f $(3-x)(1-2x)$

g $x^2 - 16$

h $1 - x^2$

i $2x - x^2$

j $x^2 - 4x + 3$

k $2 - 18x^2$

l $6x^2 + 7x + 2$

m $-3x^2 + 8x + 3$

n $2 - 2x - 4x^2$

o $-10x^2 + 9x + 9$

3 Draw sign diagrams for:

a $(x-1)^2$

b $(x+4)^2$

c $-(x+3)^2$

d $-(x-2)^2$

e $(3x-1)^2$

f $x^2 - 6x + 9$

g $-x^2 - 4x - 4$

h $-x^2 + 2x - 1$

i $-4x^2 - 4x - 1$

4 Draw sign diagrams for:

a $\dfrac{x+1}{x-2}$

b $\dfrac{x-1}{x}$

c $\dfrac{2x+5}{2-x}$

d $\dfrac{3x-1}{4-x}$

e $\dfrac{x+4}{3x-2}$

f $\dfrac{2x}{1-x}$

g $\dfrac{(x-2)^2}{x+1}$

h $\dfrac{3x}{(x+3)^2}$

i $\dfrac{x(x+2)}{4-x}$

j $\dfrac{(x-3)(x+4)}{2-x}$

k $\dfrac{5-x}{x^2-x-2}$

l $\dfrac{x^2-1}{-x}$

m $\dfrac{x^2+2x-3}{x+1}$

n $\dfrac{x^2+1}{x^2-2x+1}$

o $\dfrac{x^2-6x+9}{2x^2-x-3}$

B   INTERVAL NOTATION

Consider the set of numbers on the number line from 1 to 4 inclusive.

The filled circle shows that 4 is included.

We can represent this set using **interval notation** as

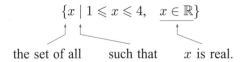

$$\{x \mid 1 \leqslant x \leqslant 4, \quad x \in \mathbb{R}\}$$

the set of all   such that x is real.

We read this notation as "the set of all real x such that x is between 1 and 4 inclusive".

If it is not stated otherwise, we assume we are dealing with real x. So, the set can be represented simply as $\{x \mid 1 \leqslant x \leqslant 4\}$.

Other examples of interval notation include:

$\{x \mid x \geqslant 3\}$ which has number line graph

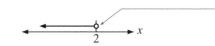

$\{x \mid x < 2\}$ which has number line graph

The non-filled or open circle shows that 2 is not included.

$\{x \mid -2 < x \leqslant 1\}$ which has number line graph

$\{x \mid x \leqslant 0 \quad \text{or} \quad x > 4\}$ which has number line graph

Note:

for numbers *between* a and b we write $a \leqslant x \leqslant b$.

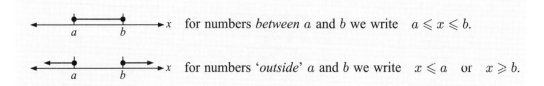

for numbers '*outside*' a and b we write $x \leqslant a$ or $x \geqslant b$.

Example 3

◀) Self Tutor

Draw a number line graph for

a $\{x \mid -2 \leqslant x < 3\}$ **b** $\{x \mid x < 2 \text{ or } x \geqslant 7\}$ **c** $\{x \mid x < 0 \text{ or } 1 \leqslant x < 4\}$

a   **b**   **c**

Example 4

◀) Self Tutor

Use interval notation to describe

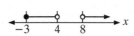

There are two possible intervals in which x could lie.

So, we have $\{x \mid -3 \leqslant x < 4 \quad \text{or} \quad x > 8\}$.

Example 5

◀) Self Tutor

Given the sign diagram alongside, use interval
notation to describe when the function is:

a > 0 **b** $\geqslant 0$

a The function is > 0 when $1 < x < 3$ or $x > 6$.
b The function is $\geqslant 0$ when $1 \leqslant x < 3$ or $x \geqslant 6$.

                                     ↑

We do not include 3 here because the
function is undefined at $x = 3$.

SQUARE BRACKET NOTATION

An alternative to using inequality signs is to use **square bracket notation**.

Instead of writing $\{x \mid 2 \leqslant x \leqslant 5\}$ we could write $x \in [2, 5]$
          and for $\{x \mid 2 < x < 5\}$ we could write $x \in \,]2, 5[$
where we reverse the brackets to show we are not including the end points.

So, for $\{x \mid 2 \leqslant x < 5\}$ we would write $x \in [2, 5[$.

For intervals which stretch to infinity we use the symbol ∞. We always use an 'outwards'
bracket for infinity.

So, for $\{x \mid x \geqslant 2\}$ we would write $x \in [2, \infty[$.

In square bracket notation, we use the union symbol $\cup$ to replace 'or'.

So, for $\{x \mid 1 \leqslant x < 3 \quad \text{or} \quad x \geqslant 5\}$ we would write $x \in [1, 3[\,\cup\, [5, \infty[$.

EXERCISE 19B

1 Draw a number line graph of:

   a $\{x \mid -2 \leqslant x \leqslant 3\}$ **b** $\{x \mid 0 < x < 3\}$

   c $\{x \mid x < 1 \quad \text{or} \quad x > 3\}$ **d** $\{x \mid x \leqslant 2 \quad \text{or} \quad x \geqslant 3\}$

   e $\{x \mid x \leqslant -2 \quad \text{or} \quad x > 1\}$ **f** $\{x \mid -1 < x \leqslant 4\}$

   g $\{x \mid -3 \leqslant x < 0\}$ **h** $\{x \mid x < 0 \quad \text{or} \quad x \geqslant 4\}$

   i $\{x \mid x \leqslant -1 \quad \text{or} \quad 0 \leqslant x \leqslant 3\}$ **j** $\{x \mid -2 \leqslant x \leqslant 2 \quad \text{or} \quad x \geqslant 4\}$

   k $\{x \mid -2 < x < 2 \quad \text{or} \quad x > 3\}$ **l** $\{x \mid x < -2 \quad \text{or} \quad -1 < x \leqslant 2\}$

2 Use interval notation to describe:

  a

  b

  c

  d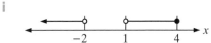

  e

  f

  g

  h

  i

  j

3 Use interval notation to describe when the functions with the following sign diagrams are: **i** > 0 **ii** $\geqslant 0$ **iii** < 0 **iv** $\leqslant 0$.

  a   **b**   **c**

4 Write these number sets using square bracket notation:

   a $\{x \mid -1 \leqslant x \leqslant 6\}$ **b** $\{x \mid 0 < x < 5\}$

   c $\{x \mid -4 < x \leqslant 7\}$ **d** $\{x \mid 4 \leqslant x < 8\}$

   e $\{x \mid x \leqslant 2 \quad \text{or} \quad x \geqslant 5\}$ **f** $\{x \mid x < -3 \quad \text{or} \quad x > 4\}$

   g $\{x \mid -1 < x \leqslant 1 \quad \text{or} \quad x \geqslant 2\}$ **h** $\{x \mid x < -4 \quad \text{or} \quad 2 \leqslant x < 7\}$

   i   **j**

   k   **l**

   m   **n**

INEQUALITIES

When dealing with inequalities we use the same basic principles as for ordinary equations. Anything we do to one side of an inequality, we also do to the other side.

However, if we multiply both sides of an inequality by a negative number then we need to reverse the inequality sign, i.e., $\geqslant$ becomes $\leqslant$, and so on.

For this reason we never multiply or divide both sides of an inequality by an expression involving the variable. It can lead to errors, as seen in the **Opening problem** on page **464**.

Example 6 ◀) **Self Tutor**

Solve for x:

   a $3x \leqslant x - 1$ b $-2x > 7 + x$ c $x^2 < 4$

a $3x \leqslant x - 1$

   $\therefore$ $2x \leqslant -1$ {subtracting x from both sides}

   $\therefore$ $x \leqslant -\frac{1}{2}$ {dividing both sides by 2}

b $-2x > 7 + x$

   $\therefore$ $-3x > 7$ {subtracting x from both sides}

   $\therefore$ $x < -\frac{7}{3}$ {dividing both sides by -3}

c $x^2 < 4$

   $\therefore$ $|x| < 2$

   $\therefore$ $-2 < x < 2$

To systematically solve more complicated inequalities, use the following procedure:

- Make the RHS zero by shifting all terms to the LHS.
- Fully factorise the LHS.
- Draw a sign diagram for the LHS.
- Determine the values required from the sign diagram.

Example 7 ◀) **Self Tutor**

Solve for x: a $3x^2 + 5x \geqslant 2$ b $x^2 + 9 < 6x$

a $3x^2 + 5x \geqslant 2$

   $\therefore$ $3x^2 + 5x - 2 \geqslant 0$ {making RHS zero}

   $\therefore$ $(3x - 1)(x + 2) \geqslant 0$ {fully factorising LHS}

Sign diagram of LHS is

So, for LHS $\geqslant 0$, $x \leqslant -2$ or $x \geqslant \frac{1}{3}$.

b
$$x^2 + 9 < 6x$$
$$\therefore \quad x^2 - 6x + 9 < 0 \qquad \text{\{making RHS zero\}}$$
$$\therefore \quad (x - 3)^2 < 0 \qquad \text{\{fully factorising LHS\}}$$

Sign diagram of LHS is

The LHS is never negative, so the inequality is **never true**.

Example 8　　　　　　　　　　　　　　　　　　　　◀》 **Self Tutor**

Solve for x:　　**a** $\dfrac{3x + 2}{x - 4} \leqslant 1$　　　**b** $\dfrac{1}{x} \leqslant 10$

a
$$\dfrac{3x + 2}{x - 4} \leqslant 1$$
$$\therefore \quad \dfrac{3x + 2}{x - 4} - 1 \leqslant 0$$
$$\therefore \quad \dfrac{3x + 2}{x - 4} - 1\left(\dfrac{x - 4}{x - 4}\right) \leqslant 0$$
$$\therefore \quad \dfrac{3x + 2 - (x - 4)}{x - 4} \leqslant 0$$
$$\therefore \quad \dfrac{2x + 6}{x - 4} \leqslant 0$$

Sign diagram of LHS is

$$\therefore \quad -3 \leqslant x < 4$$

b
$$\dfrac{1}{x} \leqslant 10$$
$$\therefore \quad \dfrac{1}{x} - 10 \leqslant 0$$
$$\therefore \quad \dfrac{1}{x} - 10\left(\dfrac{x}{x}\right) \leqslant 0$$
$$\therefore \quad \dfrac{1 - 10x}{x} \leqslant 0$$

Sign diagram of LHS is

$$\therefore \quad x < 0 \quad \text{or} \quad x \geqslant \tfrac{1}{10}$$

EXERCISE 19C

1 Solve for x:

a $2x \geqslant 6$　　　　　　**b** $-x < 3$　　　　　　**c** $2x \leqslant 1 - x$

d $x - 7 > -x$　　　　　**e** $x + 1 \leqslant -2x - 4$　　**f** $x^2 > 9$

2 Solve for x:

a $(x - 1)(x - 3) \leqslant 0$　　**b** $(2x + 3)(4 - x) > 0$　　**c** $(x + 1)(x - 2) > 0$

d $(x + 5)^2 < 0$　　　　　**e** $x^2 - 2x \geqslant 0$　　　　**f** $4x^2 + 2x < 0$

g $x^2 < 16$　　　　　　　**h** $3x^2 \leqslant 12$　　　　　**i** $x^2 + 4x - 5 > 0$

j $x^2 \leqslant x + 2$　　　　　**k** $x^2 - 4x + 4 < 0$　　　**l** $2x^2 + 7x < -6$

m $3x^2 \geqslant 2(x + 4)$　　　**n** $3x^2 - 6x + 3 > 0$　　　**o** $2x^2 - 5 \leqslant 3x$

p $4 < 5x^2 + 8x$　　　　　**q** $6(x^2 + 2) < 17x$　　　**r** $9x^2 \leqslant 12x - 4$

3 Solve for x:

a $\dfrac{x+2}{x-3} < 0$ b $\dfrac{x+3}{2-x} < 0$ c $\dfrac{x+4}{2x-1} \geqslant 0$ d $\dfrac{x-3}{2x} \leqslant 0$

e $\dfrac{x-1}{x+3} \geqslant -1$ f $\dfrac{x+2}{2x-3} < 1$ g $\dfrac{1}{x} > 3$ h $\dfrac{x}{3x+1} \geqslant -2$

i $\dfrac{5-2x}{1-x} > 4$ j $\dfrac{4}{x} \leqslant x$ k $\dfrac{x^2-4x}{x+3} > 0$ l $\dfrac{x}{x^2-1} \leqslant 0$

m $\dfrac{3}{x} > \dfrac{2}{x+2}$ n $\dfrac{x}{x+6} > \dfrac{3}{x}$ o $\dfrac{x+1}{x} \geqslant \dfrac{1}{x+4}$

4 For what values of x are the following expressions defined?

a $\sqrt{x}$ b $\sqrt{x-2}$ c $\sqrt{3-2x}$ d $\dfrac{1}{\sqrt{x}}$

e $\dfrac{1}{\sqrt{x+2}}$ f $\dfrac{1}{\sqrt{5+2x}}$ g $\sqrt{x(x-2)}$ h $\sqrt{(x+1)(x-3)}$

i $\dfrac{1}{\sqrt{x}} + \dfrac{1}{\sqrt{2-x}}$ j $\sqrt{\dfrac{x+3}{x-1}}$ k $\sqrt{x^2-3x}$ l $\sqrt{x-1}+\sqrt{5-x}$

Check your answers using the graphing package.

GRAPHING
PACKAGE

5 For what numbers is it true that:

a their square is greater than themselves

b they are greater than their reciprocals

c two more than their square is less than three times themselves?

D | THE ARITHMETIC MEAN-GEOMETRIC MEAN INEQUALITY (EXTENSION)

For any two non-negative numbers a and b,

the **arithmetic mean** is $\dfrac{a+b}{2}$ and the **geometric mean** is $\sqrt{ab}$.

INVESTIGATION   ARITHMETIC AND GEOMETRIC MEANS

What to do:

1 Copy and complete, giving $\sqrt{ab}$ to 3 significant figures if necessary:

a	b	$\dfrac{a+b}{2}$	$\sqrt{ab}$	a	b	$\dfrac{a+b}{2}$	$\sqrt{ab}$
2	4			5	5		
3	3			9	6		
4	8			7	10		
1	7			12	8		

2   Write down your observations from **1** for the cases when $a = b$ and when $a \neq b$.

3   Copy and complete:

For non-negatives a and b, ... $\geqslant$ ......,   with equality if and only if ....

From the **Investigation** you should have discovered the **arithmetic mean - geometric mean inequality** which states:

$$\text{for non-negatives } a \text{ and } b, \quad \frac{a+b}{2} \geqslant \sqrt{ab} \quad \text{with equality when} \quad a = b.$$

There are many proofs of this inequality. For example:

Proof: As $a \geqslant 0$ and $b \geqslant 0$, $\sqrt{a}$ and $\sqrt{b}$ both exist,

and $(\sqrt{a} - \sqrt{b})^2 \geqslant 0$ with equality when $\sqrt{a} = \sqrt{b}$

$\therefore$ $a - 2\sqrt{ab} + b \geqslant 0$ with equality when $a = b$

$\therefore$ $a + b \geqslant 2\sqrt{ab}$ with equality when $a = b$

$\therefore$ $\dfrac{a+b}{2} \geqslant \sqrt{ab}$ with equality when $a = b$.

This is called a **direct proof** as it starts with the known truth $(\sqrt{a} - \sqrt{b})^2 \geqslant 0$ and after a series of mathematically correct steps, ends with the required result.

Example 9   ◀⑨ **Self Tutor**

Show that the sum of a positive number and its reciprocal is never less than 2.

Let the unknown number be x, so $x > 0$.

Its reciprocal $\dfrac{1}{x}$ is also positive, so x and $\dfrac{1}{x}$ are both non-negative.

$\therefore$ using the arithmetic mean-geometric mean inequality, $\dfrac{x + \dfrac{1}{x}}{2} \geqslant \sqrt{x\left(\dfrac{1}{x}\right)}$

with equality when $x = \dfrac{1}{x}$

$\therefore$ $x + \dfrac{1}{x} \geqslant 2\sqrt{1}$ with equality when $x^2 = 1$

$\therefore$ $x + \dfrac{1}{x} \geqslant 2$ with equality when $x = 1$.

So, the sum of a positive number and its reciprocal is never less than 2.

The following example shows how the arithmetic mean - geometric mean inequality can sometimes be used instead of quadratic optimisation.

Example 10   ◀⑨ **Self Tutor**

600 m of fencing is used to make 3 identical rectangular enclosures as shown in the illustration. What dimensions should each enclosure have so that the maximum area is enclosed?

What is the maximum area?

Let each of the enclosures be x m by y m, so the area of each enclosure is $A = xy$.

The total perimeter of fencing is $4x + 6y$ m
$\therefore$ $4x + 6y = 600$

Now $4x$ and $6y$ are both non-negative.

$\therefore$ $\dfrac{4x + 6y}{2} \geqslant \sqrt{(4x)(6y)}$ with equality when $4x = 6y$

$\therefore$ $\dfrac{600}{2} \geqslant \sqrt{24xy}$ with equality when $600 - 6y = 6y$ i.e.,   when $12y = 600$

$\therefore$ $300 \geqslant \sqrt{24A}$ with equality when $y = 50$

$\therefore$ $24A \leqslant 90\,000$ with equality when $x = 75$, $y = 50$

$\therefore$ $A \leqslant 3750$ with equality when $x = 75$, $y = 50$

So, the maximum area of each enclosure is 3750 m^2 when each one is 75 m by 50 m.

EXERCISE 19D

1 If a and b are non-negative and $ab = 9$,   what is the minimum value of $a + b$?

2 If a and b are non-negative and $a + b = 4$,   what is the maximum value of ab?

3   **a** Prove that if $x > 0$ then $x + \dfrac{9}{x} \geqslant 6$.

 b Check your answer by graphing $y = x + \dfrac{9}{x}$ for $x > 0$.

4 If a and b are positive, prove that $(a + b)\left(\dfrac{1}{a} + \dfrac{1}{b}\right) \geqslant 4$.

5 In the semi-circle given, let [AP] have length a units and [PB] have length b units.

 a Find the lengths OR and PQ in terms of a and b.

 b Hence, deduce that $\dfrac{a + b}{2} \geqslant \sqrt{ab}$ with equality when $a = b$.

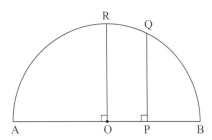

6

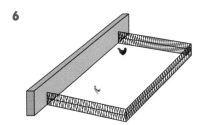

A rectangular chicken pen is constructed with 3 sides of chicken wire and the fourth side an existing brick wall. The total length of chicken wire is 100 m.
Use the AM-GM inequality to find the dimensions of the pen of maximum area. What is the maximum area?

7 Prove that for all rectangles of fixed perimeter P cm, the square has maximum area.

8 At the local EXPO, a company wishes to have three identical booths which are rectangular and open at the front as shown.

They are allocated 2500 m² of floor space.

What dimensions should each booth be to minimise the total length of walls required?

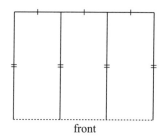

front

REVIEW SET 19A

1 Draw a sign diagram for:

    a $x^2 - 4$
    b $\dfrac{2x + 1}{3 - x}$
    c $-5x(1 - x)(2 - x)$

2 Graph on number lines:

    a $\{x \mid -1 \leqslant x \leqslant 3\}$
    b $\{x \mid x < 2 \text{ or } x \geqslant 3\}$
    c $x \in [3, 5[$

3 Solve for x:

    a $x^2 \geqslant 4x$
    b $2x^2 < 5x + 12$
    c $x^2 + 4 > 0$

    d $\dfrac{x}{x - 2} \geqslant 3$
    e $\dfrac{2x - 1}{1 - x} < \frac{1}{4}$
    f $x \geqslant \dfrac{2}{x}$

4 For what values of x are the following expressions defined?

    a $\sqrt{5 - x}$
    b $\sqrt{x(x - 4)}$
    c $\sqrt{x} + \sqrt{5 - x}$

5 Find all numbers whose squares are less than themselves.

6 If $a^2 + b^2 = 1$, what values can ab have?

REVIEW SET 19B

1 Draw a sign diagram for:

    a $x^2 + 3x$
    b $-x^2(x - 2)$
    c $\dfrac{x(x - 2)}{x - 1}$

2 Graph on number lines:

    a $\{x \mid -2 < x \leqslant 1\}$
    b $\{x \mid x < 0 \text{ or } x \geqslant 5\}$
    c $x \in [-1, 2] \cup [3, \infty[$

3 Solve for x:

    a $x < x^2$
    b $\dfrac{1}{x} > \dfrac{1}{x^2}$
    c $6x^2 \geqslant 13x + 5$

    d $2x^2 + 1 < 3x$
    e $\dfrac{3x + 2}{x - 1} \geqslant 4$
    f $x < \dfrac{10}{x}$

4 For what values of x are the following expressions defined?

    a $\sqrt{2x + 1}$
    b $\dfrac{1}{\sqrt{x(x - 4)}}$
    c $\dfrac{1}{\sqrt{x}} - \dfrac{1}{\sqrt{4 - x}}$

5 Find all numbers which are at least double their reciprocals.

6 If $a^2 + b^2 = 1$ and $c^2 + d^2 = 1$, prove that $0 \leqslant ab + cd \leqslant 1$ for positive a, b, c and d.

Chapter 20

Matrices and linear transformations

Contents:

OPENING PROBLEM

Phillip has two mens' clothing stores in Allendale and Beaumont. He sells jackets, trousers and suits. At the Allendale store he has 43 jackets, 69 trousers and 58 suits. At the Beaumont store he has 28 jackets, 57 trousers and 39 suits.

Things to think about:

1 How can Phillip represent his clothing inventory so that he can easily observe the stock levels in each store?

2 How can he use this representation to find his total stock of each clothing type and to total items sold by each store?

There are probably several different methods that Phillip could use.

One of them is to use a **matrix**, or rectangular array of numbers.

For example, to represent his present clothing stocks, Phillip could use the matrix:

$$\begin{array}{ccc} & J & T & S \\ \text{Store A} & \begin{pmatrix} 43 & 69 & 58 \\ \text{Store B} & 28 & 57 & 39 \end{pmatrix} \end{array}$$

Provided we can remember what each row and column stands for, we can omit the labels.

So, Phillip's inventory matrix is $\begin{pmatrix} 43 & 69 & 58 \\ 28 & 57 & 39 \end{pmatrix}$.

Phillip can find the total number of items in each store by adding the numbers in each row of the matrix, and the total number of each clothing type by adding the numbers in each column.

A   INTRODUCTION TO MATRICES

Matrices were originally introduced as an aid to solving linear simultaneous equations involving 3 or more unknowns. The theory has been developed and extended to applications in business, economics, transformation geometry, and various branches of Physics. Matrices are also used by computers to store and organise data.

An $m \times n$ **matrix** is a rectangular array of numbers in m **rows** and n **columns**.

The numbers of the matrix are called its **elements**.

$m \times n$ is called the **order** of the matrix.

Capital letters such as **A** and **B** are used to represent matrices.

Depending on the text, a matrix may be written with round or square brackets.

For example:

$\mathbf{A} = \begin{pmatrix} 1 & 2 & 3 \\ 4 & 5 & 6 \end{pmatrix}$ is a 2×3 matrix as it has 2 rows and 3 columns.

$\mathbf{B} = \begin{pmatrix} 1 \\ 2 \end{pmatrix}$ is a 2×1 matrix, also known as a **column matrix** or **column vector**.

$\mathbf{C} = \begin{pmatrix} 3 & 0 & -1 \end{pmatrix}$ is a 1×3 matrix, also known as a **row matrix** or **row vector**.

$\mathbf{D} = \begin{pmatrix} 1 & 3 \\ 5 & 2 \end{pmatrix}$ is a 2×2 matrix, also known as a **square matrix**.

$\mathbf{E} = \begin{pmatrix} 6 & 1 & 2 \\ 9 & 2 & 3 \\ 10 & 3 & 4 \end{pmatrix}$ has 3 rows and 3 columns and is called a 3×3 **square matrix**.

This element, 3, is in row 3, column 2.

MATRIX EQUALITY

Two matrices are **equal** if and only if the matrices have the same shape and elements in corresponding positions are equal.

Example 1   ◄) **Self Tutor**

If $\begin{pmatrix} p & q+1 \\ r^2 & 5 \end{pmatrix} = \begin{pmatrix} 9 & -2 \\ 4 & s \end{pmatrix}$,   find p, q, r and s.

Since the matrices are equal, $p = 9$, $q + 1 = -2$, $r^2 = 4$, $5 = s$

$\therefore$ $p = 9$, $q = -3$, $r = \pm 2$, $s = 5$

EXERCISE 20A

1   State the order of the following matrices:

a $\begin{pmatrix} 3 \\ 1 \end{pmatrix}$ b $\begin{pmatrix} 4 & 3 & 9 \end{pmatrix}$ c $\begin{pmatrix} 1 & 2 \\ 3 & 4 \\ 5 & 6 \end{pmatrix}$ d $\begin{pmatrix} 1 & 3 & 4 \\ 2 & 0 & 9 \\ 4 & 1 & 2 \end{pmatrix}$

2   For the matrix $\begin{pmatrix} 2 & -1 & 4 \\ 3 & 7 & -11 \end{pmatrix}$,   what element is in:

a   row 1, column 3   b   row 2, column 2   c   row 2, column 3?

3   Explain why the following pairs of matrices are not equal:

a $\begin{pmatrix} 1 & 2 \\ -1 & 3 \end{pmatrix} \neq \begin{pmatrix} 1 & 2 \\ -1 & -3 \end{pmatrix}$ b $\begin{pmatrix} 2 & -3 \\ -2 & 1 \end{pmatrix} \neq \begin{pmatrix} 2 & -3 & 0 \\ -2 & 1 & 0 \end{pmatrix}$

4 Find the unknowns if:

a $\begin{pmatrix} a & 2 \\ 3 & b \end{pmatrix} = \begin{pmatrix} 1 & c \\ d & -5 \end{pmatrix}$

b $\begin{pmatrix} x & a \\ 2a & x^2 \end{pmatrix} = \begin{pmatrix} -2 & 5 \\ b & 4 \end{pmatrix}$

c $\begin{pmatrix} x & 3 \\ 1-y & z \end{pmatrix} = \begin{pmatrix} 4 & x-1 \\ 0 & -2 \end{pmatrix}$

d $\begin{pmatrix} x^2 & x-1 \\ y & z \end{pmatrix} = \begin{pmatrix} 9 & 2 \\ -y & z^2 \end{pmatrix}$

B   OPERATIONS WITH MATRICES

MATRIX ADDITION

Suppose Phillip's inventory matrix is now $\begin{pmatrix} 11 & 17 & 12 \\ 16 & 24 & 19 \end{pmatrix}$.

He decides to purchase new stock for each store according to the matrix $\begin{pmatrix} 30 & 20 & 15 \\ 25 & 35 & 10 \end{pmatrix}$.

At the Allendale store, Phillip now has $11 + 30 = 41$ jackets, so the number in row 1, column 1 of his new inventory matrix must be $11 + 30$ or 41.

Using the same argument for each element of the new inventory matrix, it must be

$$\begin{pmatrix} 11+30 & 17+20 & 12+15 \\ 16+25 & 24+35 & 19+10 \end{pmatrix} \quad \text{or} \quad \begin{pmatrix} 41 & 37 & 27 \\ 41 & 59 & 29 \end{pmatrix}.$$

So, it is clear that $\begin{pmatrix} 11 & 17 & 12 \\ 16 & 24 & 19 \end{pmatrix} + \begin{pmatrix} 30 & 20 & 15 \\ 25 & 35 & 10 \end{pmatrix} = \begin{pmatrix} 41 & 37 & 27 \\ 41 & 59 & 29 \end{pmatrix}$

where the $+$ sign represents **matrix addition**.

> To **add** two matrices of the same shape, we add corresponding elements.
>
> We cannot add matrices of different shape.

Example 2   ◀) **Self Tutor**

If $\mathbf{A} = \begin{pmatrix} 1 & 3 \\ 2 & 0 \end{pmatrix}$, $\mathbf{B} = \begin{pmatrix} 3 & -2 \\ 4 & 1 \end{pmatrix}$,   and $\mathbf{C} = \begin{pmatrix} -1 & 2 & 1 \\ 2 & 0 & 4 \end{pmatrix}$,   find:

a $\mathbf{A} + \mathbf{B}$

b $\mathbf{B} + \mathbf{C}$

---

a $\mathbf{A} + \mathbf{B} = \begin{pmatrix} 1 & 3 \\ 2 & 0 \end{pmatrix} + \begin{pmatrix} 3 & -2 \\ 4 & 1 \end{pmatrix}$

$= \begin{pmatrix} 1+3 & 3+-2 \\ 2+4 & 0+1 \end{pmatrix}$

$= \begin{pmatrix} 4 & 1 \\ 6 & 1 \end{pmatrix}$

b $\mathbf{B} + \mathbf{C}$ cannot be done since $\mathbf{B}$ is 2×2 and $\mathbf{C}$ is 2×3.

MATRIX SUBTRACTION

Following the addition of new stock, Phillip's inventory matrix is $\begin{pmatrix} 41 & 37 & 27 \\ 41 & 59 & 29 \end{pmatrix}$.

Suppose his sales for the week are given by $\begin{pmatrix} 21 & 18 & 24 \\ 33 & 30 & 17 \end{pmatrix}$.

At the Allendale store, Phillip now has $41 - 21 = 20$ jackets, so the number in row 1, column 1 of his new inventory matrix must be $41 - 21$ or 20.

Using the same argument for each element of the new inventory matrix, it must be

$$\begin{pmatrix} 41-21 & 37-18 & 27-24 \\ 41-33 & 59-30 & 29-17 \end{pmatrix} \quad \text{or} \quad \begin{pmatrix} 20 & 19 & 3 \\ 8 & 29 & 12 \end{pmatrix}.$$

Consequently, $\begin{pmatrix} 41 & 37 & 27 \\ 41 & 59 & 29 \end{pmatrix} - \begin{pmatrix} 21 & 18 & 24 \\ 33 & 30 & 17 \end{pmatrix} = \begin{pmatrix} 20 & 19 & 3 \\ 8 & 29 & 12 \end{pmatrix}$

where the $-$ sign represents **matrix subtraction**.

> To **subtract** two matrices of the same shape we subtract corresponding elements in the correct order.

For example, if $\mathbf{A} = \begin{pmatrix} 2 & 4 \\ -1 & 5 \end{pmatrix}$ and $\mathbf{B} = \begin{pmatrix} 3 & 0 \\ 2 & 7 \end{pmatrix}$ then

$$\mathbf{A} - \mathbf{B} = \begin{pmatrix} 2-3 & 4-0 \\ -1-2 & 5-7 \end{pmatrix} = \begin{pmatrix} -1 & 4 \\ -3 & -2 \end{pmatrix}$$

$$\mathbf{B} - \mathbf{A} = \begin{pmatrix} 3-2 & 0-4 \\ 2--1 & 7-5 \end{pmatrix} = \begin{pmatrix} 1 & -4 \\ 3 & 2 \end{pmatrix}$$

We cannot subtract matrices of different shapes.

Example 3   ◀)) **Self Tutor**

If $\mathbf{P} = \begin{pmatrix} 1 & 2 & 5 \\ 0 & -1 & 2 \end{pmatrix}$ and $\mathbf{Q} = \begin{pmatrix} 3 & -1 & 2 \\ 4 & -3 & -1 \end{pmatrix}$ find $\mathbf{Q} - \mathbf{P}$.

Since $\mathbf{P}$ and $\mathbf{Q}$ have the same shape, $\mathbf{Q} - \mathbf{P}$ can be found.

$$\mathbf{Q} - \mathbf{P} = \begin{pmatrix} 3 & -1 & 2 \\ 4 & -3 & -1 \end{pmatrix} - \begin{pmatrix} 1 & 2 & 5 \\ 0 & -1 & 2 \end{pmatrix}$$

$$= \begin{pmatrix} 3-1 & -1-2 & 2-5 \\ 4-0 & -3--1 & -1-2 \end{pmatrix}$$

$$= \begin{pmatrix} 2 & -3 & -3 \\ 4 & -2 & -3 \end{pmatrix}$$

EXERCISE 20B.1

1 Find, if possible:

a $\begin{pmatrix} 2 & 3 & 1 \end{pmatrix} + \begin{pmatrix} 1 & 4 & 6 \end{pmatrix}$

b $\begin{pmatrix} 3 \\ 2 \end{pmatrix} + \begin{pmatrix} -1 \\ 4 \end{pmatrix}$

c $\begin{pmatrix} 2 & 1 \\ 3 & -1 \end{pmatrix} + \begin{pmatrix} 1 & 0 & 2 \\ 3 & -1 & 1 \end{pmatrix}$

d $\begin{pmatrix} 1 & 3 & -1 \\ 2 & 0 & 1 \end{pmatrix} + \begin{pmatrix} 3 & 5 \\ -1 & 4 \end{pmatrix}$

e $\begin{pmatrix} 1 & 2 \\ 3 & 3 \\ -1 & 4 \end{pmatrix} - \begin{pmatrix} -1 & 1 \\ 2 & -1 \\ 3 & 2 \end{pmatrix}$

f $\begin{pmatrix} 4 & 1 & 3 \\ -1 & 2 & 2 \\ 1 & 0 & 3 \end{pmatrix} - \begin{pmatrix} 1 & 3 & 5 \\ 2 & -1 & -4 \\ 3 & 2 & 0 \end{pmatrix}$

g $\begin{pmatrix} 1 & 2 \\ 3 & -1 \\ 1 & 0 \end{pmatrix} - \begin{pmatrix} 1 \\ 3 \\ 1 \end{pmatrix}$

h $\begin{pmatrix} -1 & 1 \\ 0 & 1 \end{pmatrix} + \begin{pmatrix} 2 & -1 \\ 1 & 0 \end{pmatrix} - \begin{pmatrix} 1 & -4 \\ -1 & 5 \end{pmatrix}$

2 a If $\mathbf{A} = \begin{pmatrix} 5 & 1 \\ 2 & 3 \end{pmatrix}$, find a matrix $\mathbf{B}$ such that $\mathbf{A} + \mathbf{B} = \mathbf{A}$ and $\mathbf{B} + \mathbf{A} = \mathbf{A}$.

b If $\mathbf{A}$ is any 2×3 matrix, what matrix is $\mathbf{A} - \mathbf{A}$ equal to?

3 a If $\mathbf{A} = \begin{pmatrix} 1 & 3 \\ 2 & 4 \end{pmatrix}$ find: **i** $\mathbf{A} + \mathbf{A}$ **ii** $\mathbf{A} + \mathbf{A} + \mathbf{A}$

b In ordinary algebra we write $a + a$ as $2a$ and $a + a + a$ as $3a$. If we write $\mathbf{A} + \mathbf{A}$ as $2\mathbf{A}$ and $\mathbf{A} + \mathbf{A} + \mathbf{A}$ as $3\mathbf{A}$, explain how to find $2\mathbf{A}$ and $3\mathbf{A}$ without using matrix addition.

c In words, predict a rule for finding $k\mathbf{A}$ where k is a real number and $\mathbf{A}$ is a matrix.

4 What matrix would we need to add to $\begin{pmatrix} 4 & 2 \\ -1 & 3 \end{pmatrix}$ to give a result of $\begin{pmatrix} 0 & 0 \\ 0 & 0 \end{pmatrix}$?

ZERO MATRIX

A **zero matrix** is one which has all elements zero.

For example, $\mathbf{O} = \begin{pmatrix} 0 & 0 \\ 0 & 0 \end{pmatrix}$ is the 2×2 zero matrix.

For any matrix $\mathbf{A}$, $\mathbf{A} + \mathbf{O} = \mathbf{O} + \mathbf{A} = \mathbf{A}$

MULTIPLICATION BY A SCALAR

To multiply any matrix by any real number or scalar k, we multiply every element by k.

So, for $\mathbf{A} = \begin{pmatrix} 2 & 1 & 3 \\ -1 & 2 & 4 \end{pmatrix}$, $3\mathbf{A} = \begin{pmatrix} 6 & 3 & 9 \\ -3 & 6 & 12 \end{pmatrix}$ and $\frac{1}{2}\mathbf{A} = \begin{pmatrix} 1 & \frac{1}{2} & 1\frac{1}{2} \\ -\frac{1}{2} & 1 & 2 \end{pmatrix}$.

Note that we cannot divide a matrix by a scalar. Instead, we multiply by its reciprocal.

So, instead of $\dfrac{\mathbf{A}}{k}$ we have $\frac{1}{k}\mathbf{A}$.

THE NEGATIVE OF A MATRIX

$$\text{If } \mathbf{A} \text{ is a matrix then} \quad -\mathbf{A} = -1 \times \mathbf{A}.$$

For example, if $\mathbf{A} = \begin{pmatrix} 2 & 1 & 3 \\ -1 & 2 & 4 \end{pmatrix}$ then $-\mathbf{A} = \begin{pmatrix} -2 & -1 & -3 \\ 1 & -2 & -4 \end{pmatrix}$.

Notice that $\quad \mathbf{A} + (-\mathbf{A}) = (-\mathbf{A}) + \mathbf{A} = \mathbf{O}$

Example 4 ◀) **Self Tutor**

If $\mathbf{A} = \begin{pmatrix} -1 & 2 \\ 3 & 0 \end{pmatrix}$ and $\mathbf{B} = \begin{pmatrix} 2 & -1 \\ 1 & 1 \end{pmatrix}$ find:

    a $\;3\mathbf{A}$ b $\;2\mathbf{A} + 3\mathbf{B}$ c $\;\mathbf{A} - 2\mathbf{B}$

---

a $\quad 3\mathbf{A}$	b $\quad 2\mathbf{A} + 3\mathbf{B}$	c $\quad \mathbf{A} - 2\mathbf{B}$
$= 3\begin{pmatrix} -1 & 2 \\ 3 & 0 \end{pmatrix}$	$= 2\begin{pmatrix} -1 & 2 \\ 3 & 0 \end{pmatrix} + 3\begin{pmatrix} 2 & -1 \\ 1 & 1 \end{pmatrix}$	$= \begin{pmatrix} -1 & 2 \\ 3 & 0 \end{pmatrix} - 2\begin{pmatrix} 2 & -1 \\ 1 & 1 \end{pmatrix}$
$= \begin{pmatrix} -3 & 6 \\ 9 & 0 \end{pmatrix}$	$= \begin{pmatrix} -2 & 4 \\ 6 & 0 \end{pmatrix} + \begin{pmatrix} 6 & -3 \\ 3 & 3 \end{pmatrix}$	$= \begin{pmatrix} -1 & 2 \\ 3 & 0 \end{pmatrix} - \begin{pmatrix} 4 & -2 \\ 2 & 2 \end{pmatrix}$
	$= \begin{pmatrix} 4 & 1 \\ 9 & 3 \end{pmatrix}$	$= \begin{pmatrix} -5 & 4 \\ 1 & -2 \end{pmatrix}$

EXERCISE 20B.2

1 If $\mathbf{A} = \begin{pmatrix} 1 & 0 \\ -1 & 2 \end{pmatrix}$, $\mathbf{B} = \begin{pmatrix} 4 & 1 \\ 2 & -3 \end{pmatrix}$, $\mathbf{C} = \begin{pmatrix} 0 & -2 \\ -1 & 1 \end{pmatrix}$, $\mathbf{O} = \begin{pmatrix} 0 & 0 \\ 0 & 0 \end{pmatrix}$, find:

    a $\;\mathbf{A} + \mathbf{C}$ b $\;4\mathbf{B}$ c $\;-\mathbf{C}$ d $\;-3\mathbf{A}$ e $\;\mathbf{A} - \mathbf{B}$

    f $\;2\mathbf{A} + \mathbf{B}$ g $\;3\mathbf{B} - 2\mathbf{C}$ h $\;\mathbf{A} + \mathbf{B} - \mathbf{C}$ i $\;\mathbf{C} + \mathbf{O}$ j $\;\mathbf{O} + 2\mathbf{A}$

2 Simplify the following:

    a $\;\mathbf{A} + \mathbf{O}$ b $\;\mathbf{O} + \mathbf{B}$ c $\;\mathbf{A} + 2\mathbf{A}$ d $\;2\mathbf{B} + 3\mathbf{B}$

    e $\;\mathbf{A} - \mathbf{A}$ f $\;2\mathbf{C} - 4\mathbf{C}$ g $\;\mathbf{X} - 2\mathbf{X}$ h $\;\mathbf{A} + \mathbf{B} - \mathbf{A}$

3 Show, by using $\mathbf{A} = \begin{pmatrix} a_1 & a_2 \\ a_3 & a_4 \end{pmatrix}$ and $\mathbf{B} = \begin{pmatrix} b_1 & b_2 \\ b_3 & b_4 \end{pmatrix}$, that $\mathbf{A} - \mathbf{B} = -(\mathbf{B} - \mathbf{A})$.

4 Show, by using $\mathbf{A} = \begin{pmatrix} a_1 & a_2 \\ a_3 & a_4 \end{pmatrix}$, $\mathbf{B} = \begin{pmatrix} b_1 & b_2 \\ b_3 & b_4 \end{pmatrix}$ and $\mathbf{X} = \begin{pmatrix} x_1 & x_2 \\ x_3 & x_4 \end{pmatrix}$, that:

    a $\;$ if $\;\mathbf{X} + \mathbf{A} = \mathbf{B}\;$ then $\;\mathbf{X} = \mathbf{B} - \mathbf{A}$

    b $\;$ if $\;k\mathbf{X} = \mathbf{A}\;$ then $\;\mathbf{X} = \frac{1}{k}\mathbf{A}$

    where k is any non-zero scalar.

> There is no such thing as a matrix divided by a scalar.

MATRIX ALGEBRA

Under the operations of addition, subtraction, and scalar multiplication, the algebra of matrices is exactly the same as normal algebra. Whatever we do to one side of a matrix equation we must also do to the other side.

EXERCISE 20B.3

1   Repeat **Exercise 20B.2** question **4** using matrix algebra.

2   Use matrix algebra to make **X** the subject of:

    a $\mathbf{A} + \mathbf{X} = \mathbf{B}$ **b** $\mathbf{X} - \mathbf{A} = 2\mathbf{X}$ **c** $\mathbf{A} - \mathbf{X} = \mathbf{B}$

    d $2\mathbf{X} = \mathbf{C}$ **e** $3\mathbf{X} - \mathbf{C} = \mathbf{X} + \mathbf{A}$ **f** $2\mathbf{X} + \mathbf{A} = \mathbf{B} - \mathbf{X}$

C   MATRIX MULTIPLICATION

Suppose David wants to buy 2 cans of soft drink, 1 hamburger and 3 icecreams. Store A prices them at \$3, \$6 and \$2 respectively whereas Store B prices them at \$4, \$5 and \$3 respectively.

We can represent this information by using:

a quantities matrix $\mathbf{Q} = \begin{pmatrix} \overset{D}{2} & \overset{H}{1} & \overset{I}{3} \end{pmatrix}$ and a costs matrix $\mathbf{C} = \begin{array}{c} \\ D \\ H \\ I \end{array}\begin{pmatrix} \overset{A}{3} & \overset{B}{4} \\ 6 & 5 \\ 2 & 3 \end{pmatrix}$

The total cost at Store A is $(2 \times 3 + 1 \times 6 + 3 \times 2)$ dollars $= \$18.$
The total cost at Store B is $(2 \times 4 + 1 \times 5 + 3 \times 3)$ dollars $= \$22.$

We can write this using the **matrix multiplication**

$$\mathbf{QC} = \begin{pmatrix} 2 & 1 & 3 \end{pmatrix} \times \begin{pmatrix} 3 & 4 \\ 6 & 5 \\ 2 & 3 \end{pmatrix} = \begin{pmatrix} 2 \times 3 + 1 \times 6 + 3 \times 2 & 2 \times 4 + 1 \times 5 + 3 \times 3 \end{pmatrix}$$

Orders: 1×3 3×2 1×2

           the same

The $\times$ sign used here has a different meaning to that used for multiplying numbers. In this case we multiply each element of a row by the corresponding element of a column, and then add the results.

> In matrix multiplication, two or more matrices are 'multiplied' to produce a final matrix.

If matrix **A** is $m \times n$ and matrix **B** is $n \times p$ then their product **AB** exists and is an $m \times p$ matrix.

The element in row i and column j of **AB** is obtained by multiplying the elements of row i of **A** with the elements of column j of **B** and then adding these values.

For example, $\begin{pmatrix} 1 & 2 & 3 \\ 4 & 5 & 6 \end{pmatrix} \begin{pmatrix} 7 \\ 8 \\ 9 \end{pmatrix} = \begin{pmatrix} (1)(7) + (2)(8) + (3)(9) \\ (4)(7) + (5)(8) + (6)(9) \end{pmatrix} = \begin{pmatrix} 50 \\ 122 \end{pmatrix}$

$\qquad\qquad\ \ 2 \times 3 \qquad 3 \times 1 \qquad\qquad\qquad 2 \times 1$

2×2 matrices can always be multiplied together and the result is also a 2×2 matrix.

In general, $\quad \begin{pmatrix} a & b \\ c & d \end{pmatrix} \begin{pmatrix} w & x \\ y & z \end{pmatrix} = \begin{pmatrix} aw + by & ax + bz \\ cw + dy & cx + dz \end{pmatrix}.$

$\qquad\qquad\qquad\ \ \mathbf{A} \qquad\quad \mathbf{B} \qquad\qquad\quad \mathbf{AB}$

Notice how the **scalar product** of row 1 of **A** with column 1 of **B** appears in row 1, column 1 of **AB**.

Example 5   ◀) **Self Tutor**

If $\mathbf{A} = \begin{pmatrix} 1 & 2 \\ 3 & 4 \end{pmatrix}$ and $\mathbf{B} = \begin{pmatrix} 5 & 6 \\ 7 & 8 \end{pmatrix}$, find: **a** **AB**   **b** **BA**

a $\mathbf{AB} = \begin{pmatrix} 1 & 2 \\ 3 & 4 \end{pmatrix} \begin{pmatrix} 5 & 6 \\ 7 & 8 \end{pmatrix}$

$\quad = \begin{pmatrix} 1(5) + 2(7) & 1(6) + 2(8) \\ 3(5) + 4(7) & 3(6) + 4(8) \end{pmatrix}$

$\quad = \begin{pmatrix} 19 & 22 \\ 43 & 50 \end{pmatrix}$

b $\mathbf{BA} = \begin{pmatrix} 5 & 6 \\ 7 & 8 \end{pmatrix} \begin{pmatrix} 1 & 2 \\ 3 & 4 \end{pmatrix}$

$\quad = \begin{pmatrix} 5(1) + 6(3) & 5(2) + 6(4) \\ 7(1) + 8(3) & 7(2) + 8(4) \end{pmatrix}$

$\quad = \begin{pmatrix} 23 & 34 \\ 31 & 46 \end{pmatrix}$

From the above example, we notice that in general $\mathbf{AB} \neq \mathbf{BA}$.

Example 6   ◀) **Self Tutor**

If $\mathbf{P} = \begin{pmatrix} 1 & 2 \\ 3 & 4 \end{pmatrix}$ and $\mathbf{Q} = \begin{pmatrix} 5 \\ 6 \end{pmatrix}$, find: **a** **PQ**   **b** **QP**

a $\mathbf{PQ} = \begin{pmatrix} 1 & 2 \\ 3 & 4 \end{pmatrix} \begin{pmatrix} 5 \\ 6 \end{pmatrix} = \begin{pmatrix} 1(5) + 2(6) \\ 3(5) + 4(6) \end{pmatrix} = \begin{pmatrix} 17 \\ 39 \end{pmatrix}$

b $\mathbf{QP} = \begin{pmatrix} 5 \\ 6 \end{pmatrix} \begin{pmatrix} 1 & 2 \\ 3 & 4 \end{pmatrix}$ which cannot be found since the number of columns in **Q** $\neq$ the number of rows in **P**.

$\qquad\quad 2 \times 1 \quad 2 \times 2$

EXERCISE 20C

1 If $\mathbf{A} = \begin{pmatrix} 1 & 2 \\ 3 & 4 \end{pmatrix}$, $\mathbf{B} = \begin{pmatrix} 3 & -1 \\ 2 & 0 \end{pmatrix}$, $\mathbf{C} = \begin{pmatrix} -1 & 2 \\ 1 & 4 \end{pmatrix}$, and $\mathbf{D} = \begin{pmatrix} 5 \\ -2 \end{pmatrix}$ find:

   a $\mathbf{AB}$ **b** $\mathbf{BA}$ **c** $\mathbf{BC}$ **d** $\mathbf{CB}$

   e $\mathbf{AC}$ **f** $\mathbf{CA}$ **g** $\mathbf{AD}$ **h** $\mathbf{BD}$

2 Find:

   a $\begin{pmatrix} 3 & 4 \end{pmatrix} \begin{pmatrix} 1 \\ 7 \end{pmatrix}$ **b** $\begin{pmatrix} 1 & 2 & 3 \end{pmatrix} \begin{pmatrix} 6 \\ 5 \\ 4 \end{pmatrix}$ **c** $\begin{pmatrix} a & b & c \end{pmatrix} \begin{pmatrix} 1 \\ 1 \\ 1 \end{pmatrix}$

3 **a** How could we represent the sum $a + b + c + d$ using matrix multiplication?

   b How could we represent the average of a, b, c and d using matrix multiplication?

4 If $\mathbf{A} = \begin{pmatrix} 1 & 2 & 4 \end{pmatrix}$ and $\mathbf{B} = \begin{pmatrix} 3 & 2 & 1 \\ 0 & 1 & 2 \end{pmatrix}$ explain why $\mathbf{AB}$ cannot be found.

   Can $\mathbf{BA}$ be found?

5 Find:

   a $\begin{pmatrix} 1 & 2 & 3 \end{pmatrix} \begin{pmatrix} 1 & 0 & 0 \\ 2 & 1 & 0 \\ 3 & 2 & 1 \end{pmatrix}$ **b** $\begin{pmatrix} 2 & 0 & 2 \\ 0 & 2 & 0 \\ 2 & 0 & 2 \end{pmatrix} \begin{pmatrix} 1 \\ 3 \\ 5 \end{pmatrix}$

   c $\begin{pmatrix} 1 & 0 & 2 \\ 0 & 1 & 1 \\ -1 & 1 & 0 \end{pmatrix} \begin{pmatrix} 1 & 1 \\ 2 & 3 \\ 1 & 2 \end{pmatrix}$ **d** $\begin{pmatrix} 1 & 1 & 2 \\ 2 & 1 & 1 \\ 1 & 1 & 2 \end{pmatrix} \begin{pmatrix} 1 & 0 & 3 \\ 2 & 1 & 4 \\ 3 & 2 & 0 \end{pmatrix}$

6 Suppose $\mathbf{I} = \begin{pmatrix} 1 & 0 \\ 0 & 1 \end{pmatrix}$.

   a Find $\mathbf{AI}$ and $\mathbf{IA}$ if $\mathbf{A}$ is: **i** $\begin{pmatrix} 1 & 2 \\ 3 & 4 \end{pmatrix}$ **ii** $\begin{pmatrix} a & b \\ c & d \end{pmatrix}$

   b What is special about matrix $\mathbf{I}$ when multiplied by any 2×2 matrix?

7 If $\mathbf{A}$ is $3 \times n$ and $\mathbf{B}$ is $m \times 4$:

   a when can $\mathbf{AB}$ be found and what will its order be

   b what can be said about $\mathbf{BA}$?

8 In the real number system, $ab = ba$ for **all** real numbers a and b.

   a Give an example which proves that this law is not true for all 2×2 matrices.

   b Find two non-zero 2×2 matrices $\mathbf{A}$ and $\mathbf{B}$ such that $\mathbf{AB} = \mathbf{BA}$.

9 We can write powers of square matrices in the same way we do for scalars.

   For example, $\mathbf{A}^2$ means $\mathbf{A} \times \mathbf{A}$ or $\mathbf{AA}$ and $\mathbf{A}^3$ means $\mathbf{A} \times \mathbf{A} \times \mathbf{A}$ or $\mathbf{AAA}$.

   a If $\mathbf{A} = \begin{pmatrix} 1 & 0 \\ 2 & 3 \end{pmatrix}$, find $\mathbf{A}^2$.

   b If $\mathbf{A} = \begin{pmatrix} a & b \\ c & a \end{pmatrix}$ where a, b and c are integers, and $\mathbf{A}^2 = 4\mathbf{A}$,   find the possible

   values of a, b and c.

c Hence, write down all 2×2 matrices of the form $\begin{pmatrix} a & b \\ c & a \end{pmatrix}$ which satisfy the matrix equation $\mathbf{A}^2 - 4\mathbf{A} = \mathbf{O}$, where the elements of $\mathbf{A}$ are integers.

D   THE DETERMINANT OF A MATRIX

Matrices were originally introduced to assist in the solution of linear simultaneous equations.

For example, $\begin{cases} x + 2y = 5 \\ 2x - y = 3 \end{cases}$ can be written using matrices as $\begin{pmatrix} 1 & 2 \\ 2 & -1 \end{pmatrix} \begin{pmatrix} x \\ y \end{pmatrix} = \begin{pmatrix} 5 \\ 3 \end{pmatrix}$.

Any system of linear simultaneous equations can be written in the form $\mathbf{AX} = \mathbf{B}$ where $\mathbf{A}$ is a square matrix of coefficients, $\mathbf{X}$ is a column matrix of unknowns, and $\mathbf{B}$ is a column matrix of constants.

Mathematicians found that for any such system of linear equations, the existence and nature of solutions was determined by a property of the square matrix $\mathbf{A}$. They called this property the **determinant** of the matrix.

In this course we consider the determinants of 2×2 matrices. We can define:

> The **determinant** of the 2×2 matrix $\mathbf{A} = \begin{pmatrix} a & b \\ c & d \end{pmatrix}$ is written $|\mathbf{A}|$ or $\det \mathbf{A}$
>
> or $\begin{vmatrix} a & b \\ c & d \end{vmatrix}$ and has the value $ad - bc$.

Example 7   ◀ᵍ **Self Tutor**

Find: a $\begin{vmatrix} 1 & 3 \\ 2 & -1 \end{vmatrix}$ b $\det \mathbf{A}$ if $\mathbf{A} = \begin{pmatrix} 2 & -2 \\ -1 & -3 \end{pmatrix}$

a $\begin{vmatrix} 1 & 3 \\ 2 & -1 \end{vmatrix}$
$= 1(-1) - 3(2)$
$= -1 - 6$
$= -7$

b $\det \mathbf{A} = \begin{vmatrix} 2 & -2 \\ -1 & -3 \end{vmatrix}$
$= 2(-3) - (-2)(-1)$
$= -6 - 2$
$= -8$

In the following sections we will see how the determinant of a square matrix is important for solving systems of linear equations, but first we consider one of its geometric properties.

THE AREA OF A TRIANGLE GIVEN ITS COORDINATES

Consider the triangle OAB with vertices O(0, 0), A(2, 3) and B(4, 1).

The area of $\triangle$OAB

$= \text{area}\triangle\text{OAA}' + \text{area ABB}'\text{A}' - \text{area}\triangle\text{OBB}'$

$= \frac{1}{2}(2)(3) + \left(\dfrac{3+1}{2}\right) \times 2 - \frac{1}{2}(4)(1)$

$= 3 + 4 - 2$

$= 5 \text{ units}^2$

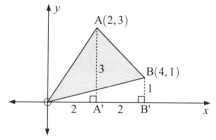

Now consider the triangle OAB given the points A(a, b) and B(c, d).

$\triangle$OAB now has area

$= \text{area}\triangle\text{OAA}' + \text{area ABB}'\text{A}' - \text{area}\triangle\text{OBB}'$

$= \frac{1}{2}ab + \left(\dfrac{b+d}{2}\right)(c-a) - \frac{1}{2}cd$

$= \frac{1}{2}(\cancel{ab} + bc - \cancel{ab} + \cancel{cd} - ad - \cancel{cd})$

$= \frac{1}{2}(bc - ad) = -\frac{1}{2}(ad - bc)$

$= -\frac{1}{2}\begin{vmatrix} a & b \\ c & d \end{vmatrix}$

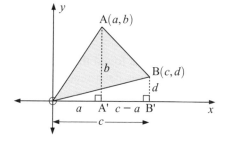

So,   for points A(a, b) and B(c, d),

$$\text{the area of } \triangle\text{OAB} = \frac{1}{2}\left\|\begin{matrix} a & b \\ c & d \end{matrix}\right\| \quad \text{where} \quad \begin{vmatrix} a & b \\ c & d \end{vmatrix} = ad - bc.$$

modulus ⌐ ⌐ determinant

Example 8   ◀)) **Self Tutor**

Find the area of the triangle with vertices:

a (0, 0), (5, 11) and (−2, 7)   **b** (2, 3), (6, −5) and (−2, 7).

a   area $= \frac{1}{2}\left\|\begin{matrix} 5 & 11 \\ -2 & 7 \end{matrix}\right\|$

           $= \frac{1}{2}|35 - (-22)|$

           $= \frac{1}{2}|57|$

           $= 28.5 \text{ units}^2$

b   We translate each point $\begin{pmatrix} -2 \\ -3 \end{pmatrix}$ so

that the first point moves to the origin O.

      $(2, 3) \rightarrow (0, 0)$

      $(6, -5) \rightarrow (4, -8)$

      $(-2, 7) \rightarrow (-4, 4)$

$\therefore$ area $= \frac{1}{2}\left\|\begin{matrix} 4 & -8 \\ -4 & 4 \end{matrix}\right\|$

           $= \frac{1}{2}(16)$

           $= 8 \text{ units}^2$

EXERCISE 20D

1 Find the value of:

$$\textbf{a} \quad \begin{vmatrix} 2 & 3 \\ 5 & 4 \end{vmatrix} \qquad \textbf{b} \quad \begin{vmatrix} 4 & 5 \\ -1 & 2 \end{vmatrix} \qquad \textbf{c} \quad \begin{vmatrix} 4 & 2 \\ 2 & 1 \end{vmatrix} \qquad \textbf{d} \quad \begin{vmatrix} -1 & 2 \\ 4 & 3 \end{vmatrix} \qquad \textbf{e} \quad \begin{vmatrix} 4 & 0 \\ -1 & 2 \end{vmatrix}$$

2 Find $|\textbf{A}|$ if: $\textbf{a} \quad \textbf{A} = \begin{pmatrix} 3 & 2 \\ -1 & 4 \end{pmatrix} \qquad \textbf{b} \quad \textbf{A} = \begin{pmatrix} -1 & 3 \\ -2 & 5 \end{pmatrix}.$

3 Find the area of the triangle with vertices:

    a O(0, 0), A(2, 5) and B(−1, 4)   **b** O(0, 0), P(−1, −2) and R(4, −3)

    c P(−1, −3), Q(2, 7) and R(5, −4)   **d** A(2, −4), B(5, 11) and C(−3, 8).

4 Devise a simple test for the collinearity of the points O(0, 0), A(a, b) and B(c, d).

5 O(0, 0), B(3, x) and C(−2, 5) are the vertices of a triangle with area 4 units². Find the possible values that x may have.

6 Find the area of the quadrilateral with vertices O(0, 0), A(5, 1), B(2, 4) and C(−7, 2).

7 For the illustrated parallelogram, find:

    a the coordinates of point C

    b its area.

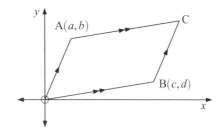

E | MULTIPLICATIVE IDENTITY AND INVERSE MATRICES

The number one (1) has the property that $a \times 1 = 1 \times a = a$ for any real number a.

1 is called the **multiplicative identity** for the set of all real numbers because under the operation of multiplication, it will leave any real number a unchanged.

In **Exercise 20C** question **6**, we found a multiplicative identity for 2×2 matrices. We call this multiplicative identity **I**.

$$\textbf{I} = \begin{pmatrix} 1 & 0 \\ 0 & 1 \end{pmatrix} \quad \text{is the } \textbf{2} \times \textbf{2 identity matrix}.$$

$$\textbf{AI} = \textbf{IA} = \textbf{A} \quad \text{for all } 2 \times 2 \text{ matrices } \textbf{A}.$$

For any real number $a \neq 0$ we can write a reciprocal or inverse that is a^{-1}.

We know that $a \times a^{-1} = a^{-1} \times a = 1$ for all real numbers $a \neq 0$.

If there is a 2×2 matrix $\textbf{A}^{-1}$ such that $\textbf{AA}^{-1} = \textbf{A}^{-1}\textbf{A} = \textbf{I}$, then we say that $\textbf{A}^{-1}$ is the **inverse** of $\textbf{A}$.

INVESTIGATION   DISCOVERING A^{-1}

 In this investigation you should discover a formula for finding A^{-1} for the 2×2 matrix A.

What to do:

1 Find the following matrix products:

a $\begin{pmatrix} 2 & 3 \\ 7 & 1 \end{pmatrix} \begin{pmatrix} 1 & -3 \\ -7 & 2 \end{pmatrix}$ **b** $\begin{pmatrix} 3 & 4 \\ 6 & 5 \end{pmatrix} \begin{pmatrix} 5 & -4 \\ -6 & 3 \end{pmatrix}$ **c** $\begin{pmatrix} -1 & 5 \\ -2 & 3 \end{pmatrix} \begin{pmatrix} 3 & -5 \\ 2 & -1 \end{pmatrix}$

2 What do you notice from **1**?

3 **a** Find $\begin{pmatrix} a & b \\ c & d \end{pmatrix} \begin{pmatrix} d & -b \\ -c & a \end{pmatrix}$.

    b State a formula for finding A^{-1} where $A = \begin{pmatrix} a & b \\ c & d \end{pmatrix}$.

    c When does A^{-1} exist?

4 Check that A^{-1} found in **3** satisfies $A^{-1}A = AA^{-1} = I$.

From the investigation you should have discovered that:

$$\text{If} \quad A = \begin{pmatrix} a & b \\ c & d \end{pmatrix} \quad \text{and} \quad |A| = ad - bc \neq 0, \quad \text{then} \quad A^{-1} = \frac{1}{|A|} \begin{pmatrix} d & -b \\ -c & a \end{pmatrix}.$$

Example 9   ◀) Self Tutor

a If $A = \begin{pmatrix} 2 & 5 \\ -3 & 1 \end{pmatrix}$, find A^{-1}.

b If $B = \begin{pmatrix} 1 & -2 \\ -2 & 4 \end{pmatrix}$, find B^{-1}.

---

a $|A| = (2)(1) - (5)(-3) = 17$

$$\therefore \quad A^{-1} = \tfrac{1}{17} \begin{pmatrix} 1 & -5 \\ 3 & 2 \end{pmatrix} = \begin{pmatrix} \frac{1}{17} & -\frac{5}{17} \\ \frac{3}{17} & \frac{2}{17} \end{pmatrix}$$

b $|B| = (1)(4) - (-2)(-2) = 0$

$\therefore \quad B^{-1}$ does not exist.

EXERCISE 20E

1 Find the inverse matrix for each of the following matrices:

a $A = \begin{pmatrix} 2 & 3 \\ 1 & 4 \end{pmatrix}$ **b** $B = \begin{pmatrix} 1 & 0 \\ 2 & -3 \end{pmatrix}$ **c** $C = \begin{pmatrix} 1 & 0 \\ 2 & 0 \end{pmatrix}$

d $D = \begin{pmatrix} 0 & 1 \\ -1 & 0 \end{pmatrix}$ **e** $E = \begin{pmatrix} 2 & 1 \\ -1 & 3 \end{pmatrix}$ **f** $F = \begin{pmatrix} 2 & 4 \\ 1 & 2 \end{pmatrix}$

2 **a** If $\mathbf{A} = \begin{pmatrix} a & -b \\ b & a \end{pmatrix}$ and $a^2 + b^2 = 1$, find $\mathbf{A}^{-1}$.

b If $\mathbf{B} = \begin{pmatrix} a & b \\ b & -a \end{pmatrix}$ and $a^2 + b^2 = 1$, find $\mathbf{B}^{-1}$.

3 Simplify the following for 2×2 matrices:

   a $\mathbf{AI}$ **b** $\mathbf{IP}$ **c** $\mathbf{A}^{-1}\mathbf{A}$ **d** $\mathbf{BB}^{-1}$

   e $\mathbf{ABB}^{-1}\mathbf{A}^{-1}$ **f** $(\mathbf{AB})^{-1}\mathbf{AB}$ **g** $\mathbf{B}^{-1}\mathbf{A}^{-1}\mathbf{AB}$ **h** $\mathbf{AO}$

4 Can $\mathbf{AB}^{-1}\mathbf{A}^{-1}\mathbf{B}$ be simplified for unknown matrices $\mathbf{A}$ and $\mathbf{B}$?

5 If $\mathbf{A} = \begin{pmatrix} 1 & -1 \\ 2 & 3 \end{pmatrix}$ and $\mathbf{B} = \begin{pmatrix} 2 & 1 \\ -1 & 1 \end{pmatrix}$ find:

   a $\mathbf{AB}$ **b** $(\mathbf{AB})^{-1}$ **c** $\mathbf{A}^{-1}\mathbf{B}^{-1}$ **d** $\mathbf{B}^{-1}\mathbf{A}^{-1}$

6 **a** Assuming $\mathbf{A}^{-1}$ and $\mathbf{B}^{-1}$ exist, use your results in **5** to make a conjecture about the inverse $(\mathbf{AB})^{-1}$.

   b Prove your conjecture is true for all 2×2 matrices $\mathbf{A}$ and $\mathbf{B}$ for which $\mathbf{A}^{-1}$ and $\mathbf{B}^{-1}$ exist.

F   SIMULTANEOUS EQUATIONS

Any pair of simultaneous equations in two unknowns can be written in the form $\mathbf{AX} = \mathbf{B}$ where $\mathbf{A}$ is a 2×2 matrix of coefficients, $\mathbf{X}$ is a 2×1 column matrix of unknowns, and $\mathbf{B}$ is a 2×1 column matrix of constants.

For example, the system $\begin{cases} x + 3y = 4 \\ 4x + 7y = 11 \end{cases}$ can be written in matrix form as

$$\begin{pmatrix} 1 & 3 \\ 4 & 7 \end{pmatrix} \begin{pmatrix} x \\ y \end{pmatrix} = \begin{pmatrix} 4 \\ 11 \end{pmatrix}.$$

Example 10	◀» **Self Tutor**

Write $\begin{cases} 3x - 4y = 17 \\ 2x + 5y = -8 \end{cases}$ in matrix form.

Matrix form is $\begin{pmatrix} 3 & -4 \\ 2 & 5 \end{pmatrix} \begin{pmatrix} x \\ y \end{pmatrix} = \begin{pmatrix} 17 \\ -8 \end{pmatrix}$

            matrix of   matrix of   matrix of
           coefficients   unknowns   constants

EXERCISE 20F.1

1 Write as a pair of simultaneous equations:

a $\begin{pmatrix} 2 & 3 \\ 1 & 4 \end{pmatrix} \begin{pmatrix} x \\ y \end{pmatrix} = \begin{pmatrix} 5 \\ 6 \end{pmatrix}$

b $\begin{pmatrix} 3 & -1 \\ -1 & 1 \end{pmatrix} \begin{pmatrix} x \\ y \end{pmatrix} = \begin{pmatrix} -3 \\ 11 \end{pmatrix}$

c $\begin{pmatrix} 4 & 7 \\ 11 & -2 \end{pmatrix} \begin{pmatrix} p \\ q \end{pmatrix} = \begin{pmatrix} -5 \\ -7 \end{pmatrix}$

d $\begin{pmatrix} 3 & -4 \\ 7 & -2 \end{pmatrix} \begin{pmatrix} c \\ d \end{pmatrix} = \begin{pmatrix} 5 \\ 17 \end{pmatrix}$

2 Write the following as matrix equations:

a $\begin{cases} 2x - 3y = 8 \\ x + 2y = -5 \end{cases}$

b $\begin{cases} 7x + 2y = -1 \\ 4x - 5y = 9 \end{cases}$

c $\begin{cases} 4c + 9d = 8 \\ 7c + 14d = -11 \end{cases}$

SOLVING SIMULTANEOUS EQUATIONS USING MATRICES

Consider the algebraic equation $ax = b$, $a \neq 0$.

To solve this for the real number x, we can multiply both sides of the equation by the inverse or reciprocal of a:

$$ax = b$$
$$\therefore \quad \frac{1}{a}ax = \frac{1}{a}b \quad \{\text{as} \quad a \neq 0\}$$
$$\therefore \quad x = \frac{b}{a}$$

The solution to the matrix equation $\mathbf{AX} = \mathbf{B}$ is very similar, but we need to be careful about how we multiply both sides by the inverse matrix $\mathbf{A}^{-1}$.

In particular, since in general $\mathbf{CD} \neq \mathbf{DC}$, we need to *pre-multiply* both sides by $\mathbf{A}^{-1}$. This means the $\mathbf{A}^{-1}$ is placed *in front of* the other matrices:

$$\mathbf{AX} = \mathbf{B}$$
$$\therefore \quad \mathbf{A}^{-1}\mathbf{AX} = \mathbf{A}^{-1}\mathbf{B}$$
$$\therefore \quad \mathbf{IX} = \mathbf{A}^{-1}\mathbf{B}$$
$$\therefore \quad \mathbf{X} = \mathbf{A}^{-1}\mathbf{B}$$

It would be incorrect, for example, to write:

$$\mathbf{AX} = \mathbf{B}$$
$$\therefore \quad \mathbf{A}^{-1}\mathbf{AX} = \mathbf{BA}^{-1}$$

If the square matrix $\mathbf{A}$ has an inverse $\mathbf{A}^{-1}$, and if $\mathbf{AX} = \mathbf{B}$,   then $\mathbf{X} = \mathbf{A}^{-1}\mathbf{B}$.

So, if we are given a system of linear equations in the form $\mathbf{AX} = \mathbf{B}$ where the square matrix $\mathbf{A}$ has an inverse, the solution to the system is $\mathbf{X} = \mathbf{A}^{-1}\mathbf{B}$.

Example 11	◀ﾟ Self Tutor

Solve for x and y: $\begin{cases} 2x + 3y = 2 \\ 5x + 4y = 12 \end{cases}$

The system $\begin{cases} 2x + 3y = 2 \\ 5x + 4y = 12 \end{cases}$ can be written in matrix form as

$$\begin{pmatrix} 2 & 3 \\ 5 & 4 \end{pmatrix} \begin{pmatrix} x \\ y \end{pmatrix} = \begin{pmatrix} 2 \\ 12 \end{pmatrix}$$

$$\therefore \quad \begin{pmatrix} x \\ y \end{pmatrix} = \begin{pmatrix} 2 & 3 \\ 5 & 4 \end{pmatrix}^{-1} \begin{pmatrix} 2 \\ 12 \end{pmatrix} \qquad \{\text{if} \quad \mathbf{AX} = \mathbf{B} \quad \text{then} \quad \mathbf{X} = \mathbf{A}^{-1}\mathbf{B}\}$$

$$\therefore \quad \begin{pmatrix} x \\ y \end{pmatrix} = \frac{1}{8 - 15} \begin{pmatrix} 4 & -3 \\ -5 & 2 \end{pmatrix} \begin{pmatrix} 2 \\ 12 \end{pmatrix}$$

$$\therefore \quad \begin{pmatrix} x \\ y \end{pmatrix} = \frac{1}{-7} \begin{pmatrix} -28 \\ 14 \end{pmatrix}$$

$$\therefore \quad \begin{pmatrix} x \\ y \end{pmatrix} = \begin{pmatrix} 4 \\ -2 \end{pmatrix}$$

$$\therefore \quad x = 4 \quad \text{and} \quad y = -2$$

Example 12 ◀)) **Self Tutor**

Write $\begin{cases} x' = 4x - y \\ y' = 2x - 3y \end{cases}$ in the form $\begin{cases} x = px' + qy' \\ y = rx' + sy' \end{cases}$.

The system $\begin{cases} x' = 4x - y \\ y' = 2x - 3y \end{cases}$ can be written in matrix form as

$$\begin{pmatrix} x' \\ y' \end{pmatrix} = \begin{pmatrix} 4 & -1 \\ 2 & -3 \end{pmatrix} \begin{pmatrix} x \\ y \end{pmatrix}$$

$$\therefore \quad \begin{pmatrix} 4 & -1 \\ 2 & -3 \end{pmatrix}^{-1} \begin{pmatrix} x' \\ y' \end{pmatrix} = \begin{pmatrix} x \\ y \end{pmatrix} \qquad \{\text{if} \quad \mathbf{AX} = \mathbf{B} \quad \text{then} \quad \mathbf{X} = \mathbf{A}^{-1}\mathbf{B}\}$$

$$\therefore \quad \begin{pmatrix} x \\ y \end{pmatrix} = \begin{pmatrix} \frac{-3}{-10} & \frac{1}{-10} \\ \frac{-2}{-10} & \frac{4}{-10} \end{pmatrix} \begin{pmatrix} x' \\ y' \end{pmatrix}$$

$$\therefore \quad \begin{cases} x = \frac{3}{10}x' - \frac{1}{10}y' \\ y = \frac{1}{5}x' - \frac{2}{5}y' \end{cases}$$

EXERCISE 20F.2

1 Solve simultaneously using matrices:

a $\begin{cases} 2x - 3y = 3 \\ 3x + 2y = 11 \end{cases}$
b $\begin{cases} 4x + 7y = 13 \\ 3x - 2y = -12 \end{cases}$
c $\begin{cases} 3x - 5y = 8 \\ 2x + 3y = 4 \end{cases}$

d $\begin{cases} 5x - 7y = 41 \\ 2x + y = 5 \end{cases}$
e $\begin{cases} 4x - 7y = 13 \\ 5x + 3y = -19 \end{cases}$
f $\begin{cases} x - y = -2 \\ 11x + 17y = 61 \end{cases}$

g $\begin{cases} 6x + 5y = 21 \\ 7x + 8y = 48 \end{cases}$
h $\begin{cases} 3x - 5y = 11 \\ 5x - 7y = -4 \end{cases}$
i $\begin{cases} 5x + 8y = 19 \\ 7x - 10y = 25 \end{cases}$

2 Write the following systems in the form $\begin{cases} x = px' + qy' \\ y = rx' + sy' \end{cases}$

   a $\begin{cases} x' = 2x + y \\ y' = x - 3y \end{cases}$
     b $\begin{cases} x' = x - 3y \\ y' = 2x + 4y \end{cases}$
     c $\begin{cases} x' = 2x + 7y \\ y' = 3x - 4y \end{cases}$

3 Consider the system $\begin{cases} x' = ax + by \\ y' = cx + dy \end{cases}$ for which the matrix of coefficients is

$\begin{pmatrix} a & b \\ c & d \end{pmatrix} = \mathbf{M}.$

If these equations are rearranged so the system is in the form $\begin{cases} x = px' + qy' \\ y = rx' + sy' \end{cases}$

what will be the new matrix of coefficients?

G   LINEAR TRANSFORMATIONS

In **Chapter 7** we considered translations, rotations, reflections and dilations. These are all examples of **linear transformations**.

In this section we consider linear transformations which move $P(x, y)$ to $P'(x', y')$ according to the equations $\begin{cases} x' = ax + by \\ y' = cx + dy \end{cases}$ where a, b, c and d are real numbers.

We will see that all rotations and reflections can be written in this form.

Consider the effect of the linear transformation with equations $\begin{cases} x' = 2x - y \\ y' = x + 3y \end{cases}$ on the 'unit square' with vertices $O(0, 0)$, $A(1, 0)$, $B(1, 1)$ and $C(0, 1)$.

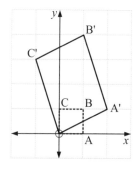

$$\begin{array}{ccc} O(0, 0) & \rightarrow & O'(0, 0) \\ A(1, 0) & \rightarrow & A'(2, 1) \\ B(1, 1) & \rightarrow & B'(1, 4) \\ C(0, 1) & \rightarrow & C'(-1, 3) \end{array}$$

The system $\begin{cases} x' = 2x - y \\ y' = x + 3y \end{cases}$ can be written in the form

$\mathbf{X'} = \mathbf{MX}$ where the matrix of coefficients $\mathbf{M} = \begin{pmatrix} 2 & -1 \\ 1 & 3 \end{pmatrix}.$

From the previous section we know that provided $\mathbf{M}^{-1}$ exists, we can rearrange the system into the form $\mathbf{X} = \mathbf{M}^{-1}\mathbf{X'}$.

For the linear transformation $\begin{cases} x' = ax + by \\ y' = cx + dy \end{cases}$ with matrix of coefficients $\mathbf{M} = \begin{pmatrix} a & b \\ c & d \end{pmatrix}$:

- straight lines are transformed onto other straight lines provided $\mathbf{M}^{-1}$ exists
- any point which does not move under the transformation is called an **invariant point**. In the above example, point O is the only invariant point.

- if the order in which vertices are labelled is kept in the same orientation (both clockwise or both anticlockwise) then we say that **sense is preserved**. If one is clockwise and the other anticlockwise we say that **sense is reversed**.

EXERCISE 20G.1

1 Consider the linear transformation $\begin{cases} x' = x + 2y \\ y' = 3x - y. \end{cases}$

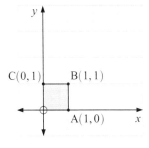

a Find the coordinates of the images of O, A, B and C in the figure alongside.

b Prove that $O'A'B'C'$ is a parallelogram.

c Find the area of $O'A'B'C'$.

d Find the determinant of the transformation.

e What does the determinant in d indicate about
the: i sense   ii area of the image under this transformation?

2 Repeat 1 for the linear transformation $\begin{cases} x' = 3x + y \\ y' = x + 4y. \end{cases}$

3 Consider the linear transformation $\begin{cases} x' = ax + by \\ y' = cx + dy. \end{cases}$

a Find the coordinates of the images of O, A, B and C in the figure alongside.

b Prove that $O'A'B'C'$ is a parallelogram.

c Prove that the area of

$$O'A'B'C' = \left\| \begin{matrix} a & b \\ c & d \end{matrix} \right\| \times \text{area of OABC.}$$

$\underset{\text{modulus}}{\nearrow} \quad \underset{\text{determinant}}{\nwarrow}$

4 a Sketch the graph of $x^2 + y^2 = a^2$ and then sketch its image under the linear transformation $\begin{cases} x' = x \\ y' = \dfrac{b}{a}y, \quad a > 0, \quad b > 0. \end{cases}$

b What is the equation of the resulting figure?

c Prove that the area of the figure is given by $A = \pi ab$.

ROTATIONS

If $P(x, y)$ moves to $P'(x', y')$ under a **rotation** about O through **an angle of** θ

then $\begin{cases} x' = x \cos \theta - y \sin \theta \\ y' = x \sin \theta + y \cos \theta. \end{cases}$

The matrix of the transformation is $\begin{pmatrix} \cos \theta & -\sin \theta \\ \sin \theta & \cos \theta \end{pmatrix}.$

Proof: Let $OP = OP' = r$ and $\widehat{PON}$ be α.

Now $\cos(\theta + \alpha) = \dfrac{x'}{r}$ and $\sin(\theta + \alpha) = \dfrac{y'}{r}$

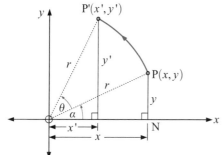

$\therefore$ $x' = r\cos(\theta + \alpha)$

$= r\left[\cos\theta\cos\alpha - \sin\theta\sin\alpha\right]$

$= r\left[\cos\theta\left(\dfrac{x}{r}\right) - \sin\theta\left(\dfrac{y}{r}\right)\right]$

$= x\cos\theta - y\sin\theta$

and $y' = r\sin(\theta + \alpha)$

$= r\left[\sin\theta\cos\alpha + \cos\theta\sin\alpha\right]$

$= r\left[\sin\theta\left(\dfrac{x}{r}\right) + \cos\theta\left(\dfrac{y}{r}\right)\right]$

$= x\sin\theta + y\cos\theta$

Note: If $\mathbf{M} = \begin{pmatrix} \cos\theta & -\sin\theta \\ \sin\theta & \cos\theta \end{pmatrix}$

then $|\mathbf{M}| = \cos^2\theta + \sin^2\theta = 1$

$\therefore$ $\mathbf{M}^{-1} = \begin{pmatrix} \cos\theta & \sin\theta \\ -\sin\theta & \cos\theta \end{pmatrix}$ We can use this inverse matrix to find the image of an equation under the given transformation.

Example 13   ◀) **Self Tutor**

Find the image of the point $(-2, 8)$ under a rotation about O through $\frac{\pi}{3}$.

Since $\cos\frac{\pi}{3} = \frac{1}{2}$ and $\sin\frac{\pi}{3} = \frac{\sqrt{3}}{2}$,
the transformation equations are:

$x' = x\left(\frac{1}{2}\right) - y\left(\frac{\sqrt{3}}{2}\right) = \frac{1}{2}\left(x - \sqrt{3}y\right)$

and $y' = x\left(\frac{\sqrt{3}}{2}\right) + y\left(\frac{1}{2}\right) = \frac{1}{2}\left(\sqrt{3}x + y\right)$

Thus $(-2, 8)$ becomes $\left(\frac{1}{2}(-2 - 8\sqrt{3}), \frac{1}{2}(-2\sqrt{3} + 8)\right)$

which is $(-1 - 4\sqrt{3},\ -\sqrt{3} + 4)$.

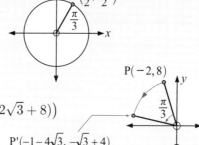

P'$(-1-4\sqrt{3},\ -\sqrt{3}+4)$

Example 14   ◀) **Self Tutor**

Find the equation of the image of $2x - 3y = 6$ under a rotation about O through an angle of $\frac{3\pi}{4}$.

Under a rotation through $\theta = \frac{3\pi}{4}$,
the transformation equations are

$\begin{cases} x' = x\left(-\frac{1}{\sqrt{2}}\right) - y\left(\frac{1}{\sqrt{2}}\right) \\ y' = x\left(\frac{1}{\sqrt{2}}\right) + y\left(-\frac{1}{\sqrt{2}}\right) \end{cases}$ with $\mathbf{M} = \begin{pmatrix} -\frac{1}{\sqrt{2}} & -\frac{1}{\sqrt{2}} \\ \frac{1}{\sqrt{2}} & -\frac{1}{\sqrt{2}} \end{pmatrix}$.

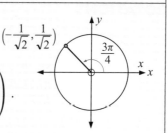

$$\therefore \quad \mathbf{M}^{-1} = \begin{pmatrix} -\frac{1}{\sqrt{2}} & \frac{1}{\sqrt{2}} \\ -\frac{1}{\sqrt{2}} & -\frac{1}{\sqrt{2}} \end{pmatrix}$$

$$\therefore \quad \begin{cases} x = \left(-\frac{1}{\sqrt{2}}\right) x' + \left(\frac{1}{\sqrt{2}}\right) y' \\ y = \left(-\frac{1}{\sqrt{2}}\right) x' + \left(-\frac{1}{\sqrt{2}}\right) y' \end{cases}$$

so we must replace x by $\dfrac{-x+y}{\sqrt{2}}$ and y by $\dfrac{-x-y}{\sqrt{2}}$.

Thus $2x - 3y = 6$ becomes $2\left(\dfrac{-x+y}{\sqrt{2}}\right) - 3\left(\dfrac{-x-y}{\sqrt{2}}\right) = 6$

i.e., $-2x + 2y + 3x + 3y = 6\sqrt{2}$

i.e., $x + 5y = 6\sqrt{2}$

Thus the image has equation $x + 5y = 6\sqrt{2}$.

EXERCISE 20G.2

1   Find the coordinates of the image of:

    a $(3, 1)$ under a rotation about O through an angle of 90°

    b $(-3, 2)$ under a rotation about O through an angle of 180°

    c $(2, 4)$ under a rotation about O through an angle of $-\frac{\pi}{3}$

    d $(1, \sqrt{3})$ under an anti-clockwise rotation about O of $\frac{\pi}{6}$

    e $(\sqrt{2}, 1)$ under a clockwise rotation about O of $\frac{3\pi}{4}$

    f $(-\sqrt{3}, 2)$ under a clockwise rotation about O of $\frac{5\pi}{6}$.

2   Find the equation of the image of:

    a $y = x^2$ under a clockwise rotation about O of 90°

    b $3x - 2y = 10$ under a half turn rotation about O

    c $y = \dfrac{4}{x}$ under an anti-clockwise rotation about O of $\frac{\pi}{2}$

    d $y = x + 1$ under a rotation of $\frac{\pi}{3}$ about O

    e $y = \dfrac{2}{x}$ under an anti-clockwise rotation of $\frac{\pi}{4}$ about O

    f $y = -x^2$ under a rotation of $-\frac{3\pi}{4}$ about O

    g $2x - 5y = 8$ under a clockwise rotation of $\frac{5\pi}{6}$ about O

    h $x + 3y = 7$ under an anti-clockwise rotation of $\frac{4\pi}{3}$ about O.

REFLECTIONS IN THE LINE $y = [\tan\theta]x$

The line $y = [\tan\theta]x$ passes through the origin and has slope $\tan\theta$.

Thus the line makes an angle of θ with the positive x-axis.

If $P(x, y)$ moves to $P'(x', y')$ under a **reflection** in the line $y = [\tan\theta]x$

$$\text{then} \quad \begin{cases} x' = x\cos 2\theta + y\sin 2\theta \\ y' = x\sin 2\theta - y\cos 2\theta. \end{cases}$$

The matrix of the transformation is $\begin{pmatrix} \cos 2\theta & \sin 2\theta \\ \sin 2\theta & -\cos 2\theta \end{pmatrix}$.

Proof: Triangle OPP′ must be isosceles since the perpendicular bisector of the base passes through the apex.

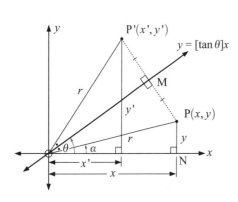

We therefore let $OP = OP' = r$,

and also we let $P\widehat{O}N$ be α.

Now $P'\widehat{O}N = P'\widehat{O}M + \theta$

$\qquad\qquad = (\theta - \alpha) + \theta$

$\qquad\qquad = 2\theta - \alpha$

$\therefore \quad \cos(2\theta - \alpha) = \dfrac{x'}{r}$ and $\sin(2\theta - \alpha) = \dfrac{y'}{r}$

$\therefore \quad x' = r\cos(2\theta - \alpha)$

$\qquad = r\left[\cos 2\theta \cos\alpha + \sin 2\theta \sin\alpha\right]$

$\qquad = r\left[\cos 2\theta \left(\dfrac{x}{r}\right) + \sin 2\theta \left(\dfrac{y}{r}\right)\right]$

$\qquad = x\cos 2\theta + y\sin 2\theta$

and $y' = r\sin(2\theta - \alpha)$

$\qquad = r\left[\sin 2\theta \cos\alpha - \cos 2\theta \sin\alpha\right]$

$\qquad = r\left[\sin 2\theta \left(\dfrac{x}{r}\right) - \cos 2\theta \left(\dfrac{y}{r}\right)\right]$

$\qquad = x\sin 2\theta - y\cos 2\theta$

Note:

- If $\mathbf{M} = \begin{pmatrix} \cos 2\theta & \sin 2\theta \\ \sin 2\theta & -\cos 2\theta \end{pmatrix}$ then $|\mathbf{M}| = -\cos^2 2\theta - \sin^2 2\theta = -1$

$\therefore \quad \mathbf{M}^{-1} = \dfrac{1}{-1}\begin{pmatrix} -\cos 2\theta & -\sin 2\theta \\ -\sin 2\theta & \cos 2\theta \end{pmatrix}$

$\qquad\quad = \begin{pmatrix} \cos 2\theta & \sin 2\theta \\ \sin 2\theta & -\cos 2\theta \end{pmatrix}$

$\qquad\quad = \mathbf{M}$

- The following trigonometric formulae will prove useful:

$$\text{If} \quad m = \tan\theta, \quad \text{then} \quad \cos 2\theta = \frac{1 - m^2}{1 + m^2} \quad \text{and} \quad \sin 2\theta = \frac{2m}{1 + m^2}.$$

Proof: [for θ acute only]

For $\tan \theta = m = \dfrac{m}{1}$ we have a triangle as shown:

$\therefore$ $\sin \theta = \dfrac{m}{\sqrt{1+m^2}}$ and $\cos \theta = \dfrac{1}{\sqrt{1+m^2}}$

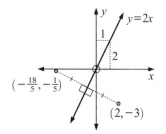

$\therefore$ $\cos 2\theta = \cos^2 \theta - \sin^2 \theta$ and $\sin 2\theta = 2 \sin \theta \cos \theta$

$$= \dfrac{1}{1+m^2} - \dfrac{m^2}{1+m^2} \qquad\qquad = 2 \left(\dfrac{m}{\sqrt{1+m^2}} \right) \left(\dfrac{1}{\sqrt{1+m^2}} \right)$$

$$= \dfrac{1-m^2}{1+m^2} \qquad\qquad\qquad\qquad = \dfrac{2m}{1+m^2}$$

Example 15   ◄ᵍ Self Tutor

Find the image of the point $(2, -3)$ under a reflection in the line $y = 2x$.
Illustrate your answer.

If $m = \tan \theta = 2$ then $\cos 2\theta = \dfrac{1-m^2}{1+m^2} = -\tfrac{3}{5}$

and $\sin 2\theta = \dfrac{2m}{1+m^2} = \tfrac{4}{5}$

The transformation equations are

$\begin{cases} x' = x \left(-\tfrac{3}{5}\right) + y \left(\tfrac{4}{5}\right) \\ y' = x \left(\tfrac{4}{5}\right) - y \left(-\tfrac{3}{5}\right) \end{cases}$

$\therefore$ $(2, -3)$ becomes

$\left(2(-\tfrac{3}{5}) + (-3)(\tfrac{4}{5}), \; 2(\tfrac{4}{5}) - (-3)(-\tfrac{3}{5}) \right),$

which is $\left(-\tfrac{18}{5}, -\tfrac{1}{5}\right)$.

Example 16   ◄ᵍ Self Tutor

Find the equation of the image of $3x - 2y = 4$ when it is reflected in the line with
equation $y = -\tfrac{1}{3}x$.

If $m = \tan \theta = -\tfrac{1}{3}$ then $\cos 2\theta = \dfrac{1-m^2}{1+m^2} = \dfrac{1-\tfrac{1}{9}}{1+\tfrac{1}{9}} = \dfrac{\tfrac{8}{9}}{\tfrac{10}{9}} = \tfrac{4}{5}$

and $\sin 2\theta = \dfrac{2m}{1+m^2} = \dfrac{-\tfrac{2}{3}}{\tfrac{10}{9}} = -\tfrac{3}{5}$

The transformation equations are

$\begin{cases} x' = x \left(\tfrac{4}{5}\right) + y \left(-\tfrac{3}{5}\right) \\ y' = x \left(-\tfrac{3}{5}\right) - y \left(\tfrac{4}{5}\right) \end{cases}$ with matrix $\mathbf{M} = \begin{pmatrix} \tfrac{4}{5} & -\tfrac{3}{5} \\ -\tfrac{3}{5} & -\tfrac{4}{5} \end{pmatrix}.$

$$\therefore \quad \mathbf{M}^{-1} = \begin{pmatrix} \frac{4}{5} & -\frac{3}{5} \\ -\frac{3}{5} & -\frac{4}{5} \end{pmatrix} \qquad \{\text{for a reflection, } \mathbf{M}^{-1} = \mathbf{M}\}$$

$$\therefore \quad \begin{cases} x = \frac{4}{5}x' - \frac{3}{5}y' \\ y = -\frac{3}{5}x' - \frac{4}{5}y' \end{cases} \qquad \text{so we must replace } x \text{ by } \quad \frac{4}{5}x - \frac{3}{5}y \quad \text{and } y \text{ by } \quad -\frac{3}{5}x - \frac{4}{5}y$$

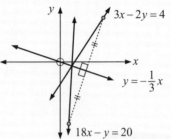

$$\therefore \quad 3x - 2y = 4 \quad \text{becomes}$$

$$3\left(\tfrac{4}{5}x - \tfrac{3}{5}y\right) - 2\left(-\tfrac{3}{5}x - \tfrac{4}{5}y\right) = 4$$

$$\text{i.e.,} \quad 12x - 9y + 6x + 8y = 20$$

$$\text{i.e.,} \quad 18x - y = 20$$

Thus the image has equation $\quad 18x - y = 20$.

EXERCISE 20G.3

TRANSFORMATION
GEOMETRY
PACKAGE

1 Find the coordinates of the image of:

    a $(2, 5)$ when reflected in the line $\quad y = x$

    b $(3, -2)$ when reflected in the line $\quad y = -x$

    c $(3, 4)$ when reflected in the line $\quad y = -2x$

    d $(-2, 3)$ when reflected in the line $\quad y = 3x$

    e $(4, 2)$ when reflected in the line $\quad y = \sqrt{2}x$

    f $(-1, 3)$ when reflected in the line $\quad y = -\frac{1}{\sqrt{3}}x$.

2 Find the equation of the image of:

    a $y = x^2 - 2x$ under a reflection in the line $\quad y = x$

    b $2x + 3y = 6$ under a reflection in the line $\quad y = -x$

    c $2x - 5y = 10$ under a reflection in the $\quad y$-axis

    d $3x + 2y = 12$ under a reflection in the line $\quad y = 3x$

    e $x - y = 8$ under a reflection in the line $\quad y = \frac{1}{2}x$

    f $y = \dfrac{4}{x}$ under a reflection in the line $\quad y = \sqrt{2}x$.

DEDUCING THE NATURE OF TRANSFORMATIONS

For some linear transformations we can use the determinant to help deduce its nature.

- If the matrix of a transformation is $\quad \mathbf{M} = \begin{pmatrix} a & -b \\ b & a \end{pmatrix}$

  where $\quad |\mathbf{M}| = 1,$ then the transformation is **a rotation**.

- If the matrix of a transformation is $\quad \mathbf{M} = \begin{pmatrix} a & b \\ b & -a \end{pmatrix}$

  where $\quad |\mathbf{M}| = -1,$ then the transformation is a **reflection**.

Example 17　　　　　　　　　　　　　　　　　　　　　🔊 **Self Tutor**

Determine the nature of the transformation if $x' = \dfrac{3x + y}{\sqrt{10}}$ and $y' = \dfrac{-x + 3y}{\sqrt{10}}$.

The transformation has matrix $\mathbf{M} = \begin{pmatrix} \frac{3}{\sqrt{10}} & \frac{1}{\sqrt{10}} \\ -\frac{1}{\sqrt{10}} & \frac{3}{\sqrt{10}} \end{pmatrix}$

$\therefore \quad |\mathbf{M}| = \frac{9}{10} - (-\frac{1}{10}) = 1$ and $\mathbf{M}$ has the form $\begin{pmatrix} a & -b \\ b & a \end{pmatrix}$

$\therefore$ it is a rotation about O and since $\cos\theta = \frac{3}{\sqrt{10}}$ and $\sin\theta = -\frac{1}{\sqrt{10}}$, $\theta \approx -0.322$

$\therefore$ it is a rotation about O through an angle of about -0.322^c.

Example 18　　　　　　　　　　　　　　　　　　　　　🔊 **Self Tutor**

Find the nature of the transformation if $x' = \dfrac{-3x - 4y}{5}$ and $y' = \dfrac{-4x + 3y}{5}$.

The transformation has matrix $\mathbf{M} = \begin{pmatrix} -\frac{3}{5} & -\frac{4}{5} \\ -\frac{4}{5} & \frac{3}{5} \end{pmatrix}$

$\therefore \quad |\mathbf{M}| = -\frac{9}{25} - \frac{16}{25} = -1$ and $\mathbf{M}$ has the form $\begin{pmatrix} a & b \\ b & -a \end{pmatrix}$

$\therefore$ it is a reflection in a line which passes through the origin.

The equation of the mirror line can be found by using $x' = x$ or $y' = y$.

In this case we substitute $x' = x$,   then $x = \dfrac{-3x - 4y}{5}$

$\therefore \quad 5x = -3x - 4y$

$\therefore \quad y = -2x$

EXERCISE 20G.4

1　Determine the nature of the transformation with equations:

　a　$\begin{cases} x' = y \\ y' = -x \end{cases}$
　　b　$\begin{cases} x' = -x \\ y' = y \end{cases}$
　　c　$\begin{cases} x' = -y \\ y' = -x \end{cases}$

　d　$\begin{cases} x' = \frac{3}{5}x - \frac{4}{5}y \\ y' = \frac{4}{5}x + \frac{3}{5}y \end{cases}$
　　e　$\begin{cases} x' = -\frac{3}{5}x + \frac{4}{5}y \\ y' = \frac{4}{5}x + \frac{3}{5}y \end{cases}$
　　f　$\begin{cases} x' = \frac{8}{17}x + \frac{15}{17}y \\ y' = \frac{15}{17}x - \frac{8}{17}y \end{cases}$

　g　$\begin{cases} x' = \dfrac{x - y}{\sqrt{2}} \\ y' = \dfrac{x + y}{\sqrt{2}} \end{cases}$
　　h　$\begin{cases} x' = \dfrac{x - y}{\sqrt{2}} \\ y' = \dfrac{-x - y}{\sqrt{2}} \end{cases}$
　　i　$\begin{cases} x' = \dfrac{2x + y}{\sqrt{5}} \\ y' = \dfrac{-x + 2y}{\sqrt{5}} \end{cases}$

2　Find the equations of a rotation about O which maps $(3, 1)$ onto $(-3, 1)$.

3 Find the equations of a reflection which maps $(1, 3)$ onto $(\sqrt{10}, 0)$.

DOUBLE TRANSFORMATIONS

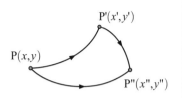

Suppose T_1 maps $P(x, y)$ onto $P'(x', y')$ and T_2 maps $P'(x', y')$ onto $P''(x'', y'')$, where T_1 and T_2 are linear transformations with matrices M_1 and M_2, respectively.

The single transformation which maps P onto P'' has matrix M_2M_1.

Proof: T_1 has equations $\begin{pmatrix} x' \\ y' \end{pmatrix} = M_1 \begin{pmatrix} x \\ y \end{pmatrix}$ and

T_2 has equations $\begin{pmatrix} x'' \\ y'' \end{pmatrix} = M_2 \begin{pmatrix} x' \\ y' \end{pmatrix}$.

$$\therefore \quad \begin{pmatrix} x'' \\ y'' \end{pmatrix} = M_2 \begin{pmatrix} x' \\ y' \end{pmatrix} = M_2M_1 \begin{pmatrix} x \\ y \end{pmatrix}.$$

Example 19   ◀》 **Self Tutor**

Find the nature of the single transformation equivalent to a reflection in the line $y = 3x$,   followed by a rotation about O through $-\frac{\pi}{2}$.

T_1:   For the reflection in the line $y = 3x$, $\tan \theta = 3$.

$$\therefore \quad \cos 2\theta = \frac{1 - m^2}{1 + m^2} = \frac{1 - 9}{1 + 9} = -\frac{4}{5} \quad \text{and} \quad \sin 2\theta = \frac{2m}{1 + m^2} = \frac{6}{10} = \frac{3}{5}$$

$$\therefore \quad \text{the matrix for this transformation is} \quad M_1 = \begin{pmatrix} -\frac{4}{5} & \frac{3}{5} \\ \frac{3}{5} & \frac{4}{5} \end{pmatrix}$$

T_2:   For a rotation about O through $-\frac{\pi}{2}$,

$$M_2 = \begin{pmatrix} 0 & 1 \\ -1 & 0 \end{pmatrix} \quad \{\text{as} \quad \cos(-\tfrac{\pi}{2}) = 0, \quad \sin(-\tfrac{\pi}{2}) = -1\}$$

Now $M_2M_1 = \begin{pmatrix} 0 & 1 \\ -1 & 0 \end{pmatrix} \begin{pmatrix} -\frac{4}{5} & \frac{3}{5} \\ \frac{3}{5} & \frac{4}{5} \end{pmatrix} = \begin{pmatrix} \frac{3}{5} & \frac{4}{5} \\ \frac{4}{5} & -\frac{3}{5} \end{pmatrix}$

which has determinant $= -\frac{9}{25} - \frac{16}{25} = -1$ and the form $\begin{pmatrix} a & b \\ b & -a \end{pmatrix}$

So, T_1 followed by T_2 is a reflection.

Substituting $x' = x$ into $x' = \frac{3}{5}x + \frac{4}{5}y$,   we find $x = \frac{3}{5}x + \frac{4}{5}y$

$$\therefore \quad 5x = 3x + 4y$$

$$\therefore \quad 2x = 4y$$

$$\therefore \quad y = \tfrac{1}{2}x$$

So, T_1 followed by T_2 is a reflection in the line $y = \frac{1}{2}x$.

EXERCISE 20G.5

1 Find the nature of the single transformation equivalent to:

  a a reflection in $y = x$ followed by a $90°$ rotation about O

  b a rotation of $\frac{\pi}{6}$ followed by a reflection in the line $y = \sqrt{3}x$

  c a reflection in $y = 4x$ followed by a reflection in the line $y = x$

  d a $-\frac{\pi}{2}$ rotation about O followed by a reflection in the line $y = -2x$

  e a reflection in $y = x$ followed by a reflection in the line $y = 2x$.

2 Determine the nature of the single transformation equivalent to:

  a a reflection followed by a rotation

  b a reflection followed by another reflection.

  Hint: $|\mathbf{AB}| = |\mathbf{A}|\,|\mathbf{B}|$ for all 2×2 matrices $\mathbf{A}$ and $\mathbf{B}$.

PROOFS WITH 2×2 MATRICES (EXTENSION)

When we prove laws of matrices, we often use general matrices such as $\begin{pmatrix} a_1 & a_2 \\ a_3 & a_4 \end{pmatrix}$.

EXERCISE 20H

1 The distributive law for 2×2 matrices is: $\mathbf{A}(\mathbf{B} + \mathbf{C}) = \mathbf{AB} + \mathbf{AC}$.

  Prove this law using the general matrices $\mathbf{A} = \begin{pmatrix} a_1 & a_2 \\ a_3 & a_4 \end{pmatrix}$, $\mathbf{B} = \begin{pmatrix} b_1 & b_2 \\ b_3 & b_4 \end{pmatrix}$

  and $\mathbf{C} = \begin{pmatrix} c_1 & c_2 \\ c_3 & c_4 \end{pmatrix}$.

2 Prove using general 2×2 matrices that $(\mathbf{AB})\mathbf{C} = \mathbf{A}(\mathbf{BC})$.

3 Prove using general 2×2 matrices that $k(\mathbf{A} + \mathbf{B}) = k\mathbf{A} + k\mathbf{B}$ for any scalar k.

4 We showed earlier that if $\mathbf{AX} = \mathbf{B}$ then $\mathbf{X} = \mathbf{A}^{-1}\mathbf{B}$.
    Prove that if $\mathbf{XA} = \mathbf{B}$ then $\mathbf{X} = \mathbf{BA}^{-1}$.

5 If $\mathbf{A} = \begin{pmatrix} a & b \\ c & d \end{pmatrix}$, $\mathbf{X} = \begin{pmatrix} w & x \\ y & z \end{pmatrix}$ and $\mathbf{AX} = \mathbf{A}$, deduce that $\mathbf{X} = \begin{pmatrix} 1 & 0 \\ 0 & 1 \end{pmatrix} = \mathbf{I}$ by
    solving simultaneous equations.

6 If $\mathbf{A} = \begin{pmatrix} a & b \\ c & d \end{pmatrix}$, $\mathbf{X} = \begin{pmatrix} w & x \\ y & z \end{pmatrix}$ and $\mathbf{AX} = \mathbf{I}$, deduce that $\mathbf{X} = \dfrac{1}{ad - bc}\begin{pmatrix} d & -b \\ -c & a \end{pmatrix}$
    by solving simultaneous equations.

7 It is known that $\mathbf{X} = \mathbf{P}^{-1}\mathbf{AP}$ where $\mathbf{A}^2 = \mathbf{I}$. Prove that $\mathbf{X}^2 = \mathbf{I}$ also.

8 It is known that **AB = A** and **BA = B** where **A** and **B** do *not* have inverses. Prove that **A**^{2} = **A**.

9 If **A** is any 2×2 matrix, show that $|k\mathbf{A}| = k^2|\mathbf{A}|$ for any scalar k.

10 For matrices **A** and **B** which have inverses, prove that $(\mathbf{AB})^{-1} = \mathbf{B}^{-1}\mathbf{A}^{-1}$.
Hint: Start with $(\mathbf{AB})(\mathbf{B}^{-1}\mathbf{A}^{-1})$.

11 **a** If **A** and **B** are any 2×2 matrices, show that $|\mathbf{AB}| = |\mathbf{A}|\,|\mathbf{B}|$.
   b Hence, show that **i** $|\mathbf{A}^2| = |\mathbf{A}|^2$ **ii** $|\mathbf{A}^3| = |\mathbf{A}|^3$ **iii** $|\mathbf{A}^{-1}| = \dfrac{1}{|\mathbf{A}|}$.
   c Suppose $\mathbf{A} = \mathbf{A}^{-1}$.
     i Show that $|\mathbf{A}| = \pm 1$.   **ii** If $|\mathbf{A}| = 1$, show that $\mathbf{A} = k\mathbf{I}$ for some k.

12 If $\mathbf{A}^2 = a\mathbf{A} + b\mathbf{I}$, find $\mathbf{A}^{-1}$ in terms of a and b.

HILL CIPHERS

LINKS
click here

Areas of interaction:
Approaches to learning/Human ingenuity

REVIEW SET 20A

1 If $\mathbf{M} = \begin{pmatrix} 2 & -3 \\ -4 & 1 \end{pmatrix}$ and $\mathbf{N} = \begin{pmatrix} 5 & -2 \\ 3 & 0 \end{pmatrix}$, find:

   a $\mathbf{M} + \mathbf{N}$ **b** $-4\mathbf{N}$ **c** $3\mathbf{M} - \frac{1}{2}\mathbf{N}$

2 Find x, y and z if:

   a $\begin{pmatrix} x^2 & 2 \\ 2y & z+1 \end{pmatrix} = \begin{pmatrix} y+6 & z \\ 6 & x \end{pmatrix}$ **b** $\begin{pmatrix} x+2 & y \\ x+y & 5 \end{pmatrix} = \begin{pmatrix} y-3 & z-2 \\ z-3 & 5 \end{pmatrix}$

3 Find:

   a $\begin{pmatrix} 5 & -1 \\ 3 & 2 \end{pmatrix}\begin{pmatrix} 3 & -4 \\ 0 & 1 \end{pmatrix}$ **b** $\begin{pmatrix} 2 & -4 & 1 \end{pmatrix}\begin{pmatrix} 5 & 2 \\ 4 & 1 \\ -1 & -1 \end{pmatrix}$

   c $\begin{pmatrix} -1 & 2 & 0 \\ -2 & 3 & -1 \\ -4 & 1 & -1 \end{pmatrix}\begin{pmatrix} -2 \\ 3 \\ 1 \end{pmatrix}$

4 Find, if possible, the inverse matrix of:

   a $\begin{pmatrix} 2 & -1 \\ 6 & 4 \end{pmatrix}$ **b** $\begin{pmatrix} -2 & -3 \\ 4 & 6 \end{pmatrix}$ **c** $\begin{pmatrix} 0 & -2 \\ -3 & 8 \end{pmatrix}$

5 If $\mathbf{A} = \begin{pmatrix} 2a & b \\ -4b & 2a \end{pmatrix}$ and $a^2 + b^2 = 1$, find $\mathbf{A}^{-1}$.

6 Find the area of a triangle with vertices $A(1, 2)$, $B(3, 5)$ and $C(6, 4)$.

7 Solve simultaneously using matrices:

a $\begin{cases} 4x + 3y = -2 \\ -6x - 5y = 5 \end{cases}$

b $\begin{cases} 9x + 7y = -3 \\ -7x - 5y = 1 \end{cases}$

8 Consider the linear transformation
$\begin{cases} x' = 2x - y \\ y' = 3x + 2y. \end{cases}$

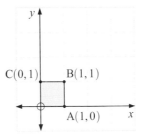

a Find the coordinates of the images of O, A, B and C in the figure alongside.

b Prove that $O'A'B'C'$ is a parallelogram.

c Find the area of $O'A'B'C'$.

9 **a** Find the coordinates of the image of $(2, -1)$ under an anticlockwise rotation about O through an angle of $\frac{\pi}{4}$.

b Find the equation of the image of $5x - 3y = 2$ under an anticlockwise rotation about O through an angle of $\frac{\pi}{4}$.

10 **a** Find the coordinates of the image of $(-3, -2)$ when reflected in the line $y = -\frac{1}{2}x$.

b Find the equation of the image of $y = x^2$ when reflected in the line $y = -\frac{1}{2}x$.

11 Determine the nature of the transformation with equations $x' = \dfrac{2x + 3y}{\sqrt{13}}$ and $y' = \dfrac{-3x + 2y}{\sqrt{13}}$.

12 Find the nature of the single transformation equivalent to a reflection in the line $y = -2x$ followed by a rotation about O through $\frac{\pi}{2}$.

13 Make **X** the subject of: **a** $\mathbf{A} = 3\mathbf{X}$ **b** $\mathbf{B} - \mathbf{X} = \mathbf{A} - 3\mathbf{X}$

REVIEW SET 20B

1 If $\mathbf{A} = \begin{pmatrix} 3 & 2 \\ 0 & -1 \end{pmatrix}$ and $\mathbf{B} = \begin{pmatrix} 1 & 0 \\ -2 & 4 \end{pmatrix}$ find:

a $\mathbf{A} + \mathbf{B}$ **b** $\mathbf{B} - 2\mathbf{A}$ **c** $3\mathbf{A} - 2\mathbf{B}$ **d** $\mathbf{AB}$

e $\mathbf{BA}$ **f** $\mathbf{A}^{-1}$ **g** $\mathbf{A}^2$ **h** $(\mathbf{AB})^{-1}$

2 Find a, b, c and d if:

a $\begin{pmatrix} a & b-2 \\ c & d \end{pmatrix} = \begin{pmatrix} -a & 3 \\ 2-c & -4 \end{pmatrix}$

b $\begin{pmatrix} 3 & 2a \\ b & -2 \end{pmatrix} + \begin{pmatrix} b & -a \\ c & d \end{pmatrix} = \begin{pmatrix} a & 2 \\ 2 & 6 \end{pmatrix}$

3 Simplify:

a $\mathbf{AI} - \mathbf{OA}$ **b** $\mathbf{BA}^{-1}\mathbf{A} + \mathbf{IB}$ **c** $\mathbf{A}^{-1}\mathbf{IA} + \mathbf{A}^2\mathbf{A}^{-1} - \mathbf{IA}$

4 If $\mathbf{B} = \begin{pmatrix} a & 2b \\ 3b & 6a \end{pmatrix}$ and $a^2 - b^2 = 1$, find $\mathbf{B}^{-1}$.

5 Solve using matrix methods:

a $\begin{cases} 3x - 4y = 2 \\ 5x + 2y = -1 \end{cases}$

b $\begin{cases} 4x - y = 5 \\ 2x + 3y = 9 \end{cases}$

6 Write the following systems in the form $\begin{cases} x = px' + qy' \\ y = rx' + sy' \end{cases}$

a $\begin{cases} x' = 2x + y \\ y' = x - y \end{cases}$

b $\begin{cases} x' = ax + by \\ y' = cx + dy \end{cases}$

7 $O(0, 0)$, $A(4, 2)$ and $B(x, -3)$ are the vertices of a triangle with area 5 units^2. Find the possible values that x may have.

8 Consider the linear transformation
$\begin{cases} x' = 2x + y \\ y' = x + 3y. \end{cases}$

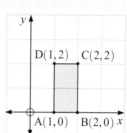

a Find the coordinates of the images of A, B, C and D in the figure alongside.

b Find the area of ABCD.

c Hence find the area of $A'B'C'D'$.

9 Find the coordinates of the image of:

a $(4, 0)$ when rotated clockwise about O through $\frac{3\pi}{4}$

b $(-4, -2)$ when reflected in the line $y = \frac{1}{4}x$.

10 Find the equation of the image of:

a $4x + 5y = 10$ under a clockwise rotation of $\frac{\pi}{4}$ about O

b $3x + y = 4$ under a reflection in the line $y = -4x$.

11 Find the nature of the single transformation equivalent to a reflection in the line $y = x$ followed by a reflection in $y = 3x$.

Chapter **21**

Deductive geometry

Contents:

The geometry of triangles, quadrilaterals and circles has been used for at least 3000 years in art, design and architecture. Simple geometrical figures often have very interesting and useful properties.

In **deductive geometry** we use logical reasoning to prove that certain observations about geometrical figures are indeed true. In the process we use special results called **theorems**.

Many amazing, yet sometimes quite useless, discoveries have been made by mathematicians and non-mathematicians who were simply drawing figures with rulers and compasses.

For example:

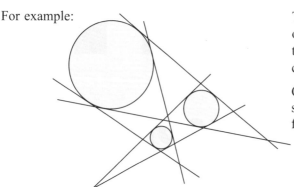

This figure consists of three circles of unequal radii. Common external tangents are drawn between each pair of circles and extended until they meet.

Click on the icon to see what interesting fact emerges.

GRAPHING PACKAGE

HISTORICAL NOTE

Euclid was one of the great mathematical thinkers of ancient times. He founded a school in Alexandria during the reign of Ptolemy I, which lasted from 323 BC until 284 BC.

Euclid's most famous mathematical writing is the *Elements*. This work is the most complete study of geometry ever written and has been a major source of information for the study of geometric techniques, logic, and reasoning. Despite writing a large number of books on various mathematical topics, Euclid's fame is still for geometry, and he is often called "Father of Geometry".

A large proportion of the information in the *Elements* was derived from previously written works but the organisation of the material and the discovery of new proofs is credited to Euclid.

The importance of the *Elements* is emphasized by the fact that it was used as a text book for 2000 years until the middle of the 19th century. At this time a number of other texts adapting Euclid's original ideas began to appear, and the study and teaching of geometry has since begun to follow a variety of paths.

Like many of the great mathematicians and philosophers, Euclid believed in study and learning for its own merit rather than for the rewards it may bring.

OPENING PROBLEM

Market gardener Joe has four long straight pipes of different lengths. He places the pipes on the ground and joins them with rubber hose to form a garden bed in the shape of a quadrilateral. A sprinkler which casts water in semi-circles of diameter equal to that of the length of a pipe is placed at the midpoint of each pipe.

Joe draws a rough sketch of the watering system and decides that his sprinklers will water the whole of the garden. His son Clinton is sceptical of his father's idea, and draws his own sketch which suggests that there will be an unwatered patch in the centre.

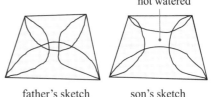

father's sketch   son's sketch

Can you:

1 draw a quadrilateral and use a compass to find the midpoint of each side

2 draw the four semi-circles using a compass

3 make a conjecture as to who you think is correct, father or son

4 prove that your conjecture is true using the theorems of deductive geometry?

A   CIRCLE THEOREMS

Before we can talk about the properties and theorems of circles, we need to learn the appropriate language for describing them.

- A **circle** is the set of all points which are equidistant from a fixed point called the **centre**.

- The **circumference** is the distance around the entire circle boundary.

- An **arc** of a circle is any continuous part of the circle.

- A **chord** of a circle is a line segment joining any two points on the circle.

- A **semi-circle** is a half of a circle.

- A **diameter** of a circle is any chord passing through its centre.

- A **radius** of a circle is any line segment joining its centre to any point on the circle.

- A **tangent** to a circle is any line which touches the circle in exactly one point.

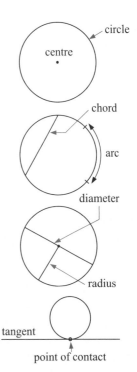

CIRCLE THEOREMS

Name of theorem	Statement	Diagram
Angle in a semi-circle	The angle in a semi-circle is a right angle.	$\widehat{ABC} = 90^o$
Chords of a circle	The perpendicular from the centre of a circle to a chord bisects the chord.	$AM = BM$
Radius-tangent	The tangent to a circle is perpendicular to the radius at the point of contact.	$\widehat{OAT} = 90^o$
Tangents from an external point	Tangents from an external point are equal in length.	$AP = BP$

Two useful **converses** are:

- If line segment [AB] subtends a right angle at C then the circle through A, B and C has diameter [AB].

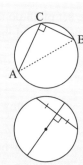

- The perpendicular bisector of a chord of a circle passes through its centre.

Example 1   ◀)) **Self Tutor**

Find x, giving brief reasons for your answer.

$\widehat{ABC}$ measures 90° {angle in semi-circle}

$\therefore \quad (x+10) + 3x + 90 = 180$ {angles in triangle}

$\therefore \quad 4x + 100 = 180$

$\therefore \quad 4x = 80$

$\therefore \quad x = 20$

Example 2   ◀) **Self Tutor**

A circle has radius 4 cm and a chord of length 6 cm. Find the shortest distance from the circle's centre to the chord.

The shortest distance is the perpendicular distance.

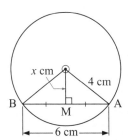

$\therefore$ M is the midpoint of [AB]   {chord of a circle}

$\therefore$ AM $= 3$ cm

In $\triangle$OMA, $x^2 + 3^2 = 4^2$ {Pythagoras}

$\therefore$ $x^2 + 9 = 16$

$\therefore$ $x^2 = 7$

$\therefore$ $x = \pm\sqrt{7}$

$\therefore$ $x = \sqrt{7}$ {as $x > 0$}

So, the shortest distance is $\sqrt{7}$ cm.

Example 3   ◀) **Self Tutor**

The tangent from point M to a circle of radius 5 cm is 12 cm long.
Find the distance from M to the centre of the circle.

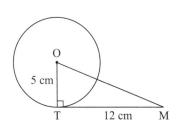

$\widehat{OTM} = 90^o$ {radius-tangent theorem}

$\therefore$ $OM^2 = OT^2 + TM^2$ {Pythagoras}

$\therefore$ $OM^2 = 5^2 + 12^2$

$\therefore$ $OM^2 = 169$

$\therefore$ $OM = 13$ {OM > 0}

So, M is 13 cm from the centre of the circle.

EXERCISE 21A

1   Find x, giving brief reasons for your answers:

a

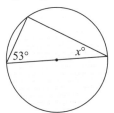

b

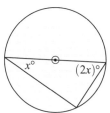

c

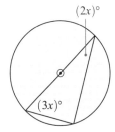

d

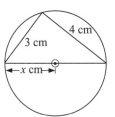

e

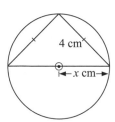

f

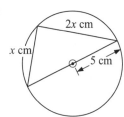

2 Find x in the following, giving brief reasons for your answers:

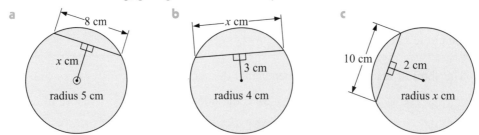

a   8 cm x cm   radius 5 cm

b x cm   3 cm   radius 4 cm

c   10 cm   2 cm   radius x cm

3 A circle has a chord of length 8 cm and the shortest distance from the centre of the circle to the chord is 2 cm. Find the radius of the circle.

4 The shortest distance from the centre of a circle to a chord is 2 cm. Find the length of the chord given that the radius has length 5 cm.

5 In each of the following questions, C is the centre of the circle and [XY] is a tangent. Give reasons for your answers.

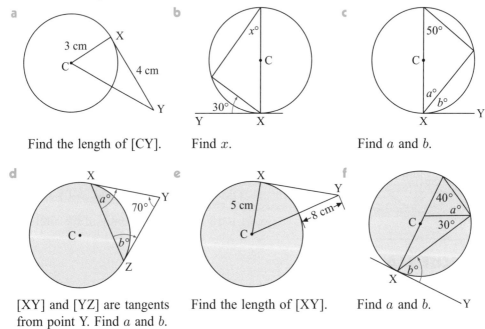

a   3 cm   X   C   4 cm   Y

Find the length of [CY].

b $x°$ C   30°   Y   X

Find x.

c   50°   C $a°$ $b°$ X   Y

Find a and b.

d   X $a°$ 70°   Y   C• $b°$ Z

[XY] and [YZ] are tangents from point Y. Find a and b.

e   X   5 cm   Y   8 cm   C

Find the length of [XY].

f   40° $a°$ C•   30°   X $b°$ Y

Find a and b.

6 Point P is 10 cm from the centre of a circle of radius 6 cm. A tangent is drawn from P to touch the circle at Q. Find the length of [PQ].

7 Find x, giving reasons:

a   point of contact x cm   6 cm $2x$ cm

b   point of contact x cm   8 cm   5 cm

8

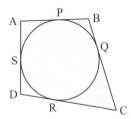

A circle is drawn and four tangents to it are constructed as shown.

Deduce that   AB + CD = BC + AD.

9 Find the radius of the circle which touches the three sides of the triangle as shown.

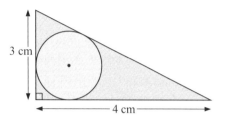

10

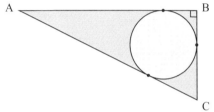

A circle is inscribed in a right angled triangle. The radius of the circle is 3 cm, and [BC] has length 8 cm.

Find the perimeter of the triangle ABC.

<h1>B   FURTHER CIRCLE THEOREMS</h1>

Any continuous part of a circle is called an **arc**.

If the arc is less than half the circle it is called a **minor arc**.

If it is greater than half the circle it is called a **major arc**.

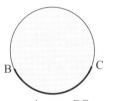

a minor arc BC

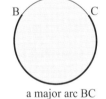

a major arc BC

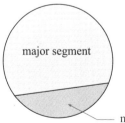

A chord divides the interior of a circle into two regions called **segments**. The larger region is called a **major segment** and the smaller region is called a **minor segment**.

In the diagram opposite:

- the minor arc BC **subtends** the angle BAC, where A is on the circle

- the minor arc BC also subtends angle BOC at the centre of the circle.

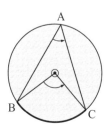

INVESTIGATION 1   CIRCLE THEOREMS

The use of the **geometry package** on the CD is recommended, but this investigation can also be done using a ruler, compass and protractor.

Part 1:   Angle at the centre theorem

What to do:

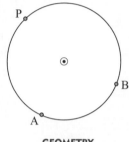

1   Use a compass to draw a large circle with centre O. Mark on it points A, B and P.

2   Join [AO], [BO], [AP] and [BP] with a ruler. Measure angles AOB and APB.

3   What do you notice about the measured angles?

GEOMETRY PACKAGE

4   Repeat the above steps with another circle.

5   Copy and complete:
"The angle at the centre of a circle is ...... the angle on the circle subtended by the same arc."

Part 2:   Angles subtended by the same arc theorem

What to do:

1   Use a compass to draw a circle with centre O. Mark on it points A, B, C and D.

2   Draw angles ACB and ADB with a ruler.

3   Measure angles ACB and ADB. What do you notice?

4   Repeat the above steps with another circle.

GEOMETRY PACKAGE

5   Copy and complete:
"Angles subtended by an arc on the circle are ...... in size."

Part 3:   Angle between a tangent and a chord theorem

What to do:

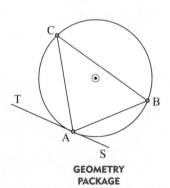

1   Use a compass to draw a circle. Mark on it points A, B and C.

2   Draw carefully tangent TAS at A and join [AB], [BC] and [CA].

3   Measure angles BAS and ACB. What do you notice?

GEOMETRY PACKAGE

4   Repeat the above steps with another circle.

5   Copy and complete:
"The angle between a tangent and a chord at the point of contact is ...... to the angle subtended by the chord in the alternate ......"

From the investigation you should have discovered the following theorems:

Name of theorem	Statement	Diagram
Angle at the centre	The angle at the centre of a circle is twice the angle on the circle subtended by the same arc.	$\text{A}\widehat{\text{O}}\text{B} = 2 \times \text{A}\widehat{\text{C}}\text{B}$
Angles subtended by the same arc	Angles subtended by an arc on the circle are equal in size.	$\text{A}\widehat{\text{D}}\text{B} = \text{A}\widehat{\text{C}}\text{B}$
Angle between a tangent and a chord	The angle between a tangent and a chord at the point of contact is equal to the angle subtended by the chord in the alternate segment.	$\text{B}\widehat{\text{A}}\text{S} = \text{B}\widehat{\text{C}}\text{A}$

Note: • The following diagrams show other cases of **the angle at the centre theorem**. These cases can be easily shown using the **geometry package**.

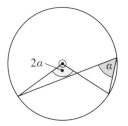 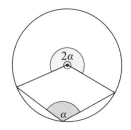 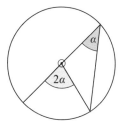

• The **angle in a semi-circle theorem** is a special case of the angle at the centre theorem.

Example 4   ◀) **Self Tutor**

Find x:

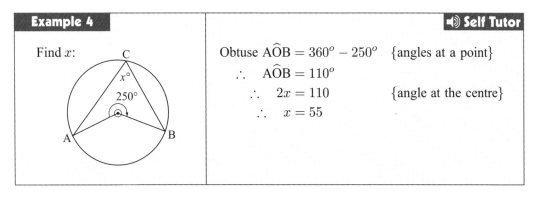

Obtuse $\text{A}\widehat{\text{O}}\text{B} = 360° - 250°$ {angles at a point}

$\therefore \quad \text{A}\widehat{\text{O}}\text{B} = 110°$

$\therefore \quad 2x = 110$ {angle at the centre}

$\therefore \quad x = 55$

Example 5   ◀) **Self Tutor**

Find x:

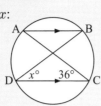

$\widehat{BDC} = \widehat{ABD}$ {equal alternate angles}

But $\widehat{ABD} = \widehat{ACD}$ {angles on the same arc}

$\therefore$ $\widehat{BDC} = \widehat{ACD}$

$\therefore$ $x = 36$

Example 6   ◀) **Self Tutor**

Find x if [AT] is a tangent and A is the point of contact.

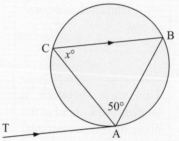

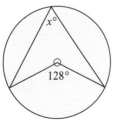

Since   [CB] ∥ [TA], $\widehat{CAT} = x^o$

{equal alternate angles}

But $\widehat{CAT} = \widehat{ABC}$

{angle between a tangent and a chord}

$\therefore$ $\widehat{ABC} = x^o$

$\therefore$ $x + x + 50 = 180$ {angles of a $\triangle$}

$\therefore$ $2x = 130$

$\therefore$ $x = 65$

EXERCISE 21B

1 Find, giving reasons, the value of x in each of the following:

a

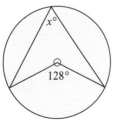

b

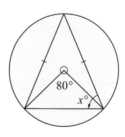

c

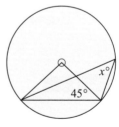

d

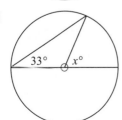

e

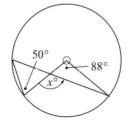

f

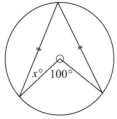

2 Find, giving reasons, the values of the pronumerals in the following:

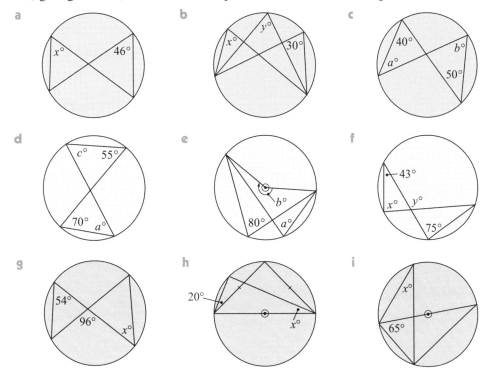

3 In each diagram, C is the point of contact of tangent [CT]. Find x, giving reasons:

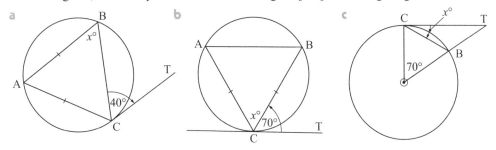

C GEOMETRIC PROOF

The circle theorems and other geometric facts can be formally **proven** using theorems we have already seen, such as the isosceles triangle theorem and congruence.

Example 7	◀)) **Self Tutor**

Use the given figure to prove the *angle in a semi-circle theorem*.

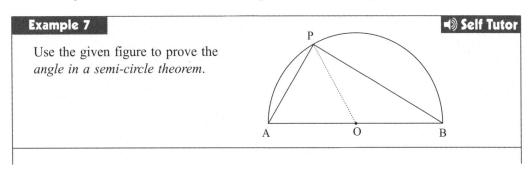

Proof:

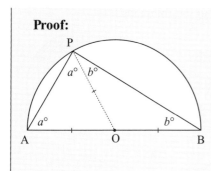

Let $P\hat{A}O = a^o$ and $P\hat{B}O = b^o$

Now $OA = OP = OB$ {equal radii}

$\therefore$ Δs OAP and OBP are isosceles.

$\therefore$ $O\hat{P}A = a^o$ and $B\hat{P}O = b^o$ {isosceles Δ}

Now $a + (a + b) + b = 180$ {angles of ΔAPB}

$\therefore$ $2a + 2b = 180$

$\therefore$ $a + b = 90$

So, $A\hat{P}B$ is a right angle.

Example 8   ◀ **Self Tutor**

ΔABC is isosceles and is inscribed in a circle.
[TC] is a tangent to the circle.

Prove that [AC] bisects angle $B\hat{C}T$.

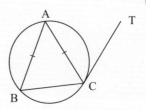

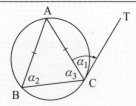

Now $\alpha_1 = \alpha_2$ {tangent and chord theorem}

and $\alpha_2 = \alpha_3$ {isosceles Δ theorem}

$\therefore$ $\alpha_1 = \alpha_3$

Thus [AC] bisects $B\hat{C}T$.

EXERCISE 21C

1 In this question we prove the *chords of a circle* theorem.

a For the given figure join [OA] and [OB] and classify ΔOAB.

b Apply the isosceles triangle theorem to triangle OAB. What geometrical facts result?

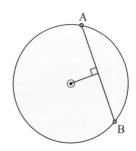

2 In this question we prove the *tangents from an external point* theorem.

a Join [OP], [OA] and [OB].

b Assuming the *tangent-radius* theorem, prove that Δs POA and POB are congruent.

c What are the consequences of the congruence in **b**?

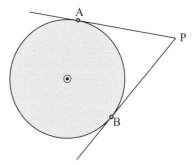

3 In this question we prove the *angle at the centre* theorem.

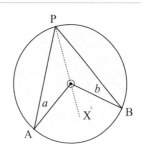

    a Explain why Δs OAP and OBP are isosceles.

    b Find the measure of the following angles in terms of a and b:

      i $A\widehat{P}O$ **ii** $B\widehat{P}O$ **iii** $A\widehat{O}X$

      iv $B\widehat{O}X$ **v** $A\widehat{P}B$ **vi** $A\widehat{O}B$

    c What can be deduced from **b v** and **b vi**?

4 In this question we prove the *angles in the same segment* theorem.

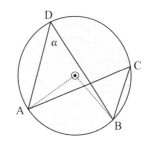

    a Using the results of question **3**, find the size of $A\widehat{O}B$ in terms of α.

    b Find the size of $A\widehat{C}B$ in terms of α.

    c State the relationship between $A\widehat{D}B$ and $A\widehat{C}B$.

5 In this question we prove the *angle between a tangent and a chord* theorem.

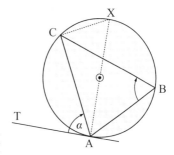

    a We draw diameter [AX] and join [CX].

      Find the size of   **i** $T\widehat{A}X$ **ii** $A\widehat{C}X$

    b If $T\widehat{A}C = \alpha$, find in terms of α:

      i $C\widehat{A}X$ **ii** $C\widehat{X}A$ **iii** $C\widehat{B}A$

      Give reasons for your answers.

6 [AB] is the diameter of a circle with centre O. X is a point on the circle and [AX] is produced to Y such that OX = XY.

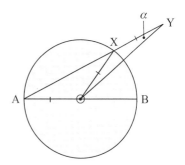

    a If $X\widehat{Y}O = \alpha$, find in terms of α:

      i $X\widehat{O}Y$ **ii** $A\widehat{X}O$ **iii** $X\widehat{A}O$

      iv $X\widehat{O}B$ **v** $B\widehat{O}Y$

    b What is the relationship between $B\widehat{O}Y$ and $Y\widehat{O}X$?

7 Revisit the **Opening Problem** on page **509**. Consider the two semi-circles in the figure alongside.

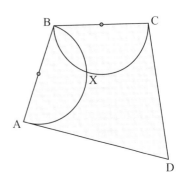

    a Determine the measure of $B\widehat{X}A$ and $B\widehat{X}C$.

    b What does **a** tell us about the points A, X and C?

    c Do the two illustrated sprinklers water all of the area on one side of the diagonal [AC]?

    d Will the four sprinklers water the whole garden? Explain your answer.

8 [AB] is a diameter of a circle with centre O.
[CD] is a chord parallel to [AB].
Prove that [BC] bisects angle DCO.

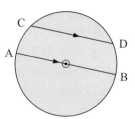

9 P is any point on a circle. [QR] is a chord of the circle parallel to the tangent at P. Prove that triangle PQR is isosceles.

10 Two circles intersect at A and B.
Straight lines [PQ] and [XY] are drawn
through A to meet the circles as shown.
Show that $X\hat{B}P = Y\hat{B}Q$.

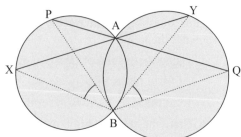

11 A, B and C are three points on a circle. The bisector of angle BAC cuts [BC] at P and the circle at Q. Prove that $A\hat{P}C = A\hat{B}Q$.

12 Triangle ABC is inscribed in a circle with AB = AC. The bisector of angle ACB meets the tangent from A at D. Prove that [AD] and [BC] are parallel.

13 Two circles intersect at A and B. [AX] and
[AY] are diameters as shown. Prove that X,
B and Y are collinear, i.e., lie on a straight
line.

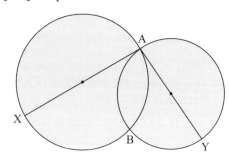

14

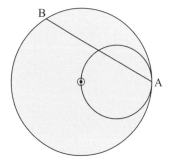

Two circles touch at A. O is the centre of
the larger circle. The smaller circle passes
through O. Prove that any chord [AB] of the
larger circle is bisected by the smaller circle.

15 Triangle PQR is isosceles with PQ = PR.
A semi-circle with diameter [PR] is drawn which
cuts [QR] at X.
Prove that X is the midpoint of [QR].

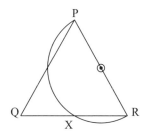

16   Brigitta notices that her angle of view of a picture on a
wall depends on how far she is standing in front of the
wall. When she is close to the wall the angle of view
is small. When she moves backwards so that she is a
long way from the wall, the angle of view is also small.

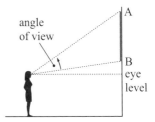

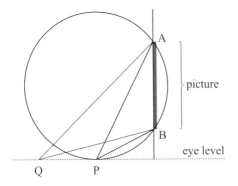

It becomes clear to Brigitta that there must be a
point in front of the picture for which her angle
of view is greatest. This position can be found
by drawing the circle through A and B which
touches the 'eye level' line at P. $A\hat{P}B$ is the
largest angle of view.

Prove this result by choosing any other point
Q on the 'eye level' line and showing that this
angle must be less than $A\hat{P}B$.

<h1>D   CYCLIC QUADRILATERALS</h1>

A circle can always be drawn through any three points
that are not collinear.

To find the circle's centre we draw the perpendicular
bisectors of the lines joining two pairs of points.

Using the chords of a circle theorem, the centre is at
the intersection of these two lines.

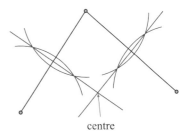

However, a circle may or may not
be drawn through any four points
in a plane.

For example:

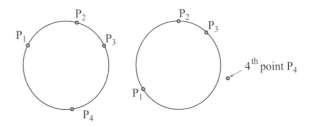

If a circle can be drawn through four points we say that the points are **concyclic**.

If any four points on a circle are joined to form a
convex quadrilateral then the quadrilateral is said to
be a **cyclic quadrilateral**.

INVESTIGATION 2   **CYCLIC QUADRILATERALS**

This investigation can be done using a compass, ruler and protractor, or you can use the **geometry package** by clicking on the icon.

GEOMETRY
PACKAGE

What to do:

1 Draw several cyclic quadrilaterals with vertices A, B, C and D. Make sure that you have different shaped quadrilaterals and make them large enough so that angle measurement is easy with a protractor.

2 Measure all angles to the nearest $\frac{1}{2}$ degree, and record your results in a table like the one following.

Figure	$\widehat{A}$	$\widehat{B}$	$\widehat{C}$	$\widehat{D}$	$\widehat{A} + \widehat{C}$	$\widehat{B} + \widehat{D}$
1						
2						
⋮						

3 Write a sentence to summarise your results.

From the investigation you should have discovered the following theorem:

OPPOSITE ANGLES OF A CYCLIC QUADRILATERAL THEOREM

The opposite angles of a cyclic quadrilateral are **supplementary**.

$$\alpha + \beta = 180^o \quad \text{and} \quad \theta + \phi = 180^o.$$

Example 9	◀) **Self Tutor**

Find x given:

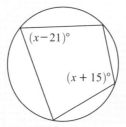

The angles given are opposite angles of a cyclic quadrilateral.

$$\therefore \quad (x+15) + (x-21) = 180$$
$$\therefore \quad 2x - 6 = 180$$
$$\therefore \quad 2x = 186$$
$$\therefore \quad x = 93$$

TESTS FOR CYCLIC QUADRILATERALS

A quadrilateral is a **cyclic quadrilateral** if one of the following is true:

- one pair of opposite angles is supplementary

If $\alpha + \beta = 180°$ then ABCD is a cyclic quadrilateral.

- one side subtends equal angles at the other two vertices

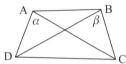

If $\alpha = \beta$ then ABCD is a cyclic quadrilateral.

Example 10   ◄⑨ **Self Tutor**

Triangle ABC is isosceles with AB = AC. X and Y lie on [AB] and [AC] respectively such that [XY] is parallel to [BC]. Prove that XYCB is a cyclic quadrilateral.

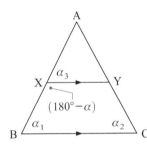

$\triangle$ABC is isosceles with AB = AC.

$$\therefore \quad \alpha_1 = \alpha_2 \quad \{\text{equal base angles}\}$$

Since [XY] || [BC], $\alpha_1 = \alpha_3$ {equal corresp. angles}

$$\therefore \quad Y\hat{X}B = 180° - \alpha.$$

$$\therefore \quad Y\hat{X}B + Y\hat{C}B = 180° - \alpha + \alpha$$

$$= 180°$$

$\therefore$ XYCB is a cyclic quadrilateral   {opposite angles supplementary}

EXERCISE 21D

1 A, B, C and D are distinct points on a circle with centre O.

   a Use the given figure to find $D\hat{O}B$ and reflex $D\hat{O}B$.

   b Write an equation connecting the angles in **a** and simplify it.

   You should have established the *opposite angles of a cyclic quadrilateral* theorem.

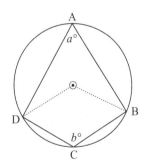

2 An alternative method for establishing the *opposite angles of a cyclic quadrilateral* theorem is to use the figure alongside. Show how this can be done.

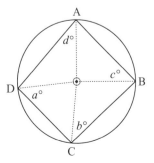

3 Find x, giving reasons:

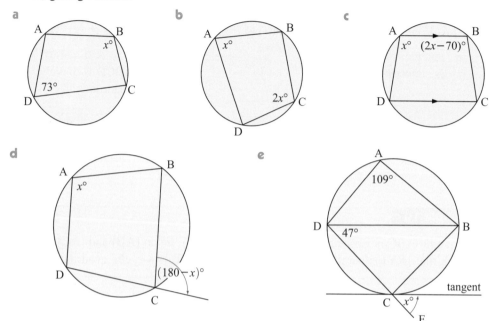

4 Is ABCD a cyclic quadrilateral? Explain your answers.

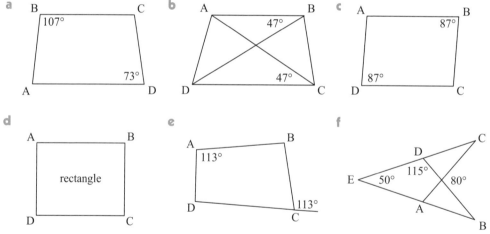

5 Can a circle be drawn through the vertices of a non-rectangular parallelogram? Explain your answer.

6 Prove that a parallelogram inscribed in a circle is a rectangle.

7 ABCD is a cyclic quadrilateral and X is any point on diagonal [CA]. [XY] is drawn parallel to [CB] to meet [AB] at Y, and [XZ] is drawn parallel to [CD] to meet [AD] at Z. Prove that XYAZ is a cyclic quadrilateral.

8 ABC is an isosceles triangle in which AB = AC. The angle bisectors at B and C meet the sides [AC] and [AB] at X and Y respectively. Show that BCXY is a cyclic quadrilateral.

9 The non-parallel sides of a trapezium have equal length. Prove that the trapezium is a cyclic quadrilateral.

10 OABC is a parallelogram.
A circle with centre O and radius OA is drawn.
[BA] produced meets the circle at D.
Prove that DOCB is a cyclic quadrilateral.

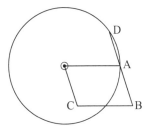

11 [AB] and [CD] are two parallel chords of a circle with centre O. [AD] and [BC] meet at E. Prove that AEOC is a cyclic quadrilateral.

12 [AB] and [AC] are chords of a circle with centre O. X and Y are the midpoints of [AB] and [AC] respectively. Prove that OXAY is a cyclic quadrilateral.

13 [RX] is the bisector of angle QRT.
Prove that [PX] bisects angle QPS.

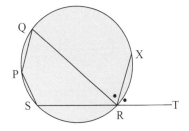

14 Two circles meet at points X and Y. [AXB] and [CYD] are two line segments which meet one circle at A and C and the other at B and D. Prove that [AC] is parallel to [BD].

15 Two circles intersect at X and Y. A line segment [AXB] is drawn which cuts the circles at A and B respectively. The tangents at A and B meet at C. Prove that AYBC is a cyclic quadrilateral.

INVESTIGATION 3   **CIRCLES AND TRIANGLES**

Triangles and circles which are related to them have many fascinating properties. In this investigation you should discover one of them.

What to do:

1 Given three points A, B and C, explain how to use a ruler and geometrical compass to locate the centre of the circle passing through A, B and C.
Clearly state any geometrical theorems you have used.
Check your construction by drawing the circle.

2 Draw any triangle PQR with sides between 6 cm and 10 cm.
Label any points X, Y and Z on [PR], [PQ] and [RQ] respectively.
Use **1** to accurately construct circles through:

    a P, X and Y   **b** Q, Y and Z

    c R, X and Z

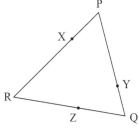

3 What do you notice about the three circles?

4 Repeat **2** with a different acute-angled triangle.

5 Prove your assertion in **3** to be true.
   Hint: Do **not** draw all three circles on your figure.

REVIEW SET 21A

1 Find the value of a, giving reasons:

a
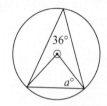

b

c

d
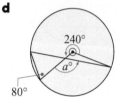

e
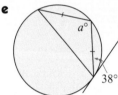

f
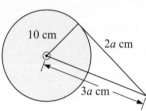

g
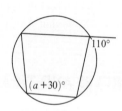

h
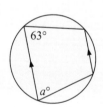

i

2 [AB] and [AC] are tangents to the circle.
   Find an equation connecting α, β and γ.

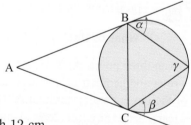

3 A circle of radius 14 cm has a chord of length 12 cm.
   What is the shortest distance from the chord to the circle's centre?

4 [AB] is the diameter of a circle with centre O.
   [AC] and [BD] are any two chords.
   If $B\widehat{D}O = \alpha$:

   a find $D\widehat{B}O$

   b show that $B\widehat{D}O = A\widehat{C}D$.

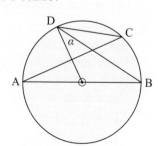

5 [AB] and [CM] are common tangents to two circles. Show that:

   a M is the midpoint of [AB]

   b A$\widehat{\text{C}}$B is a right angle.

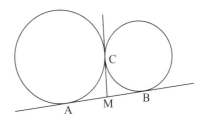

6 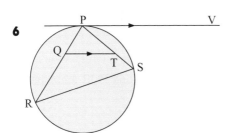 [PV] is a tangent to the circle and [QT] is parallel to [PV].

Prove that QRST is a cyclic quadrilateral.

7 In the figure alongside, E and F are the midpoints of [AB] and [AC] respectively. [BF] and [CE] intersect at G. A line is drawn through A and G, extended to H such that [HC] ∥ [BF]. We join [BH].

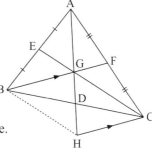

   a Prove that   [BH] ∥ [EC].
     Hint: Use the midpoint theorem and its converse.

   b Hence show that   BD = DC.

   c A **median** of a triangle is a line segment from a vertex to the midpoint of the opposite side. What can you conclude from **b** about the three medians of a triangle?

REVIEW SET 21B

1 Find the value of x, giving reasons:

  a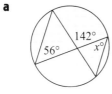

  b

  c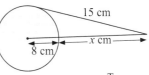

  d

  e

  f

2 Given the figure alongside:

   a find the size of obtuse B$\widehat{\text{O}}$D

   b find the size of reflex B$\widehat{\text{O}}$D

   c find the value of $\alpha + \beta$.

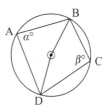

3 In triangle PQR, PQ = PR. A circle is drawn
with diameter [PQ], and the circle cuts [QR]
at S.

Show that S is the midpoint of [QR].

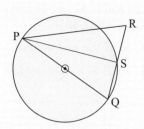

4

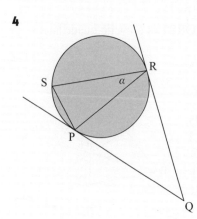

[QP] and [QR] are tangents to a circle. S is a point
on the circle such that $P\widehat{S}R$ and $P\widehat{Q}R$ are equal and
both are double $P\widehat{R}S$.

Let $P\widehat{R}S$ be α.

a Find in terms of α:

    i $P\widehat{S}R$ **ii** $P\widehat{Q}R$

    iii $P\widehat{R}Q$ **iv** $Q\widehat{P}R$

b Use triangle PQR to show that $\alpha = 30°$.

c Find the measure of $Q\widehat{R}S$.

d What can you conclude about [RS]?

5 **a** Copy and complete: *"The angle
between a tangent and a chord through
the point of contact is equal to ......"*

  b Two circles intersect at points P and Q.
A line segment [APB] is drawn through
P and the tangents at A and B meet at C.

    i Given that $A\widehat{B}C = \alpha$ and $B\widehat{A}C = \beta$,
find expressions for $P\widehat{Q}B$, $P\widehat{Q}A$ and
$A\widehat{Q}B$ in terms of α and β.

    ii Show that $A\widehat{C}B + A\widehat{Q}B = 180°$.

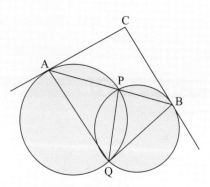

6 In the figure alongside, [XT] and [XP] are
tangents.

Prove that:

  a BTXP is a cyclic quadrilateral

  b [PT] bisects angle CTX.

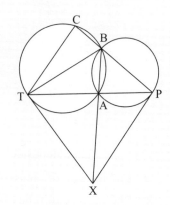

Chapter 22

Introduction to calculus

Contents:

Calculus is the branch of mathematics which connects the equation of a function with the gradient of the tangent at any point on its graph. **Sir Isaac Newton** and **Gottfried Wilhelm Leibniz** were instrumental in developing this theory in the 17th century.

Calculus has two major branches called **differential calculus** and **integral calculus**. We use differential calculus to find special features of functions, find tangents to curves, and to solve optimisation and rates of change problems. We use integral calculus to find areas under curves and volumes of revolution.

OPENING PROBLEM

A sheet of metal 30 cm by 20 cm has squares cut out of its 4 corners as shown. The resulting shape is bent along the dashed lines to form an open rectangular dish.

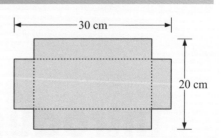

What size squares should be removed to obtain the dish of maximum capacity?

A   ESTIMATING GRADIENTS OF TANGENTS TO CURVES

A **tangent** to a smooth curve at a given point is a straight line which touches the curve at that point.

For example:

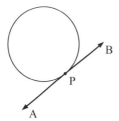

(AB) is the tangent to the circle at the **point of contact** P.

(CD) is the tangent to this parabola at the point Q.

To estimate the **gradient** of a tangent to a curve, we must:

- obtain an accurate graph of the curve on 1 to 1 graph paper
- draw, as accurately as possible, a tangent to the curve at the given point
- construct a right angled triangle with legs parallel to the axes, and use it to find the gradient.

Example 1 ◀)) Self Tutor

Consider $y = x^2$, $x > 0$. Estimate the gradient of the tangent at $(1, 1)$.

We draw an accurate graph of $y = x^2$.

At $(1, 1)$ we draw a right angled triangle.

The x-step $= 1$. The y-step ≈ 2.

$\therefore$ the gradient $\approx \frac{2}{1}$ or 2.

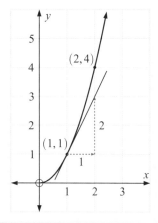

EXERCISE 22A

Click on the icon to obtain printed pages for the curves in this exercise.

PRINTABLE
CURVES

1 Consider $y = -x^2$.
  Estimate the gradient of the tangent to the curve at:

  a $x = 1$　　　b $x = 2$　　　c $x = 1\frac{1}{2}$

2 Consider $y = \dfrac{4}{x}$.
  Estimate the gradient of the tangent to the curve at:

  a $x = 1$　　　b $x = 2$　　　c $x = 3$

3 Consider $y = 2^x$.
  Estimate the gradient of the tangent to the curve at:

  a $x = 1$　　　b $x = 2$　　　c $x = -\frac{1}{2}$

4 Consider $y = \sqrt{x}$.
  Estimate the gradient of the tangent to the curve at:

  a $x = 1$　　　b $x = 4$　　　c $x = 6$.

B　GRADIENTS USING QUADRATIC THEORY

For two types of functions we can use **quadratic theory** to obtain the gradients of tangents. These are the **quadratic functions** of the form $y = ax^2 + bx + c$, $a \neq 0$, and the **reciprocal functions** of the form $y = \dfrac{a}{x}$.

To find the gradient of a tangent, we suppose the tangent has equation $y = mx + c$ and then find where this tangent meets the curve.

Example 2   ◀⟩ **Self Tutor**

Find the gradient of the tangent to $y = x^2$ at the point $(1, 1)$ using quadratic theory.

Suppose the tangent has equation $y = mx + k$.
$y = x^2$ and $y = mx + k$ meet when $x^2 = mx + k$
$\therefore \quad x^2 - mx - k = 0$

This is a quadratic in x with $a = 1$, $b = -m$
and $c = -k$.

The quadratic must have one solution as the line
touches the curve.

$\therefore \quad \triangle = b^2 - 4ac = 0$ and hence $x = -\dfrac{b}{2a}$

But the tangent is at $(1, 1)$, so $1 = \dfrac{-(-m)}{2}$

$\therefore \quad m = 2$

So, the gradient of the tangent at $(1, 1)$ is 2.

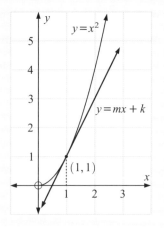

EXERCISE 22B

1 Use quadratic theory to find the gradient of the tangent to:

    a $y = x^2$ at the point $(2, 4)$ **b** $y = x^2$ at the point $(3, 9)$.

2 Using **Example 2**, question **1**, and arguments of symmetry, find the gradient of the tangent to $y = x^2$ at the point:

    a $(-1, 1)$ **b** $(-2, 4)$ **c** $(-3, 9)$.

3 Find, using quadratic theory, the gradient of the tangent to the curve:

    a $y = x^2 + 3x$ at the point $(0, 0)$ **b** $y = x^2 - 2x + 1$ at the point $(2, 1)$

    c $y = \dfrac{4}{x}$ at the point $(1, 4)$ **d** $y = \dfrac{6}{x}$ at the point $(2, 3)$.

4 Explain why the quadratic theory above cannot be used to find the gradient of the tangent to $y = x^3$ at the point $(1, 1)$.

C   GRADIENTS USING LIMIT THEORY

In **Example 1** we saw that the gradient of the tangent to $y = x^2$ at the point $(1, 1)$ is approximately 2.

In **Example 2** we used quadratic theory to show that this gradient is exactly 2. However, this quadratic theory can only be used for a small selection of functions.

So, we need another exact method for finding gradients which can be used for all functions. **Sir Isaac Newton** discovered such a method which uses the idea of a **limit**.

Consider the tangent to $y = x^2$ at the point F(1, 1).

Let M be a point on the curve close to F.
We let M have x-coordinate $1 + h$, so M is $(1 + h, (1 + h)^2)$.

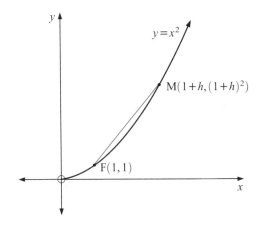

[FM] has gradient $= \dfrac{y_M - y_F}{x_M - x_F}$

$$= \dfrac{(1 + h)^2 - 1}{1 + h - 1}$$

$$= \dfrac{1 + 2h + h^2 - 1}{h}$$

$$= \dfrac{2h + h^2}{h}$$

$$= \dfrac{\cancel{h}(2 + h)}{\cancel{h}}$$

$$= 2 + h \qquad \{\text{as } h \neq 0\}$$

We now let M move along the curve towards F.

As M gets extremely close to F, we say in mathematics that "M approaches F", and write this as M $\to$ F.

> The symbol $\to$ reads "approaches" or "tends to".

Geometrically:

As   M $\to$ F, $h \to 0$
$\therefore$ the slope of [FM] $\to$ the slope of the tangent at F.

Algebraically:

As $h \to 0$, $2 + h \to 2$
$\therefore$ the slope of [FM] $\to$ 2

Comparing the two approaches, the slope of the tangent at $(1, 1)$ equals 2.

> The gradient of the **tangent** at F equals the slope of [FM] as h approaches 0.
>
> We write this as $\lim\limits_{h \to 0}$ **(slope of [FM])**,
>
> which reads   "the limit as h approaches 0 of the slope of [FM]".

Example 3	◀》 **Self Tutor**

Find the gradient of the tangent to $y = x^2$ at the point $(2, 4)$.

Let F be the point $(2, 4)$ and M have the x-coordinate $2 + h$, so M is $(2 + h, (2 + h)^2)$.

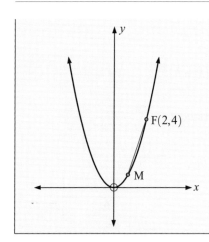

The gradient of $[FM] = \dfrac{y_M - y_F}{x_M - x_F}$

$$= \frac{(2+h)^2 - 4}{(2+h) - 2}$$

$$= \frac{4 + 4h + h^2 - 4}{h}$$

$$= \frac{\cancel{h}(4+h)}{\cancel{h}}$$

$$= 4 + h \qquad \{\text{as } h \neq 0\}$$

$\therefore$ the gradient of the tangent at F $= \lim\limits_{h \to 0} (4+h) = 4.$

EXERCISE 22C

1 F$(3, 9)$ lies on the graph of $y = x^2$. M also lies on the graph, and has x-coordinate $3+h$.

   a State the y-coordinate of M.

   b Find the gradient of the chord [MF].

   c Use the limit method to find the gradient of the tangent to $y = x^2$ at $(3, 9)$.

2 F$(1, 1)$ lies on the graph of $y = x^3$. M also lies on the graph, and has x-coordinate $1+h$.

   a State the y-coordinate of M.

   b Find the gradient of the chord [MF] in simplest form.

   c Use the limit method to find the gradient of the tangent to $y = x^3$ at $(1, 1)$.

3 F$(1, 4)$ lies on the graph of $y = \dfrac{4}{x}$. M also lies on the graph, and has x-coordinate $1+h$.

   a State the y-coordinate of M.

   b Find the gradient of the chord [MF] in simplest form.

   c Use the limit method to find the gradient of the tangent to $y = \dfrac{4}{x}$ at $(1, 4)$.

4 Find, using the limit method, the slope of the tangent to:

   a $y = x^2$ at the point where $x = 4$

   b $y = x^3$ at the point where $x = 2$

   c $y = x^4$ at the point where $x = 1$.

5 Find, using the limit method, the slope of the tangent to:

   a $y = x^2$ at the point (a, a^2)

   b $y = x^3$ at the point (a, a^3)

   c $y = x^4$ at the point (a, a^4).

6 From 5, predict the slope of the tangent to $y = x^n$, $n \in \mathbb{Z}^+$ at the point (a, a^n).

D   DIFFERENTIATION

Using the methods we have already seen, we can find the gradient of the tangent to a curve at any particular point. We could hence construct a gradient table for a curve like the one shown for $y = x^2$.

The results suggest that for $y = x^2$, the tangent at $x = a$ is $2a$, or in other words, that the gradient is always double the x-coordinate.

So, for $f(x) = x^2$ the gradient function is $2x$.

This gradient function is called the **derivative** or **derivative function** and is given the notation $f'(x)$.

For $f(x) = x^2$, $f'(x) = 2x$.

$y = x^2$	
at	gradient
$x = -2$	-4
$x = -1$	-2
$x = 0$	0
$x = 1$	2
$x = 2$	4
$x = 3$	6

INVESTIGATION 1   DERIVED FUNCTIONS

In this investigation we attempt to find the derived functions for the family of functions of the form $f(x) = x^n$, $n = 1, 2, 3, 4, 5, \ldots\ldots$

What to do:

1 If $n = 1$, $f(x) = x$. Find $f'(x)$, giving reasons for your answer.

2 If $n = 2$, $f(x) = x^2$.

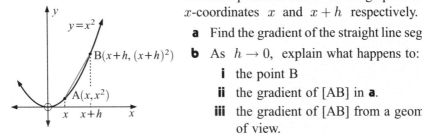

Consider points A and B on the graph with x-coordinates x and $x + h$ respectively.

a Find the gradient of the straight line segment [AB].

b As $h \to 0$, explain what happens to:

  i the point B

  ii the gradient of [AB] in **a**.

  iii the gradient of [AB] from a geometric point of view.

c Deduce $f'(x)$ for $f(x) = x^2$.

3 If $n = 3$, $f(x) = x^3$

a

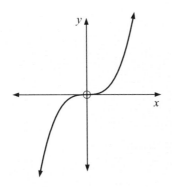

Use the graphing package to complete this table:

GRAPHING PACKAGE

$y = x^3$	
at	gradient
$x = -2$	
$x = -1$	
$x = 0$	
$x = 1$	
$x = 2$	

b Use the table in **a** to draw a graph of the gradient against the x-values. Hence predict the nature and equation of the derived function for $f(x) = x^3$.

c

Consider points A and B on $y = x^3$.

i Find the gradient of the straight line segment [AB].

ii As $h \to 0$, explain what happens to:

  A the point B

  B the gradient of [AB] in **i**

  C the gradient of [AB] from a geometric point of view.

iii Deduce $f'(x)$ for $f(x) = x^3$.

4 Repeat **3** for $n = 4$, $f(x) = x^4$.

From the investigation you should have found the derived functions shown alongside:

$f(x)$	$f'(x)$
x	1
x^2	$2x$
x^3	$3x^2$
x^4	$4x^3$

THE DERIVATIVE FUNCTION $f'(x)$

Consider now the general function $y = f(x)$.

P and M are points on the curve, with P at $(x,\ f(x))$ and M at $(x + h,\ f(x + h))$.

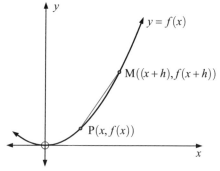

$\therefore$ the gradient of [PM] $= \dfrac{f(x + h) - f(x)}{(x + h) - x}$

$\qquad\qquad\qquad\quad = \dfrac{f(x + h) - f(x)}{h}$

As M approaches P, $h \to 0$ and the gradient of [PM] $\to$ the gradient of the tangent at P.

Thus, the gradient of the tangent at P $= \lim\limits_{h \to 0} \dfrac{f(x + h) - f(x)}{h}$.

When simplified, this limit provides a new function which is *derived* from $f(x)$. It is thus called the **derivative** of $f(x)$ and is denoted by $f'(x)$.

The **derivative** of $y = f(x)$ is $\boldsymbol{f'(x) = \lim\limits_{h \to 0} \dfrac{f(x + h) - f(x)}{h}}$.

$f'(x)$ gives the gradient of the tangent at any point on the curve with equation $y = f(x)$.

The process of finding the derivative or derived function is called **differentiation**.

When we find the derivative using limit theory, we say we are performing differentiation from **first principles**.

Example 4   ◀) **Self Tutor**

Find the derivative of the function $f(x) = x^2$.

$$
\begin{aligned}
f'(x) &= \lim_{h \to 0} \frac{f(x+h) - f(x)}{h} \\
&= \lim_{h \to 0} \frac{(x+h)^2 - x^2}{h} \\
&= \lim_{h \to 0} \frac{\cancel{x^2} + 2hx + h^2 - \cancel{x^2}}{h} \\
&= \lim_{h \to 0} \frac{\cancel{h}(2x+h)}{\cancel{h}} \\
&= \lim_{h \to 0} (2x+h) \qquad \{\text{as } h \neq 0\} \\
&= 2x
\end{aligned}
$$

Example 5   ◀) **Self Tutor**

Prove that if $f(x) = x^4$ then $f'(x) = 4x^3$.

Proof:
$$
\begin{aligned}
f'(x) &= \lim_{h \to 0} \frac{f(x+h) - f(x)}{h} \\
&= \lim_{h \to 0} \frac{(x+h)^4 - x^4}{h} \\
&= \lim_{h \to 0} \frac{\cancel{x^4} + 4x^3h + 6x^2h^2 + 4xh^3 + h^4 - \cancel{x^4}}{h} \qquad \{\text{binomial expansion}\} \\
&= \lim_{h \to 0} \frac{4x^3h + 6x^2h^2 + 4xh^3 + h^4}{h} \\
&= \lim_{h \to 0} \frac{\cancel{h}(4x^3 + 6x^2h + 4xh^2 + h^3)}{\cancel{h}} \\
&= \lim_{h \to 0} (4x^3 + 6x^2h + 4xh^2 + h^3) \qquad \{\text{as } h \neq 0\} \\
&= 4x^3
\end{aligned}
$$

EXERCISE 22D.1

1 Use limit theory to find the derivative of:

     a $f(x) = x^3$ **b** $f(x) = x^{-1}$ **c** $f(x) = x^{\frac{1}{2}} = \sqrt{x}$ **d** $f(x) = c$, a constant

2 **a** From the worked **Examples 4** and **5** and from question **1** above, copy and complete the table alongside:

     b If $f(x) = x^n$, predict a general formula for $f'(x)$.

3 Using $f'(x) = \lim_{h \to 0} \dfrac{f(x+h) - f(x)}{h}$, find the derivative of:

     a $f(x) = 2x + 3$ **b** $f(x) = 3x^2 + 5x + 1$

     c $f(x) = 2x^3 + 4x^2 + 6x - 1$

$f(x)$	$f'(x)$
x^1	
x^2	
x^3	
x^{-1}	
$x^{\frac{1}{2}}$	

4 From the results of **3**, copy and complete:

    a If $f(x) = ax + b$ then $f'(x) = \ldots\ldots$

    b If $f(x) = ax^2 + bx + c$ then $f'(x) = \ldots\ldots$

    c If $f(x) = ax^3 + bx^2 + cx + d$ then $f'(x) = \ldots\ldots$

5 Use the limit definition of $f'(x)$ to show that:

    a if $f(x) = cg(x)$ where c is a constant, then $f'(x) = cg'(x)$

    b if $f(x) = g(x) + h(x)$ then $f'(x) = g'(x) + h'(x)$.

RULES FOR DIFFERENTIATION

In **Exercise 22D.1** we derived the rules shown in the table opposite. Note that c represents a constant.

The last rule tells us that to differentiate a sum or difference, we can simply differentiate '*term by term*'.

$f(x)$	$f'(x)$
c	0
$x^n, \quad n \neq 0$	nx^{n-1}
$kx^n, \quad n \neq 0$	nkx^{n-1}
$cg(x)$	$cg'(x)$
$g(x) + h(x)$	$g'(x) + h'(x)$

Example 6   ◀) **Self Tutor**

Use the rules of differentiation to find $f'(x)$ if $f(x)$ is:

    a $x^3 + 2x^2 - 3x + 4$
        b $f(x) = \dfrac{x+4}{\sqrt{x}}$

  a $f(x) = x^3 + 2x^2 - 3x + 4$

     $\therefore \quad f'(x) = 3x^2 + 2(2x) - 3(1) + 0$

              $= 3x^2 + 4x - 3$

  b $f(x) = \dfrac{x+4}{\sqrt{x}} = \dfrac{x+4}{x^{\frac{1}{2}}} = x^{\frac{1}{2}} + 4x^{-\frac{1}{2}}$

         $\therefore \quad f'(x) = \tfrac{1}{2}x^{-\frac{1}{2}} + 4(-\tfrac{1}{2})x^{-\frac{3}{2}}$

                 $= \tfrac{1}{2}x^{-\frac{1}{2}} - 2x^{-\frac{3}{2}}$

Example 7   ◀) **Self Tutor**

Consider the curve $y = \sqrt{x}$ whose graph is drawn alongside.

    a Find the equation of the tangent at $x = 1$.

    b Find the point on $y = \sqrt{x}$ at which the tangent has gradient $\tfrac{1}{4}$.

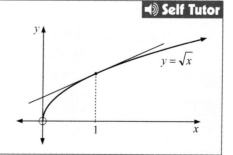

If $f(x) = \sqrt{x} = x^{\frac{1}{2}}$ then $f'(x) = \frac{1}{2}x^{-\frac{1}{2}} = \dfrac{1}{2\sqrt{x}}$

a $f(1) = 1$ and $f'(1) = \frac{1}{2}$, so the gradient at $(1, 1)$ is $\frac{1}{2}$

and the equation of the tangent is $\dfrac{y-1}{x-1} = \frac{1}{2}$

$$\therefore \quad y - 1 = \tfrac{1}{2}x - \tfrac{1}{2}$$

$$\therefore \quad y = \tfrac{1}{2}x + \tfrac{1}{2}$$

b If the gradient is $\frac{1}{4}$, then $f'(x) = \frac{1}{4}$

$$\therefore \quad \dfrac{1}{2\sqrt{x}} = \tfrac{1}{4}$$

$$\therefore \quad \sqrt{x} = 2$$

$$\therefore \quad x = 4$$

When $x = 4$, $y = \sqrt{4} = 2$, so the point of contact is $(4, 2)$.

EXERCISE 22D.2

1 Use the rules of differentiation to find $f'(x)$ for $f(x)$ equal to:

a $5x^3$
b $5x - x^2$
c $x^3 + 4x$
d $\frac{1}{2}x^4$

e $x^2 + 3$
f $x + \dfrac{1}{x}$
g $\dfrac{x+1}{x}$
h $\dfrac{x^2+5}{x}$

i $\dfrac{10}{x^2}$
j $6\sqrt{x}$
k $(x+1)(x-2)$
l $3 - \dfrac{4}{x^2}$

m $\dfrac{4}{\sqrt{x}}$
n $3x^3 - 2x - \dfrac{2}{x^2}$
o $3 - x - \dfrac{2}{\sqrt{x}}$
p $x(x+1)^2$

q $(2x-1)^2$
r $(x+2)^3$

2 Consider $f(x) = x^3 + 2x^2 - 3x + 1$

   a Find $f'(x)$.
          b Find $f(2)$ and $f'(2)$.

   c Copy and complete:
      For $f(x) = x^3 + 2x^2 - 3x + 1$, the gradient of the tangent at $(2, ...)$ is ....

3 Find the gradient of the tangent to:

   a $f(x) = 3x^2$ at $x = -1$
         b $f(x) = \dfrac{6}{x}$ at $x = 2$

   c $f(x) = x^3 + 2x + 1$ at $x = 1$
      d $f(x) = x^2 + 7x$ at $x = -2$

   e $f(x) = \dfrac{x^2+1}{x}$ at $x = 2$
      f $f(x) = \sqrt{x} + \dfrac{8}{x}$ at $x = 4$.

4 Find the equation of the tangent to $y = f(x)$ where $f(x)$ equals:

   a $x^3 + 2x$ at the point where $x = 0$
   b $\sqrt{x}$ at the point where $x = 4$

   c $2x^2 + 5x + 3$ at the point where $x = -2$

   d $x + \dfrac{2}{x}$ at the point where $x = 2$
      e $\dfrac{x^2+4}{x}$ at the point where $x = -1$.

5 Find the coordinates of the point(s) on:

    a $f(x) = x^2 + 3x + 5$ where the tangent is horizontal

    b $f(x) = \sqrt{x}$ where the tangent has gradient $\frac{1}{2}$

    c $f(x) = x^3 + x^2 - 1$ where the tangent has gradient 1

    d $f(x) = x^3 - 3x + 1$ where the tangent has gradient 9

    e $f(x) = ax^2 + bx + c$ where the tangent has zero gradient.

6 Find a if:

    a $f(x) = ax^2 + 6x - 3$ has a tangent with gradient 2 at the point where $x = -1$

    b $f(x) = \dfrac{a}{x}$ has a tangent with gradient 3 at the point where $x = 2$.

E   OPTIMISATION

Optimisation problems where we need to find a maximum or minimum value are not just restricted to problems involving quadratic functions. As quadratic optimisation cannot be used in the majority of cases, we need a more universal approach. Differential calculus provides us with a useful method.

Consider the function $y = f(x)$ alongside:

Notice that at the turning points of the graph, the gradient of the tangent is zero.

$\therefore$ $f'(x) = 0$ at the turning points.

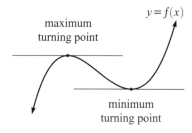

To find the maximum and minimum turning points of $y = f(x)$, we need to find x such that $f'(x) = 0$.

The method used to solve maxima-minima problems is:

    Step 1:   Draw a large, clear diagram (or diagrams) of the situation.

    Step 2:   Construct an equation with the variable to be **maximised** or **minimised** as the subject of the formula in terms of a single variable, x say.

    Step 3:   Find the **derivative** and hence find x when this derivative is **zero**. Let this value be a.

    Step 4:   Use a **sign diagram of the derivative** to show whether a maximum or minimum value occurs when $x = a$.

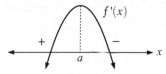

indicates a maximum turning point

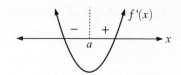

indicates a minimum turning point

Example 8 ◄⑴ Self Tutor

When a small business employs x workers to manufacture its goods, the profit made is given by $P(x) = -2x^3 + 2400x - 4000$ euros per week.

a How many employees should they use to maximise profits?

b What is the maximum profit?

a
$$P(x) = -2x^3 + 2400x - 4000 \quad \text{euros per week, and} \quad x \geqslant 0$$
$$\therefore \quad P'(x) = -6x^2 + 2400$$
So, $P'(x) = 0$ when $6x^2 = 2400$
$$\therefore \quad x^2 = 400$$
$$\therefore \quad x = \pm 20$$
But $x \geqslant 0$, so $x = 20$

Sign diagram for $P'(x)$:

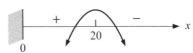

From the sign diagram, $P'(x)$ changes sign from $+$ to $-$ when $x = 20$. This indicates a maximum turning point, so the profit per week is maximised when 20 employees are used.

b As $P(20) = 28\,000$, the maximum profit per week is $28\,000$ euros.

Example 9 ◄⑴ Self Tutor

Square corners are cut from a piece of 12 cm by 12 cm tinplate which is then bent to form an open dish. What size squares should be removed to maximise the capacity of the dish?

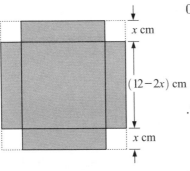

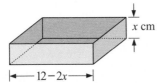

Suppose we cut out x cm by x cm squares, so $0 \leqslant x \leqslant 6$.

Capacity = length × width × depth
$$\therefore \quad V = (12 - 2x)^2 \times x$$
$$\therefore \quad V = (144 - 48x + 4x^2) \times x$$
$$\therefore \quad V = 144x - 48x^2 + 4x^3$$
$$\therefore \quad V'(x) = 144 - 96x + 12x^2$$
$$= 12(x^2 - 8x + 12)$$
$$= 12(x - 2)(x - 6)$$

which has sign diagram

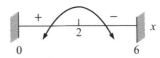

$\therefore$ the maximum capacity occurs when $x = 2$ cm
$\therefore$ we should cut out 2 cm squares.

EXERCISE 22E

1   If a business employs x workers to manufacture furniture then the profit made by the business is given by $P(x) = -3x^3 + 6084x - 5000$ dollars per week.

GRAPHING
PACKAGE

a   How many employees should the business have to maximise profit?

b   What is the maximum profit?

c   Use the graphing package to check your answers to a and b.

2   Two numbers have a sum of 10. What is the minimum value that the sum of their cubes could be?

3   What is the least possible value of the sum of a positive number and its reciprocal?

4   Answer the **Opening Problem** on page **530**.

5   A rectangle sits on the x-axis under the graph of $y = 9 - x^2$.

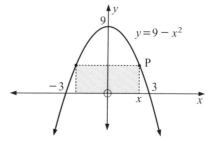

a   Find the coordinates of point P.

b   Write down a formula for the area of the rectangle in terms of x.

c   Find the maximum possible area of the rectangle.

6   A beam with a rectangular cross-section is to be cut from a log of diameter 1 m.

The strength of the beam varies in proportion to the width and to the square of the depth.

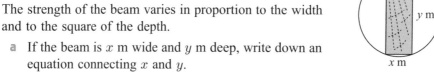

a   If the beam is x m wide and y m deep, write down an equation connecting x and y.

b   The strength S of the beam is given by the width times the square of the depth. Write down a formula for S in terms of x only.

c   Find the dimensions of the strongest possible beam that can be cut from the log.

7   An open rectangular box has a square base, and its outer surface area must be 108 cm^2.

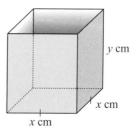

a   Find an equation connecting x and y.

b   Write y in terms of x.

c   Find a formula for the capacity C in terms of x only.

d   What size must the base be in order to maximise the capacity?

8   The slant edge of a cone has length 12 cm. If the cone has height x cm, find:

a   an expression for the volume of the cone in terms of x

b   the value of x for which the cone has the maximum possible volume.

Click on the demo icon to see the changing shape of the cone and how it affects the volume.

DEMO

F   AREAS UNDER CURVES

INVESTIGATION 2   THE AREA UNDER $y = x^2$ FROM $x = 0$ TO $x = 1$

Consider the area A under the curve $y = x^2$ and above the x-axis from $x = 0$ to $x = 1$. The region is shaded in the diagram alongside.

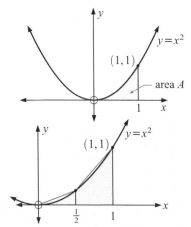

What to do:

1 Explain why $A < \frac{1}{2}$ units^2.

2 Use the graph alongside to explain why $A < \frac{3}{8}$.

3 Subdivide the interval $0 \leqslant x \leqslant 1$ into 3, 4, and then 5 equal parts, finding an upper bound for A in each case.

4 Consider the upper bounds for A found in **1**, **2** and **3**. These numbers are approaching the actual value of A. Can you predict what this is?

From the **Investigation** above, you may have guessed that the area under the curve $y = x^2$ and above the x-axis from $x = 0$ to $x = 1$ is $\frac{1}{3}$ units^2.

To prove that this is the case, we can use our knowledge of limit theory. We will also need a formula we saw in **Chapter 13**: $1^2 + 2^2 + 3^2 + \ldots\ldots + n^2 = \dfrac{n(n+1)(2n+1)}{6}$.

Consider a more general case where we want to find the area under $y = x^2$ and above the x-axis from $x = 0$ to $x = a$.

We subdivide the interval $0 \leqslant x \leqslant a$ into n equal intervals of width h units, so $a = nh$.

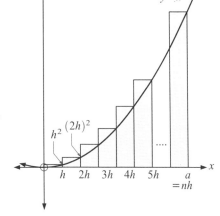

We draw rectangular strips on each interval with height equal to the value of the function at the right hand side of the interval. The sum of the areas of the rectangles will therefore overestimate the required area. However, in the limit as h approaches zero, the rectangles will give the area exactly.

The sum of the areas of the rectangles is

$$S = h(h^2) + h(2h)^2 + h(3h)^2 + \ldots\ldots + h(nh)^2$$
$$= h^3(1^2 + 2^2 + 3^2 + \ldots\ldots + n^2)$$
$$= \left(\frac{a}{n}\right)^3 \frac{n(n+1)(2n+1)}{6} \qquad \{\text{using formula}\}$$

DEMO

$$\therefore \quad S = \frac{a^3}{6} \left(\frac{n+1}{n} \right) \left(\frac{2n+1}{n} \right)$$

$$= \frac{a^3}{6} \left(1 + \frac{1}{n} \right) \left(2 + \frac{1}{n} \right)$$

As $h \to 0$, n becomes infinitely large. We write this as $n \to \infty$.

At the same time, $\dfrac{1}{n} \to 0$, so $\displaystyle\lim_{n \to \infty} S = \dfrac{a^3}{6}(1)(2) = \dfrac{a^3}{3}$.

So, the area under $y = x^2$ and above the x-axis from $x = 0$ to $x = a$, is $\dfrac{a^3}{3}$ units^2.

When $a = 1$, we see the area is $\frac{1}{3}$ units^2, as you may have predicted from the **Investigation**.

EXERCISE 22F

1 Consider the area under $y = x^3$ and above the x-axis from $x = 0$ to $x = a$.

    a Sketch $y = x^3$ and divide the interval into n subdivisions as for $y = x^2$ above.

    b Write down the sum of the areas of the strips which overestimates the required area.

    c Use the formula $1^3 + 2^3 + 3^3 + \ldots\ldots + n^3 = \dfrac{n^2(n+1)^2}{4}$ to show that the sum

       of the areas of the strips is $\dfrac{a^4}{4} \left(1 + \dfrac{1}{n} \right)^2$.

    d Hence, find the exact area under the curve.

2 Find the shaded area:

    a
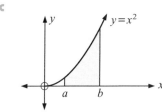

    b
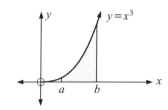

    c

    d

3 Using the results of **2** above, predict these areas:

    a
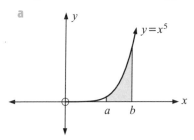

    b
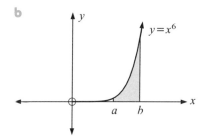

G | INTEGRATION

The table below summarises the results obtained in **Exercise 22F**.

Function	Area
$y = 1$	$b - a$
$y = x$	$\dfrac{b^2}{2} - \dfrac{a^2}{2}$
$y = x^2$	$\dfrac{b^3}{3} - \dfrac{a^3}{3}$
$y = x^3$	$\dfrac{b^4}{4} - \dfrac{a^4}{4}$

Looking carefully at the results, you may be able to see a pattern.

For example, in this case both terms are of the form $\dfrac{x^3}{3}$.

Notice that the derivative of $\dfrac{x^3}{3}$ is $\dfrac{3x^2}{3} = x^2$, which was the original function.

Check that this pattern holds for the other functions in the table.

From this observation, we conclude that to make finding areas easier, we need a process that is the reverse of differentiation. We call such a process **anti-differentiation** or **integration**.

> **Integration** is the reverse process of differentiation.

Unlike differentiation, when we integrate we do not obtain a unique answer. For example, we know the derivative of $\frac{1}{3}x^3$ is x^2, but the derivatives of $\frac{1}{3}x^3 - 1$, $\frac{1}{3}x^3 + 10$ and $\frac{1}{3}x^3 - 5$ are all also x^2.

In fact, all functions of the form $\frac{1}{3}x^3 + c$ where c is any real number constant, have the derivative x^2.

We say that $\frac{1}{3}x^3 + c$ is the integral of x^2 and write $\int x^2 dx = \frac{1}{3}x^3 + c$.

$\int x^2 dx$ reads "the integral of x^2 with respect to x".

In general, if $F(x)$ and $f(x)$ are functions such that $F'(x) = f(x)$ then

- $f(x)$ is the **derivative** of $F(x)$ and
- $F(x)$ is the **integral** or **anti-derivative** of $f(x)$.

$\int f(x) dx$ reads "the integral of $f(x)$ with respect to x".

If $\boldsymbol{F'(x) = f(x)}$ then $\int \boldsymbol{f(x) dx = F(x) + c}$.

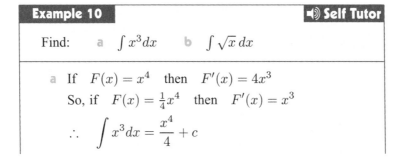

Example 10　　　　　　　　　　　　　🔊 **Self Tutor**

Find:　　a $\int x^3 dx$　　b $\int \sqrt{x}\, dx$

a　If $F(x) = x^4$ then $F'(x) = 4x^3$

So, if $F(x) = \frac{1}{4}x^4$ then $F'(x) = x^3$

$\therefore \int x^3 dx = \dfrac{x^4}{4} + c$

> **b** $\sqrt{x} = x^{\frac{1}{2}}$,   so we try $F(x) = x^{\frac{3}{2}}$
>
> If $F(x) = x^{\frac{3}{2}}$ then $F'(x) = \frac{3}{2}x^{\frac{1}{2}}$
>
> So, if $F(x) = \frac{2}{3}x^{\frac{3}{2}}$ then $F'(x) = \frac{2}{3} \times \frac{3}{2}x^{\frac{1}{2}} = x^{\frac{1}{2}}$
>
> $\therefore \quad \int \sqrt{x}\,dx = \frac{2}{3}x^{\frac{3}{2}} + c$

EXERCISE 22G.1

1 **a** Use the 'trial and error' approach of **Example 10** to find:

     i $\int x\,dx$ **ii** $\int x^2\,dx$ **iii** $\int x^6\,dx$ **iv** $\int x^{-2}\,dx$

   b Predict a formula for $\int x^n\,dx$.

   c Does this formula work for $n = -1$?

2 **a** Find:

     i $\int(5x^2 + 4x)dx$ **ii** $5\int x^2 dx + 4\int x\,dx$

   b Can you draw any conclusions from your results?

3 Find $\int k\,dx$ where k is a constant.

RULES FOR INTEGRATION

From the results in the exercise above, we observe the following rules:

- $\int \boldsymbol{k\,dx = kx + c}$ $\{k$ a constant$\}$

- $\int \boldsymbol{x^n\,dx = \dfrac{x^{n+1}}{n+1} + c}$ $\{n \neq -1\}$

- $\int \boldsymbol{k\,f(x)\,dx = k\int f(x)\,dx}$ $\{k$ a constant$\}$

- $\int \boldsymbol{[f(x) \pm g(x)]dx = \int f(x)\,dx \pm \int g(x)\,dx}$

Example 11	◀)) **Self Tutor**

Integrate: **a** $x^3 + 3x + 4$ **b** $(x^2 - 4)^2$ **c** $\dfrac{4}{\sqrt{x}}$

a $\displaystyle\int (x^3 + 3x + 4)dx$ **b** $\displaystyle\int (x^2 - 4)^2\,dx$

$= \displaystyle\int x^3 dx + \int 3x\,dx + \int 4\,dx$ $= \displaystyle\int (x^4 - 8x^2 + 16)dx$

$= \dfrac{x^4}{4} + \dfrac{3x^2}{2} + 4x + c$ $= \dfrac{x^5}{5} - \dfrac{8x^3}{3} + 16x + c$

c $\int \dfrac{4}{\sqrt{x}}\,dx = \int 4x^{-\frac{1}{2}}\,dx = \dfrac{4 \times x^{\frac{1}{2}}}{\frac{1}{2}} + c = 8\sqrt{x} + c$

EXERCISE 22G.2

1 Integrate:

    a $x^2 + 3x - 2$ **b** $x^3 - x$ **c** $5\sqrt{x}$ **d** $3x^2$

    e $\dfrac{1}{x^2}$ **f** $x^2 + \dfrac{1}{\sqrt{x}}$ **g** $2x^3 + 3x - \dfrac{4}{x^2}$ **h** $\dfrac{x^4 - 3x + 4}{x^3}$

    i $\dfrac{x^2 - 2}{\sqrt{x}}$ **j** $(2 - x)^2$ **k** $(2x + 1)^2$ **l** $(x + 2)^3$

H | THE DEFINITE INTEGRAL

If $F(x) = \int f(x)\,dx$ then the **definite integral** of $f(x)$ on the interval $a \leqslant x \leqslant b$ is

$$\int_a^b f(x)\,dx = F(b) - F(a).$$

We often write $F(b) - F(a)$ as $[F(x)]_a^b$.

If $f(x) \geqslant 0$ on the interval $a \leqslant x \leqslant b$ then the definite integral $\int_a^b f(x)\,dx$ will give the **area under the curve** and above the x-axis from $x = a$ to $x = b$.

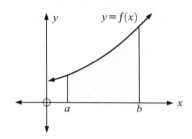

For example, we saw earlier that if $f(x) = x^2$ then the area under the curve and above the x-axis from $x = a$ to $x = b$ is $\dfrac{b^3}{3} - \dfrac{a^3}{3}$.

This can be written as $F(b) - F(a)$ or $[F(x)]_a^b$ where $F(x) = \dfrac{x^3}{3}$, and indeed $\dfrac{x^3}{3}$ is an anti-derivative of x^2.

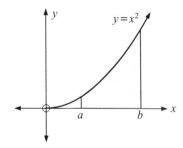

Example 12   ◀◈ **Self Tutor**

Evaluate: **a** $\int_1^2 x^2\,dx$ **b** $\int_1^4 (2\sqrt{x} + 5)\,dx$

a $\displaystyle\int_1^2 x^2\,dx = \left[\dfrac{x^3}{3}\right]_1^2$

$\qquad\qquad\quad = \left(\dfrac{2^3}{3}\right) - \left(\dfrac{1^3}{3}\right)$

$\qquad\qquad\quad = \dfrac{8}{3} - \dfrac{1}{3}$

$\qquad\qquad\quad = \dfrac{7}{3}$

$\qquad\qquad\quad = 2\tfrac{1}{3}$

b $\displaystyle\int_1^4 (2\sqrt{x} + 5)\,dx = \int_1^4 (2x^{\frac{1}{2}} + 5)\,dx$

$\qquad\qquad\qquad\qquad = \left[\dfrac{2x^{\frac{3}{2}}}{\frac{3}{2}} + 5x\right]_1^4$

$\qquad\qquad\qquad\qquad = \left[\tfrac{4}{3}x\sqrt{x} + 5x\right]_1^4$

$\qquad\qquad\qquad\qquad = \left(\tfrac{32}{3} + 20\right) - \left(\tfrac{4}{3} + 5\right)$

$\qquad\qquad\qquad\qquad = 24\tfrac{1}{3}$

Example 13   ◀)) **Self Tutor**

Find the area bounded by $y = x^2$,   the x-axis, $x = 1$ and $x = 2$.

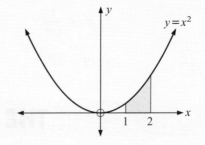

$x^2 > 0$ for all $x \in [1, 2]$

$\therefore$ Area $= \int_1^2 x^2 \, dx$

$\qquad = \left[\dfrac{x^3}{3} \right]_1^2$

$\qquad = \dfrac{8}{3} - \dfrac{1}{3}$

$\qquad = 2\frac{1}{3}$ units^2

EXERCISE 22H

1 Evaluate:

  a $\int_2^5 x \, dx$ **b** $\int_1^3 (2x + 4) \, dx$ **c** $\int_{-1}^2 (x^2 + 3) \, dx$

  d $\int_1^6 (2 - x) \, dx$ **e** $\int_1^4 \sqrt{x} \, dx$ **f** $\displaystyle\int_4^9 \frac{4}{\sqrt{x}} \, dx$

2 Evaluate:

  a $\displaystyle\int_1^4 \left(\sqrt{x} - \frac{1}{\sqrt{x}} \right) dx$ **b** $\displaystyle\int_0^2 (2x + 3)^2 \, dx$ **c** $\displaystyle\int_{-2}^{-1} \frac{x^2 + 4}{x^2} \, dx$

  d $\displaystyle\int_{-1}^1 (x^3 - x) \, dx$ **e** $\displaystyle\int_4^9 \frac{\sqrt{x} - x^2}{x} \, dx$ **f** $\displaystyle\int_1^2 (x + 2)^3 \, dx$

3 Find the area bounded by:

  a $y = x^2$, the x-axis, $x = 1$ and $x = 3$

  b $y = \sqrt{x}$, the x-axis, $x = 1$ and $x = 4$

  c $y = 4x - x^2$ and the x-axis

  d $y = x\sqrt{x}$, the x-axis, $x = 1$ and $x = 9$

  e $y = x^3 + 1$, the x-axis, $x = 0$ and $x = 2$

  f $y = 2x^2 + 3x + 1$, the x-axis, $x = 2$ and $x = 4$

  g $y = \dfrac{1}{x^2}$, the x-axis, $x = \frac{1}{2}$ and $x = 2\frac{1}{2}$

  h $y = \dfrac{4}{\sqrt{x}}$, the x-axis, $x = 1$ and $x = 4$.

LINKS
click here

ARCHIMEDES' NESTED CYLINDER, HEMISPHERE AND CONE

Areas of interaction:
Approaches to learning/Human ingenuity

REVIEW SET 22A

1 Find, using the limit method, the slope of the tangent to $y = \dfrac{4}{x}$ at $(-2, -2)$.

2 Find, from the limit definition $f'(x) = \displaystyle\lim_{h \to 0} \dfrac{f(x+h) - f(x)}{h}$, the derivative function of $f(x) = x^2 - 2x$.

3 Use the rules of differentiation to find $f'(x)$ for $f(x)$ equal to:

    a $7x^3$
    b $3x^2 - x^3$
    c $(2x - 3)^2$
    d $\dfrac{7x^3 + 2x^4}{x^2}$

4 Consider the function $y = \dfrac{4}{x}$.

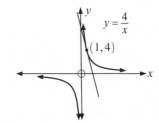

    a Find the equation of the tangent to the curve at the point $(1, 4)$.

    b Find the points on $y = \dfrac{4}{x}$ at which the tangent has slope $-\frac{1}{2}$.

5   A rectangular gutter is formed by bending a 24 cm wide sheet of metal as illustrated. Find the dimensions of the gutter which maximise the water capacity.

    ←————24 cm————→

6 A 200 m fence is to be placed around a lawn which has the shape of a rectangle with a semi-circle on one of its sides.

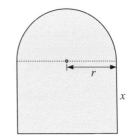

    a Find the expression for the perimeter of the lawn in terms of r and x.

    b Find x in terms of r.

    c Show that the area of the lawn A can be written as $A = 200r - r^2 \left(2 + \frac{\pi}{2}\right)$.

    d Find the dimensions of the lawn such that its area is a maximum.

7 Integrate with respect to x:

    a $\sqrt{x}(1 - x)$
    b $(x^2 + 5)^2$
    c $-\dfrac{1}{x^3}$
    d $\dfrac{(x - 1)^2}{\sqrt{x}}$

8 Find:

    a $\int x^3 + 3x^2 - 1\,dx$
    b $\int x\sqrt{x}\,dx$
    c $\displaystyle\int \left(x - \dfrac{1}{x}\right)^2 dx$

9 Evaluate:

    a $\displaystyle\int_{-1}^{2} (2x + 1)\,dx$
    b $\displaystyle\int_{1}^{2} \left(x - \dfrac{1}{\sqrt{x}}\right) dx$
    c $\displaystyle\int_{1}^{2} \dfrac{(x + 1)^2}{\sqrt{x}}\,dx$

10 Find the area of the region bounded by $y = x^2$, the x-axis, and $x = 2$.

11 Find the area of the finite region bounded by $y = -2(x+1)(x-3)$ and the x-axis.

REVIEW SET 22B

1 Use the rules of differentiation to find $f'(x)$ for $f(x)$ equal to:

    a $\sqrt{x}$ **b** $(2x-1)^3$ **c** $\dfrac{1}{x} - \dfrac{4}{x^2}$ **d** $\dfrac{2x+1}{\sqrt{x}}$

2 Use the definition $f'(x) = \lim\limits_{h\to 0} \dfrac{f(x+h) - f(x)}{h}$ to show that if $f(x) = x^3$ then $f'(x) = 3x^2$.

3 Find the equation of the tangent to $y = x^3 - 3x + 5$ at the point where $x = 2$.

4 Find all points on the curve $y = \dfrac{2x+1}{\sqrt{x}}$ which have a tangent parallel to the x-axis.

5 An open box is made by cutting squares out of the corners of a 36 cm by 36 cm square sheet of tinplate. What is the size of the squares that should be removed if the capacity is to be a maximum?

6 A sheet of poster paper is to have a total area of 1 m². A 10 cm margin is to be left blank at the top and bottom, and a 5 cm margin is to be left blank at each side.

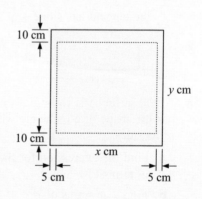

    a Show that $y = \dfrac{10\,000}{x}$.

    b Find an expression for the printing area A, in terms of x and y.

    c Show that the printing area $A = 10\,200 - 20x - \dfrac{100\,000}{x}$.

    d Find the dimensions of the paper such that the printing area is maximised.

7 Integrate with respect to x:

    a $x^2 - 2x + 4$ **b** -3 **c** $3x^2 + \dfrac{4}{x^2}$ **d** $2x - \dfrac{1}{\sqrt{x}}$

8 Find:

    a $\int x^2(2x-1)\,dx$ **b** $\displaystyle\int \dfrac{(x-2)^2}{\sqrt{x}}\,dx$ **c** $\int(1-x)^3\,dx$

9 Evaluate:

    a $\int_0^1 x^2\,dx$ **b** $\int_0^2 (x^2 - x)\,dx$ **c** $\int_4^9 \sqrt{x}\,dx$

10 Find the area of the region bounded by the x-axis and the part of $y = 6 + x - x^2$ which lies above the x-axis.

11

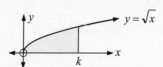

The shaded region has area 5 units².
Find k correct to 3 decimal places.

Chapter 23

Counting and probability

Click on the icon to access this printable chapter

Contents:

Chapter 24

Click on the icon to access this printable chapter

Locus

Contents:

Chapter **25**

Click on the icon to access this printable chapter

Networks

Contents:

EXERCISE 1A

1 **a** true **b** true **c** true **d** true
e false **f** false **g** true **h** true

2 **a, b, c, d, f, g, h** are rational; **e** is irrational

3 **a** $S = \{1, 2, 3, 6\}$ **b** $S = \{6, 12, 18, 24, ...\}$
c $S = \{1, 17\}$ **d** $S = \{17, 34, 51, 68, ...\}$
e $S = \{2, 3, 5, 7, 11, 13, 17, 19\}$
f $S = \{12, 14, 15, 16, 18, 20, 21, 22, 24, 25, 26, 27, 28\}$

4 **a** 4 **b** is infinite **c** 2 **d** is infinite **e** 8 **f** 13

5 **a** $0.\overline{7} = \frac{7}{9}$ **b** $0.\overline{41} = \frac{41}{99}$ **c** $0.\overline{324} = \frac{12}{37}$

6 **a** 0.527 can be written as $\frac{527}{1000}$, and 527, 1000 are integers
b $0.\overline{9} = 1$

7 **a** e.g., $\sqrt{2} + (-\sqrt{2}) = 0$ which is rational
b e.g., $\sqrt{2} \times \sqrt{50} = \sqrt{100} = 10$ which is rational

EXERCISE 1B

1 **a** The set of all real x such that x is greater than 4.
b The set of all real x such that x is less than or equal to 5.
c The set of all real y such that y lies between 0 and 8.
d The set of all real x such that x lies between 1 and 4 or is equal to 1 or 4.
e The set of all real t such that t lies between 2 and 7.
f The set of all real n such that n is less than or equal to 3 or n is greater than 6.

2 **a** $\{x \mid x > 3\}$ **b** $\{x \mid 2 < x \leqslant 5\}$
c $\{x \mid x \leqslant -1 \text{ or } x \geqslant 2\}$ **d** $\{x \mid -1 \leqslant x < 5, x \in \mathbb{Z}\}$
e $\{x \mid 0 \leqslant x \leqslant 6, x \in \mathbb{N}\}$ **f** $\{x \mid x < 0\}$

3 **a** **b**

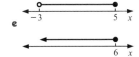

c **d**

e **f**

EXERCISE 1C

1 **a**
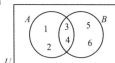
$A = \{2, 3, 5, 7\}$
b $A' = \{1, 4, 6, 8\}$

2 **a**
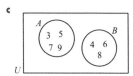

b $V' = \{b, c, d, f, g, h, j, k, l, m, n, p, q, r, s, t, v, w, x, y, z\}$

3 **a** **i** $U = \{1, 2, 3, 4, 5, 6, 7, 8, 9, 10\}$
ii $N = \{3, 8\}$ **iii** $M = \{1, 3, 4, 7, 8\}$
b $n(N) = 2$, $n(M) = 5$ **c** No, $N \subseteq M$.

4 **a**

b

c

5 **a/b**
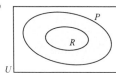

c **i** true
ii true
iii true

d (shaded section of diagram alongside)

6 **a**
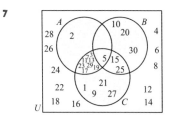
b

7

EXERCISE 1D.1

1 **a** **i** $C = \{1, 3, 7, 9\}$ **ii** $D = \{1, 2, 5\}$
iii $U = \{1, 2, 3, 4, 5, 6, 7, 8, 9\}$ **iv** $C \cap D = \{1\}$
v $C \cup D = \{1, 2, 3, 5, 7, 9\}$
b **i** $n(C) = 4$ **ii** $n(D) = 3$ **iii** $n(U) = 9$
iv $n(C \cap D) = 1$ **v** $n(C \cup D) = 6$

2 **a** **i** $A = \{2, 7\}$ **ii** $B = \{1, 2, 4, 6, 7\}$
iii $U = \{1, 2, 3, 4, 5, 6, 7, 8\}$ **iv** $A \cap B = \{2, 7\}$
v $A \cup B = \{1, 2, 4, 6, 7\}$
b **i** $n(A) = 2$ **ii** $n(B) = 5$ **iii** $n(U) = 8$
iv $n(A \cap B) = 2$ **v** $n(A \cup B) = 5$

3 **a**

b **i** $A \cap B = \{2, 9, 11\}$
ii $A \cup B = \{1, 2, 7, 9, 10, 11, 12\}$
iii $B' = \{3, 4, 5, 6, 7, 8, 10\}$
c **i** $n(A) = 5$ **ii** $n(B') = 7$
iii $n(A \cap B) = 3$ **iv** $n(A \cup B) = 7$

4 **a** $A \cap B = \{1, 3, 9\}$

b $A \cup B = \{1, 2, 3, 4, 6, 7, 9, 12, 18, 21, 36, 63\}$

5 **a** $X \cap Y = \{$B, M, T, Z$\}$
  b $X \cup Y = \{$A, B, C, D, M, N, P, R, T, W, Z$\}$

6 **a** **i** $n(A) = 8$ **ii** $n(B) = 10$
  iii $n(A \cap B) = 3$ **iv** $n(A \cup B) = 15$
  b $n(A) + n(B) - n(A \cap B) = 8 + 10 - 3 = 15 = n(A \cup B)$

7 **a** $n(A) + n(B) - n(A \cap B) = (a+b) + (b+c) - b$
  $= a + b + c = n(A \cup B)$
  b $A \cap B = \varnothing, \ \therefore \ n(A \cap B) = 0$

8 **a** $\varnothing$ **b** U **c** $\varnothing$

EXERCISE 1D.2

1 **a** not in A - shaded pink   **b** in both A and B

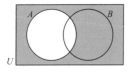 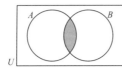

c $A \cap B'$ **d** in either A or B

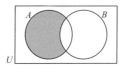 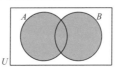

e $A \cup B'$ **f** $(A \cup B)'$

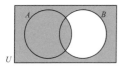 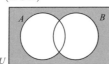

g $(A \cap B)'$ **h** in exactly one of A or B

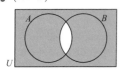 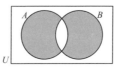

2 **a** in X but not in Y
  b the complement of 'in exactly one of X and Y'
  c in exactly two or three of X, Y and Z

3 **a** A' **b** $A' \cap B$

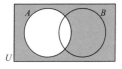 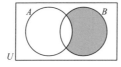

c $A \cup B'$ **d** $A' \cap B'$

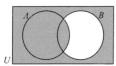 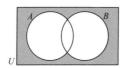

4 **a** A **b** B'

c $B \cap C$ **d** $A \cup C$

e $A \cap B \cap C$ **f** $(A \cup B) \cap C$

5 **a**

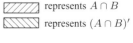

represents $A \cap B$
represents $(A \cap B)'$

represents A'
represents B'
whole shaded region is $A' \cup B'$

b

represents $B \cap C$
represents A
whole shaded region represents
$A \cup (B \cap C)$

represents $A \cup B$
represents $A \cup C$
represents
$(A \cup B) \cap (A \cup C)$

c

represents A
represents $B \cup C$
represents $A \cap (B \cup C)$

represents $A \cap B$
represents $A \cap C$
whole shaded region represents
$(A \cap B) \cup (A \cap C)$

EXERCISE 1E

1 **a** 18 **b** 2 **c** 17 **d** 12
2 **a** 75 **b** 9 **c** 24 **d** 42
3

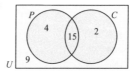

a 15   **b** 21
c 4   **d** 6
e 9

4 a 19 **b** 20 **c** 32 **d** 25 **e** 13

5 10 play both **6 a** 18 **b** 38 **7 a** 22 **b** 18

8 a 15 **b** 14 **c** 8 **9** 200 families had both

10 a 65% **b** 35% **c** 22% **d** 28% **e** 9%

11 11 violin players **15 a** 15 students

12 at least 24 places **b** 55 students

13 43%

14 14 members

16 The number who participate in all three sports must be less than or equal to 30.

EXERCISE 1F

1 a

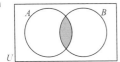

$A \cap B = B \cap A$
The common area
is the same.

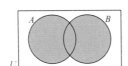

$A \cup B = B \cup A$
The combined area
is the same.

b

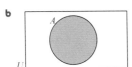

$A \cap A = A$
$A \cup A = A$

The intersection is the area common to both $= A$.
The union is the total area in both $= A$.

c

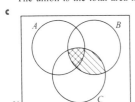

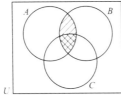

☐ represents $B \cap C$
☒ represents $A \cap (B \cap C)$

☐ represents $A \cap B$
☒ represents $(A \cap B) \cap C$

Area shaded is the same in each case.

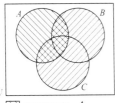

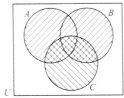

☐ represents A
☐ represents $B \cup C$
whole shaded region
represents $A \cup (B \cup C)$

☐ represents C
☐ represents $A \cup B$
whole shaded region
represents $(A \cup B) \cup C$

Total shaded area is the same in each case.

d

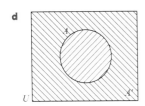

☐ represents A
☐ represents A'
A and A' are the complement
of each other. When com-
bined, they make up the universal set U,
i.e., $(A')' = A$.

1 a 1.3 can be written as $\frac{13}{10}$, and 13, 10 are integers

  b false **c** $\{23, 29, 31, 37\}$

  d The set of all real t such that t lies between -1 and 3, including -1.

  e $\{x \mid 0 < x \leqslant 5\}$ **f**

2 a

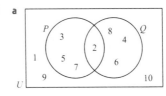

  b $A' = \{1, 2, 4, 5, 7, 8, 10, 11\}$ **c** $n(A') = 8$ **d** false

3 a false **b** false

4 a i $A = \{1, 2, 3, 4, 5\}$ **ii** $B = \{1, 2, 7\}$

  iii $U = \{1, 2, 3, 4, 5, 6, 7\}$

  iv $A \cup B = \{1, 2, 3, 4, 5, 7\}$ **v** $A \cap B = \{1, 2\}$

  b i $n(A) = 5$ **ii** $n(B) = 3$ **iii** $n(A \cup B) = 6$

5 a

  b i $P \cap Q = \{2\}$ **ii** $P \cup Q = \{2, 3, 4, 5, 6, 7, 8\}$

  iii $Q' = \{1, 3, 5, 7, 9, 10\}$

  c i $n(P') = 6$ **ii** $n(P \cap Q) = 1$ **iii** $n(P \cup Q) = 7$

  d true

6 a shaded region is the complement of X, i.e., everything not in X

  b shaded region represents 'in exactly one of X or Y but not both'

  c shaded region represents everything in X or in neither set

1 a false **b** false **c** $0.\overline{51} = \frac{51}{99}$, and 51, 99 are integers

  d $\{t \mid t \leqslant -3 \text{ or } t > 4\}$ **e**

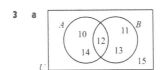

2

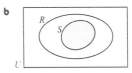

3 a   **b**

  Image

4 a $A \cap B = \{1, 2, 3, 6\}$

  b $A \cup B = \{1, 2, 3, 4, 6, 8, 9, 12, 18, 24\}$

5 a

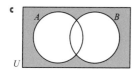

b

c

6

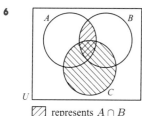

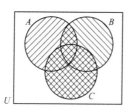

▨ represents $A \cap B$
▩ represents C

whole shaded region
represents $(A \cap B) \cup C$

▨ represents $A \cup C$
▩ represents $B \cup C$
▩ represents
$(A \cup C) \cap (B \cup C)$

Area shaded is the same in each case.

EXERCISE 2A

1 a $6x + 15$ **b** $4x^2 - 12x$ **c** $-6 - 2x$ **d** $-3x^2 - 3xy$
e $2x^3 - 2x$ **f** $x^3 - x$ **g** $a^2b - ab^2$ **h** $x^3 - 3x^2$

2 a $7x - 14$ **b** $-5x - 6$ **c** $4x - x^2$ **d** $2x^3$
e $a^2 + b^2$ **f** $x^5 - 3x^4 + 2x^3$

3 a $x^2 + 7x + 10$ **b** $x^2 + x - 12$ **c** $x^2 + 2x - 15$
d $x^2 - 12x + 20$ **e** $2x^2 - 5x - 3$ **f** $6x^2 - 23x + 20$
g $2x^2 - xy - y^2$ **h** $-2x^2 - 7x - 3$ **i** $-x^2 - x - 2xy - 2y$

4 a $x^2 - 49$ **b** $9 - a^2$ **c** $25 - x^2$ **d** $4x^2 - 1$
e $16 - 9y^2$ **f** $9x^2 - 16z^2$

5 a $x^2 + 10x + 25$ **b** $4x^2 + 12x + 9$ **c** $x^2 + 2xy + y^2$
d $9x^2 + 24x + 16$ **e** $25 + 10x^2 + x^4$ **f** $9x^2 + 12xz + 4z^2$

6 a $x^2 - 6x + 9$ **b** $4 - 4x + x^2$ **c** $9x^2 - 6x + 1$
d $x^2 - 2xy + y^2$ **e** $4x^2 - 20xy + 25y^2$ **f** $a^2b^2 - 4ab + 4$

EXERCISE 2B

1 a $3(x - 3)$ **b** $2x(x + 3)$ **c** $2x(2 - y)$
d $3b(a - 2)$ **e** $2x^2(1 + 4x)$ **f** $6x(2 - x)$
g $x(x^2 + 2)$ **h** $x^2(x + 1)$ **i** $2x^2(1 - 2x)$

2 a $(x + 5)(3 + x)$ **b** $(b + 3)(a - 5)$ **c** $(x + 4)(x + 1)$
d $(x + 2)(2x + 5)$ **e** $(c - d)(a + b)$ **f** $(2 + y)(y - 1)$
g $(x - 1)(ab + c)$ **h** $(x + 2)(a - 1)$

3 a $(x + 4)(x - 4)$ **b** $(8 + x)(8 - x)$ **c** $(3x + 1)(3x - 1)$
d $(7 + 2x)(7 - 2x)$ **e** $(y + 2x)(y - 2x)$
f $(2a + 5b)(2a - 5b)$ **g** $(9x + 4y)(9x - 4y)$
h $(2x^2 + y)(2x^2 - y)$ **i** $(3ab + 4)(3ab - 4)$

4 a $2(x + 2)(x - 2)$ **b** $3(y + 3)(y - 3)$ **c** $2(1 + 3x)(1 - 3x)$
d $x(2 + 3x)(2 - 3x)$ **e** $ab(a + b)(a - b)$
f $(5 + xy)(5 - xy)$ **g** $b(3b + 2)(3b - 2)$
h $(2xy + 1)(2xy - 1)$ **i** $(x^2 + y^2)(x + y)(x - y)$

5 a $(x + 2)^2$ **b** $(x - 5)^2$ **c** $(3x + 5)^2$ **d** $(x - 4)^2$
e $(2x + 7)^2$ **f** $(x - 10)^2$

6 a $-(3x - 1)^2$ **b** $3(x + 3)^2$ **c** $-2(3x - 1)^2$
d $2(x + 5)(x - 5)$ **e** $2(x - 4)^2$ **f** $-3(x + 3)^2$

EXERCISE 2C

1 a $x^3 + 3x^2 + 6x + 8$ **b** $x^3 + 5x^2 + 3x - 9$
c $x^3 + 5x^2 + 7x + 3$ **d** $2x^3 + x^2 - 6x - 5$
e $2x^3 + 7x^2 + 8x + 3$ **f** $2x^3 - 9x^2 + 4x + 15$
g $3x^3 + 14x^2 - x + 20$ **h** $8x^3 - 14x^2 + 7x - 1$

2 a $x^3 + 6x^2 + 8x$ **b** $x^3 - x^2 - 6x$ **c** $x^3 - 9x^2 + 20x$
d $2x^3 + 14x^2 + 20x$ **e** $-3x^3 + 15x^2 - 18x$
f $x^3 - 4x^2 - 12x$ **g** $-9x^3 - 33x^2 + 12x$
h $-10x^3 - 13x^2 + 3x$ **i** $x^3 - 3x^2 - 4x + 12$

3 a $x^3 + 9x^2 + 26x + 24$ **b** $x^3 - x^2 - 14x + 24$
c $x^3 - 10x^2 + 31x - 30$ **d** $2x^3 + x^2 - 12x + 9$
e $3x^3 + 14x^2 + 21x + 10$ **f** $12x^3 + 11x^2 - 2x - 1$
g $-3x^3 + 26x^2 - 33x - 14$ **h** $-3x^3 + 16x^2 - 12x - 16$

4 a 4 **b** 6 **c** 6 **d** 9 **e** 8 **f** 12 **g** 8 **h** 12

EXERCISE 2D

1 a $x^3 + 3x^2 + 3x + 1$ **b** $x^3 + 9x^2 + 27x + 27$
c $x^3 + 12x^2 + 48x + 64$ **d** $x^3 + 3x^2y + 3xy^2 + y^3$
e $x^3 - 3x^2 + 3x - 1$ **f** $x^3 - 15x^2 + 75x - 125$
g $x^3 - 12x^2 + 48x - 64$ **h** $x^3 - 3x^2y + 3xy^2 - y^3$
i $8 + 12y + 6y^2 + y^3$ **j** $8x^3 + 12x^2 + 6x + 1$
k $27x^3 + 27x^2 + 9x + 1$ **l** $8y^3 + 36y^2 + 54x^2y + 27x^3$
m $8 - 12y + 6y^2 - y^3$ **n** $8x^3 - 12x^2 + 6x - 1$
o $27x^3 - 27x^2 + 9x - 1$ **p** $8y^3 - 36xy^2 + 54x^2y - 27x^3$

2 $(a + b)^4 = a^4 + 4a^3b + 6a^2b^2 + 4ab^3 + b^4$

3 a $x^4 + 4x^3y + 6x^2y^2 + 4xy^3 + y^4$
b $x^4 + 4x^3 + 6x^2 + 4x + 1$
c $x^4 + 8x^3 + 24x^2 + 32x + 16$
d $x^4 + 12x^3 + 54x^2 + 108x + 81$
e $x^4 - 4x^3y + 6x^2y^2 - 4xy^3 + y^4$
f $x^4 - 4x^3 + 6x^2 - 4x + 1$
g $x^4 - 8x^3 + 24x^2 - 32x + 16$
h $16x^4 - 32x^3 + 24x^2 - 8x + 1$

4 a $\quad 1 \quad 5 \quad 10 \quad 10 \quad 5 \quad 1$
$\qquad 1 \quad 6 \quad 15 \quad 20 \quad 15 \quad 6 \quad 1$
b i $a^5 + 5a^4b + 10a^3b^2 + 10a^2b^3 + 5ab^4 + b^5$
ii $a^5 - 5a^4b + 10a^3b^2 - 10a^2b^3 + 5ab^4 - b^5$
iii $a^6 + 6a^5b + 15a^4b^2 + 20a^3b^3 + 15a^2b^4 + 6ab^5 + b^6$
iv $a^6 - 6a^5b + 15a^4b^2 - 20a^3b^3 + 15a^2b^4 - 6ab^5 + b^6$

EXERCISE 2E

1 a $(b + 2)(a + 1)$ **b** $(a + 4)(c + d)$ **c** $(a + 2)(b + 3)$
d $(m + p)(n + 3)$ **e** $(x + 3)(x + 7)$ **f** $(x + 4)(x + 5)$
g $(2x + 1)(x + 3)$ **h** $(3x + 2)(x + 4)$ **i** $(5x + 3)(4x + 1)$

2 a $(x + 5)(x - 4)$ **b** $(x + 2)(x - 7)$ **c** $(x - 3)(x - 2)$
d $(x - 5)(x - 3)$ **e** $(x + 7)(x - 8)$ **f** $(2x + 1)(x - 3)$
g $(3x + 2)(x - 4)$ **h** $(4x - 3)(x - 2)$ **i** $(9x + 2)(x - 1)$

EXERCISE 2F

1 a $3, 4$ **b** $3, 5$ **c** $2, 8$ **d** $2, 9$ **e** $-3, 7$
f $3, -7$ **g** $-6, 2$ **h** $-2, 15$

2 **a** $(x+1)(x+3)$ **b** $(x+3)(x+8)$ **c** $(x+3)(x+7)$
d $(x+6)(x+9)$ **e** $(x+4)(x+5)$ **f** $(x+3)(x+5)$
g $(x+4)(x+6)$ **h** $(x+2)(x+7)$ **i** $(x+2)(x+4)$

3 **a** $(x-1)(x-2)$ **b** $(x-1)(x-3)$ **c** $(x-2)(x-3)$
d $(x-3)(x-11)$ **e** $(x-3)(x-13)$ **f** $(x-3)(x-16)$
g $(x-4)(x-7)$ **h** $(x-2)(x-12)$ **i** $(x-2)(x-18)$

4 **a** $(x-8)(x+1)$ **b** $(x+7)(x-3)$ **c** $(x-2)(x+1)$
d $(x-4)(x+2)$ **e** $(x+8)(x-3)$ **f** $(x-5)(x+2)$
g $(x+9)(x-6)$ **h** $(x+9)(x-8)$ **i** $(x-7)(x+3)$
j $(x-3)(x+2)$ **k** $(x-12)(x+5)$ **l** $(x+12)(x-5)$
m $(x+6)(x-3)$ **n** $(x+2)(x-9)$ **o** $(x-5)(x-7)$

5 **a** $2(x+1)(x+4)$ **b** $3(x-1)(x-6)$ **c** $2(x+3)(x+4)$
d $2(x-10)(x-12)$ **e** $4(x-3)(x+1)$ **f** $3(x-3)(x-11)$
g $2(x-10)(x+9)$ **h** $3(x-4)(x+2)$ **i** $2(x+4)(x+5)$
j $x(x-8)(x+1)$ **k** $4(x-3)^2$ **l** $7(2x-1)(x+1)$
m $5(x-8)(x+2)$ **n** $x(x-7)(x+4)$ **o** $x^2(x+1)^2$

6 **a** $-(x+9)(x-6)$ **b** $-(x+2)(x+5)$ **c** $-(x+3)(x+7)$
d $-(x-3)(x-1)$ **e** $-(x-2)^2$ **f** $-(x+3)(x-1)$
g $-(x-8)(x+6)$ **h** $-(x-3)^2$ **i** $-(x-3)(x-7)$
j $-2(x-9)(x+7)$ **k** $-2(x-5)^2$ **l** $-x(x-2)(x+1)$

EXERCISE 2G

1 **a** $(2x+3)(x+1)$ **b** $(2x+5)(x+1)$ **c** $(7x+2)(x+1)$
d $(3x+4)(x+1)$ **e** $(3x+1)(x+4)$ **f** $(3x+2)(x+2)$
g $(4x+1)(2x+3)$ **h** $(7x+1)(3x+2)$ **i** $(3x+1)(2x+1)$
j $(6x+1)(x+3)$ **k** $(5x+1)(2x+3)$ **l** $(7x+1)(2x+5)$

2 **a** $(2x+1)(x-5)$ **b** $(3x-1)(x+2)$ **c** $(3x+1)(x-2)$
d $(2x-1)(x+2)$ **e** $(2x+5)(x-1)$ **f** $(5x+1)(x-3)$
g $(5x-3)(x-1)$ **h** $(11x+2)(x-1)$ **i** $(3x+2)(x-3)$
j $(2x+3)(x-3)$ **k** $(3x-2)(x-5)$ **l** $(5x+2)(x-3)$
m $(3x-2)(x+4)$ **n** $(2x-1)(x+9)$ **o** $(2x-3)(x+6)$
p $(2x-3)(x+7)$ **q** $(5x+2)(3x-1)$ **r** $(21x+1)(x-3)$

3 **a** $(3x+2)(5x+3)$ **b** $(3x+2)(5x-3)$ **c** $(3x-2)(5x+3)$
d $2(3x-2)(5x-3)$ **e** $2(3x-1)^2$ **f** $3(4x+3)^2$
g $2(4x+1)(2x+1)$ **h** $2(4x-1)(2x+1)$
i $5(4x+1)(2x-1)$ **j** $4(4x-1)(2x-1)$
k $(5x+3)(5x+2)$ **l** $(5x-3)(5x-2)$ **m** $(5x-4)(5x+2)$
n $(25x+1)(x-6)$ **o** $(6x+5)(6x-1)$ **p** $(9x+5)(4x-1)$
q $(12x-5)(3x+2)$ **r** $(18x-1)(2x+3)$

EXERCISE 2H

1 **a** $x(3x+2)$ **b** $(x+9)(x-9)$ **c** $2(p^2+4)$
d $3(b+5)(b-5)$ **e** $2(x+4)(x-4)$
f $n^2(n+2)(n-2)$ **g** $(x-9)(x+1)$ **h** $(d+7)(d-1)$
i $(x+9)(x-1)$ **j** $4t(1+2t)$ **k** $3(x+6)(x-6)$
l $2(g-11)(g+5)$ **m** $(2a+3d)(2a-3d)$
n $5(a-2)(a+1)$ **o** $2(c-3)(c-1)$
p $x^2(x+1)(x-1)$ **q** $d^2(d+3)(d-1)$ **r** $x(x+2)^2$

2 **a** $(x-3)^2$ **b** $(x+11)(x-11)$ **c** $(x-1)^2$
d $(y+5)^2$ **e** $(x+11)^2$ **f** $(x-y)^2$ **g** $(1+x)(1-x)$
h $(5y+1)(5y-1)$ **i** $(7y+6z)(7y-6z)$ **j** $(2d+7)^2$
k $a(2b+c)(2b-c)$ **l** $2\pi(R+r)(R-r)$

3 **a** $a(b+c-2)$ **b** $ab(ab-2)$ **c** $2x(3+x)(3-x)$
d $(x+7)^2$ **e** $4a(a+b)(a-b)$ **f** $xy(x+2)(x-2)$
g $4x^2(x+1)(x-1)$ **h** $(x-2)(y-z)$ **i** $(a+b)(x+1)$
j $(x-y)(a+1)$ **k** $(x+2)(x+3)$ **l** $(x^2+1)(x+1)$

4 **a** $7(x-5y)$ **b** $2(g+2)(g-2)$ **c** $-5x(x+2)$
d $m(m+3p)$ **e** $(a+3)(a+5)$ **f** $(m-3)^2$

g $5x(x+y-xy)$ **h** $(x+2)(y+2)$ **i** $(y+5)(y-9)$
j $(2x+1)(x+5)$ **k** $3(y+7)(y-7)$ **l** $3(p+q)(p-q)$
m $(2c+1)(2c-1)$ **n** $3(x+4)(x-3)$ **o** $2(b+5)(x-3)$

5 **a** $-(x-1)(x+12)$ **b** $-2(x-1)(x-3)$
c $-(x+7)(x-2)$ **d** $-2x(x-1)^2$
e $(a+b+3)(a+b-3)$ **f** $x(x+4)$

6 **a** $(2x+3)(x+7)$ **b** $(2x+5)(x+3)$
c $(2x+1)(2x+5)$ **d** $(4x+3)(3x+1)$
e $(x-5)(6x+1)$ **f** $(4x+1)^2$
g $(5x+4)(5x-4)$ **h** $(12x+1)(x-6)$
i $2(6x-1)(x-3)$ **j** $3(3x+4)(x-1)$
k $(3x-5)(4x-3)$ **l** $(3x+2)(12x-7)$

REVIEW SET 2A

1 **a** $3x^2-6x$ **b** $15x-3x^2$ **c** $x^2-5x-24$
d x^2+6x+9 **e** $-x^2+4x-4$ **f** $16x^2-1$
g $12x^2-5x-2$ **h** $2x^2+3x-15$

2 **a** $3x(x-4)$ **b** $3x(5-2x)$ **c** $2(x+7)(x-7)$
d $(x-3)^2$ **e** $(a+b)^2$ **f** $(x+2)(x-1)$

3 **a** $(x-1)(5+y)$ **b** $(3x+7)(1+2b)$

4 **a** $(x+3)(x+7)$ **b** $(x-3)(x+7)$ **c** $(x-7)(x+3)$
d $(x-2)(x-3)$ **e** $4(x-3)(x+1)$ **f** $-(x+4)(x+9)$

5 **a** $(4x+5)(2x+3)$ **b** $(6x-1)(2x-3)$ **c** $(4x-5)(3x+2)$

6 **a**
    1 1
  1 2 1
1 3 3 1
b **i** $a^3+3a^2b+3ab^2+b^3$
ii $8x^3+60x^2+150x+125$
iii $x^3+3x+\dfrac{3}{x}+\dfrac{1}{x^3}$

7 **b** **i** $12\frac{1}{4}$ **ii** $110\frac{1}{4}$
c To find the square of an integer plus $\frac{1}{2}$ we multiply the integer by the integer increased by 1 and then add $\frac{1}{4}$ to the result.

REVIEW SET 2B

1 **a** $9x^2-6xy+y^2$ **b** $2a^2-2ab$ **c** $-12x^2+x+1$
d $4x^2+28x+49$ **e** $-25+10x-x^2$ **f** $1-49x^2$
g $20x^2-11x-4$ **h** $-x^2+7x+18$

2 **a** $5b(a+2b)$ **b** $3(x+2)(x-2)$ **c** $(x+4)^2$
d $2(a-b)^2$ **e** $3x(x+3)(x-1)$ **f** $(x-3)(x-6)$

3 $(y-z)(2x+1)$

4 **a** $(x+5)(x+7)$ **b** $(x+7)(x-5)$ **c** $(x-5)(x-7)$
d $2(x-7)(x+5)$ **e** $(x-5)(x-6)$ **f** $-(x-2)(x-10)$

5 **a** $(3x+2)(4x-1)$ **b** $(3x-2)(4x+3)$
c $4(3x-1)(2x+3)$

6 **a** $16x^4+32x^3+24x^2+8x+1$
b $x^4-12x^3+54x^2-108x+81$
c $x^4-4x^2+6-\dfrac{4}{x^2}+\dfrac{1}{x^4}$

7 Consider $x^3-x=x(x^2-1)$ etc.

EXERCISE 3A.1

1 **a** 7 **b** 13 **c** 15 **d** 24 **e** $\frac{1}{3}$ **f** $\frac{1}{11}$
g $\frac{1}{17}$ **h** $\frac{1}{23}$

2 **a** 2 **b** -5 **c** $\frac{1}{5}$

3 **a** 24 **b** -30 **c** -30 **d** 12 **e** 18
f $54\sqrt{2}$ **g** 12 **h** $24\sqrt{3}$ **i** 64

EXERCISE 3A.2

1 a $2\sqrt{2}$ **b** 0 **c** $\sqrt{2}$ **d** $\sqrt{3}$ **e** $7\sqrt{7}$ **f** $-3\sqrt{5}$
g $6\sqrt{2}$ **h** $-3\sqrt{2}$ **i** $8\sqrt{5}$ **j** $-3\sqrt{2}$ **k** $4\sqrt{3}$
l $10\sqrt{5} - 10$

2 a $2\sqrt{2} + 7\sqrt{3}$ **b** $5\sqrt{2} - \sqrt{3}$ **c** $-7\sqrt{2} + 4\sqrt{3}$
d $11\sqrt{5} - 5\sqrt{2}$ **e** $2\sqrt{2} - 10\sqrt{7}$ **f** $2\sqrt{2} + 3\sqrt{11} + 3$
g $\sqrt{6} - 3\sqrt{2} + 4$ **h** $9\sqrt{3} - 5\sqrt{7} - 13$

EXERCISE 3B.1

1 a $\sqrt{10}$ **b** $\sqrt{21}$ **c** $\sqrt{33}$ **d** 7
e 6 **f** $2\sqrt{10}$ **g** $6\sqrt{6}$ **h** $6\sqrt{15}$
i $\sqrt{30}$ **j** $4\sqrt{3}$ **k** -12 **l** $162\sqrt{6}$

2 a 2 **b** $\frac{1}{2}$ **c** 3 **d** $\frac{1}{3}$ **e** 2 **f** $\frac{1}{2}$
g 3 **h** $\sqrt{6}$ **i** $\frac{1}{\sqrt{10}}$ **j** 5 **k** 1 **l** 25

3 a $2\sqrt{2}$ **b** $3\sqrt{2}$ **c** $5\sqrt{2}$ **d** $7\sqrt{2}$
e $10\sqrt{2}$ **f** $12\sqrt{2}$ **g** $100\sqrt{2}$ **h** $\frac{1}{2}\sqrt{2}$

4 a $2\sqrt{3}$ **b** $3\sqrt{3}$ **c** $5\sqrt{3}$ **d** $\frac{1}{3}\sqrt{3}$

5 a $2\sqrt{5}$ **b** $3\sqrt{5}$ **c** $5\sqrt{5}$ **d** $\frac{1}{5}\sqrt{5}$

6 a i 7 **ii** 5 **iii** 2 **iv** 4 **b i** no **ii** no
c $\sqrt{a+b} \neq \sqrt{a} + \sqrt{b}$ and $\sqrt{a-b} \neq \sqrt{a} - \sqrt{b}$

EXERCISE 3B.2

1 a $2\sqrt{6}$ **b** $5\sqrt{2}$ **c** $3\sqrt{6}$ **d** $2\sqrt{10}$ **e** $2\sqrt{14}$ **f** $3\sqrt{7}$
g $2\sqrt{13}$ **h** $2\sqrt{11}$ **i** $2\sqrt{15}$ **j** $3\sqrt{10}$ **k** $4\sqrt{6}$ **l** $2\sqrt{17}$
m $5\sqrt{7}$ **n** $9\sqrt{2}$ **o** $8\sqrt{2}$ **p** $10\sqrt{7}$

2 a $\frac{\sqrt{5}}{3}$ **b** $\frac{3\sqrt{2}}{2}$ **c** $\frac{\sqrt{3}}{2}$ **d** $\frac{5\sqrt{3}}{6}$

EXERCISE 3C

1 a $\sqrt{10} + 2$ **b** $3\sqrt{2} - 2$ **c** $3 + \sqrt{3}$ **d** $\sqrt{3} - 3$
e $7\sqrt{7} - 7$ **f** $2\sqrt{5} - 5$ **g** $22 - \sqrt{11}$ **h** $\sqrt{6} - 12$
i $3 + \sqrt{6} - \sqrt{3}$ **j** $6 - 2\sqrt{15}$ **k** $6\sqrt{5} - 10$ **l** $30 + 3\sqrt{10}$

2 a $2 - 3\sqrt{2}$ **b** $-2 - \sqrt{6}$ **c** $2 - 4\sqrt{2}$ **d** $-3 - \sqrt{3}$
e $-3 - 2\sqrt{3}$ **f** $-5 - 2\sqrt{5}$ **g** $-3 - \sqrt{2}$ **h** $-5 + 4\sqrt{5}$
i $\sqrt{7} - 3$ **j** $11 - 2\sqrt{11}$ **k** $\sqrt{7} - \sqrt{3}$ **l** $4 - 2\sqrt{2}$
m $9 - 15\sqrt{3}$ **n** $-14 - 14\sqrt{3}$ **o** $4 - 6\sqrt{2}$

3 a $4 + 3\sqrt{2}$ **b** $7 + 4\sqrt{3}$ **c** $1 + \sqrt{3}$ **d** $10 + \sqrt{2}$ **e** -2
f $3 - 3\sqrt{7}$ **g** $-1 - \sqrt{5}$ **h** 4 **i** 5 **j** $14 - 7\sqrt{2}$

4 a $3 + 2\sqrt{2}$ **b** $7 - 4\sqrt{3}$ **c** $7 + 4\sqrt{3}$ **d** $6 + 2\sqrt{5}$
e $5 - 2\sqrt{6}$ **f** $27 - 10\sqrt{2}$ **g** $9 + 2\sqrt{14}$ **h** $22 - 8\sqrt{6}$
i $8 - 4\sqrt{3}$ **j** $13 + 4\sqrt{10}$ **k** $13 - 4\sqrt{10}$ **l** $44 + 24\sqrt{2}$
m $51 - 10\sqrt{2}$ **n** $17 - 12\sqrt{2}$ **o** $19 + 6\sqrt{2}$

5 a 13 **b** 23 **c** 1 **d** -9 **e** 14
f 19 **g** -2 **h** -28 **i** -174

6 a 1 **b** -4 **c** $x - y$

EXERCISE 3D

1 a $\frac{\sqrt{2}}{2}$ **b** $\sqrt{2}$ **c** $2\sqrt{2}$ **d** $5\sqrt{2}$ **e** $\frac{\sqrt{14}}{2}$
f $\frac{\sqrt{3}}{3}$ **g** $\sqrt{3}$ **h** $\frac{4\sqrt{3}}{3}$ **i** $6\sqrt{3}$ **j** $\frac{\sqrt{33}}{3}$
k $\frac{\sqrt{5}}{5}$ **l** $\frac{3\sqrt{5}}{5}$ **m** $\frac{\sqrt{15}}{5}$ **n** $3\sqrt{5}$ **o** $25\sqrt{5}$
p $\sqrt{5}$ **q** $\frac{\sqrt{3}}{6}$ **r** $\frac{2\sqrt{6}}{3}$ **s** $\frac{3\sqrt{5}}{2}$ **t** $\frac{\sqrt{2}}{4}$

2 a $\frac{3 + \sqrt{5}}{4}$ **b** $2 - \sqrt{3}$ **c** $\frac{4 + \sqrt{11}}{5}$ **d** $\frac{5\sqrt{2} - 2}{23}$
e $\frac{\sqrt{3} - 1}{2}$ **f** $\frac{10 + 15\sqrt{2}}{-14}$ **g** $\frac{3\sqrt{5} - 10}{11}$ **h** $\frac{5\sqrt{7} - 13}{3}$

3 a $4 + 2\sqrt{2}$ **b** $5 - 5\sqrt{2}$ **c** $-3 + 2\sqrt{2}$ **d** $-\frac{4}{7} + \frac{1}{7}\sqrt{2}$
e $1 + \sqrt{2}$ **f** $3 + 2\sqrt{2}$ **g** $\frac{9}{7} + \frac{3}{7}\sqrt{2}$ **h** $\frac{10}{7} + \frac{6}{7}\sqrt{2}$

4 a -6 **b** $-14 - 2\sqrt{5}$ **c** $12 + 8\sqrt{2} - 9\sqrt{3} + 2\sqrt{6}$

5 $3 + 2\sqrt{2}$ **6** $\sqrt{6} = \dfrac{12}{5 - 6p^2}$ $\left(\text{or } \sqrt{6} = \dfrac{\sqrt{2} - \sqrt{3}}{p}\right)$

7 $x^2 = 8 - 2\sqrt{15}$ and so $2\sqrt{15} = 8 - x^2$
Now square both sides.

8 $u_1 = 1$, $u_2 = 1$, $u_3 = 2$, $u_4 = 3$

EXERCISE 3E

1 a $x = 3, y = 2$ **b** $x = 15, y = -4$ **c** $x = -11, y = -3$
d $x = 6, y = 0$ **e** $x = 0, y = -3$ **f** $x = y = 0$

2 a $x = 2$, $y = \frac{3}{2}$ **b** $x = \frac{3}{7}$, $y = -\frac{1}{7}$
c $x = -\frac{3}{7}$, $y = -\frac{1}{7}$ **d** $x = -\frac{8}{7}$, $y = -\frac{12}{7}$

3 a $a = 3$, $b = 1$ **b** $a = 4$, $b = 5$
c $a = 5$, $b = 2$ or $a = -5$, $b = -2$
d $a = 3$, $b = -4$ or $a = -3$, $b = 4$

4 a $90 + 34\sqrt{7}$ **b** $9\sqrt{3} - 11\sqrt{2}$ **5** $3 - \sqrt{2}$

6 a $\sqrt{11 + 4\sqrt{6}} = 2\sqrt{2} + \sqrt{3}$
b No. (Suppose it can and see what happens.)

REVIEW SET 3A

1 a 18 **b** -24 **c** $\sqrt{2}$ **d** $4\sqrt{3}$

2 a $8\sqrt{3} - 6$ **b** $16 - 6\sqrt{7}$ **c** 1 **d** $\sqrt{5} - 4$ **e** $8 + 5\sqrt{2}$

3 a $4\sqrt{2}$ **b** $5\sqrt{3}$ **c** $\frac{\sqrt{6}}{2}$ **d** $\frac{30 + 5\sqrt{3}}{33}$ **4** $\frac{1}{7}\sqrt{7}$

5 a $7 + 4\sqrt{3}$ **b** 13

6 $x = -2, y = 1$ or $x = -\frac{3}{5}, y = \frac{10}{3}$ **7** $155 + 77\sqrt{2}$

REVIEW SET 3B

1 a $6\sqrt{15}$ **b** 20 **c** $-2\sqrt{2}$ **d** $2 - 2\sqrt{2}$ **e** 9 **f** 15

2 $5\sqrt{3}$ **3 a** 22 **b** $4\sqrt{5} - 9$ **c** $6 - 4\sqrt{3}$ **d** $7\sqrt{2} - 9$

4 a $7\sqrt{2}$ **b** $\frac{\sqrt{6}}{3}$ **c** $\frac{3\sqrt{2} - 2}{7}$ **d** $\frac{-20 - 5\sqrt{3}}{13}$

5 a $-\frac{1}{11} + \frac{1}{11}\sqrt{5}$ **b** $\frac{1}{2} - \frac{5}{2}\sqrt{5}$ **c** $\frac{3}{2} - \frac{1}{2}\sqrt{5}$

6 $p = 2$, $q = -3$ or $p = -\frac{63}{5}$, $q = \frac{10}{21}$ **7** $49 + 20\sqrt{6}$

EXERCISE 4A

1 a $\sqrt{65}$ cm **b** $\sqrt{50}$ cm **c** $\sqrt{233}$ km

2 a $\sqrt{85}$ cm **b** $\sqrt{4.23}$ km **c** $\sqrt{45.125}$ cm

3 a $x = \sqrt{11}$ **b** $x = \sqrt{2}$ **c** $x = \sqrt{5}$

4 a $x = \sqrt{\frac{5}{4}}$ **b** $x = \sqrt{\frac{5}{2}}$ **c** $x = \frac{1}{2}$

5 a $x = \sqrt{27}$ **b** $x = \sqrt{52}$ **c** $x = 2$

6 a $x = \sqrt{17}$, $y = \sqrt{8}$ **b** $x = \sqrt{29}$, $y = \sqrt{45}$
c $x = \sqrt{5}$, $y = \sqrt{6}$

7 a $x = \sqrt{2}$ **b** $x = 14$ **8** $AC = \sqrt{39}$ m

9 a $AB = \sqrt{17}$ cm **b** $AB = \sqrt{29}$ m **c** $AB = \sqrt{41}$ m

EXERCISE 4B.1

1 b, e, f are right angled. **2 a** $\widehat{BAC}$ **b** $\widehat{ABC}$ **c** $\widehat{ACB}$

EXERCISE 4B.2

1 a, b, d, f are Pythagorean triples.

2 a $k = 17$ **b** $k = 10$ **c** $k = 48$
d $k = 25$ **e** $k = 24$ **f** $k = 60$

3 $n = 3$

4 Hint: Let $(n+3)^2 = n^2 + (n+1)^2$ and solve for n.

XERCISE 4C.1

1 8.54 cm **2** 3.16 cm × 9.49 cm
3 a 53.7 cm **b** 160 cm² **4** 6.63 cm **5** 7.07 cm
6 25.6 cm **7** 9.43 km **8** 42.2 km
9 By car, $1.\overline{4}$ h; by train, $1.41\overline{6}$ h ∴ quicker to go by train.
10 11.2 km h⁻¹ and 22.4 km h⁻¹
11 a $x = \sqrt{2}$, $y = 45$ **b** $x = 6$, $h = \sqrt{13}$
c $x = \frac{1}{2}$, $y = \frac{\sqrt{3}}{2}$
12 10.4 cm **13** 22.2 cm² **14** 6.03 m **15** 8 cm
16 a 240 m **b** 40 m **c** 202 m

EXERCISE 4C.2

1 19.2 km **2** 6.09 km **3** ≈ 190 km h⁻¹

EXERCISE 4D

1 6 cm **2** $\frac{1}{2}\sqrt{157} \approx 6.26$ cm

3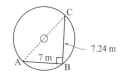
Using the converse of the angle in a semi-circle theorem, [AC] is a diameter of the circle, $d \approx 10.07$ m.

4 3.71 cm **5** 4.24 cm **6** 12.5 cm **7** 8.49 cm
8 10.6 cm **9** 717 km **10** 0.414 m **11** 10.05 m
12 5.29 cm **13** 5 cm

EXERCISE 4E

1 15 cm **2** 10 cm **3** 4.21 cm **4** 5.20 cm **5** 6.80 m
6 4.12 cm **7** 8.06 m **8** 71 m **9** 15.8 cm **10** 2.45 m

EXERCISE 4F

1 17 km from B **2** 80.3 m
3 Hint: Find area of trapezium ABED. **4** 10.8 cm
5 Use Area A + Area B = total area − area of semi-circle
6 4.24 cm or 5.66 cm **7 b** 3.00 m **8 b** $\frac{13}{18}$

REVIEW SET 4A

1 a $\sqrt{29}$ cm **b** $\sqrt{33}$ cm **c** $\sqrt{27}$ cm, $2\sqrt{27}$ cm
2 Yes, $1^2 + 4^2 = (\sqrt{17})^2$ **3** $5^2 + 11^2 \neq 13^2$ **4** 41.4 cm
5 7.07 cm **6** 14.1 km, 315° **7** 9.90 cm **8** 181 km
9 a $x = \sqrt{20} = 2\sqrt{5}$ **b** $x = \sqrt{56} = 2\sqrt{14}$
10 a $\sqrt{61}$ m **b** $\sqrt{70}$ m

REVIEW SET 4B

1 a $x = \sqrt{18}$ **b** $x = \sqrt{61}$ **c** $x = \sqrt{2}$
2 $2^2 + 5^2 = (\sqrt{29})^2$, $\widehat{ABC}$ is a right angle **3** 6 cm
4 1.431 m (to nearest mm) **5** 42.4 m **6** 34.2 km
7 13.4 m **8** Yes, diagonal of shed is 11.05 m.
9 9.95 cm **10 a** $y = 10\sqrt{2}$ **b** $y = 15$

11 a i PQ $= \sqrt{a^2 + b^2}$ units **ii Hint:** Equate areas.
b $\frac{100\sqrt{2}}{\sqrt{3}}$ m ≈ 81.6 m

EXERCISE 5A.1

1 a 2 units **b** $\sqrt{37}$ units **c** $\sqrt{13}$ units **d** 3 units
e $2\sqrt{2}$ units **f** $\sqrt{29}$ units **g** 5 units **h** 7 units
i $5\sqrt{2}$ units
2 a $\sqrt{2}$ units **b** $\sqrt{29}$ units **c** $3\sqrt{5}$ units

EXERCISE 5A.2

1 a $2\sqrt{2}$ units **b** 7 units **c** $2\sqrt{5}$ units **d** 6 units
e 7 units **f** $\sqrt{5}$ units **g** $\sqrt{10}$ units **h** $3\sqrt{5}$ units
2 a isosceles (AB = AC) **b** scalene
c isosceles (AB = BC) **d** isosceles (BC = AC)
e equilateral **f** isosceles (AC = BC)

3 a $\widehat{ABC}$ **b** $\widehat{ABC}$ **c** $\widehat{BAC}$ **d** $\widehat{BAC}$
4 a $a = 2$ **b** $a = 3$ or -5 **c** $a = \pm 2$ **d** $a = -1$

EXERCISE 5B

1 a $(-1\frac{1}{2}, 3\frac{1}{2})$ **b** $(-1, -2)$ **c** $(1, 1\frac{1}{2})$ **d** $(2, 1)$
e $(1, -1\frac{1}{2})$ **f** $(-4, 1\frac{1}{2})$ **g** $(-4\frac{1}{2}, \frac{1}{2})$ **h** $(-1\frac{1}{2}, \frac{1}{2})$
2 a $(5, 3)$ **b** $(1, -1)$ **c** $(1\frac{1}{2}, 3)$ **d** $(0, 4)$
e $(2, -1\frac{1}{2})$ **f** $(1, 1)$ **g** $(1, 2\frac{1}{2})$ **h** $(2, -3\frac{1}{2})$
3 a B$(0, -6)$ **b** B$(5, -2)$ **c** B$(0, 6)$ **d** B$(0, 7)$
e B$(-7, 3)$ **f** B$(-3, 0)$
4 a P$(-9, 10)$ **b** P$(6, 3)$ **5** C$(1, -3)$ **6** P$(7, -3)$
7 S$(-2, 0)$ **8** $\frac{\sqrt{89}}{2}$ units **9** $a = 2\frac{1}{3}$, $b = 5\frac{1}{2}$

EXERCISE 5C.1

1 a $\frac{1}{3}$ **b** 0 **c** -3 **d** $\frac{2}{3}$ **e** $-\frac{3}{4}$ **f** undefined
g -4 **h** $-\frac{2}{5}$

2 a **b** **c**

d **e** **f**

3 a $\frac{1}{5}$ **b** $\frac{1}{4}$ **c** 4 **d** 0 **e** undefined **f** $\frac{2}{7}$ **g** $-\frac{2}{7}$
h 1

4 **5**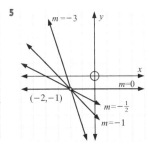

EXERCISE 5C.2

1 a -2 **b** $-\frac{5}{2}$ **c** $-\frac{1}{3}$ **d** $-\frac{1}{7}$ **e** $\frac{5}{2}$ **f** $\frac{3}{7}$ **g** $\frac{1}{5}$
h 1

2 c, **d**, **f** and **h** are perpendicular.

3 a $a = 9$ **b** $a = 1$ **c** $a = 6\frac{1}{3}$
4 a $t = \frac{1}{5}$ **b** $t = 5$ **c** $t = 3\frac{3}{5}$
5 a $t = 4$ **b** $t = 4$ **c** $t = 14$ **d** $t = 3\frac{1}{7}$

EXERCISE 5C.3

1 a not collinear **b** collinear **c** not collinear **d** collinear

2 a $c = 3$ **b** $c = -5$

EXERCISE 5D

1 a $PQ = PR = \sqrt{20}$ **d**

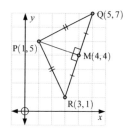

b $(4, 4)$

c slope of $[PM] = -\frac{1}{3}$,
slope of $[QR] = 3$

2 a **i** gradient of $[AB] = -\frac{1}{4}$
= gradient of $[DC]$

ii gradient of $[BC] = \frac{3}{5}$
= gradient of $[AD]$

b a parallelogram

c $AB = \sqrt{68}$ units $= DC$, $BC = \sqrt{306}$ units $= AD$

d **i** $(\frac{5}{2}, \frac{5}{2})$ **ii** $(\frac{5}{2}, \frac{5}{2})$ **e** diagonals bisect each other

3 a gradient of $[MN] = 0 =$ gradient of $[AC]$

b $MN = 3$ units, $AC = 6$ units

4 a $AB = BC = CD = DA = 5$ units **b** $(2, 1)$ and $(2, 1)$

c gradient of $[AC] = -2$, gradient of $[BD] = \frac{1}{2}$

5 a **i** $P(0, 5)$ **ii** $Q(4\frac{1}{2}, 2)$ **iii** $R(\frac{1}{2}, -2\frac{1}{2})$ **iv** $S(-4, \frac{1}{2})$

b **i** $-\frac{2}{3}$ **ii** $\frac{9}{8}$ **iii** $-\frac{2}{3}$ **iv** $\frac{9}{8}$

c PQRS is a parallelogram

6 a $s = 6$ **b** **i** $\frac{1}{2}$ **ii** -2

c gradient of $[PS] \times$ gradient of $[SQ] = \frac{1}{2} \times -2 = -1$

EXERCISE 5E.1

1 a $y = 5x - 15$ **b** $y = -2x - 4$ **c** $y = -4x + 25$

d $y = \frac{1}{2}x + \frac{5}{2}$ **e** $y = -\frac{1}{3}x + \frac{7}{3}$ **f** $y = -1$

2 a $3x - 4y = -14$ **b** $2x - 5y = -22$ **c** $x + 2y = 5$

d $3x + 4y = 10$ **e** $5x - y = -14$ **f** $3x + y = 12$

3 a $x - y = -4$ **b** $x + y = 4$ **c** $y = 7$

d $x = -3$ **e** $y = -2$ **f** $x + 9y = 6$

g $x - 3y = 5$ **h** $2x - y = -7$

4 a $y = \frac{1}{2}x + 3$ **b** $y = 2x + 6$ **c** $2x - 5y = 10$

d $y = -2x - 2$ **e** $4x + 3y = 20$ **f** $x - 2y = -8$

5 a 3 **b** -2 **c** 0 **d** undefined **e** $\frac{2}{3}$ **f** -3 **g** $\frac{2}{7}$

h $-\frac{2}{7}$ **i** $\frac{3}{4}$ **j** $-\frac{3}{4}$ **k** $\frac{A}{B}$ **l** $-\frac{A}{B}$

8 $(3, 3)$

EXERCISE 5E.2

1 a $y = 3x + 5$ **b** $y = 2x - 5$ **c** $y = -3x - 2$

d $y = -\frac{1}{2}x - 1$ **e** $y = 4$ **f** $x = -1$

2 a $y = \frac{2}{3}x + 2$ **b** $y = \frac{5}{4}x - 2$ **c** $y = -\frac{3}{5}x + 3$

d $x - y = -5$ **e** $5x + 3y = -10$ **f** $5x + 7y = -15$

3 a $M = \frac{1}{3}t + 4$ **b** $N = \frac{2}{3}x - 2$ **c** $G = -\frac{3}{4}s + 3$

d $H = -g + 2$ **e** $F = \frac{3}{10}x + 5$ **f** $P = -\frac{1}{3}t - 2$

EXERCISE 5E.3

1 a $x - 2y = 2$ **b** $2x - 3y = -19$ **c** $3x - 4y = 15$

d $3x - y = 11$ **e** $x + 3y = 13$ **f** $3x + 4y = -6$

g $2x + y = 4$ **h** $3x + y = 4$

2 a $-\frac{2}{3}$ **b** $\frac{3}{7}$ **c** $\frac{6}{11}$ **d** $-\frac{5}{6}$ **e** $-\frac{1}{2}$ **f** 3

3 a parallel lines have the same gradient of $-\frac{3}{5}$

b $-\frac{3}{5} \times \frac{5}{3} = -1$ for perpendicular lines, $\therefore$ $m = \frac{5}{3}$

4 a $3x + 4y = 10$ **b** $2x - 5y = 3$

c $3x + y = -12$ **d** $x - 3y = 0$

5 a $\frac{2}{3}, -\frac{6}{k}$ **b** $k = -9$ **c** $k = 4$

6 a $x - 3y = -16$ **b** $3x - 2y = 13$

c $2x - y = -3$ **d** $x = 5$

EXERCISE 5E.4

1 a $x - y = 4$ **b** $2x - y = -6$

c $12x - 10y = -35$ **d** $y = 1$

2 $2x - 3y = -5$

3 a $x + 2y = 5$, $3x + y = 10$, $x - 3y = 0$ **b** $(3, 1)$

4 $(3, 3)$

5 a $P(5, 3)$, $Q(4, 0)$, $R(2, 2)$

b **i** $x - y = 2$ **ii** $3x + y = 12$ **iii** $x + 3y = 8$

c $X(3\frac{1}{2}, 1\frac{1}{2})$ **d** yes

e The perpendicular bisectors meet at a point.

f X is the centre of the circle which could be drawn through A, B and C.

EXERCISE 5F

1 a $2\sqrt{10}$ units **b** $3\sqrt{5}$ units **c** $3\sqrt{5}$ units

d $2\sqrt{17}$ units **e** $2\sqrt{10}$ units **f** 5 units

2 a $\sqrt{10}$ units **b** 4 units

3 a $N(4.44, 0.92)$ **b** 3.8 km

EXERCISE 5G

1 a **b**

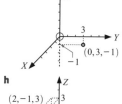

c **d**

e

f

g **h**

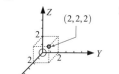

i

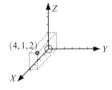

(4, 1, 2)

j

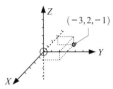

(−2, 2, 3)

k

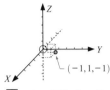

(−1, 1, −1)

l

Z

(−3, 2, −1)

f

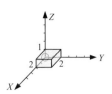

All points on and within a $2 \times 2 \times 1$ rectangular prism (as shown).

2 **a** $2\sqrt{14}$ units, M(1, 1, −1)   **b** 6 units, M(1, −2, 2)
c $2\sqrt{3}$ units, M(2, 2, 2)   **d** $\sqrt{35}$ units, M($\frac{3}{2}$, $\frac{1}{2}$, $\frac{7}{2}$)

3 **a** Isosceles with AC = BC.
b Right angled with A the right angle.

4 $k = 1 \pm \sqrt{19}$

5 **a** $x^2 + y^2 + z^2 = 4$ and must be the equation of a sphere, centre (0, 0, 0), radius 2 units
b $(x-1)^2 + (y-2)^2 + (z-3)^2 = 16$ which is the equation of a sphere, centre (1, 2, 3), radius 4 units.

6 **a**

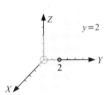

$y = 2$

A plane parallel to the XOZ plane passing through (0, 2, 0).

b

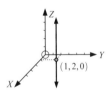

(1, 2, 0)

A line parallel to the Z-axis passing through (1, 2, 0).

c

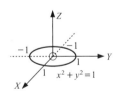

$x^2 + y^2 = 1$

A circle in the XOY plane, centre (0, 0, 0), radius 1 unit.

d

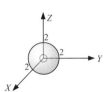

A sphere, centre (0, 0, 0), radius 2 units.

e

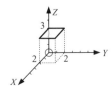

A 2 by 2 square plane 3 units above the XOY plane (as shown).

REVIEW SET 5A

1 **a** $x = -1$ **b** $\sqrt{73}$ units   **c** $(0, \frac{1}{2})$ **d** 2   **e** 3
f $-\frac{4}{5}$ **g** x-intercept is 3, y-intercept is 2, gradient is $-\frac{2}{3}$

2 $a = -2 \pm 2\sqrt{5}$ **3** $y = -\frac{1}{2}x + 4$ **4** $3x - y = 5$

5 gradient of [AB] = gradient of [BC] = 2   and B is common

6 $b = -3$

7 $2x - 5y = 10$

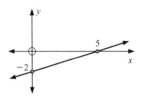

8 **a** AB = BC = 5 units   **b** X($\frac{1}{2}$, $\frac{1}{2}$)
c gradient [BX] × gradient [AC] = $7 \times -\frac{1}{7} = -1$

9 **a** $y = 4x - 11$ **b** $6x - 16y = -11$ **10** $\sqrt{13}$ units

11 **a** **i** $2\sqrt{14}$ units   **ii** M(0, 0, 0)   **b** $k = 4$ or -6

REVIEW SET 5B

1 **a** $(-3, 3)$ **b** $\sqrt{58}$ units   **c** $y = 0$ **d** $-\frac{3}{2}$
e gradient is -2, y-intercept is 5

2 $y = 2x + 2$ **3** $m = 2 \pm 3\sqrt{5}$ **4** $a = -8$

5 **a** $y = -2x + 7$ **b** $2x + 3y = 7$ **c** $3x - 2y = 15$

6 $k = -1$ **7** $2t + 3P = 10$

8 **a** gradient [AB] = gradient [DC] = $\frac{1}{5}$
b gradient [AD] = gradient [BC] = -2
c [AB] ∥ [DC]   and   [AD] ∥ [BC]
∴ ABCD is a parallelogram.
d $(\frac{1}{2}, \frac{1}{2})$; diagonals bisect each other

9 **a** $3x + 2y = 4$ **b** $x - 2y = -7$

10 **a** N($\frac{66}{13}$, $\frac{18}{13}$)   **b** $\frac{7}{\sqrt{13}}$ units **11** **a** $\sqrt{30}$ units

EXERCISE 6A

1 **a** and **d**, **b** and **e**   **2** A, D and M, C and O, I and L

3 **a** **i** QR   **ii** QR̂S   **b** **i** NO   **ii** MÔN
c **i** QR   **ii** QR̂P   **d** **i** HE   **ii** HÊF
e **i** DE   **ii** DÊF   **f** **i** ON   **ii** ON̂M

EXERCISE 6B

1 **a**   **b**

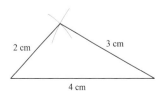

c cannot form a triangle

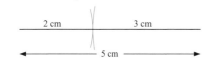

d cannot form a triangle

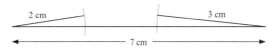

2 The sum of the lengths of any two sides of a triangle must be greater than the length of the third side.

EXERCISE 6C.1

1 **a** A and C, SAS   **b** B and C, AAcorS   **c** A and B, RHS
d A and C, SSS   **e** B and C, AAcorS   **f** A and C, SAS
g A and C, SSS   **h** B and C, RHS

2 **a** $\triangle ABC \cong \triangle FED$ (AAcorS)   **b** $\triangle PQR \cong \triangle ZYX$ (SAS)
c $\triangle ABC \cong \triangle EDF$ (AAcorS)
d $\triangle ABC \cong \triangle LKM$ (SSS)   **e** $\triangle XYZ \cong \triangle FED$ (RHS)
f no   **g** no   **h** no   **i** $\triangle ABC \cong \triangle PQR$ (SSS)
j $\triangle ABC \cong \triangle FED$ (AAcorS)

EXERCISE 6C.2

1 **a** $BC = DC$ {given}, $A\widehat{C}B = E\widehat{C}D$ {vert. opposite},
$A\widehat{B}C = E\widehat{D}C$ {alternate}
$\therefore$ $\triangle$s congruent {AAcorS}

b **i** 5 cm   **ii** $37°$

2 **a** SSS   **b** $P\widehat{Q}S = R\widehat{Q}S$, $Q\widehat{P}S = Q\widehat{R}S$, $P\widehat{S}Q = R\widehat{S}Q$

3 **a** AAcorS
b $A\widehat{B}C = E\widehat{D}C$, $A\widehat{C}B = E\widehat{C}D$, $C\widehat{A}B = C\widehat{E}D$, $DC = BC$, $AC = EC$

4 **a** $AC = BC = CD = CE$, $A\widehat{C}B = D\widehat{C}E$, i.e., SAS
b $AB = DE$, $A\widehat{B}C = B\widehat{A}C = C\widehat{D}E = C\widehat{E}D$, AB $\parallel$ DE

5 **a** SSS   **b** $W\widehat{Z}X = Y\widehat{X}Z$ so   WZ $\parallel$ XY
and $W\widehat{X}Z = Y\widehat{Z}X$ so   WX $\parallel$ ZY

8 **c** ACBD is a parallelogram   **9** **c** a parallelogram

EXERCISE 6C.3

2 **a** No, as none of the 4 congruency tests can be used.
b Yes.   (Show this!)

EXERCISE 6D

2 **a** $x = 1.2$ **b** $x = 10.8$ **c** $x = 3\frac{1}{3}$ **d** $x = 10.5$
e $x = 12$ **f** $x = 2\frac{6}{7}$ **g** $x = 7.5$ **h** $x = 5$ **i** $x = 6$

3 1.8 m   **4** 7 m   **5** ≈ 2.67 m

6 **a**   **b** 1.76 m

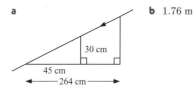

7 Triangles are equiangular and so are similar.

Width = 40 m.

8 ≈ 1.62 m   **9** ≈ 651 m

EXERCISE 6E

1 **a** ≈ 14.2 m^2 **b** ≈ 30.7 m^2 **c** ≈ 41.5 m^2
d ≈ 8.45 m^2

2 **a** ≈ 12.5 cm^2 **b** 6.14 cm^2

3 **a** $x = 1.5$ **b** 17.6 m^2

4 **a** It is multiplied by 8.   **b** It is increased by 72.8%.
c It is divided by 8.
d It is multiplied by 3.375, i.e., increased by 237.5%.

5 **a** 10 cm   **b** 0.003 m$^2 = 30$ cm^2
c 6 mm, 2.25 mm   **d** 1.25 mL

REVIEW SET 6A

1 A, B and E   and   C and D

2

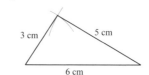

3 **a** B and C (AAcorS)
b A and C (AAcorS)

5 **a** $U\widehat{Y}V = W\widehat{X}V$ {given}, $U\widehat{V}Y = W\widehat{V}X$ {vert. opp.}
$\therefore$ $\triangle$s UYV and WXV are equiangular $\therefore$ similar.
b $J\widehat{L}K = N\widehat{L}M$ {vertically opposite},
$J\widehat{K}L = N\widehat{M}L$ {alternate angles, JK $\parallel$ MN}
$\therefore$ $\triangle$s JLK, NLM are equiangular $\therefore$ similar.
c $C\widehat{B}D = C\widehat{E}A$ {given}, $\widehat{C}$ is common to both
$\therefore$ $\triangle$s CBD and CEA are equiangular $\therefore$ similar.

6 ≈ 117 m   **7** **a** $5 : 4$ **b** $25 : 16$ **c** $125 : 64$

8 **a** 38.4 cm^2 **b** 28.8 cm^2

REVIEW SET 6B

1 **a** DF   **b** $D\widehat{F}E$

2 **a** (RHS)   **b** PB $=$ QB, $P\widehat{A}B = Q\widehat{A}B$, $P\widehat{B}A = Q\widehat{B}A$

3

The triangle is right angled.

4 **a** $x = 1\frac{5}{8}$ **b** $x = 7\frac{2}{3}$ **c** $x = 13\frac{1}{3}$

5 **c** $V = \frac{2}{3}\pi x^3$ **6** 2 cm   **7** 4.74 m

8 **Hint:** The midpoint theorem should be used.

EXERCISE 7A

1 **a** $(2, -1)$ $\begin{pmatrix} 3 \\ 4 \end{pmatrix}$ $(5, 3)$ **b** $(5, 2)$ $\begin{pmatrix} -1 \\ 4 \end{pmatrix}$ $(4, 6)$
c $(3, -2)$ $\begin{pmatrix} 0 \\ 3 \end{pmatrix}$ $(3, 1)$ **d** $(0, 1)$ $\begin{pmatrix} -3 \\ 1 \end{pmatrix}$ $(-3, 2)$

2 **a** $3x + 2y = 11$ **b** $x = 6$ **c** $y = 2x$ **d** $y = 0$
e $y = x^2 + 3$ **f** $y = -2(x-3)^2 + 2$ **g** $y = \dfrac{x+9}{x+4}$
h $y = \dfrac{-2x-2}{x-3}$ **i** $y = 2^x - 3$
j $y = 9 \times 3^{-x}$ or $y = 3^{2-x}$

3 A translation of $\begin{pmatrix} 5 \\ 5 \end{pmatrix}$.

EXERCISE 7B

1 a $(4, 1)$ **b** $(-4, -1)$ **c** $(-1, 4)$ **d** $(1, -4)$
  e $(-1, 3)$ **f** $(1, -3)$ **g** $(-3, -1)$ **h** $(3, 1)$

2 a $y = -2x - 3$ **b** $y = -x^2$ **c** $xy = -5$ **d** $x = 2^y$
  e $3x + 2y = -4$ **f** $x^2 + y^2 = 4$ **g** $y = x^2$
  h $2x + 3y = -4$ **i** $y = -3$ **j** $x = 2y^2$

3 a $(1, -1)$ **b** $(5, -1)$ **c** $(3, -9)$ **d** $(1, 7)$ **e** $(5, 1)$

EXERCISE 7C

1 a R_{90}: $(-3, -2)$, R_{-90}: $(3, 2)$, R_{180}: $(2, -3)$
  b R_{90}: $(1, 4)$, R_{-90}: $(-1, -4)$, R_{180}: $(-4, 1)$

2 a $4x + 3y = -7$ **b** $x = 3$ **c** $x = -7$
  d $y = -x^2$ **e** $3x - 2y = 12$

3 a $(-3, -2)$ **b** $(2, 5)$ **c** $(1, 3)$ **d** $(0, 1)$
  e $x - y = 13$ **f** $2x - y = 5$ **g** $y = x - 3$

EXERCISE 7D

1 a $(6, 9)$ **b** $(-\frac{1}{3}, \frac{4}{3})$ **c** $(3, -4)$ **d** $(4, 10)$
  e $(-1, 1)$ **f** $(\frac{9}{2}, -4)$

2 a $y = 2x + 6$ **b** $y = -2x^2$ **c** $y = \frac{1}{8}x^2$
  d $xy = 4$ **e** $y = 2^{x+1}$

3 a circle, centre O,   **b** ellipse, centre O,
   radius 3 is $x^2 + y^2 = 9$ $9x^2 + 4y^2 = 36$

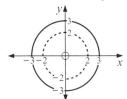
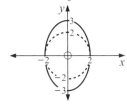

  c ellipse, centre O,
   $4x^2 + 9y^2 = 36$

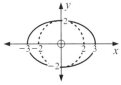

REVIEW SET 7A

1 a $3x - 2y = -5$ **b** $y = 3$
  c $2x + y = 12$ **d** $y = 2(x - 2)^2 - 5$

2 a $(-2, -5)$ **b** $(6, -3)$ **c** $(5, 1)$ **d** $(5, 3)$

3 a $y = -3x + 2$ **b** $y = -3x^2$ **c** $x = 3^y$ **d** $xy = 6$

4 a $(-3, 2)$ **b** $(2, -4)$

5 a $(4, -2)$ **b** $(3, 20)$ **c** $(-8, -7)$

6 a $y = 3x + 6$ **b** $4x - 5y = 20$ **c** $y = -4x + 1$
  d $y = -x^2 + 3x - 5$ **e** $(x - 5)^2 + (y + 2)^2 = 4$

REVIEW SET 7B

1 a $(3, 2)$ **b** $(4, -5)$ **c** $(2, 5)$ **d** $(7, 2)$

2 a $5x - 2y = 27$ **b** $y = -(x + 2)^2 + 5$
  c $y = -2 - \dfrac{4}{x - 1}$ **d** $(x + 3)^2 + (y + 4)^2 = 9$

3 a $4x - 3y = -8$ **b** $xy = -12$
  c $3x - 2y = -9$ **d** $y = 2x^2$

4 a $(-1, -13)$ **b** $(-3, -2)$

5 a $(9, 15)$ **b** $(-4, 3)$ **c** $(-5, -\frac{3}{2})$

6 a $y = -6x + 3$ **b** $y = 2 - 15x$ **c** $x - 3y = 7$
  d $x = 1 + 3y - 2y^2$ **e** $(x + 3)^2 + (y + 4)^2 = 8$

EXERCISE 8A.1

1 a numerical   **b** numerical   **c** categorical   **d** numerical
  e numerical   **f** categorical   **g** categorical   **h** numerical

2 a male, female
  b soccer, gridiron, rugby, Australian, Gaelic, etc.
  c black, blonde, brown, grey, brunette
  d unleaded, premium unleaded, diesel, LPG, super

3 a quantitative discrete   **b** quantitative continuous
  c categorical   **d** quantitative discrete
  e quantitative discrete   **f** categorical
  g quantitative discrete   **h** quantitative continuous
  i quantitative discrete   **j** quantitative continuous
  k categorical   **l** categorical
  m quantitative continuous   **n** quantitative discrete
  o quantitative discrete

4 a sample   **b** census   **c** sample   **d** census
  e census   **f** sample

EXERCISE 8A.2

1 a type of fruit, frequency   **b** frequency   **c** 80
  d It may be, as the sample is from one school only.
  e No, provided all year groups are properly represented.
  f banana
  g

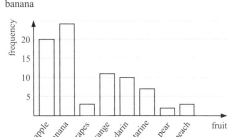

2 a favourite subject, frequency
  b dependent: frequency;   independent: subject
  c Science   **d** randomly selected   **e** yes
  f

Art   Science   Mathematics   English   Language   Geography   Music   History

3 a i $\geqslant 1690$ **ii** $\geqslant 3759$ **iii** $\geqslant 2019$
  b

% of households of corresponding size			
Number of	Year		
persons	1935	1960	1985
1	2.1%	0.8%	9.8%
2	15.6%	17.6%	26.2%
3	16.7%	16.1%	35.4%
4	24.9%	37.3%	23.1%
5+	40.7%	28.2%	5.4%
Totals	1	1	1

EXERCISE 8B

1 a continuous   **b** continuous   **c** continuous
   d continuous   **e** discrete   **f** discrete   **g** continuous

2 a number of TV sets in a household
   b Discrete, since you can't have part of a TV set.
   c

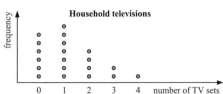

   d positively skewed, no outliers   **e** 30%   **f** 15%

3 a 45 shoppers   **b** 18 shoppers   **c** 15.6%
   d positively skewed, no outliers

4 a The number of business appointments each day.
   b You can only have whole appointments.
   c 22.2%   **d** 4.44%   **e** 2 appointments
   f positively skewed with an outlier
   g Data value 10 is an outlier.

5 a number of toothpicks in a box   **b** discrete
   c

No. of toothpicks	Tally	Freq.
47	|	1
48	⊞	5
49	⊞ ⊞	10
50	⊞ ⊞ ⊞ ⊞ |||	23
51	⊞ ⊞	10
52	⊞ ||||	9
53	||	2

   d

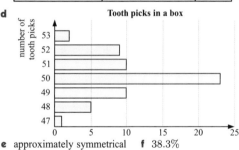

   e approximately symmetrical   **f** 38.3%

6 a

No. of pumpkins	Tally	Frequency
2	|	1
3		0
4	||	2
5	|||	3
6	⊞	5
7	⊞ |||	8
8	⊞ ||	7
9	⊞	5
10	⊞ ||	7
11	|	1
12		0
13		0
14		0
15	|	1
	Total	40

   b

   c Yes, data value 15 is an outlier.
   d It is slightly negatively skewed.
   e On average the number of pumpkins is higher in the "with fertiliser" group.
   f Yes, assuming the fertiliser is not too expensive and the pumpkins are as big as they were previously.

EXERCISE 8C

1 a

Test Score	Tally	Freq.
0 - 9		0
10 - 19		0
20 - 29	|	1
30 - 39	||	2
40 - 49	|||	3
50 - 59	⊞ ||||	9
60 - 69	⊞ ⊞ |||	13
70 - 79	⊞ |||	8
80 - 89	⊞ ⊞	10
90 - 100	||||	4
	Total	50

   b 28%
   c 12%
   d More students had a test score in the interval 60 - 69 than in any other interval.

2 a

Stem	Leaf
2	9 7 4 1 7 5
3	3 0 5 4 6 4
4	6 0 2 8
5	8 7 1 0

   b

Stem	Leaf
2	1 4 5 7 7 9
3	0 3 4 4 5 6
4	0 2 6 8
5	0 1 7 8

   5 | 8   represents 58

3 a 1   **b** 43   **c** 10   **d** 1   **e** 21.4%

4 a

Stem	Leaf
0	
1	8
2	9 9 7
3	4 7 9 3 7 5 9 1 4 7 4
4	4 0 2 3 3 7 1 3 8 4 4 4 5 9 1 2 2 3 3 5
5	1 3 8 0 5 2 4 9 7 1

   b

Stem	Leaf
0	
1	8
2	7 9 9
3	1 3 4 4 4 5 7 7 7 9 9
4	0 1 1 2 2 2 3 3 3 3 3 4 4 4 5 5 7 8 9
5	0 1 1 2 3 4 5 7 8 9

   c The stem-and-leaf plot shows all the actual data values.
   d i 59   **ii** 18   **e** 22.2%   **f** 8.9%
   g negatively skewed with no outliers

EXERCISE 8D

1 a Weights can take any value from 75 kg to 105 kg.

b

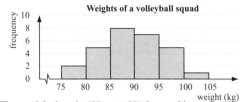

Weights of a volleyball squad

c The modal class is (85 - < 90) kg as this occurred most frequently.

d approximately symmetrical with no outliers

2 **a** continuous numerical

b

Stem	Leaf
0	3 6 8 8 8
1	0 0 0 0 0 2 2 4 4 4 5 5 5 6 6 6 6 6 7 8 8 8 8 9
2	0 0 0 1 4 5 5 5 6 7 7
3	2 2 3 4 7
4	0 2 5 5 6

c positively skewed, no outliers

d The modal travelling time was between 10 and 20 minutes.

3 **a** column graph

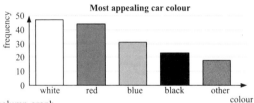

Most appealing car colour

b column graph

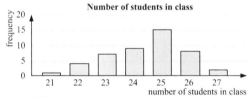

Number of students in class

c frequency histogram

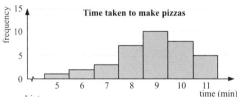

Time taken to make pizzas

d frequency histogram

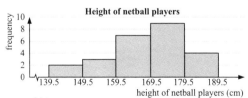

Height of netball players

e frequency histogram

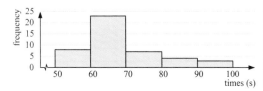

4 **a**

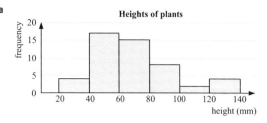

Heights of plants

b 46   **c** 30%   **d** **i** 754   **ii** 686

EXERCISE 8E.1

1 **a** **i** 24   **ii** 24   **iii** no mode
   b **i** 13.3   **ii** 11.5   **iii** 8
   c **i** 10.3   **ii** 10.0   **iii** 11.2
   d **i** 428.6   **ii** 428   **iii** 415 and 427

2 **a** A: 7.73   B: 8.45   **b** A: 7   B: 7
   c The data sets are the same except for the last value, and the last value of A is less than the last value of B, so the mean of A is less than the mean of B.
   d The middle value of the data sets is the same, so the median is the same.

3 **a** mean: \$582 000, median: \$420 000, mode: \$290 000
   b The mode is the second lowest value, so does not take the higher values into account.
   c No, since the data is unevenly distributed, the median is not in the centre.

4 **a** mean: 3.11,   median: 0,   mode: 0
   b The data is very positively skewed so the median is not in the centre.
   c The mode is the lowest value so does not take the higher values into account.
   d yes, 15 and 27   **e** no

5 **a** 44   **b** 44   **c** 40.6   **d** increase mean to 40.75

6 105.6   **7** 2275 km   **8** \$2 592 000   **9** $x = 12$ **10** $a = 8$

11 27   **12** **a** 1696 km   **b** 1632 km   **c** 475.4 km   **13** 7.875

14 15

EXERCISE 8E.2

1 **a** 1   **b** 1   **c** 1.4

2 **a** **i** 5.74
       ii 7
       iii 8

   b

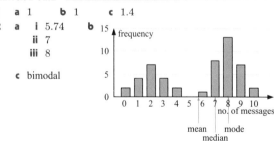

   c bimodal

   d The mean takes into account the full range of numbers of text messages and is affected by extreme values. Also the values which are lower than the median are well below it.
   e median

3 **a**

Donation (\$)	Frequency
1	7
2	9
3	2
4	4
5	8

   b 30
   c **i** \$2.90
       ii \$2
       iii \$2
   d mode

4 **a** **i** 4.25   **ii** 5   **iii** 5   **b** Yes, negatively skewed.
   c The mean is less than the mode and median.

EXERCISE 8F

1 a i

Age	Frequency	Cum. Freq.
0 - < 1	1	1
1 - < 2	3	4
2 - < 3	3	7
3 - < 4	6	13
4 - < 5	12	25
5 - < 6	15	40
6 - < 7	8	48
7 - < 8	5	53
8 - < 9	2	55

ii

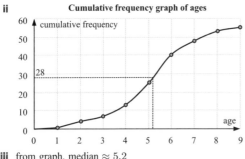

Cumulative frequency graph of ages

iii from graph, median ≈ 5.2

b i

Time	Frequency	Cum. Freq.
$0 \leqslant t < 1$	7	7
$1 \leqslant t < 2$	11	18
$2 \leqslant t < 3$	20	38
$3 \leqslant t < 4$	22	60
$4 \leqslant t < 5$	12	72
$5 \leqslant t < 6$	9	81
$6 \leqslant t < 7$	5	86

ii

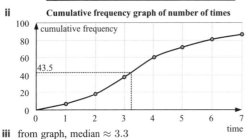

Cumulative frequency graph of number of times

iii from graph, median ≈ 3.3

c i

Height	Frequency	Cum. Freq.
$0 \leqslant h < 5$	4	4
$5 \leqslant h < 10$	8	12
$10 \leqslant h < 15$	14	26
$15 \leqslant h < 20$	16	42
$20 \leqslant h < 25$	10	52
$25 \leqslant h < 30$	6	58
$30 \leqslant h < 35$	2	60

ii

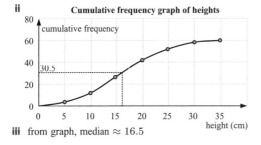

Cumulative frequency graph of heights

iii from graph, median ≈ 16.5

2 a

Salmon lengths (cm)	Freq.	Cum. Freq.
$24 \leqslant x < 27$	2	2
$27 \leqslant x < 30$	5	7
$30 \leqslant x < 33$	7	14
$33 \leqslant x < 36$	11	25
$36 \leqslant x < 39$	12	37
$39 \leqslant x < 42$	2	39
$42 \leqslant x < 45$	1	40

b

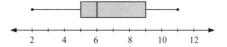

Cumulative frequency graph of lengths of salmon

c median ≈ 35

d Median is 34. The graph is assuming a constant change over the interval whereas original data is not uniform over the interval.

3 a 70   **b** 76   **c** 61   **d** 26   **e** 84

4 a $7\frac{1}{2}$ **b i** 43   **ii** 43

5 a 32 min   **b** 77 runners   **c** 27 min

6 a 56 m   **b** 15   **c** 29   **d** 46

EXERCISE 8G

1 a i 9   **ii** $Q_1 = 7, Q_3 = 10$ **iii** 7   **iv** 3
   b i 18.5   **ii** $Q_1 = 16, Q_3 = 20$ **iii** 14   **iv** 4
   c i 26.9   **ii** $Q_1 = 25.5, Q_3 = 28.1$ **iii** 7.7   **iv** 2.6

2 a median = 2.35, $Q_1 = 1.4$, $Q_3 = 3.7$
   b range = 5.1,   IQR = 2.3
   c i ...... greater than 2.35 minutes
      ii ...... less than 3.7 minutes
      iii The minimum waiting time was 0.1 minutes and the maximum waiting time was 5.2 minutes. The waiting times were spread over 5.1 minutes.

3 a 20   **b** 58   **c** 40   **d** 30   **e** 49   **f** 38   **g** 19

EXERCISE 8H.1

1 a i 31   **ii** 54   **iii** 16   **iv** 40   **v** 26
   b i 38   **ii** 14

2 a ...... 89 points   **b** ...... 25 points
   c ...... 62 points   **d** ...... 73 points
   e ...... between 45 and 73 points   **f** 64   **g** 28

3 a i min = 2, $Q_1 = 5$, median = 6, $Q_3 = 9$, max = 11
      ii

   iii range = 9   **iv** IQR = 4
   b i min = 0, $Q_1 = 4$, median = 7, $Q_3 = 8$, max = 9
      ii

   iii range = 9   **iv** IQR = 4

4 a median = 20.2 kg, Q_1 = 19.8 kg, Q_3 = 21.1 kg,
max. weight = 22.3 kg, min. weight = 18.8 kg

b

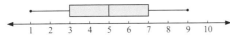

c i IQR = 1.3 kg   **ii** range = 3.5 kg
d i ...... 20.2 kg   **ii** 31.8% of the bags ......
iii ...... 1.3 kg   **iv** ...... 19.8 kg or less
e positively skewed

EXERCISE 8H.2

1 a

Statistic	A	C
min value	2	8
Q_1	7	10
median	10	14
Q_3	12	16
max value	16	17

b i A: 14, C: 9
ii A: 5, C: 6

2 a i class B   **ii** class B   **iii** class B   **b i** 49   **ii** 13
c 75%   **d i** almost symmetrical   **ii** almost symmetrical
e The students in class A generally scored higher marks. The
marks in class B were more varied.

3 a

Statistic	Boys	Girls
min value	160	152
Q_1	167	163
median	171	166
Q_3	174	170
max value	188	177

b The distributions show that in general, the boys are taller than
the girls and are more varied in their heights.

EXERCISE 8I.1

1 $\overline{x} \approx 4.87$, min = 1, Q_1 = 3, median = 5, Q_3 = 7, max = 9
2

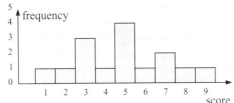

3

frequency / score

4 $\overline{x} \approx 5.24$, min = 2, Q_1 = 4, median = 5, Q_3 = 6.5, max = 9

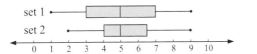

EXERCISE 8I.2

1 Set 1
mean = 6.63, mode = 7, min = 3, Q_1 = 6, median = 7, Q_3 = 8,
max = 9, range = 6, IQR = 2
Set 2
mean = 7.7, mode = 7, min = 2, Q_1 = 6, median = 8, Q_3 = 9,
max = 15, range = 13, IQR = 3

2 Set 1
mean = 11.9, mode = 11.9, min = 11.6, Q_1 = 11.8,
median = 11.9, Q_3 = 12, max = 12.2, range = 0.6, IQR = 0.2
Set 2
mean = 11.8, mode = 11.8, min = 11.5, Q_1 = 11.7,
median = 11.8, Q_3 = 11.9, max = 12.2, range = 0.7, IQR = 0.2

EXERCISE 8J.1

1 a Sample A   **b** A: 7,   B: 5
c i A: 8, B: 4   **ii** A: 2, B: 1   **d** A: 1.90, B: 0.894
e s takes all values into account, whereas the range and IQR
each use only 2 values.

2 a 5.74   **b** 1.41
c The standard deviation is much less, indicating the outlier had
a marked effect on the standard deviation.

3 a Colin: mean = 25.4, SD = 4.63
Imran: mean = 29.8, SD = 11.0
b The standard deviation and so Colin is more consistent.

4 a Mickey: mean = 3, range = 5
Julio: mean = 3, range = 5
b Mickey's   **c** Mickey: SD = 1.95, Julio: SD = 1.26
d standard deviation

EXERCISE 8J.2

1 1.5   **2** mean = 28.8, SD = 1.64
3 mean length = 38.3 cm, SD = 2.66 cm
4 mean wage = €412.11, SD = €16.35

EXERCISE 8K

1 a

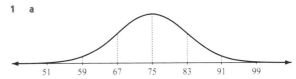

b i 80   **ii** 12 or 13   **iii** 407 or 408
2 a

b i 286   **ii** 252   **c** 16%
3 a 2.5%   **b** 84%   **c** 97.35%   **d** 84%   **4** once

REVIEW SET 8A

1 a categorical   **b** numerical   **c** numerical
2 a 49   **b** 15   **c** 26.5%   **d** positively skewed
3 a the number of children in the household
b Discrete, since you cannot have part of a child.
c

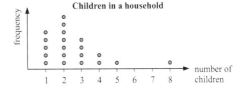

Children in a household

frequency / number of children

d positively skewed, one outlier at 8

4 a

Stem	Leaf
0	9
1	8 8
2	5 8 4 9 2 6 5 0 3 8 7
3	5 2 4 9 3 4 9 1 6 5 6 3 5 2
4	0 0

4 | 0   represents 40

b

Stem	Leaf
0	9
1	8 8
2	0 2 3 4 5 5 6 7 8 8 9
3	1 2 2 3 3 4 4 5 5 5 6 6 9 9
4	0 0

4 | 0   represents 40

c The stem-and-leaf plot displays all the actual data values.
d **i** 40 **ii** 9 **e** 20%

5 $x = 7$ **6** **a** 32 kg **b** 91 kg **c** 20 **d** 5 **e** 20%

7 **a** Mass can be any decimal of a gram.
b

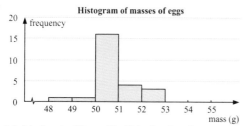

Histogram of masses of eggs

c Modal class is 50 - < 51. This class has the most eggs.
d approximately symmetrical

8 **a** 29.6 **b** 16 and 28 **c** 29 **d** 45
  e $Q_1 = 22$, $Q_3 = 41.5$ **f** 19.5

9 **a** **i** 48 **ii** 98 **iii** 15 **iv** 66 **v** 42
  b **i** 83 **ii** 24

10 **a** mean = 0.88, SD = 0.0980
  b mean = 1.76, SD = 0.196
  c Both mean and standard deviation doubled when the individual scores were doubled.

REVIEW SET 8B

1 **a** sample
  b It may depend on the time of day the sample was carried out.

2

Stem	Leaf
3	1
4	9 5
5	8 8 7 8 3 5
6	9 0 8 5 9 6 4 1 6 4 1 6 3
7	0 1 2 5 6 7 8 4 0
8	0 2 3 9 2 2
9	1 4 0 2 4 1 1 7

9 | 1   represents 91

a

Stem	Leaf
3	1
4	5 9
5	3 5 7 8 8 8
6	0 1 1 3 4 4 5 6 6 6 8 9 9
7	0 0 1 2 4 5 6 7 8
8	0 2 2 2 3 9
9	0 1 1 1 2 4 4 7

9 | 1   represents 91

b **i** 97 **ii** 31 **c** 20%
d **iii** neither symmetric nor skewed

3 **a** 14.55 **b** 14.5 **c** 14 and 15

4 13.56 **5** mean = 6, $x = 2$

6 **a** **i** 8.47 **ii** 9 **iii** 9 **iv** 4 **b** well above average
  c negatively skewed

7 **a**

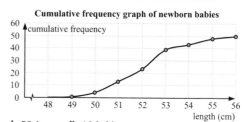

Histogram of lengths of newborn babies

b 27
c 70%

d

Length (cm)	Frequency	Cum. Freq.
$48 \leqslant l < 49$	1	1
$49 \leqslant l < 50$	3	4
$50 \leqslant l < 51$	9	13
$51 \leqslant l < 52$	10	23
$52 \leqslant l < 53$	16	39
$53 \leqslant l < 54$	4	43
$54 \leqslant l < 55$	5	48
$55 \leqslant l < 56$	2	50

e

Cumulative frequency graph of newborn babies

f **i** 52.1 cm **ii** 18 babies

8 **a** min = \$8.60, Q_1 = \$9.60, median = \$10.15, Q_3 = \$11.45, max = \$12.00

b

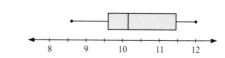

c range = \$3.40 **d** IQR = \$1.85

9 **a** Comparing the median swim times for girls and boys shows that, in general, boys swim 2.5 seconds faster than the girls.
  b The range of the girls' swim times is 10 seconds compared to the range of 7 seconds for the boys.
  c The fastest 25% of the boys swim faster than 100% of the girls.
  d 100% of the boys swim faster than 60 seconds whereas 75% of the girls swim faster than 60 seconds.

10 **a** 80 **b** 12 **c** 238

EXERCISE 9A

1 **a** $x = \pm 10$ **b** $x = \pm 5$ **c** $x = \pm 2$
  d $x = \pm 3$ **e** no solution **f** $x = 0$
  g $x = \pm 3$ **h** no solution **i** $x = \pm\sqrt{2}$
2 **a** $x = 4$ or -2 **b** $x = 0$ or -8 **c** no solution
  d $x = 4 \pm \sqrt{5}$ **e** no solution **f** $x = -2$
  g $x = 2\frac{1}{2}$ **h** $x = 0$ or $-\frac{4}{3}$ **i** $x = \dfrac{\pm\sqrt{6} - 3}{2}$

EXERCISE 9B.1

1 **a** $x = 0$ **b** $a = 0$ **c** $y = 0$ **d** $a = 0$ or $b = 0$
  e $x = 0$ or $y = 0$ **f** $a = 0$ or $b = 0$ or $c = 0$ **g** $a = 0$
  h $p = 0$ or $q = 0$ or $r = 0$ or $s = 0$ **i** $a = 0$ or $b = 0$

2　**a** $x = 0$ or 5　　**b** $x = 0$ or -3　　**c** $x = -1$ or 3
　d $x = 0$ or 7　　**e** $x = 0$ or -1　　**f** $x = -6$ or $\frac{3}{2}$
　g $x = \pm\frac{1}{2}$　　**h** $x = -2$ or 7　　**i** $x = 5$ or $-\frac{2}{3}$
　j $x = 0$　　**k** $x = 5$　　**l** $x = \frac{1}{3}$

EXERCISE 9B.2

1　**a** $x = 0$ or 7　　**b** $x = 0$ or 5　　**c** $x = 0$ or 8
　d $x = 0$ or 4　　**e** $x = 0$ or -2　　**f** $x = 0$ or $-\frac{5}{2}$
　g $x = 0$ or $\frac{3}{4}$　　**h** $x = 0$ or $\frac{5}{4}$　　**i** $x = 0$ or 3

2　**a** $x = 1$ or -1　　**b** $x = 3$ or -3　　**c** $x = 5$
　d $x = -2$　　**e** $x = -1$ or -2　　**f** $x = 1$ or 2
　g $x = -2$ or -3　　**h** $x = 2$ or 3　　**i** $x = -1$ or -6
　j $x = -2$ or -7　　**k** $x = -5$ or -6　　**l** $x = -5$ or 3
　m $x = -6$ or 2　　**n** $x = 3$ or 8　　**o** $x = 7$

3　**a** $x = -4$ or -5　　**b** $x = -4$ or -7　　**c** $x = -4$ or 2
　d $x = -4$ or 3　　**e** $x = 3$ or 2　　**f** $x = 2$
　g $x = 3$ or -2　　**h** $x = 12$ or -5　　**i** $x = 10$ or -7
　j $x = -5$ or 2　　**k** $x = 3$ or 4　　**l** $x = 12$ or -3

4　**a** $x = \frac{1}{2}$ or 2　　**b** $x = -3$ or $\frac{1}{3}$　　**c** $x = -4$ or $-\frac{5}{3}$
　d $x = \frac{1}{2}$ or -3　　**e** $x = \frac{1}{2}$ or 5　　**f** $x = -1$ or $-\frac{5}{2}$
　g $x = -\frac{1}{3}$ or -4　　**h** $x = -\frac{2}{5}$ or 3　　**i** $x = \frac{1}{2}$ or -9
　j $x = 1$ or $-\frac{5}{2}$　　**k** $x = \frac{4}{3}$ or -2　　**l** $x = \frac{3}{2}$ or -6

5　**a** $x = \frac{1}{3}$ or $-\frac{5}{2}$　　**b** $x = \frac{2}{3}$ or $-\frac{1}{2}$　　**c** $x = -\frac{1}{2}$ or $-\frac{1}{3}$
　d $x = -\frac{1}{21}$ or 3　　**e** $x = \frac{2}{5}$ or $-\frac{1}{2}$　　**f** $x = -\frac{3}{10}$ or 1

6　**a** $x = -4$ or -3　　**b** $x = -3$ or 1　　**c** $x = \pm 3$
　d $x = -1$ or $\frac{2}{3}$　　**e** $x = -\frac{1}{2}$　　**f** $x = \frac{5}{2}$ or 4

7　**a** $x = \pm\sqrt{6}$　　**b** $x = \pm\sqrt{8}$　　**c** $x = \pm\sqrt{10}$
　d $x = 4$ or -3　　**e** $x = -1$ or -5　　**f** $x = 2$ or -1
　g $x = \frac{1}{2}$ or -1　　**h** $x = 1$ or $-\frac{1}{3}$　　**i** $x = -1$ or 4

8　**a** $x = \pm 1$ or ± 2　　**b** $x = \pm\sqrt{3}$ or ± 2　　**c** $x = \pm\sqrt{5}$

EXERCISE 9C

1　**a** **i** 1　**ii** $(x+1)^2 = 6$　**b** **i** 1　**ii** $(x-1)^2 = -6$
　c **i** 9　**ii** $(x+3)^2 = 11$　**d** **i** 9　**ii** $(x-3)^2 = 6$
　e **i** 25　**ii** $(x+5)^2 = 26$
　f **i** 16　**ii** $(x-4)^2 = 21$
　g **i** 36　**ii** $(x+6)^2 = 49$
　h **i** $\frac{25}{4}$　**ii** $(x+\frac{5}{2})^2 = 4\frac{1}{4}$
　i **i** $\frac{49}{4}$　**ii** $(x-\frac{7}{2})^2 = 16\frac{1}{4}$

2　**a** $x = 2 \pm \sqrt{3}$　　**b** $x = 1 \pm \sqrt{3}$　　**c** $x = 2 \pm \sqrt{7}$
　d $x = -1 \pm \sqrt{2}$　　**e** no solution　　**f** $x = -2 \pm \sqrt{3}$
　g $x = -3 \pm \sqrt{6}$　　**h** no solution　　**i** $x = -4 \pm \sqrt{2}$

3　**a** $x = -1$ or -2　　**b** $x = 2 \pm \sqrt{12}$　　**c** $x = 2$ or 3
　d $x = \dfrac{-1 \pm \sqrt{5}}{2}$　　**e** $x = \dfrac{-3 \pm \sqrt{13}}{2}$　　**f** $x = \dfrac{-5 \pm \sqrt{33}}{2}$

4　**b** **i** $x = \dfrac{-2 \pm \sqrt{6}}{2}$　　**ii** $x = \dfrac{6 \pm \sqrt{15}}{3}$
　　iii $x = \dfrac{5 \pm \sqrt{10}}{5}$　　**iv** $x = \dfrac{1 \pm \sqrt{5}}{2}$
　　v $x = \dfrac{3 \pm \sqrt{17}}{4}$　　**vi** $x = \dfrac{1 \pm \sqrt{7}}{2}$

EXERCISE 9D

1　-11 or 10　　**2**　-13 or 9　　**3**　-3 or 8
4　$x = 3 + \sqrt{5}$ or $3 - \sqrt{5}$
5　The numbers are -2 and 5 or 2 and -5.
6　8 cm　　**7**　10 m　　**8**　18 m by 12 m
9

7.10 m　　or　　16.90 m
8.45 m　　　　　　3.55 m

10　17.9 cm　　**11**　5 cm or 16 cm
12　**a** $x = 2$　**b** $x = 5$　**c** $x = 6$　**13**　5 m
14　**a** Each triangle has a right angle and a common angle at A. So, the third angles of each triangle are equal.
　　∴　triangles are similar.
15　13 years　　**16**　$n = 6$
17　**a** $n = 7$　**b** 3 hours　**c** 14 km h^{-1}　**18**　$\frac{2}{5}$ or $\frac{-9}{-6}$
19　13　**20**　40　**21**　$\frac{3}{4}$ or $\frac{4}{3}$　**22**　$\frac{2}{3}$ or 3　**23**　2 cm by 2 cm
24　**c** $1\frac{1}{2}$ m　**25**　$x = 5$

EXERCISE 9E.1

1　**a** $x = -1 \pm \sqrt{3}$　　**b** $x = 3 \pm \sqrt{7}$　　**c** $x = 2 \pm \sqrt{5}$
　d $x = \dfrac{3 \pm \sqrt{5}}{2}$　　**e** $x = -4 \pm \sqrt{11}$　　**f** $x = \dfrac{1 \pm \sqrt{3}}{2}$
　g $x = \dfrac{1 \pm \sqrt{2}}{3}$　　**h** $x = \dfrac{2 \pm \sqrt{3}}{5}$　　**i** $x = \dfrac{-3 \pm \sqrt{7}}{2}$
　j $x = \dfrac{-1 \pm \sqrt{7}}{3}$　　**k** $x = \dfrac{3 \pm \sqrt{5}}{2}$　　**l** $x = \dfrac{1 \pm \sqrt{13}}{2}$

2　**a** $x = \dfrac{-1 \pm \sqrt{29}}{2}$　　**b** $x = \dfrac{-1 \pm \sqrt{5}}{2}$　　**c** $x = 1 \pm \sqrt{3}$
　d $x = 1 \pm 2\sqrt{2}$　　**e** $x = \dfrac{7 \pm \sqrt{217}}{6}$　　**f** $x = \dfrac{3 \pm \sqrt{13}}{2}$

3　**a** $x = \sqrt{31} - 1$　　**b** $x = \dfrac{3 + \sqrt{5}}{2}$

4　$2 + \frac{1}{2}\sqrt{14}$　and　$2 - \frac{1}{2}\sqrt{14}$

5
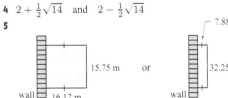
7.88 m
15.75 m　　or　　32.25 m
wall　16.12 m　　wall

EXERCISE 9E.2

1　**a** $x = \dfrac{3 \pm \sqrt{-39}}{2}$　∴　no real solutions exist
　b $x = -1 \pm \sqrt{-3}$　∴　no real solutions exist
　c $x = \dfrac{1 \pm \sqrt{-7}}{4}$　∴　no real solutions exist

2　**a** $x = \pm 5$　　**b** no real solutions exist　　**c** $x = \pm\sqrt{7}$
　d no real solutions exist　　**e** $x = \pm\frac{3}{2}$
　f no real solutions exist　　**g** no real solutions exist
　h $x = 5$ or -1　　**i** no real solutions exist
　j no real solutions exist　　**k** $x = \dfrac{3 \pm \sqrt{19}}{2}$
　l $x = \dfrac{-1 \pm \sqrt{17}}{4}$

EXERCISE 9E.3

1 **a** 32 **b** −39 **c** 44 **d** 68 **e** 61 **f** −127

2 **a** 2 distinct real roots **b** a repeated root
c 2 distinct real roots **d** 2 distinct real roots
e no real roots **f** a repeated root

3 a, b, d, f

4 **a** $k = 18$ **b** $k = 21\frac{1}{3}$ **c** $k > -3,\ k \neq 0$
d $k < 9$ **e** $k > 3\frac{1}{8}$ **f** never true

REVIEW SET 9A

1 **a** $x = \pm\sqrt{2}$ **b** no real solutions **c** $x = 0$ or 3
d $x = 3$ or 8 **e** $x = -\frac{2}{5}$ or $\frac{3}{2}$ **f** $x = -\frac{7}{3}$ or 3

2 **a** $x = 0$ or 1 **b** no real solutions **c** $x = 2 \pm \sqrt{5}$

3 **a** $x = -4 \pm \sqrt{11}$ **b** $x = 7 \pm \sqrt{42}$

4 $3\sqrt{3}$ cm $\times \sqrt{3}$ cm **5** $\dfrac{3+\sqrt{5}}{2}$ or $\dfrac{3-\sqrt{5}}{2}$

6 The number is $2 + \sqrt{3}$ or $2 - \sqrt{3}$.

7 **a** 2 real distinct roots **b** no real roots

8 **a** $x = \dfrac{-1 \pm \sqrt{3}}{2}$ **b** $x = \dfrac{2 \pm \sqrt{2}}{2}$

9 $\dfrac{15 + 30\sqrt{2}}{7}$ cm **10** **a** $k = -5$ **b** $k > -5,\ k \neq 0$

11 **a** **i** $2\sqrt{70}$ cm **ii** $20 + 2\sqrt{70}$ cm
b Assume it can. So, $x^2 - 20x + 102 = 0$
where $\Delta = -8$ ∴ no real roots.
So, the area cannot be 51 cm².

REVIEW SET 9B

1 **a** $x = 3$ **b** $x = -5$ or 4 **c** no real solutions
d $x = 8$ or -3 **e** $x = \pm 2$ **f** $x = -\frac{1}{2}$ or $\frac{2}{3}$

2 **a** $x = 2 \pm \sqrt{14}$ **b** $x = \dfrac{-1 \pm \sqrt{37}}{2}$

3 $\dfrac{\sqrt{345}-5}{2}$ cm by $\dfrac{\sqrt{345}+5}{2}$ cm **4** $\frac{4}{5}$ or -1
5 5 cm, 12 cm, 13 cm

6 **a** no real solution **b** 2 distinct real solutions

7 **a** $x = 1 \pm 2\sqrt{2}$ **b** no real solutions **c** $x = \dfrac{-5 \pm \sqrt{85}}{6}$

8 $k = \pm 6\sqrt{2}$ **9** **a** $x = \dfrac{29 + \sqrt{865}}{6}$ **b** $r = \dfrac{3 + 3\sqrt{3}}{2}$

10 $-\frac{3}{2} + \sqrt{3}$ and $\frac{3}{2} + \sqrt{3}$ **11** 12 people

EXERCISE 10A.1

1 **a** **i** $\dfrac{p}{r}$ **ii** $\dfrac{q}{r}$ **iii** $\dfrac{p}{q}$ **iv** $\dfrac{q}{r}$ **v** $\dfrac{p}{r}$ **vi** $\dfrac{q}{p}$

b **i** $\dfrac{y}{x}$ **ii** $\dfrac{z}{x}$ **iii** $\dfrac{y}{z}$ **iv** $\dfrac{z}{x}$ **v** $\dfrac{y}{x}$ **vi** $\dfrac{z}{y}$

c **i** $\dfrac{4}{5}$ **ii** $\dfrac{3}{5}$ **iii** $\dfrac{4}{3}$ **iv** $\dfrac{3}{5}$ **v** $\dfrac{4}{5}$ **vi** $\dfrac{3}{4}$

d **i** $\dfrac{4}{7}$ **ii** $\dfrac{\sqrt{33}}{7}$ **iii** $\dfrac{4}{\sqrt{33}}$ **iv** $\dfrac{\sqrt{33}}{7}$ **v** $\dfrac{4}{7}$ **vi** $\dfrac{\sqrt{33}}{4}$

e **i** $\dfrac{5}{\sqrt{34}}$ **ii** $\dfrac{3}{\sqrt{34}}$ **iii** $\dfrac{5}{3}$ **iv** $\dfrac{3}{\sqrt{34}}$ **v** $\dfrac{5}{\sqrt{34}}$ **vi** $\dfrac{3}{5}$

f **i** $\dfrac{7}{\sqrt{65}}$ **ii** $\dfrac{4}{\sqrt{65}}$ **iii** $\dfrac{7}{4}$ **iv** $\dfrac{4}{\sqrt{65}}$ **v** $\dfrac{7}{\sqrt{65}}$ **vi** $\dfrac{4}{7}$

2 **a** $\sin 70^\circ = \dfrac{x}{a}$ **b** $\sin 35^\circ = \dfrac{x}{b}$ **c** $\tan 64^\circ = \dfrac{x}{c}$
d $\cos 40^\circ = \dfrac{d}{x}$ **e** $\cos 49^\circ = \dfrac{x}{e}$ **f** $\tan 73^\circ = \dfrac{f}{x}$
g $\cos 54^\circ = \dfrac{g}{x}$ **h** $\tan 30^\circ = \dfrac{h}{x}$ **i** $\sin 68^\circ = \dfrac{i}{x}$

3 **a** 15.52 **b** 12.99 **c** 9.84 **d** 6.73 **e** 11.86
f 22.94 **g** 24.41 **h** 16.86 **i** 5.60 **j** 16.37
k 22.66 **l** 10.43

4 **a** $\theta = 62$, $a \approx 10.6$, $b \approx 5.63$
b $\theta = 27$, $a \approx 16.8$, $b \approx 7.64$
c $\theta = 65$, $a \approx 49.65$, $b \approx 21.0$

EXERCISE 10A.2

1 **a** 56.3° **b** 34.8° **c** 48.2° **d** 34.8° **e** 41.1°
f 48.6° **g** 25.3° **h** 37.1° **i** 35.5°

2 **a** $x \approx 6.2$, $\theta \approx 38.7^\circ$, $\phi \approx 51.3^\circ$
b $x \approx 5.9$, $\alpha \approx 53.9^\circ$, $\beta \approx 36.1^\circ$
c $x \approx 7.5$, $a \approx 38.4^\circ$, $b \approx 51.6^\circ$

4 The 3 triangles do not exist.

EXERCISE 10B.1

1 110 m **2** 32.9° **3** 238 m **4** 2.65 m **5** 761 m
6 280 m **7** 6.89° **8** 1.92 m **9** 23.5 m **10** 73.2 m
11 **a** 10.8 cm **b** 21.8° **12** 106° **13** 15.8 cm **14** 6.10 m
15 5 cuts (including the cut to fell the tree) **16** 252 m **17** 14.3°
18 41.4° **19** 53.2° **20** **a** 247.5 m **b** 128 m **21** 7.48 m
22 163 m **23** 729 m **24** 1.66 units

EXERCISE 10B.2

1 **a**

b

c

d

2 **a** 234° **b** 293° **c** 083° **d** 124°
3 **a** **i** 041° **ii** 142° **iii** 322° **iv** 099° **v** 221°
vi 279°
b **i** 027° **ii** 151° **iii** 331° **iv** 066° **v** 207°
vi 246°

4 123° **5** 7.81 km, 130° **6** 22.4 km **7** 38.6 km
8 221 km **9** **a** 36.1 km, 058° **b** 238°

EXERCISE 10C.1

1 **a** 21.2 cm **b** 35.3°
2 **a** 9.43 cm **b** 32.5° **c** 10.8 cm **d** 29.1°
3 **a** 8.94 cm **b** 18.5° **4** 69.2 cm **5** **a** 45°

EXERCISE 10C.2

1 **a** **i** [GF] **ii** [HG] **iii** [HF] **iv** [GM]
b **i** [MA] **ii** [MN]
c **i** [CD] **ii** [DE] **iii** [DF] **iv** [DX]

2 **a** **i** $\hat{DEH}$ **ii** $\hat{CEG}$ **iii** $\hat{AGE}$ **iv** $\hat{BXF}$

b **i** $P\widehat{Y}S$ **ii** $Q\widehat{W}R$ **iii** $Q\widehat{X}R$ **iv** $Q\widehat{Y}R$

c **i** $A\widehat{Q}X$ **ii** $A\widehat{Y}X$

3 **a** **i** 45° **ii** 35.3^o **iii** 63.4^o **iv** 41.8^o

 b **i** 21.8^o **ii** 18.9^o **iii** 21.0^o

 c **i** 36.9^o **ii** 33.9^o **iii** 33.9^o

 d **i** 58.6^o **ii** 64.9^o

EXERCISE 10D

1 **a** 1 **b** 0 **c** 0 **d** 1 **e** 0 **f** -1
 g -1 **h** 0 **i** 1 **j** 0 **k** 0 **l** 1

2 **a** 0.64 **b** 0.77 **c** -0.34 **d** 0.94
 e 0.17 **f** -0.98 **g** -0.77 **h** -0.64
 i 0.77 **j** -0.64 **k** 0.87 **l** -0.5

4 **a** y-coordinate is the same
 b x-coordinates are negatives of each other
 c x-coordinate is the same
 d y-coordinates are negatives of each other

5 **a** $-\sin\theta$ **b** $-\cos\theta$

6 **a** $\theta = 60^o$ **b** $\theta = 120^o$ **c** $\theta = 30^o$ or 150°

7 **a** $\theta \approx 47.8^o$ **b** $\theta \approx 132.2^o$ **c** $\theta \approx 82.1^o$
 d $\theta \approx 97.9^o$ **e** $\theta \approx 18.5^o$ or 161.5^o
 f $\theta \approx 62.5^o$ or 117.5^o **g** $\theta \approx 85.6^o$ **h** $\theta \approx 111.7^o$
 i $\theta \approx 68.3^o$ or 111.7^o

8 **a** 0 **b** 1 **c** very large number

9 **a** **i** $\cos\theta$ **ii** $\sin\theta$ **iii** $\tan\theta$

10 $\tan(180^o - \theta) = -\tan\theta$

EXERCISE 10E

1 **a** 55.2 cm^2 **b** 347 km^2 **c** 23.1 cm^2
 d 430 m^2 **e** 53.0 cm^2 **f** 1.15 m^2

2 50.0 cm^2 **3** $x \approx 22.2$ **4** $\theta = 30^o$ or 150°

5 $A\widehat{B}C \approx 41.6^o$ or 138.4^o

6 **a** **i** area $= \frac{1}{2}bc\sin A$ **ii** area $= \frac{1}{2}ab\sin C$
 b Equate areas.

EXERCISE 10F

1 **a** $x \approx 11.1$ **b** $x \approx 11.5$ **c** $x \approx 5.19$

2 **a** $a \approx 28.4$ cm **b** $b \approx 52.2$ cm **c** $c \approx 5.23$ cm

3 **a** $\theta \approx 31.4^o$ **b** $\theta \approx 77.5^o$ or 102.5^o
 c $\theta \approx 43.6^o$ or 136.4^o

4 **a** $\widehat{A} \approx 49.1^o$ **b** $\widehat{B} \approx 71.6^o$ or 108.4^o **c** $\widehat{C} \approx 44.8^o$

EXERCISE 10G

1 **a** 27.5 cm **b** 4.15 km **c** 15.2 m

2 $\widehat{A} \approx 51.8^o$, $\widehat{B} \approx 40.0^o$, $\widehat{C} \approx 88.3^o$ **3** **a** 43.0^o **b** 120°

4 **a** $\cos\theta = \dfrac{m^2 + c^2 - a^2}{2cm}$

 b $\cos(180^o - \theta) = \dfrac{m^2 + c^2 - b^2}{2cm}$

 d **i** $x \approx 9.35$ **ii** $x \approx 4.24$

5 **b** $x = 5 \pm \sqrt{6}$

c

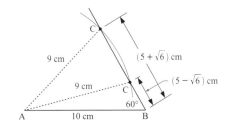

EXERCISE 10H

1 $AC \approx 14.3$ km **2** $AC \approx 1280$ m **3** $B\widehat{C}A \approx 107.5^o$
4 **a** 35.69^o **b** 4 ha **5** ≈ 1010 m
6 **a** 8.08 km **b** 099° **7** $\approx 214^o$
8 **a** 4° **b** $11\,286$ m **c** $10\,353$ m **d** 6792 m
 f 6792 m
9 ≈ 14.3 km **10** ≈ 63.4 m

EXERCISE 10I.1

1 **a** $\cos\theta = \frac{\sqrt{5}}{3}$ **b** $\cos\theta = -\frac{\sqrt{5}}{3}$ **2** $\cos\theta = -\frac{\sqrt{6}}{3}$
3 $\sin\theta = \frac{4}{5}$

EXERCISE 10I.2

1 **a** $2\cos\theta$ **b** $5\sin\theta$ **c** $3\sin\theta$
 d $2\sin\theta$ **e** $-3\cos\theta$ **f** $5\cos\theta$

2 **a** 5 **b** -3 **c** -1 **d** $7\cos^2\theta$
 e $6\sin^2\theta$ **f** $\sin\theta$ **g** $-\cos^2\theta$ **h** $3\cos^2\theta$
 i $-6\sin^2\theta$ **j** 1 **k** $2\sin\theta$ **l** $-\sin\theta$

3 **a** $4 + 4\sin\theta + \sin^2\theta$ **b** $\sin^2\alpha - 6\sin\alpha + 9$
 c $\cos^2\alpha - 8\cos\alpha + 16$ **d** $1 + 2\sin\beta\cos\beta$
 e $1 - 2\sin\phi\cos\phi$ **f** $-1 + 2\cos\alpha - \cos^2\alpha$

4 **a** $(1 + \sin\phi)(1 - \sin\phi)$ **b** $(\sin\theta + \cos\theta)(\sin\theta - \cos\theta)$
 c $(\cos\beta + 1)(\cos\beta - 1)$ **d** $\sin\beta(3\sin\beta - 1)$
 e $3\cos\phi(2 + \cos\phi)$ **f** $2\sin\theta(2\sin\theta - 1)$
 g $(\sin\theta + 2)(\sin\theta + 4)$ **h** $(2\cos\theta + 3)(\cos\theta + 2)$
 i $(4\cos\alpha - 1)(2\cos\alpha + 1)$

5 **a** $1 + \cos\alpha$ **b** $\sin\theta - 1$ **c** $\dfrac{1}{\cos\alpha + \sin\alpha}$

 d $\cos\theta - \sin\theta$ **e** $\dfrac{1}{\cos\phi - \sin\phi}$ **f** $2\cos\theta$

REVIEW SET 10A

1 $\sin\theta = \frac{5}{13}$, $\cos\theta = \frac{12}{13}$, $\tan\theta = \frac{5}{12}$
2 **a** $x \approx 14.0$ **b** $x \approx 35.2$
3 $\theta = 36^o$, $x \approx 12.4$, $y \approx 21.0$ **4** 80.9 m **5** $\theta \approx 125.3^o$
6 22.4 km **7** **a** 56.3^o **b** 33.9^o **8** 3.88 km^2
9 **a** a **b** b **c** $\dfrac{b}{a}$ **d** b **e** $-a$ **f** $-\dfrac{b}{a}$ **10** 15.8 km
11 **a** 278 m **b** $46\,658$ m$^2 \approx 4.67$ ha
12 **a** $\cos\theta - 1$ **b** $2\cos\theta$

REVIEW SET 10B

1 **a** 0.2756 **b** 0.7431 **c** -8.1443
2 **a** $x \approx 38.7^o$ **b** $x \approx 37.1^o$
3 $x \approx 25.7$, $\alpha \approx 36.4^o$, $\theta \approx 53.6^o$ **4** 638 m **5** 32.2^o
6 $\cos\theta = -\frac{\sqrt{7}}{4}$ **7** **a** 76.1 km **b** 053°
8 **a** 45° **b** 60° **9** **a** 275 m **b** $28\,558$ m$^2 \approx 2.86$ ha
10 $x \approx 2.83$ or 15.56 **11** **a** $\tan\theta$ **b** $1 - \sin\theta$ **c** $3\sin\theta$

EXERCISE 11A

1 0.55   **2** 0.84   **3** 0.0894   **4** 0.256   **5** 0.331

6 a 0.243   **b** 0.486

EXERCISE 11B

1 a 407 people   **b**

Brand	Freq	Rel Freq
Silktouch	125	0.307
Super	107	0.263
Just Soap	93	0.229
Indulgence	82	0.201
Total	407	1

c i 0.229
ii 0.201
iii 0.307

2 a

Outcome	Freq	Rel Freq
0 heads	121	0.247
1 head	259	0.530
2 heads	109	0.223
Total	489	1

b i 0.247
ii 0.530
iii 0.223

3 a 1083 people   **b**

Colour	Freq	Rel Freq
Green	361	0.25
Red	1083	0.75
Total	1444	1

c i 0.25
ii 0.75

4 a 5235 tickets   **b**

Ticket Type	Freq	Rel Freq
Adult	3762	0.719
Concession	1084	0.207
Child	389	0.074
Total	5235	1

c 0.207

5 a

Councillor	Freq	Rel Freq
Mr Tony Trimboli	2167	0.361
Mrs Andrea Sims	724	0.121
Mrs Sara Chong	2389	0.398
Mr John Henry	720	0.12
Total	6000	1

b 0.519

EXERCISE 11C

1 a {A, B, C, D}   **b** {BB, BG, GB, GG}
c {ABCD, ABDC, ACBD, ACDB, ADBC, ADCB, BACD, BADC, BCAD, BCDA, BDAC, BDCA, CABD, CADB, CBAD, CBDA, CDAB, CDBA, DABC, DACB, DBAC, DBCA, DCAB, DCBA}
d {GGG, GGB, GBG, BGG, GBB, BGB, BBG, BBB}
e i {HH, HT, TH, TT}
ii {HHH, HHT, HTH, THH, HTT, THT, TTH, TTT}
iii {HHHH, HHHT, HHTH, HTHH, THHH, HHTT, HTHT, HTTH, THHT, THTH, TTHH, HTTT, THTT, TTHT, TTTH, TTTT}

2 a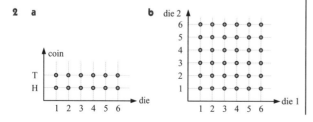
b

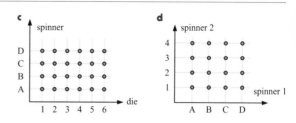

c   **d**

3 a    **b**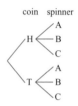

c   **d**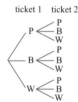

e

4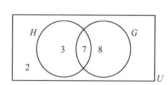

EXERCISE 11D

1 a {ODG, OGD, DOG, DGO, GOD, GDO}
b i $\frac{1}{6}$ **ii** $\frac{1}{3}$ **iii** $\frac{2}{3}$ **iv** $\frac{1}{3}$

2 a $\frac{17}{43}$ **b** $\frac{5}{43}$ **c** $\frac{24}{43}$ **d** $\frac{19}{43}$ **e** $\frac{19}{43}$ **f** $\frac{17}{24}$ **g** $\frac{5}{17}$

3 50c coin / 10c coin diagram
a $\frac{1}{4}$ **b** $\frac{1}{4}$
c $\frac{1}{2}$ **d** $\frac{3}{4}$

4 a coin / spinner diagram

b 10 outcomes   **c i** $\frac{1}{10}$ **ii** $\frac{3}{10}$ **iii** $\frac{2}{5}$ **iv** $\frac{3}{5}$

5 {ABK, AKB, BAK, BKA, KAB, KBA}
a $\frac{1}{3}$ **b** $\frac{1}{3}$ **c** $\frac{1}{3}$ **d** $\frac{2}{3}$

6 **a** {GGG, GGB, GBG, BGG, GBB, BGB, BBG, BBB}

   b **i** $\frac{1}{8}$ **ii** $\frac{1}{8}$ **iii** $\frac{1}{8}$ **iv** $\frac{3}{8}$ **v** $\frac{1}{2}$ **vi** $\frac{7}{8}$

7 **a** $\frac{3}{8}$ **b** $\frac{19}{24}$

8 **a** {PQRS, PQSR, PRQS, PRSQ, PSQR, PSRQ, QPRS, QPSR, QRPS, QRSP, QSPR, QSRP, RPQS, RPSQ, RQPS, RQSP, RSPQ, RSQP, SPQR, SPRQ, SQPR, SQRP, SRPQ, SRQP}

   b **i** $\frac{1}{2}$ **ii** $\frac{1}{2}$ **iii** $\frac{1}{2}$ **iv** $\frac{1}{2}$

9 **a**

die 2 grid with dots for all combinations of die 1 (1–6) and die 2 (1–6)

   b **i** $\frac{1}{18}$ **ii** $\frac{1}{6}$ **iii** $\frac{11}{36}$ **iv** $\frac{5}{9}$ **v** $\frac{1}{4}$ **vi** $\frac{1}{6}$

10 **a** $\frac{4}{15}$ **b** $\frac{3}{10}$ **c** $\frac{7}{10}$

11 {HHHH, HHHT, HHTH, HTHH, THHH, HHTT, HTHT, HTTH, THTH, TTHH, THHT, TTTH, TTHT, THTT, HTTT, TTTT}

   a $\frac{1}{16}$ **b** $\frac{3}{8}$ **c** $\frac{5}{16}$ **d** $\frac{15}{16}$ **e** $\frac{1}{4}$

12 **a**

suit vs card value grid (♥ ♦ ♣ ♠ against A 2 3 4 5 6 7 8 9 10 J Q K)

   b **i** $\frac{1}{13}$ **ii** $\frac{1}{52}$ **iii** $\frac{1}{4}$ **iv** $\frac{3}{13}$ **v** $\frac{1}{26}$
   vi $\frac{1}{2}$ **vii** $\frac{4}{13}$ **viii** 0

13 **a** $\frac{11}{14}$ **b** $\frac{5}{28}$ **c** $\frac{1}{28}$

EXERCISE 11E.1

1 **a** $\frac{1}{10}$ **b** $\frac{1}{5}$ **2** **a** $\frac{3}{14}$ **b** $\frac{4}{21}$

3 **a** $\frac{8}{21}$ **b** $\frac{1}{7}$ **c** $\frac{2}{7}$ **4** **a** 0.0441 **b** 0.6241

5 **a** $\frac{2}{15}$ **b** $\frac{2}{5}$ **c** $\frac{1}{5}$ **d** $\frac{4}{15}$

6 **a** **i** 0.405 **ii** 0.595 **b** 0.164 **c** 0.354

EXERCISE 11E.2

1 **a** **i** $\frac{5}{14}$ **ii** $\frac{15}{56}$ **iii** $\frac{15}{56}$ **iv** $\frac{3}{28}$
   b Because these 4 events are the only possible outcomes. One of them must occur.

2 **a** **i** $\frac{1}{3}$ **ii** $\frac{4}{15}$ **iii** $\frac{8}{15}$
   b The possibilities are: WW, WY, YW, YY.
   The 3 events do not cover all these possibilities.
   So, the probability sum should not be 1.

3 **a** $\frac{1}{14}$ **b** $\frac{1}{56}$ **c** $\frac{1}{28}$

EXERCISE 11F

1 **a**

1st spin / 2nd spin tree diagram:
B ($\frac{2}{5}$) → B ($\frac{2}{5}$), Y ($\frac{2}{5}$), G ($\frac{1}{5}$)
Y ($\frac{2}{5}$) → B ($\frac{2}{5}$), Y ($\frac{2}{5}$), G ($\frac{1}{5}$)
G ($\frac{1}{5}$) → B ($\frac{2}{5}$), Y ($\frac{2}{5}$), G ($\frac{1}{5}$)

   b $\frac{4}{25}$ **c** $\frac{1}{25}$ **d** $\frac{16}{25}$ **e** $\frac{16}{25}$

2 **a** **i** $\frac{5}{9}$ **ii** $\frac{4}{9}$

   b

tile 1 / tile 2 tree diagram:
G ($\frac{5}{9}$) → G ($\frac{5}{9}$), B ($\frac{4}{9}$)
B ($\frac{4}{9}$) → G ($\frac{5}{9}$), B ($\frac{4}{9}$)

   c **i** $\frac{25}{81}$ **ii** $\frac{16}{81}$ **iii** $\frac{20}{81}$ **iv** $\frac{40}{81}$

3 **a**

tree diagram:
muddy ($\frac{1}{4}$) → win ($\frac{2}{5}$), lose ($\frac{3}{5}$)
not muddy ($\frac{3}{4}$) → win ($\frac{1}{20}$), lose ($\frac{19}{20}$)

   b $\frac{11}{80}$

4 0.034 **5** $\frac{23}{60}$ **6** **a** $\frac{23}{42}$ **b** $\frac{19}{42}$

EXERCISE 11G

1

1st ticket / 2nd ticket tree diagram:
R ($\frac{2}{3}$) → R ($\frac{2}{3}$), Y ($\frac{1}{3}$)
Y ($\frac{1}{3}$) → R ($\frac{2}{3}$), Y ($\frac{1}{3}$)

   a $\frac{4}{9}$ **b** $\frac{1}{9}$ **c** $\frac{2}{9}$ **d** $\frac{4}{9}$

2 **a** $\frac{2}{7}$ **b** $\frac{1}{7}$ **c** $\frac{2}{7}$ **d** $\frac{4}{7}$

3 **a** $\frac{1}{6}$ **b** $\frac{5}{18}$ **c** $\frac{5}{18}$ **d** $\frac{5}{18}$
   These cases cover all possibilities, so their probabilities must add up to 1.

4 **a**

1st egg / 2nd egg tree diagram:
S ($\frac{7}{12}$) → S ($\frac{6}{11}$), D ($\frac{5}{11}$)
D ($\frac{5}{12}$) → S ($\frac{7}{11}$), D ($\frac{4}{11}$)

   b $\frac{5}{33}$ **c** $\frac{7}{22}$

5 **a**

1st chocolate / 2nd chocolate tree diagram:
H ($\frac{8}{19}$) → H ($\frac{7}{18}$), S ($\frac{11}{18}$)
S ($\frac{11}{19}$) → H ($\frac{4}{9}$), S ($\frac{5}{9}$)

   b $\frac{28}{171}$ **c** $\frac{55}{171}$

6 **a** $\frac{1}{25}$ **b** $\frac{24}{25}$ **c** $\frac{8}{199}$

EXERCISE 11H

1 a A and B, A and D, A and E, A and F, B and D,
     B and F, C and D

 b i $\frac{2}{3}$ **ii** $\frac{5}{6}$ **iii** $\frac{2}{3}$ **iv** $\frac{1}{2}$ **v** 1   **vi** $\frac{5}{6}$

2 a

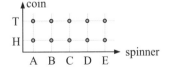

coin

T • • • • • •
H • • • • • •
   1 2 3 4 5 6 → die

 b i $\frac{1}{12}$

   ii $\frac{7}{12}$

 c $P(H) + P(5) - P(H \text{ and } 5) = \frac{6}{12} + \frac{2}{12} - \frac{1}{12}$
             $= \frac{7}{12} = P(H \text{ or } 5)$

3 a

die 2

6 • • • • • •
5 • • • • • •
4 • • • • • •
3 • • • • • •
2 • • • • • •
1 • • • • • •
   1 2 3 4 5 6 → die 1

 b i $\frac{1}{18}$

   ii $\frac{5}{9}$

 c $P(3) + P(4) - P(3 \text{ and } 4) = \frac{11}{36} + \frac{11}{36} - \frac{2}{36}$
             $= \frac{5}{9} = P(3 \text{ or } 4)$

EXERCISE 11I.1

1 a $\frac{2}{5}$ **b** $\frac{17}{35}$ **c** $\frac{27}{35}$ **d** $\frac{22}{35}$ **e** $\frac{13}{35}$

2 a $\frac{8}{25}$ **b** $\frac{7}{50}$ **c** $\frac{12}{25}$

3 a i $\dfrac{b+c}{a+b+c+d}$ **ii** $\dfrac{b}{a+b+c+d}$

   iii $\dfrac{a+b+c}{a+b+c+d}$ **iv** $\dfrac{a+b+c}{a+b+c+d}$

 b $P(A \text{ or } B) = P(A) + P(B) - P(A \text{ and } B)$

EXERCISE 11I.2

1 a 11   **b i** $\frac{29}{50}$ **ii** $\frac{11}{40}$

2 a $\frac{12}{25}$ **b** $\frac{3}{25}$ **c** $\frac{7}{25}$ **d** $\frac{12}{19}$

3 a $\frac{5}{7}$ **b** $\frac{13}{14}$ **c** $\frac{1}{14}$ **d** $\frac{5}{23}$ **e** $\frac{9}{10}$

4 a $\frac{24}{25}$ **b** $\frac{1}{25}$

5 a $\frac{1}{20}$ **b** $\frac{19}{20}$ **c** $\frac{31}{50}$ **d** $\frac{39}{50}$ **e** $\frac{12}{19}$ **f** $\frac{17}{78}$

6 a $\frac{3}{4}$ **b** $\frac{5}{9}$ **7 a** $\frac{13}{15}$ **b** $\frac{7}{52}$ **8** $\frac{35}{47}$

REVIEW SET 11A

1 a 39 days   **b i** $\frac{1}{39}$ **ii** $\frac{11}{39}$ **iii** $\frac{19}{39}$

2

coin

T • • • • •
H • • • • •
   A B C D E → spinner

3 The occurrence of either event does not affect the occurrence of
   the other event.

4 a $\frac{1}{16}$ **b** $\frac{3}{8}$ **c** $\frac{5}{16}$

5 a 0.72   **b** 0.02   **c** 0.98   **d** 0.18

6 $\frac{1}{6}$ **7 a** $\frac{16}{49}$ **b** $\frac{24}{49}$

8 a

coin

T • • • • •
H • • • • •
   1 2 3 4 5 → spinner

 b i $\frac{1}{10}$

   ii $\frac{3}{5}$

9

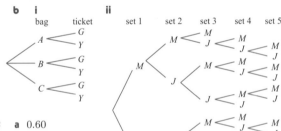

bag   1st marble   2nd marble

          $\frac{1}{4}$ — R $\frac{9}{20}$
$\frac{2}{5}$ — R
    X < $\frac{3}{4}$ — W
          $\frac{3}{5}$ — W $\frac{2}{4}$ — R
$\frac{1}{2}$ $\frac{2}{4}$ — W
    <
$\frac{1}{2}$ $\frac{3}{4}$ — R $\frac{2}{3}$ — R
    Y < $\frac{1}{3}$ — W
          $\frac{1}{4}$ — W — 1 — R

10

N T
20% (45%) 15%
U 20%

 a $\frac{13}{20}$ **b** $\frac{1}{5}$

 c $\frac{4}{5}$ **d** $\frac{7}{20}$

 e $\frac{9}{13}$

REVIEW SET 11B

1 a 0.364   **b** 0.551   **c** 0.814

2 a {AH, BH, CH, DH, AT, BT, CT, DT}

 b i   **ii**

bag   ticket   set 1 set 2 set 3 set 4 set 5

        G
   A <
        Y   M — M < M
   B < G   M < M <   J — J < M
        Y   M <   M — M <   J
   C < G   J < M <   J — M < M
        Y   J < J
                       M — M < M
                  J <   J — M <   J
                       J < M — M < M
                            J — M <   J
                                     J < J

3 a 0.60

 b 0.40

4 a $\frac{3}{14}$

 b

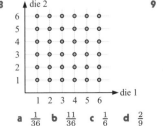

   1st draw   2nd draw   **c i** $\frac{33}{91}$

                 vowel $\left(\frac{2}{13}\right)$ **ii** $\frac{36}{91}$
  vowel $\left(\frac{3}{14}\right)$
                 non-vowel $\left(\frac{11}{13}\right)$

                 vowel $\left(\frac{3}{13}\right)$
  non-vowel $\left(\frac{11}{14}\right)$
                 non-vowel $\left(\frac{10}{13}\right)$

5 a $\frac{1}{9}$ **b** $\frac{4}{9}$ **c** $\frac{4}{9}$ **6** $\frac{5}{12}$ **7 a** $\frac{1}{20}$ **b** $\frac{3}{10}$

8

die 2

6 • • • • • •
5 • • • • • •
4 • • • • • •
3 • • • • • •
2 • • • • • •
1 • • • • • •
   1 2 3 4 5 6 → die 1

 a $\frac{1}{36}$ **b** $\frac{11}{36}$ **c** $\frac{1}{6}$ **d** $\frac{2}{9}$

9

B F
12 3 6
U 4

 a $\frac{4}{25}$ **b** $\frac{12}{25}$

 c $\frac{1}{5}$ **d** $\frac{2}{5}$

EXERCISE 12A.1

1 **a** $2a$ **b** $2b$ **c** $\dfrac{1}{2x}$ **d** 8 **e** cannot be simplified

f $2a$ **g** $\dfrac{1}{2b}$ **h** 2 **i** $\dfrac{1}{3a^2}$ **j** $\dfrac{x}{2}$

k cannot be simplified **l** $\dfrac{a}{b}$ **m** cannot be simplified

n $\dfrac{5x}{y}$ **o** $2ac$ **p** $4a$ **q** 1 **r** $3a^3$ **s** a^2 **t** $\dfrac{a}{2}$

2 **a** $\dfrac{x}{3}+1$ **b** $2a+\dfrac{1}{2}$ **c** $\dfrac{a}{c}+\dfrac{b}{c}$ **d** $\dfrac{a}{b}+2$

e $a+2$ **f** $a+2b$ **g** $m+2n$ **h** $2+\dfrac{4n}{m}$

3 **e, f** and **g** produce simplified answers. They have common factors in the numerator and denominator.

4 **a** $x+2$ **b** $2(x-1)$ **c** $\dfrac{b+2}{2}$ **d** $\dfrac{n+5}{6}$ **e** $\dfrac{2}{x+2}$

f $\dfrac{3}{3-a}$ **g** 6 **h** $\dfrac{1}{2}$ **i** $\dfrac{2}{x}$ **j** $\dfrac{x(x-5)}{3}$

k $\dfrac{x+3}{2(x+2)}$ **l** $\dfrac{x+2}{5}$ **m** $\dfrac{x+2}{x+3}$ **n** $\dfrac{x+5}{3}$

o $\dfrac{x+6}{3}$ **p** $\dfrac{x}{x-1}$ **q** $\dfrac{(x+2)(x+1)}{4}$ **r** $\dfrac{(x+2)^2}{x^2}$

EXERCISE 12A.2

1 **a** $\dfrac{3}{x+2}$ **b** $x+3$ **c** $x+4$ **d** $\dfrac{x+2}{2}$

e $\dfrac{x+4}{2}$ **f** $\dfrac{a+4}{3}$ **g** $y+z$ **h** x

i $\dfrac{a+c}{a-c}$ **j** $\dfrac{1}{2(x-4)}$ **k** $\dfrac{x+3}{6}$ **l** $\dfrac{x-y}{3}$

2 **a** 2 **b** $\dfrac{m+n}{2}$ **c** x **d** $\dfrac{1}{m}$ **e** $x+2$ **f** $x+2$

g x **h** $\dfrac{1}{b+c}$ **i** $3x$ **j** $x+3$ **k** $2x$ **l** x

3 **a** -2 **b** $-\dfrac{1}{2}$ **c** -1 **d** cannot be simplified

e $-\dfrac{1}{2}$ **f** -3 **g** $-\dfrac{3}{x}$ **h** $-\dfrac{xy}{3}$ **i** $-3x$ **j** $\dfrac{2x+3}{2}$

k cannot be simplified **l** $x+2$ **m** $x-2$ **n** $-(x+2)$

o $\dfrac{1}{x-3}$ **p** $m-n$ **q** $-(m+n)$ **r** $\dfrac{3}{2-x}$

s $-\dfrac{x+4}{x}$ **t** -1 **u** $\dfrac{x+y}{2y}$ **v** $-\dfrac{2(a+d)}{a}$

w $\dfrac{4x}{x+2}$ **x** $\dfrac{-3x}{x+2}$

4 **a** $\dfrac{x}{x+1}$ **b** $\dfrac{x+1}{x+2}$ **c** $\dfrac{x-2}{2x}$ **d** $\dfrac{x+3}{x+4}$

e $\dfrac{x-2}{x-5}$ **f** $\dfrac{x+4}{2x}$ **g** $\dfrac{x-1}{2(x-2)}$ **h** $\dfrac{x+3}{x}$

i $\dfrac{2x+1}{x+2}$ **j** $\dfrac{x+2}{x-1}$ **k** $\dfrac{2x+5}{x+3}$ **l** $\dfrac{4x+1}{x-2}$

EXERCISE 12B

1 **a** $\dfrac{ab}{6}$ **b** $\dfrac{1}{2}$ **c** $\dfrac{1}{2}$ **d** $\dfrac{a^2}{6}$ **e** $\dfrac{ax}{by}$ **f** 1

g $\dfrac{x^2}{3}$ **h** $\dfrac{2x}{y}$ **i** $\dfrac{1}{2n}$ **j** 3 **k** $\dfrac{m}{n}$ **l** 2

m $5t$ **n** $\dfrac{x^2}{y^2}$ **o** $\dfrac{16}{d^2}$ **p** 1

2 **a** $\dfrac{2}{3}$ **b** $\dfrac{1}{2}$ **c** $3x$ **d** $3y$ **e** 3 **f** $\dfrac{c}{n^2}$

g $\dfrac{d^2}{5}$ **h** 3 **i** $\dfrac{b}{a}$ **j** $\dfrac{3}{2d}$ **k** $\dfrac{8}{x^3}$ **l** $\dfrac{x}{2}$

m $\dfrac{3}{a}$ **n** $\dfrac{1}{x}$ **o** $\dfrac{10}{a^2}$ **p** $\dfrac{3a}{5}$

EXERCISE 12C

1 **a** $\dfrac{7x}{10}$ **b** $\dfrac{x}{6}$ **c** $\dfrac{17x}{20}$ **d** $\dfrac{3x}{10}$ **e** $\dfrac{t}{12}$ **f** $\dfrac{8n}{21}$ **g** $\dfrac{5a}{6}$

h $\dfrac{2a+b}{4}$ **i** $\dfrac{7n}{15}$ **j** $\dfrac{g}{2}$ **k** $\dfrac{2s}{15}$ **l** $\dfrac{2a}{5}$ **m** x

n $\dfrac{5y}{12}$ **o** $\dfrac{z}{12}$ **p** $\dfrac{41q}{21}$

2 **a** $\dfrac{3b+2a}{ab}$ **b** $\dfrac{4d+3a}{ad}$ **c** $\dfrac{5b-3a}{ab}$ **d** $\dfrac{a}{m}$

e $\dfrac{3a+b}{3y}$ **f** $\dfrac{3}{2a}$ **g** $\dfrac{3b-2}{ab}$ **h** $\dfrac{dc+ab}{ad}$

i $\dfrac{4+a}{b}$ **j** $\dfrac{2d-ac}{ad}$ **k** $\dfrac{15+x^2}{3x}$ **l** $\dfrac{pd-12}{6d}$

m $\dfrac{m^2+3n}{3m}$ **n** $\dfrac{2mn-mp}{np}$ **o** $\dfrac{17b}{20}$ **p** $\dfrac{16b}{15}$

3 **a** $\dfrac{x+6}{3}$ **b** $\dfrac{m-2}{2}$ **c** $\dfrac{4a}{3}$ **d** $\dfrac{b-10}{5}$

e $\dfrac{x-18}{6}$ **f** $\dfrac{12+x}{4}$ **g** $\dfrac{30-x}{6}$ **h** $\dfrac{2x+3}{x}$

i $\dfrac{6x-3}{x}$ **j** $\dfrac{b^2+3}{b}$ **k** $\dfrac{5+x^2}{x}$ **l** $-\dfrac{11y}{6}$

4 **a** $\dfrac{14x}{15}$ **b** $\dfrac{11x}{35}$ **c** $\dfrac{11}{2a}$ **d** $\dfrac{21}{4y}$

e $\dfrac{3c+4b}{bc}$ **f** $\dfrac{5b-24a}{4ab}$ **g** $\dfrac{x+30}{10}$ **h** $\dfrac{12-x}{3}$

EXERCISE 12D.1

1 **a** $\dfrac{9x-4}{20}$ **b** $\dfrac{5x+10}{6}$ **c** $\dfrac{20x-7}{42}$ **d** $\dfrac{a+5b}{6}$

e $\dfrac{13x-9}{20}$ **f** $\dfrac{5x+11}{14}$ **g** $\dfrac{x+15}{30}$ **h** $\dfrac{x-7}{42}$

i $\dfrac{2-3x}{10}$ **j** $\dfrac{3x-1}{12}$ **k** $\dfrac{2x+1}{15}$ **l** $\dfrac{25x+5}{24}$

2 **a** $\dfrac{5x-1}{(x+1)(x-2)}$ **b** $\dfrac{12x+17}{(x+1)(x+2)}$

c $\dfrac{x+14}{(x-1)(x+2)}$ **d** $\dfrac{-6}{(x+2)(2x+1)}$

e $\dfrac{7x+8}{(x-1)(x+4)}$ **f** $\dfrac{15x+6}{(1-x)(x+2)}$ **g** $\dfrac{4x+3}{x(x+1)}$

h $\dfrac{3x+15}{x(x+3)}$ **i** $\dfrac{x^2-x+6}{(x+2)(x-4)}$ **j** $\dfrac{2x-2}{x-3}$

k $\dfrac{2x-2}{x+2}$ **l** $\dfrac{2x^2+4x-3}{(x+3)(x+2)}$ **m** $\dfrac{x+2}{x(x+1)}$

n $\dfrac{x^2+1}{x(x-1)(x+1)}$ **o** $\dfrac{4x^2-x-9}{(x+1)(x-1)(x+2)}$

p $\dfrac{2x^3-x^2+1}{x(x+1)(x-1)}$

EXERCISE 12D.2

1 **a** $\dfrac{2+x}{x(x+1)}$ **b** $\dfrac{2+x^2}{x(x+1)}$ **c** $\dfrac{2(x^2+2x+2)}{(x+2)(x-3)}$

d $\dfrac{2(x+5)}{x+2}$ **e** $\dfrac{x^2-2x+3}{(x-2)(x+3)}$ **f** $\dfrac{x-5}{x-2}$

g $\dfrac{2(x-5)}{x-1}$ **h** $\dfrac{x+14}{x+7}$

2 a $\dfrac{2(x+1)^2}{(x+2)(x-3)}$ **b**   **i** $x=-2$ or 3 **ii** $x=-1$

3 a $\dfrac{-2}{x-2}$ **b** $\dfrac{2}{x+4}$ **c** $\dfrac{x-2}{x+2}$

d $\dfrac{x-6}{2-x}$ **e** $\dfrac{-(x+2)}{4x^2}$ **f** $\dfrac{12-x}{16x^2}$

REVIEW SET 12A

1 a $3x$ **b** $3n$ **c** $\dfrac{x}{6}$ **d** $\dfrac{2}{x}$

2 a $\dfrac{2}{c+3}$ **b** cannot be simplified   **c** $x+2$ **d** $\dfrac{x}{3(x+2)}$

3 a $\dfrac{19x}{15}$ **b** $\dfrac{2x^2}{5}$ **c** $\dfrac{10}{9}$ **d** $\dfrac{x}{15}$

4 a 4 **b** -5 **c** $2x$

5 a $\dfrac{11x+1}{12}$ **b** $\dfrac{16x-9}{14}$ **c** $\dfrac{3x+2}{x(x+2)}$

6 a $\dfrac{-2}{x+4}$ **b** $\dfrac{x+3}{x}$ **c** $\dfrac{2x+1}{3x+2}$

7 a $\dfrac{3(x+5)}{x+1}$ **b**   **i** $x=-1$ or 4 **ii** $x=-5$

REVIEW SET 12B

1 a $\dfrac{2}{3}$ **b** $2x$ **c** $3n$ **d** $2x$

2 a cannot be simplified   **b** $x+5$ **c** $\dfrac{2}{a+4}$ **d** $\dfrac{b}{2(b-a)}$

3 a $\dfrac{11x}{4}$ **b** $\dfrac{-5x}{4}$ **c** $\dfrac{3x^2}{2}$ **d** $\dfrac{3}{8}$

4 a -1 **b** $\dfrac{5}{2}$ **c** $\dfrac{3x}{a}$

5 a $\dfrac{13x-5}{15}$ **b** $-\dfrac{5x+3}{6}$ **c** $\dfrac{x+6}{2x(x+2)}$

6 a $2(x-2)$ **b** $\dfrac{x-7}{x-2}$ **c** $\dfrac{3x+1}{4x+1}$

7 a $\dfrac{2(x-7)}{x-2}$ **b**   **i** $x=7$ **ii** $x=-5$ or 2

8 a $\dfrac{-10}{x-1}$ **b** $\dfrac{2x+3}{2(3-x)}$

EXERCISE 13A

1 a 26.4 cm   **b** 17.8 cm   **c** 127.3 m

2 a 19.6 m   **b** 113 m

3 a 71.4 km h^{-1} **b** 220 km   **c** 8 h 19 min

4 a 128.7 cm^2 **b** 7.14 m

5 a 4263 cm^3 **b** 1.06 cm   **c** 4.99 mm

6 a 706.9 cm^2 **b** 39.9 cm   **7**   **a** 55.8 m^3 **b** 8.42 cm

8 a 15.9 km   **b** 49.3 m   **9**   **a** 1.34 sec   **b** 81 cm

EXERCISE 13B.1

1 a $y=2-\dfrac{2}{5}x$ **b** $y=5-\dfrac{3}{4}x$ **c** $y=2x-8$

d $y=2-\dfrac{2}{7}x$ **e** $y=10-\dfrac{5}{2}x$ **f** $y=\dfrac{2}{3}x+4$

2 a $x=r-p$ **b** $x=\dfrac{z}{y}$ **c** $x=\dfrac{d-a}{3}$

d $x=\dfrac{d-2y}{5}$ **e** $x=\dfrac{p-by}{a}$ **f** $x=\dfrac{y-c}{m}$

g $x=\dfrac{s-2}{t}$ **h** $x=\dfrac{m-p}{q}$ **i** $x=\dfrac{6-a}{b}$

3 a $y=mx-c$ **b** $y=\dfrac{c-p}{2}$ **c** $y=\dfrac{a-t}{3}$

d $y=\dfrac{n-5}{k}$ **e** $y=\dfrac{a-n}{b}$ **f** $y=\dfrac{a-p}{n}$

4 a $z=\dfrac{b}{ac}$ **b** $z=\dfrac{a}{d}$ **c** $z=\dfrac{2d}{3}$

d $z=\pm\sqrt{2a}$ **e** $z=\pm\sqrt{bn}$ **f** $z=\pm\sqrt{m(a-b)}$

5 a $a=\dfrac{F}{m}$ **b** $r=\dfrac{C}{2\pi}$ **c** $d=\dfrac{V}{lh}$

d $K=\dfrac{b}{A}$ **e** $h=\dfrac{2A}{b}$ **f** $T=\dfrac{100I}{PR}$

EXERCISE 13B.2

1 $y=-\dfrac{5}{3}x+6$ **a** $-\dfrac{5}{3}$ **b** 6

2 a $a=\dfrac{d^2}{2bK}$ **b**   **i** 1.29   **ii** 16.2

3 a $d=st$ **i** 180 km   **ii** 120 km   **iii** 126.7 km

b $t=\dfrac{d}{s}$ **i** 3 hours   **ii** 4 hours   **iii** 2 hours 12 mins

4 a $n=\dfrac{I}{Cr}$ **b**   **i** 2.05 years   **ii** 10 years

EXERCISE 13C

1 a $A=200\times17$ **b** $A=200m$ **c** $A=Dm$

2 a $A=2000+150\times8$ **b** $A=2000+150w$

c $A=2000+dw$ **d** $A=P+dw$

3 a $C=40+60\times5$ **b** $C=40+60t$

c $C=40+xt$ **d** $C=F+xt$

4 a $A=200-8\times5$ **b** $A=200-5x$

c $A=200-bx$ **d** $A=P-bx$

5 a $C=5000-10\times200$ **b** $C=5000-200r$

c $C=5000-mr$ **d** $C=L-mr$

6 a $V=Al$ **b** $V=\pi r^2 h$ **c** $V=\frac{1}{2}abc$

7 a $A=2ab+2bc+2ac$

b $A=ab+bc+ac+c\sqrt{a^2+b^2}$ **c** $A=2\pi r(r+h)$

EXERCISE 13D

1 a $3, 5, 7$ **b** $9, 11$ **c** 21 **d** $M=2n+1$

2 a $2+4+6+8+10=30=5\times6$
$2+4+6+8+10+12=42=6\times7$
$2+4+6+8+10+12+14=56=7\times8$

b $2+4+6+8+\dots\dots+2n=n(n+1)$

c $1+2+3+4+\dots\dots+n=\dfrac{n(n+1)}{2}$ **d** 20 100

3 a $22, 27$ **b** 102 **c** $M=5n+2$

4 a $1+3+5+7=16=4^2$
$1+3+5+7+9=25=5^2$
$1+3+5+7+9+11=36=6^2$

b $1+3+5+7+\dots\dots+99=50^2=2500$

c The nth odd number is $2n-1$.

d $1+3+5+7+\dots\dots+(2n-3)+(2n-1)$

e $1+3+5+7+\dots\dots+(2n-3)+(2n-1)=n^2$

5 a $M = 46$ **b** $M = 6n - 2$

6 a $S_1 = \frac{1}{2}$, $S_2 = \frac{2}{3}$, $S_3 = \frac{3}{4}$, $S_4 = \frac{4}{5}$

   b i $S_{10} = \frac{10}{11}$ **ii** $S_n = \dfrac{n}{n+1}$

7 b $338\,350$ **8 b** $1\,625\,625$ **c** $13\,005\,000$

EXERCISE 13E

1 a $x = \dfrac{c-a}{3-b}$ **b** $x = \dfrac{c}{a+b}$ **c** $x = \dfrac{a+2}{n-m}$

   d $x = \dfrac{-a}{b+8}$ **e** $x = \dfrac{b-a}{c-1}$ **f** $x = \dfrac{e-d}{r+s}$

2 a $r = \sqrt{\dfrac{A}{\pi}}$ **b** $x = \sqrt[5]{aN}$ **c** $r = \sqrt[3]{\dfrac{3V}{4\pi}}$

   d $x = \sqrt[3]{\dfrac{n}{D}}$ **e** $x = \pm\sqrt{\dfrac{y+7}{4}} = \pm\dfrac{\sqrt{y+7}}{2}$

   f $Q = \pm\sqrt{P^2 - R^2}$

3 a $a = d^2 n^2$ **b** $l = 25T^2$ **c** $a = \pm\sqrt{b^2+c^2}$

   d $d = \dfrac{25a^2}{k^2}$ **e** $l = \dfrac{gT^2}{4\pi^2}$ **f** $b = \dfrac{16a}{A^2}$

4 a $a = \dfrac{P}{2} - b$ **b** $h = \dfrac{A - \pi r^2}{2\pi r}$ **c** $r = \dfrac{E}{I} - R$

   d $q = p - \dfrac{B}{A}$ **e** $x = \dfrac{3 - Ay}{2A}$ **f** $y = \sqrt{\dfrac{4}{M} - x^2}$

5 a $x = \dfrac{y}{1-y}$ **b** $x = \dfrac{2y+3}{1-y}$ **c** $x = \dfrac{3y+1}{3-y}$

   d $x = \dfrac{y-2}{y-5}$ **e** $x = \dfrac{2y+1}{y+4}$ **f** $x = \dfrac{3y-7}{2y+3}$

   g $x = \dfrac{3y-1}{y-1}$ **h** $x = \dfrac{5}{y+2} - 4$ **i** $x = \dfrac{2y}{y+3}$

6 a $r = \sqrt[3]{\dfrac{3V}{4\pi}}$ **b i** 2.12 cm   **ii** 62.0 cm

7 a $t = \sqrt{\dfrac{2S}{a}}$ **b i** 3.16 sec   **ii** 15.8 sec

8 a $v = \sqrt{c^2\left(1 - \dfrac{m_0^2}{m^2}\right)} = \dfrac{c}{m}\sqrt{m^2 - m_0^2}$

   b $v = \dfrac{\sqrt{8}}{3}c$ **c** 2.998×10^8 m s^{-1}

REVIEW SET 13A

1 a 11.4 g cm^{-3} **b** 37.9 g   **c** 9230.8 cm^3

2 a 1.72 sec   **b** 156.3 cm

3 a $x = \dfrac{y-c}{m}$ **b** $x = \pm\sqrt{\dfrac{2}{a}}$

4 a i $V = 6 \times 8$ **ii** $V = 8n$ **iii** $V = ln$

   b $V = 25 + ln$

5 a $M = 20$ **b** $M = 2n$

6 a $p = 3r - q$ **b** $p = \sqrt[3]{y^2 - 3}$ **7** $x = \dfrac{2y-3}{y-2}$

8 a i 9, 11, 13   **ii** $2n - 1$

   b i $T_4 = \dfrac{1}{7 \times 9}$, $T_5 = \dfrac{1}{9 \times 11}$, $T_6 = \dfrac{1}{11 \times 13}$

   ii $T_{20} = \dfrac{1}{39 \times 41}$ **iii** $T_n = \dfrac{1}{(2n-1)(2n+1)}$

REVIEW SET 13B

1 a 7226 cm^3 **b** 0.943 m

2 a $x = \dfrac{3q - y}{2}$ **b** $x = \dfrac{4}{3y}$

3 a $C = 2 + 1 \times 1.20$ **b** $C = 2 + 5 \times 1.20$
   c $C = p + 1.2b$ **d** $C = p + bx$

4 $y = \frac{2}{3}x - \frac{4}{3}$ **a** $m = \frac{2}{3}$ **b** $c = -\frac{4}{3}$

5 a $M = 25$ **b** $M = 3n + 1$ **6** $y = \dfrac{64}{x^2}$

7 a $r = \sqrt{\dfrac{A}{4\pi}}$ **b** 34.5 cm   **8** $b = \dfrac{ac}{c-a}$

EXERCISE 14A

1 a Domain $= \{-3, -2, -1, 0, 6\}$ Range $= \{-1, 3, 4, 5, 8\}$
   b Domain $= \{-3, -1, 0, 2, 4, 5, 7\}$ Range $= \{3, 4\}$

2 a Domain is $\{x \mid x > -4\}$. Range is $\{y \mid y > -2\}$.
   b Domain is $\{x \mid x = 2\}$. Range is $\{y \mid y$ is in $\mathbb{R}\}$.
   c Domain is $\{x \mid -3 \leqslant x \leqslant 3\}$. Range is $\{y \mid -3 \leqslant y \leqslant 3\}$.
   d Domain is $\{x \mid x$ is in $\mathbb{R}\}$. Range is $\{y \mid y \leqslant 0\}$.
   e Domain is $\{x \mid x$ is in $\mathbb{R}\}$. Range is $\{y \mid y = -5\}$.
   f Domain is $\{x \mid x$ is in $\mathbb{R}\}$. Range is $\{y \geqslant 1\}$.
   g Domain is $\{x \mid x$ is in $\mathbb{R}\}$. Range is $\{y \mid y \leqslant 4\}$.
   h Domain is $\{x \mid x \geqslant -5\}$. Range is $\{y \mid y$ is in $\mathbb{R}\}$.
   i Domain is $\{x \mid x$ is in $\mathbb{R}$, $x \neq 1\}$.
   Range is $\{y \mid y$ is in $\mathbb{R}$, $y \neq 0\}$.

3 a Domain is $\{x \mid 0 \leqslant x \leqslant 2\}$. Range is $\{y \mid -3 \leqslant y \leqslant 2\}$.
   b Domain is $\{x \mid -2 < x < 2\}$. Range is $\{y \mid -1 < y < 3\}$.
   c Domain is $\{x \mid -4 \leqslant x \leqslant 4\}$. Range is $\{y \mid -2 \leqslant y \leqslant 2\}$.

EXERCISE 14B

1 a, b, e are functions as no two ordered pairs have the same x-coordinate.

2 a, b, d, e, g, h, i are functions.

3 No, a vertical line is not a function as it does not satisfy the vertical line test.

EXERCISE 14C.1

1 a 3   **b** 7   **c** 1   **d** -7 **e** 2

2 a 3   **b** $4\frac{1}{2}$ **c** -3 **d** $-4\frac{1}{2}$ **e** $-4\frac{1}{2}$

3 a 2   **b** 11   **c** 29   **d** 121   **e** 1

4 a $5 - 2a$ **b** $5 + 2a$ **c** $3 - 2a$ **d** $11 - 2x$ **e** $5 - 4x$

5 a $x^2 + 8x + 9$ **b** $x^2 - 6x + 2$ **c** $x^2 - 4x - 3$
   d $x^4 + 4x^2 - 3$ **e** $x^4 + 6x^2 + 2$

6 a i $-\frac{3}{2}$ **ii** $-\frac{1}{3}$ **iii** $-\frac{8}{3}$ **b** $x = -2$ **c** $2 - \dfrac{7}{x}$
   d $x = -1$

7 a $V(4) = \$12\,000$, the value of the car after 4 years.
   b $t = 5$; the car is worth $8000 after 5 years   **c** \$28\,000

EXERCISE 14C.2

1 a $\{x \mid x \geqslant 2\}$ **b** $\{x \mid x \leqslant 3\}$
   c $\{x \mid 0 \leqslant x \leqslant 2\}$ **d** $\{x \mid x > 0\}$
   e $\{x \mid x > 0\}$ **f** $\{x \mid x < 4,$ but $x \neq 0\}$

EXERCISE 14D

1 **a** $2 - 3x$ **b** $6 - 3x$ **c** $9x - 16$ **d** x

2 **a** $\sqrt{4x - 3}$ **b** $4\sqrt{x} - 3$ **c** $\sqrt[4]{x}$ **d** $16x - 15$

3 **a** $f(x) = \sqrt{x}, \ g(x) = x - 3$ **b** $f(x) = x^3, \ g(x) = x + 5$

c $f(x) = \dfrac{5}{x}, \ g(x) = x + 7$ **d** $f(x) = 3 - 4x, \ g(x) = \dfrac{1}{\sqrt{x}}$

e $f(x) = x^2, \ \ g(x) = 3^x$ **f** $f(x) = \dfrac{x + 1}{x - 1}, \ \ g(x) = x^2$

4 $x = -3$ or 1 **5** $g(x) = x^2 + 2$ **6** $f(x) = x^2 - 3$

EXERCISE 14E

1 **a** $y = -3x^2 + 30x - 77$ **b** $y = -\sqrt{x}$ **c** $y = 2x + 1$
d $x = 3 - 5y$ **e** $y = 4x^2 - 6x + 1$ **f** $y = x^2 - x$

2 **a** $y = f(-x) = x^2$ **b** $y = -f(x) = -x^2$

c $y = f(3x) = 9x^2$ **d** $y = 2f(x) = 2x^2$

3

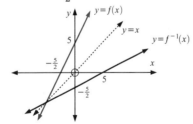

── $y = f(x)$
── $y = f(x - 1) - 2$
── $y = f(-x)$
── $y = -f(x)$
── $y = 2f(x)$
── $y = f(2x)$

EXERCISE 14F

1 **a** **i** $f^{-1}(x) = \dfrac{x - 5}{2}$

ii

b **i** $f^{-1}(x) = -2x + \frac{3}{2}$

ii
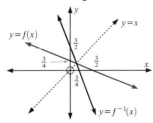

c **i** $f^{-1}(x) = x - 3$ **ii**
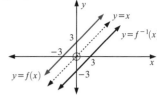

2 **a**
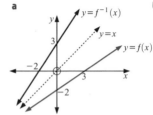

b
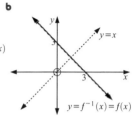

c
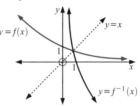

3 **a** $f^{-1}(x) = \dfrac{x - 7}{2}$ **b** x **c** x

4 **a** $f^{-1}(x) = \dfrac{1 - 3x}{x - 2}$ **b** x **c** x

5 **a**
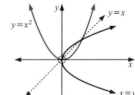

b No, as the vertical line test fails.

c Yes, it is $y = \sqrt{x}$ (not $y = \pm\sqrt{x}$).

6 **b** **i** and **iii**

7 **a** Is a function as it passes the vertical line test, but does not have an inverse as it fails the horizontal line test.
b No horizontal line cuts it more than once.

EXERCISE 14G.1

1 **a** 2 **b** 10 **c** 5 **d** 11 **e** 11 **f** 40 **g** 40 **h** -2

2 **a** **i** both 9   **ii** both 0   **iii** both 4   **iv** both 81
v both 81   **vi** both 400
b $|a|^2 = a^2$

3 **a**

a	b	$|ab|$	$|a|\,|b|$	$\left|\dfrac{a}{b}\right|$	$\dfrac{|a|}{|b|}$
12	3	36	36	4	4
12	-3	36	36	4	4
-12	3	36	36	4	4
-12	-3	36	36	4	4

b It is likely that $|ab| = |a|\,|b|$ and $\left|\dfrac{a}{b}\right| = \dfrac{|a|}{|b|}, \ b \neq 0.$

5 a

a	b	$|a+b|$	$|a|+|b|$	$|a-b|$	$|a|-|b|$
2	5	7	7	3	−3
2	−5	3	7	7	−3
−2	5	3	7	7	−3
−2	−5	7	7	3	−3

b $|a+b| \neq |a|+|b|$, $|a-b| \neq |a|-|b|$

6 a

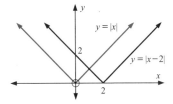

Translation $\begin{pmatrix} 2 \\ 0 \end{pmatrix}$

b

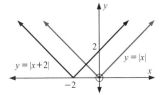

Translation $\begin{pmatrix} -2 \\ 0 \end{pmatrix}$

c

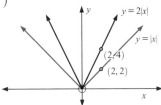

All y-coordinates double

d

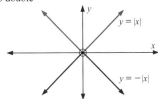

Reflection in the x-axis

e

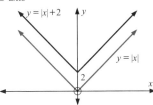

Translation $\begin{pmatrix} 0 \\ 2 \end{pmatrix}$

f

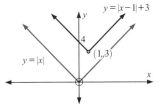

Translation $\begin{pmatrix} 1 \\ 3 \end{pmatrix}$

7 a $y = \begin{cases} -x & \text{if } x \geqslant 0 \\ x & \text{if } x < 0 \end{cases}$

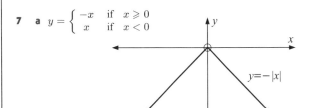

b $y = \begin{cases} 2x & \text{if } x \geqslant 0 \\ 0 & \text{if } x < 0 \end{cases}$

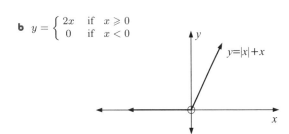

c $y = \begin{cases} 1 & \text{if } x > 0 \\ \text{undefined} & \text{if } x = 0 \\ -1 & \text{if } x < 0 \end{cases}$

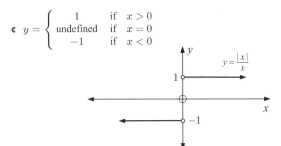

d $y = \begin{cases} -x & \text{if } x \geqslant 0 \\ 3x & \text{if } x < 0 \end{cases}$

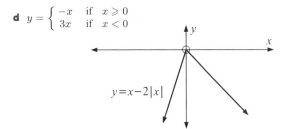

8 a

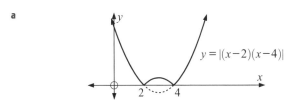

b

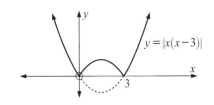

The part of the graph $y = (x - 2)(x - 4)$ or
$y = x(x - 3)$ below the x-axis is reflected in the x-axis.

EXERCISE 14G.2

1 a $x = \pm 5$ **b** no solution as $|x|$ cannot be < 0

c $x = 0$ **d** $x = 3$ or -5 **e** $x = 9$ or -1

f no solution as $|x + 6|$ cannot be < 0 **g** $x = \frac{7}{3}$ or 1

h $x = \frac{7}{2}$ or $-\frac{1}{2}$ **i** $x = \frac{17}{7}$ or 1 **j** $x = -\frac{5}{3}$ or $-\frac{5}{7}$

k $x = -\frac{5}{4}$ **l** $x = -\frac{13}{10}$ or $\frac{19}{2}$

2 a

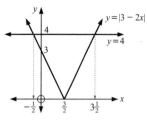

b

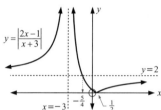

EXERCISE 14H

1 a at $(-3, 2)$ and $(2, 7)$ **b** at $(2, 1)$ and $(-1, -2)$

c at $(-\frac{1}{2}, -\frac{9}{4})$ and $(-3, 14)$ **d** at $(1, 1)$ and $(-\frac{1}{5}, -5)$

2 a at $(-1.62, -1.24)$ and $(0.62, 3.24)$ **b** at $(4.71, 0.64)$

c They do not intersect, $\therefore$ no solutions exist.

d at $(-0.75, -0.43)$

EXERCISE 14I.1

1 a common difference is 7 **b** $u_n = 7n - 3$ **c** 207

d yes, the 49th term   **e** no

2 a common difference is -4 **b** $u_n = 71 - 4n$ **c** -169

d no   **e** no, as n would be < 0

3 a $u_1 = 4$ and $d = 11$ **b** 400 **c** $u_{24} = 257$

4 a Show that $u_{n+1} - u_n$ is a constant.

b $u_1 = \frac{17}{2}$, $d = -2$ **c** $-99\frac{1}{2}$ **d** $n \geqslant 156$

5 a $k = 22$ **b** $k = 2\frac{1}{2}$ **c** $k = \frac{13}{3}$

6 a $u_n = 17 + 5n$ **b** $u_n = 10 - 4n$

c $u_n = 3n - 16$ **d** $u_n = -\frac{17}{2} - \frac{3}{4}n$

7 a $u_1 = 3$, $d = -\frac{1}{2}$ **b** 19 terms   **8** $u_{5713} = 40\,001$

EXERCISE 14I.2

1 a $b = 12$, $c = 24$ **b** $b = \frac{1}{2}$, $c = \frac{1}{8}$ **c** $b = \frac{5}{3}$, $c = -\frac{5}{9}$

2 a consecutive terms have a common ratio of 3

b $u_n = 3^{n-1}$, $u_{10} = 3^9 = 19\,683$

3 a consecutive terms have a common ratio of $-\frac{1}{2}$

b $u_n = 40 \times (-\frac{1}{2})^{n-1}$, $u_{12} = -\frac{5}{256}$

4 consecutive terms have a common ratio of $-\frac{1}{4}$,

$u_8 = -0.000\,976\,562\,5$

5 $u_n = 3 \times 2^{\frac{n-1}{2}}$

6 a $k = \frac{2}{3}$ **b** $k = 9$ **c** $k = 2$

d $k = \pm 9$ **e** $k = -7$ **f** $k = -\frac{8}{7}$ or 2

7 a $u_n = 4 \times 2^{n-1}$ ($= 2^{n+1}$)   **b** $u_n = 128 \times (-\frac{1}{2})^{n-1}$

c $u_n = 3 \times (\pm\sqrt{2})^{n-1}$ **d** $u_n = 6 \times (\pm\frac{1}{\sqrt{2}})^{n-1}$

8 $\pm\frac{3}{128}$ **9 a** $-\frac{5}{512}$ **b** -7 **c** $118\,098$

EXERCISE 14J

1 a $5, 8, 11$ **b** $9.6, 7.5, 5.4$ **c** $1291.9, 1315.8, 1339.7$

d $12, 36, 108$ **e** $100, 10, 1$ **f** $-64, 32, -16$

2 a $u_n = 5n + 36$ **b** $u_n = -1.7n + 13.5$

c $u_n = 12 \times (\frac{1}{3})^{n-1}$ **d** $u_n = 36 \times (-\frac{1}{2})^{n-1}$

3 a $1, 1, 1$ **b** $1, 2, 1$ **c** $0, -1, -\frac{4}{3}$ **d** $0, -1, 0$

4 a $-1, -1, 0, 1$ **b** $5, 13, 41, 121$

REVIEW SET 14A

1 a i Range is $\{y \mid y \geqslant -2\}$.   Domain is $\{x \mid x$ is in $\mathbb{R}\}$.

   ii function

b i Range is $\{y \mid y$ is in $\mathbb{R}\}$.   Domain is $\{x \mid x \geqslant 0\}$.

   ii not a function

c i Range is $\{y \mid y$ is in $\mathbb{R}\}$.   Domain is $\{x \mid x$ is in $\mathbb{R}\}$.

   ii function

d i Range is $\{y \mid y = 2, 4, 6\}$.   Domain is $\{x \mid x \geqslant 0\}$.

   ii not a function

2 a 2 **b** -4 **c** $1\frac{1}{4}$ **3 a** $x^2 + 3x$ **b** $x^2 + x - 2$

4 a $5 - 2x^2 - 4x$ **b** $x = -1 \pm \sqrt{21}$ **c** $f^{-1}(x) = -\frac{1}{2}x + \frac{5}{2}$

5 a

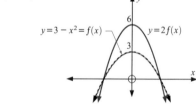

$f(x) = |2x - 4|$

b $x = -\frac{1}{2}$ or $\frac{9}{2}$

c $x = -\frac{1}{2}$ or $\frac{9}{2}$

6 a common difference is 4 **b** $u_n = 4n - 10$

c $u_{100} = 390$ **d** $u_{127} = 498$

7 $u_n = -3 \times (-2)^{n-1}$ **8** $8, 20, 44$ **9** $(-3, -5)$ and $(1, 3)$

10 a i $y = 2x^2 + 4x + 5$ **b**

   ii $y = 6x^2$

$y = 3 - x^2 = f(x)$

$y = 2f(x)$

REVIEW SET 14B

1 a i Range is $\{y \mid y > -2\}$.   Domain is $\{x \mid x > -6\}$.

   ii function

b i Range is $\{y \mid y \neq 3\}$.   Domain is $\{x \mid x \neq -2\}$.

   ii function

c i Range is $\{y \mid y$ is in $\mathbb{R}\}$.   Domain is $\{x \mid x = -3\}$.

   ii not a function

d i Range is $\{y \mid y$ is in $\mathbb{R}\}$.   Domain is $\{x \mid x \leqslant 1\}$.

   ii not a function

2 a -24 **b** $-5x - x^2$ **c** $-x^2 + 3x + 4$

3 a $9x^2 + 12x + 3$ **b** $3x^2 - 1$ **c** $h^{-1}(x) = \frac{1}{3}x - \frac{2}{3}$

4 a

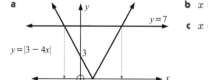

$y = |3 - 4x|$

b $x = -1$ or $2\frac{1}{2}$

c $x = -1$ or $2\frac{1}{2}$

5 $u_n = 39 - \frac{15}{2}(n-1)$

6 consecutive terms have a common ratio of $-\frac{1}{2}$; $u_{16} = -\frac{1}{512}$

7 $k = -5$ or 10; if $k = -5$, terms are $-3, 6, -12$;
if $k = 10$, terms are $27, -9, 3$

8 **a** $u_n = 10 - 3n$ **b** $u_n = 24 \times (-\frac{2}{3})^{n-1}$

9 $(\frac{3}{2}, 2)$ and $(-1, -3)$

10 **a** **i** $y = -\dfrac{5}{x}$ **b**
ii $y = \dfrac{45}{16x}$

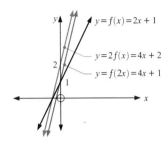

EXERCISE 15A

1 **a** *Scale:* 1 cm $\equiv 10$ km h^{-1} **b** *Scale:* 1 cm $\equiv 10$ m s^{-1}

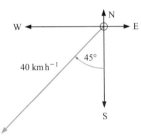

Scale: 1 cm $\equiv 10$ m

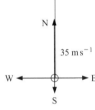

c

d

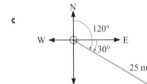

Scale: 1 cm $\equiv 10$ m s^{-1}

2 **a** *Scale:* 1 cm $\equiv 15$ Newtons

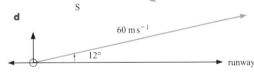

b *Scale:* 1 cm $\equiv 15$ Newtons

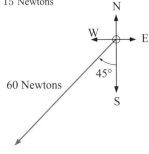

3 **a** *Scale:* 1 cm $\equiv 20$ km h^{-1} **b** *Scale:* 1 cm $\equiv 15$ kg m s^{-1}

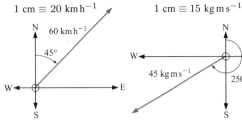

c *Scale:* 1 cm $\equiv 10$ km **d** *Scale:* 1 cm $\equiv 30$ km h^{-1}

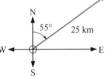
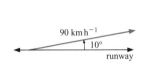

EXERCISE 15B

1 **a** **a**, **c** and **e**; **b** and **d** **b** **a**, **b**, **c** and **d**
c **a** and **b**; **c** and **d** **d** none are equal **e** **a** and **c**; **b** and **d**

2 **a** false **b** true **c** false **d** true **e** true

EXERCISE 15C

1 **a** **b**

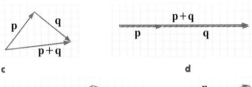

c **d**

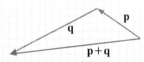

e **f**

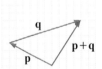

2 **a** $\overrightarrow{QS}$ **b** $\overrightarrow{PR}$ **c** $\overrightarrow{PQ}$ **d** $\overrightarrow{PS}$

3 **a** **i** **ii**

b $\mathbf{p} + \mathbf{q} = \mathbf{q} + \mathbf{p}$ for any two vectors **p** and **q**

4 Paolo is 25 km from his starting point at a bearing of $347°$.

5 Gina is 6.76 km from her starting point at a bearing of $006.60°$.

6 **a** 600 km h^{-1} due north **b** 400 km h^{-1} due north
c 510 km h^{-1} at a bearing of $011.3°$

7 **a** 0 km h^{-1} **b** 20 km h^{-1} east **c** 14.1 km h^{-1} north east

8 The aircraft is travelling at a speed of 404 km h^{-1} at a bearing of $098.5°$.

9 The ship is travelling at a speed of 23.3 knots at a bearing of $134°$.

EXERCISE 15D

1 **a**
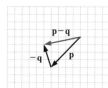

b
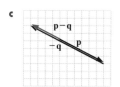

c   **d**
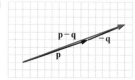

e   **f**
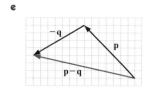

2 **a** $\overrightarrow{QS}$ **b** $\overrightarrow{PR}$ **c** $\mathbf{0}$ (zero vector) **d** $\overrightarrow{RQ}$ **e** $\overrightarrow{QS}$
   f $\overrightarrow{RQ}$

3 The plane must fly 4.57^o west of north at 501.6 km h^{-1}.

4 **a** The boat must head 25.5^o west of north. **b** 28.3 km h^{-1}

EXERCISE 15E.1

1 **a**   **b**   **c**   **d**
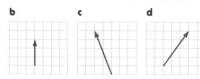

2 **a** $\binom{4}{2}$ **b** $\binom{0}{-3}$ **c** $\binom{-3}{-4}$ **d** $\binom{-6}{0}$ **e** $\binom{-6}{4}$
   f $\binom{2}{-4}$

3 **a** $\binom{3}{4}$ **b** $\binom{-4}{-2}$ **c** $\binom{-2}{1}$ **d** $\binom{3}{-3}$ **e** $\binom{1}{5}$

4 **a**   **b**
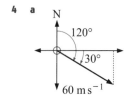
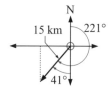

The vector is $\binom{52.0}{-30}$.   The vector is $\binom{-9.84}{-11.3}$.

c
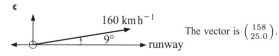

The vector is $\binom{158}{25.0}$.

EXERCISE 15E.2

1 **a** $\binom{5}{-4}$ **b** $\binom{5}{-4}$ **c** $\binom{1}{-4}$ **d** $\binom{1}{-4}$ **e** $\binom{0}{-6}$
   f $\binom{0}{-6}$ **g** $\binom{4}{-6}$ **h** $\binom{3}{-7}$

2 **a** $\binom{1}{6}$ **b** $\binom{-5}{1}$ **c** $\binom{-6}{4}$ **d** $\binom{-2}{10}$ **e** $\binom{-4}{-2}$
   f $\binom{2}{-10}$

3 **a** $\binom{-3}{-3}$ **b** $\binom{-4}{9}$

4 **a** $\sqrt{17}$ units **b** 6 units **c** $\sqrt{13}$ units
   d $\sqrt{26}$ units **e** $\sqrt{20}$ units **f** $\sqrt{37}$ units

5 **a** **i** $\binom{-2}{-3}$ **ii** $\sqrt{13}$ units **b** **i** $\binom{5}{-2}$ **ii** $\sqrt{29}$ units
   c **i** $\binom{-3}{-4}$ **ii** 5 units **d** **i** $\binom{-12}{5}$ **ii** 13 units

EXERCISE 15F

1 **a**   **b**
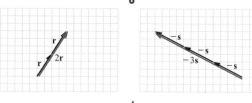

c   **d**
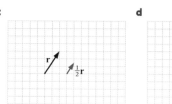

e   **f**
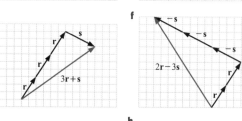

g   **h**
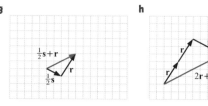

So,

a $\binom{4}{6}$ **b** $\binom{-12}{6}$ **c** $\binom{1}{1\frac{1}{2}}$ **d** $\binom{-6}{7}$

e $\binom{10}{7}$ **f** $\binom{-8}{12}$ **g** $\binom{4}{2}$ **h** $\binom{4}{2}$

3 **a**   **b**   **c**
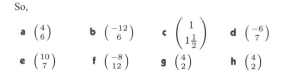

d   **e**
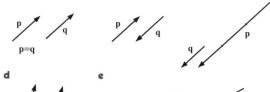
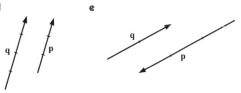

EXERCISE 15G

1 **a** $x = \frac{1}{4}p$ **b** $x = -\frac{1}{3}q$ **c** $x = 2p$

   d $x = -\frac{3}{2}r$ **e** $x = \frac{1}{2}(q - p)$ **f** $x = \frac{1}{3}(4p - q)$

   g $x = \frac{1}{3}(p - q)$ **h** $x = 2(3m - n)$ **i** $x = 3(e - 2d)$

2 **a** $y = \begin{pmatrix} 1 \\ 2 \\ \frac{2}{3} \end{pmatrix}$ **b** $y = \begin{pmatrix} 6 \\ -3 \end{pmatrix}$ **c** $y = \begin{pmatrix} -\frac{1}{2} \\ -\frac{3}{2} \end{pmatrix}$

   d $y = \begin{pmatrix} 5 \\ \frac{9}{2} \end{pmatrix}$

3 **a** $x = \begin{pmatrix} 8 \\ 4 \end{pmatrix}$ **b** $x = \begin{pmatrix} \frac{5}{2} \\ \frac{5}{2} \end{pmatrix}$ **c** $x = \begin{pmatrix} 26 \\ 18 \end{pmatrix}$

   d $x = \begin{pmatrix} 3 \\ -1 \end{pmatrix}$ **e** $x = \begin{pmatrix} \frac{5}{4} \\ \frac{5}{4} \end{pmatrix}$ **f** $x = \begin{pmatrix} -\frac{9}{4} \\ -\frac{7}{4} \end{pmatrix}$

EXERCISE 15H

1 **a** $p \parallel q$ and $|p| = 2|q|$ **b** $p \parallel q$ and $|p| = \frac{1}{2}|q|$
   c $p \parallel q$ and $|p| = 3|q|$ **d** $p \parallel q$ and $|p| = \frac{1}{3}|q|$

2 $k = -10$ **3** **a** $t = 6$ **b** $t = 20$ **4** $a = -\frac{12}{5}$ or 2

5 $\overrightarrow{PQ} = \begin{pmatrix} 5 \\ -4 \end{pmatrix}$, $\overrightarrow{SR} = \begin{pmatrix} 5 \\ -4 \end{pmatrix}$ $\Rightarrow$ $\overrightarrow{PQ} \parallel \overrightarrow{SR}$ and $|\overrightarrow{PQ}| = |\overrightarrow{SR}|$
   which is sufficient to deduce that PQRS is a parallelogram.

6 **a** C(2, 5) **b** D(9, 0)

EXERCISE 15I.1

1 **a** **i** 5 **ii** $45°$ **b** **i** 10 **ii** $0°$ **c** **i** 0 **ii** $90°$
   d **i** 5 **ii** $70.3°$ **e** **i** 33 **ii** $59.5°$
   f **i** -11 **ii** $137.7°$

2 **a** $t = 6$ **b** $t = \pm 2\sqrt{3}$ **c** $t = -8$ **d** $t = -\frac{4}{3}$ or 2

3 $k = -\frac{11}{4}$ **4** **a** $37.9°$ **b** $121.0°$ **c** $14.5°$ **d** $4.40°$

5 **a** $\widehat{P} \approx 8.13°$, $\widehat{Q} \approx 18.4°$, $\widehat{R} \approx 153.4°$
   b $\widehat{P} \approx 66.8°$, $\widehat{Q} \approx 31.3°$, $\widehat{R} \approx 81.9°$

EXERCISE 15I.2

1 **a** $\begin{pmatrix} 1 \\ 1 \end{pmatrix}$ **b** $\begin{pmatrix} 1 \\ -2 \end{pmatrix}$ **c** $\begin{pmatrix} 1 \\ 3 \end{pmatrix}$ **d** $\begin{pmatrix} 3 \\ -2 \end{pmatrix}$

2 **a** $18.4°$ **b** $59.0°$ **c** $45°$ **d** $49.4°$

EXERCISE 15I.3

Hint: Let $a = \begin{pmatrix} a_1 \\ a_2 \end{pmatrix}$, $b = \begin{pmatrix} b_1 \\ b_2 \end{pmatrix}$, etc.

EXERCISE 15J

1 $\overrightarrow{BC} = s$, etc. **2** $\overrightarrow{OB} = a + c$, $\overrightarrow{OM} = \frac{1}{2}a + \frac{1}{2}c$

3 **a** **i** $\overrightarrow{PC} = r$, $\overrightarrow{DP} = s$ **ii** $\overrightarrow{AB} = r + s$, $\overrightarrow{DC} = r + s$
   b [AB] $\parallel$ [DC], AB = DC
   c ...... the quadrilateral is a parallelogram.

4 **a** $\overrightarrow{AD} = 2p + 2q + 2r$ **b** $\overrightarrow{AS} = p + q + r$
   c $\overrightarrow{PQ} = p + q$
   d $\overrightarrow{SR} = p + q$, SR $\parallel$ PQ, SR = PQ
   so PQRS is a parallelogram

5 **b** 1 : 2 **6** $\overrightarrow{OM} = \frac{1}{2}a + \frac{1}{2}b$, $\overrightarrow{AB} = -a + b$, $\overrightarrow{OM} \bullet \overrightarrow{AB} = 0$

7 $\overrightarrow{AC} = -a + c$, $\overrightarrow{OB} = a + c$

8 **a** $\overrightarrow{AB} = -r + s$, $\overrightarrow{OQ} = \frac{3}{4}s + \frac{3}{4}r$ **b** Show $\overrightarrow{AB} \bullet \overrightarrow{OQ} = 0$!

9 **a** Hint: $|c + d|^2 = |c - d|^2$
   $\therefore$ $(c + d) \bullet (c + d) = (c - d) \bullet (c - d)$, etc.

  b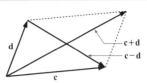

REVIEW SET 15A

1 **a**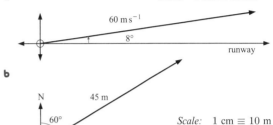
   Scale: 1 cm $\equiv 10$ m s^{-1}

  b
   Scale: 1 cm $\equiv 10$ m

2 **a**  **b**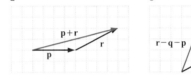

3 **a** $\overrightarrow{CA} = -c$ **b** $\overrightarrow{AB} = -a + b$
   c $\overrightarrow{OC} = a + c$ **d** $\overrightarrow{BC} = -b + a + c$

4 **a** $\overrightarrow{AD}$ **b** $\overrightarrow{BD}$ **c** 0 (the zero vector)

5 Speed is 12.3 km h^{-1} at a bearing of $145°$.

6 $a \parallel b$ and $|a| = \frac{1}{3}|b|$

7 **a** $\begin{pmatrix} 11 \\ 1 \end{pmatrix}$ **b** $\begin{pmatrix} 1 \\ 12 \end{pmatrix}$ **c** $\sqrt{34}$ units

8 **a** $x = \frac{1}{3}a$ **b** $x = \frac{1}{2}(a - c)$ **9** **a** $k = -4$ **b** $k = 9$

10 A($-2, -4$) **11** **a** -1 **b** $97.1°$ **12** $55.6°$

REVIEW SET 15B

1 **a** They have the same length. **b** $p \parallel q$ and $|p| = 2|q|$

2 $\overrightarrow{BA} = -\overrightarrow{AB}$

3 **a** He must fly in the direction $11.3°$ south of east.
   b 204 km h^{-1}

4

5 **a** $\begin{pmatrix} -1 \\ -9 \end{pmatrix}$ **b** $\sqrt{34}$ units

6 **a** $t = \frac{3}{2}$ **b** $t = -\frac{8}{3}$

7 **a** $x = 2n$ **b** $x = \frac{1}{3}(a - b)$

8 **a** $\begin{pmatrix} 3 \\ -4 \end{pmatrix}$ **b** 5 units **9** $108.4°$ **10** $26.6°$

11 **a** $2p$ **b** $p + q$ **c** $q - p$ **12** $78.7°$

EXERCISE 16A

1 **a** 3^7 **b** 4^5 **c** x^9 **d** x^{10} **e** y^9
   f x^{n+5} **g** y^{m+2} **h** t^{12}

2 **a** 3^4 **b** 7^4 **c** 8 **d** x^4 **e** y^5
   f t^{6-x} **g** p^{n-2} **h** t^{3m-1}

3 **a** 5^6 **b** 3^{20} **c** 2^{18} **d** t^{12} **e** x^{14}
   f y^{3m} **g** m^{5a} **h** a^{12m}

4   **a** 2^2 **b** 2^4 **c** 3^3 **d** 2^4 **e** 5^4 **f** 2^{t+3}
   g 3^{a-1} **h** 2^{3n} **i** 3^{2-x} **j** 5^4 **k** 3^{4a+4} **l** 3^4
   m 2^{2a-b} **n** 2^{3x-4y} **o** 5^2 **p** 3^{-6}

5   **a** x^2y^2 **b** a^3b^3 **c** r^4s^4 **d** $x^2y^2z^2$
   e $8a^3$ **f** $27b^3$ **g** $625a^4$ **h** $27x^3y^3$
   i $10^5x^5y^5$ **j** $\dfrac{p^2}{q^2}$ **k** $\dfrac{m^3}{n^3}$ **l** $\dfrac{16a^4}{b^4}$

6   **a** x^3 **b** $8b^5$ **c** a^2b^2 **d** $6x^3$ **e** $\dfrac{x^2y}{3}$
   f $\dfrac{8r^2}{5}$ **g** $15p^6q^3$ **h** x^6 **i** t^4

7   **a** 1 **b** $\frac{1}{6}$ **c** $\frac{1}{4}$ **d** 1 **e** 9 **f** $\frac{1}{9}$
   g 125 **h** $\frac{1}{125}$ **i** 49 **j** $\frac{1}{49}$ **k** 1000 **l** $\frac{1}{1000}$

8   **a** 1 **b** 1 **c** 2 **d** 1 **e** 1 **f** 3 **g** $\frac{1}{25}$
   h $\frac{1}{16}$ **i** 4 **j** $\frac{8}{3}$ **k** $\frac{3}{2}$ **l** 5 **m** 3 **n** $\frac{4}{5}$
   o $\frac{11}{3}$ **p** 9 **q** $\frac{27}{8}$ **r** $\frac{8}{27}$ **s** $\frac{25}{16}$ **t** $\frac{4}{25}$

9   **a** $\dfrac{1}{3b}$ **b** $\dfrac{3}{b}$ **c** $\dfrac{7}{a}$ **d** $\dfrac{1}{7a}$ **e** t^2 **f** $\dfrac{1}{16t^2}$
   g $\dfrac{1}{25t^2}$ **h** $\dfrac{t^2}{5}$ **i** $\dfrac{x}{y}$ **j** $\dfrac{1}{xy}$ **k** $\dfrac{x}{y^3}$ **l** $\dfrac{1}{x^3y^3}$
   m $\dfrac{1}{3pq}$ **n** $\dfrac{3}{pq}$ **o** $\dfrac{3p}{q}$ **p** x^3y^5

10 3^{75}

EXERCISE 16B

1   **a** 2 **b** $\frac{1}{2}$ **c** 4 **d** $\frac{1}{4}$ **e** 5 **f** $\frac{1}{5}$
   g 2 **h** $\frac{1}{2}$ **i** 4 **j** $\frac{1}{4}$ **k** 2 **l** $\frac{1}{2}$
   m 5 **n** -5 **o** no real solution   **p** -1

2   **a** $10^{\frac{1}{2}}$ **b** $10^{-\frac{1}{2}}$ **c** $15^{\frac{1}{3}}$ **d** $15^{-\frac{1}{3}}$ **e** $19^{\frac{1}{4}}$
   f $19^{-\frac{1}{4}}$ **g** $13^{\frac{1}{5}}$ **h** $13^{-\frac{1}{5}}$

3   **a** 4 **b** 3 **c** 4 **d** 5.848 **e** 4.472
   f 3.981 **g** 2 **h** 2.212

4   **a** 16 **b** $\frac{1}{4}$ **c** 8 **d** $\frac{1}{8}$ **e** 9 **f** $\frac{1}{9}$
   g 4 **h** $\frac{1}{8}$ **i** 32 **j** $\frac{1}{25}$ **k** 27 **l** $\frac{1}{27}$

EXERCISE 16C

1   **a** 3 **b** 11 **c** $2\frac{1}{3}$ **2**   **a** -2 **b** $-2\frac{4}{5}$ **c** 22

3   **a** $\frac{1}{9}$ **b** 9 **c** $\frac{1}{27}$

4   **a**

x	-3	-2	-1	0	1	2	3
y	$\frac{1}{27}$	$\frac{1}{9}$	$\frac{1}{3}$	1	3	9	27

b, c

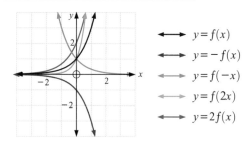

   $\longleftrightarrow y = f(x)$
   $\longleftrightarrow y = -f(x)$
   $\longleftrightarrow y = f(-x)$
   $\longleftrightarrow y = f(2x)$
   $\longleftrightarrow y = 2f(x)$

5   **a**   **i** ≈ 1.6 **ii** ≈ 3.5 **iii** ≈ 0.7
   b   **i** ≈ 1.62 **ii** ≈ 3.48 **iii** ≈ 0.707

   c   **i** $x \approx 2.3$ **ii** $x \approx 0.6$ **iii** no solution
6   **a** $y = 2^{x+1} + 3$ **b** $y = 3^{x-2} - 4$
   c   **i** $y = -2^{-x}$ **ii** $y = 2^x$ **iii** $x = 2^{-y}$
   d   **i** $y = 2(3^x)$ **ii** $y = 27^x$

7   If $x = \frac{1}{2}$, $(-2)^{\frac{1}{2}} = \sqrt{-2}$ which is undefined.

EXERCISE 16D

1   **a** 40 mongooses   **b**   **i** ≈ 61 **ii** 160 **iii** 2560
   c

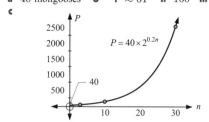

2   **a** 50 echidnas   **b**   **i** ≈ 100 **ii** ≈ 400 **iii** ≈ 5080
   c

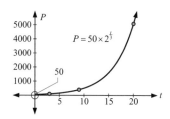

3   **a** $G_0 = 28$ **b**   **i** ≈ 39 **ii** ≈ 86 **iii** ≈ 822
   c

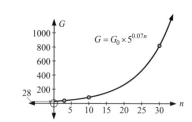

4   **a** 2.3 grams
   b   **i** 1.00 grams   **ii** $0.000\,562$ grams
     iii 1.73×10^{-36} grams
   c   **d** $\approx 56.5\%$

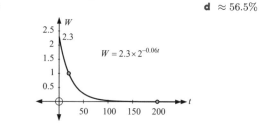

5   **a** $100°C$ **b**   **i** $70.7°C$ **ii** $17.7°C$ **iii** $0.003\,05°C$
   c

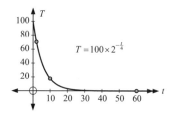

EXERCISE 16E

1

After year	Interest paid	Future Value
0	-	€8000
1	5% of €8000 = €400	€8400
2	5% of €8400 = €420	€8820
3	5% of €8820 = €441	€9261

2 a £53 240 **b** £13 240 **3** ¥8320 **4** $14 976.01
5 €11 477.02 **6** 20.5% **7** 15.8% **8** 7.85%

EXERCISE 16F

1 $5684.29

2 a

Number of owners	Depreciation or annual loss in value	Value after n years
0	-	£8495
1	£1019.40	£7475.60
2	£897.07	£6578.53
3	£789.42	£5789.11
4	£694.69	£5094.42

b £694.69 **c** £3055.10
d $F_9 - F_{10}$ is the depreciation in the tenth year.
3 a $19 712 **b** $18 788 **4** 11.5% **5** 4.81%

EXERCISE 16G

1 a $x = 1$ **b** $x = 2$ **c** $x = 3$ **d** $x = 0$
e $x = -1$ **f** $x = -1$ **g** $x = -4$ **h** $x = 0$
i $x = -4$ **j** $x = -2$ **k** $x = 6$ **l** $x = 2$
m $x = -\frac{3}{4}$ **n** $x = \frac{7}{2}$ **o** $x = 0$ **p** $x = 4$

2 a $x = 3$ **b** $x = 0$ **c** $x = -2$ **d** $x = 3$
e $x = 3$ **f** $x = -2$ **g** $x = \frac{2}{7}$ **h** $x = \frac{1}{3}$
i $x = 1$ **j** $x = 1$ **k** no solution **l** $x = 3$ or -1

EXERCISE 16H.1

1 a $4^x + 2^x$ **b** $3^x - 1$ **c** $1 + 3(2^{-x})$
d $7^{2x} + 1$ or $49^x + 1$

2 a $9^x + 3^{x+1} + 2$ **b** $4^x + 6(2^x) + 5$ **c** $25^x - 10(5^x) + 21$
d $4^x + 2^{x+1} + 1$ **e** $9^x + 4(3^x) + 4$ **f** $16^x - 14(4^x) + 49$
g $9^x + 2(3^x) + 1$ **h** $9^x - 16(3^x) + 64$ **i** $25^x - 6(5^x) + 9$
j $4^x - 25$ **k** $7^{2x} + 2 + 7^{-2x}$ **l** $9 - 6(2^{-x}) + 2^{-2x}$

EXERCISE 16H.2

1 a $3^x(3^x + 1)$ **b** $5(2^n)$ **c** $4^n(1 + 4^{2n})$
d $6(6^n - 1)$ **e** $7(7^{n+1} - 1)$ **f** $9(3^n - 1)$
g $9(2^n)$ **h** $13(3^n)$ **i** $11(2^{n-1})$

2 a $(2^x + 3)(2^x - 3)$ **b** $(3^x + 5)(3^x - 5)$
c $(8 + 3^x)(8 - 3^x)$ **d** $(4 + 5^x)(4 - 5^x)$
e $(2^x + 3^x)(2^x - 3^x)$ **f** $(5^x + 3)^2$
g $(2^x + 5)^2$ **h** $(6^x - 7)^2$ **i** $(7^x - 2)^2$

3 a $(2^x + 3)(2^x + 5)$ **b** $(2^x + 7)(2^x - 1)$ **c** $(3^x - 5)(3^x + 2)$
d $(3^x - 2)(3^x - 4)$ **e** $(5^x + 6)(5^x - 2)$ **f** $(8^x + 4)(8^x - 1)$

4 a $1 + 2^n$ **b** $1 + 2^m$ **c** 4^m **d** $1 + 3^b$ **e** 15 **f** 4^n
g $2^m - 1$ **h** $2\frac{2}{3}$ **i** 2 **j** $\frac{2}{3}$ **k** $2^x - 1$ **l** 2^y

5 a $x = 0$ or 1 **b** $x = 1$ or 3 **c** $x = 2$
d no solutions exist **e** $x = 0$ **f** $x = 2$ **g** $x = 0$ or 1
h $x = \frac{1}{3}$ or $\frac{2}{3}$ **i** $x = 1$

EXERCISE 16I.1

1 a $8 = 10^{0.9031}$ **b** $80 = 10^{1.903}$
c $800 = 10^{2.903}$ **d** $80 000 = 10^{4.903}$
e $0.03 = 10^{-1.523}$ **f** $0.003 = 10^{-2.523}$
g $0.3 = 10^{-0.5229}$ **h** $0.000 003 = 10^{-5.523}$
i $37 = 10^{1.568}$ **j** $0.0614 = 10^{-1.212}$
k $26 700 = 10^{4.427}$ **l** $0.006 372 1 = 10^{-2.196}$

2 a $x \approx 1.903$ **b** $x \approx 3.903$ **c** $x \approx -1.602$
d $x \approx 2.659$ **e** $x \approx -0.057 30$ **f** $x \approx -3.747$

3 a $x = 1.585$ **b** $x = 3.322$ **c** $x = 8.644$
d $x = -7.059$ **e** $x = 4.292$ **f** $x = -0.099 97$
g $x = 6.511$ **h** $x = 4.923$ **i** $x = 49.60$
j $x = 4.376$ **k** $x = 8.497$ **l** $x = 230.7$

4 a 17.0 hours **b** 64.6 hours
5 a 17.6 hours **b** 36.9 hours

EXERCISE 16I.2

1 a $\log 30$ **b** $\log 5$ **c** $\log 12$ **d** $\log(\frac{5}{4})$ **e** $\log 1 = 0$
f $\log 30$ **g** $\log 4$ **h** $-\log 6$ or $\log(\frac{1}{6})$ **i** $\log(\frac{1}{512})$
j $\log 2000$ **k** $\log(\frac{64}{125})$ **l** $\log 20$ **m** $\log 5$ **n** $\log 20$
o $\log(14 000)$

2 $\log 30 = \log(3 \times 10) = \log 3 + \log 10$, etc.

3 a 3 **b** 2 **c** $\frac{2}{3}$ **d** -1 **e** -1
f $-1\frac{1}{2}$ **g** $\frac{b}{3}$ **h** $\frac{2}{a}$

5 Hint: $2400 = 2^3 \times 3 \times 5^2$

EXERCISE 16I.3

1 a $\log y = \log a + 2 \log b$ **b** $\log y = 2 \log a - \log b$
c $\log y = \log d + \frac{1}{2} \log p$ **d** $\log M = 2 \log a + 5 \log b$
e $\log P = \frac{1}{2}(\log a + \log b)$ **f** $\log Q = \frac{1}{2} \log m - \log n$
g $\log R = \log a + \log b + 2 \log c$
h $\log T = \log 5 + \frac{1}{2}(\log d - \log c)$

2 a $Q = 10^{x+2}$ or $Q = 100(10^x)$
b $J = 10^{2x-1}$ or $J = \frac{1}{10}(100^x)$
c $M = 10^{2-x}$ or $M = \frac{100}{10^x}$
d $P \approx 10^{0.301+x}$ or $P \approx 2(10^x)$
e $R \approx 10^{x+1.477}$ or $R \approx 30(10^x)$
f $K \approx 10^{\frac{1}{2}x+1}$ or $K \approx 10(10^{\frac{x}{2}})$

3 a $A = \frac{B}{C^2}$ **b** $p^2 q = s$ **c** $\frac{m^3}{d} = \frac{n}{p^2}$

EXERCISE 16I.4

1 a $\log_2 8 = 3$ **b** $\log_3 9 = 2$ **c** $\log_5(\frac{1}{5}) = -1$
d $\log_2 32 = 5$ **e** $\log_7 1 = 0$ **f** $\log_3(\frac{1}{81}) = -4$
g $\log_2(\frac{1}{64}) = -6$ **h** $\log_2(\sqrt{2}) = \frac{1}{2}$

2 a $10^3 = 1000$ **b** $2^4 = 16$ **c** $3^{-1} = \frac{1}{3}$
d $4^0 = 1$ **e** $7^{-2} = \frac{1}{49}$ **f** $(\frac{1}{7})^2 = \frac{1}{49}$

3 a 2 **b** 5 **c** $\frac{1}{2}$ **d** $\frac{1}{4}$ **e** $\frac{3}{2}$ **f** 0
g 1 **h** -1 **i** 1 **j** -1 **k** $-\frac{1}{2}$ **l** $-\frac{1}{6}$

4 a $x = 4$ **b** $x = \frac{1}{25}$ **c** $x = 2$ **d** $x = \frac{1}{10}$

EXERCISE 16I.5

1

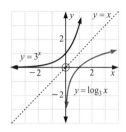

2

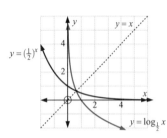

3   **a** $x \approx 0.137$ or 1 **b** $x \approx 1.32$

4   **a**

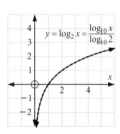

b $\dfrac{\log_{10} x}{\log_{10} 2} = \log_2 x$ **c** $\log_2 20$

REVIEW SET 16A

1   **a** $2a^9$ **b** a^{b-x} **c** $27a^6$ **2** 2^2

3   **a** $\dfrac{4}{3}$ **b** $\dfrac{25}{4}$ **c** $\dfrac{1}{4}$ **4**   **a** 0 **b** 26 **c** $-\dfrac{2}{3}$ **d** $-\dfrac{8}{9}$

5

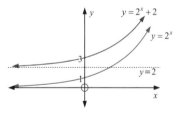

a For $y = 2^x$: y-intercept 1, horizontal asymptote $y = 0$
For $y = 2^x + 2$: y-intercept 3, horizontal asymptote $y = 2$
b a vertical translation of $\begin{pmatrix} 0 \\ 2 \end{pmatrix}$

6   **a** 1000 grams
b   **i** 812 grams   **ii** 125 grams   **iii** 9.31×10^{-7} grams
c

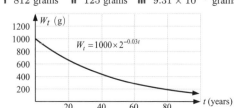

d 144 years

7   £51 475.73   **8** \$6273.18   **9** $x = \dfrac{1}{3}$

10   **a** $4^x - 1$ **b** $9^x + 3^x - 2$ **c** $25^x - 4(5^x) + 4$

11   **a** $24(5^n)$ **b** $(5 + 4^x)(5 - 4^x)$ **c** $(2^x - 2)(2^x - 4)$

12 $x = 1$ **13**   **a** $50 = 10^{1.699}$ **b** $x = 0.4325$

14   **a** $\log 8$ **b** $\log a$ **c** 4   **15** $x = -\dfrac{7}{8}$

REVIEW SET 16B

1   **a** $15x^3 y^5$ **b** $\dfrac{x}{2y^2}$ **c** $\dfrac{8a^2}{b^2}$

2   **a** $\dfrac{1}{25x^2}$ **b** $3x^2 y^5$ **c** $\dfrac{1}{5}$

3   **a** 2   **b** $\dfrac{2}{3}$ **c** $\dfrac{2}{9}$ **d** 6   **e** 18

4

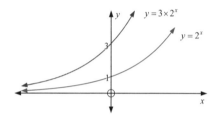

a For $y = 2^x$: y-intercept 1; horizontal asymptote $y = 0$
For $y = 3 \times 2^x$: y-intercept 3; horizontal asymptote $y = 0$
b vertical dilation by a factor of 3

5   **a** W_0 grams
b   **i** 71.9% of W_0 **ii** 19.2% of W_0 **iii** 3.70% of W_0
c

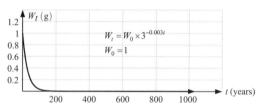

6   **a** €130 258.96   **b** €669 741.04   **7** \$11 219.88

8 $x = -2$

9   **a** $9^x + 2(3^x) + 1$ **b** $25 - 10(2^x) + 4^x$
c $16^x - 2^{x+1} + 4^{-x}$

10   **a** 2   **b** 3^n **c** 2   **11** $x = 0$ or 3

12 $x = -0.3652$ **13**   **a** $\log 4$ **b** $\log 3$ **c** 4

EXERCISE 17A

1 a, c, d and e are quadratic functions.

2   **a** $y = 0$ **b** $y = 5$ **c** $y = -15$ **d** $y = 12$

3   **a** No   **b** Yes   **c** Yes   **d** No   **e** No   **f** No

4   **a** $x = -3$ **b** $x = -3$ or -2 **c** $x = 1$ or 4
d no solution

5   **a** $x = 0$ or 1   **b** $x = 3$ or -1 **c** $x = \dfrac{1}{2}$ or -7
d $x = 2$ or 3

6   **a**   **i** 75 m   **ii** 195 m   **iii** 275 m
b   **i** at $t = 2$ sec and at $t = 14$ sec
ii at $t = 0$ sec and at $t = 16$ sec
c Height 0 m is ground level and the time of flight is 16 sec.

7   **a**   **i** $-\$40$, a loss of \$40   **ii** \$480 profit
b 10 or 62 cakes

1 a

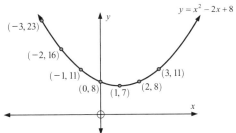

$y = x^2 - 2x + 8$

$(-3, 23)$
$(-2, 16)$
$(-1, 11)$
$(3, 11)$
$(0, 8)$ $(1, 7)$ $(2, 8)$

b

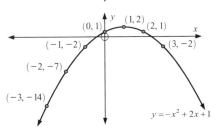

$(0, 1)$ $(1, 2)$ $(2, 1)$
$(-1, -2)$ $(3, -2)$
$(-2, -7)$
$(-3, -14)$
$y = -x^2 + 2x + 1$

c

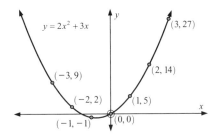

$y = 2x^2 + 3x$
$(3, 27)$
$(-3, 9)$ $(2, 14)$
$(-2, 2)$ $(1, 5)$
$(-1, -1)$ $(0, 0)$

d

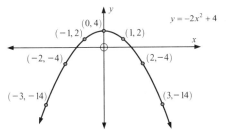

$(0, 4)$
$(-1, 2)$ $(1, 2)$
$y = -2x^2 + 4$
$(-2, -4)$ $(2, -4)$
$(-3, -14)$ $(3, -14)$

e

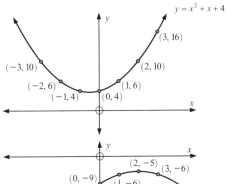

$y = x^2 + x + 4$
$(3, 16)$
$(-3, 10)$ $(2, 10)$
$(-2, 6)$ $(1, 6)$
$(-1, 4)$ $(0, 4)$

f

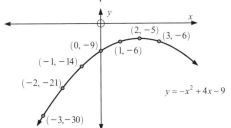

$(2, -5)$ $(3, -6)$
$(0, -9)$ $(1, -6)$
$(-1, -14)$
$(-2, -21)$
$y = -x^2 + 4x - 9$
$(-3, -30)$

1 a

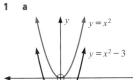

$y = x^2$
$y = x^2 - 3$
$(0, -3)$

b

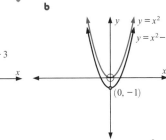

$y = x^2$
$y = x^2 - 1$
$(0, -1)$

c

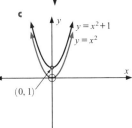

$y = x^2 + 1$
$y = x^2$
$(0, 1)$

d

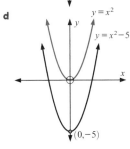

$y = x^2$
$y = x^2 - 5$
$(0, -5)$

e

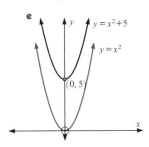

$y = x^2 + 5$
$y = x^2$
$(0, 5)$

f

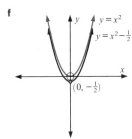

$y = x^2$
$y = x^2 - \frac{1}{2}$
$(0, -\frac{1}{2})$

3 a

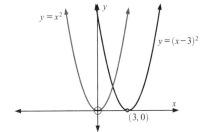

$y = x^2$
$y = (x - 3)^2$
$(3, 0)$

b

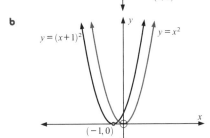

$y = (x + 1)^2$
$y = x^2$
$(-1, 0)$

c

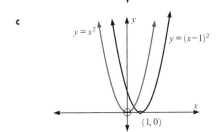

$y = x^2$
$y = (x - 1)^2$
$(1, 0)$

d

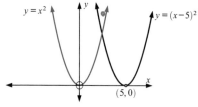

$y = x^2$ $y = (x-5)^2$ $(5, 0)$

e

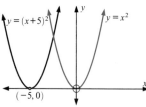

$y = (x+5)^2$ $y = x^2$ $(-5, 0)$

f

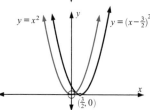

$y = x^2$ $y = (x-\frac{3}{2})^2$ $(\frac{3}{2}, 0)$

5 a $y = (x - 1)^2 + 3$

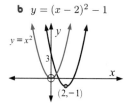

$y = x^2$ 4 $(1, 3)$

vertex is at $(1, 3)$

b $y = (x - 2)^2 - 1$

$y = x^2$ 3 $(2, -1)$

vertex is at $(2, -1)$

c $y = (x + 1)^2 + 4$

$(-1, 4)$ 5 $y = x^2$

vertex is at $(-1, 4)$

d $y = (x + 2)^2 - 3$

$y = x^2$ 1 $(-2, -3)$

vertex is at $(-2, -3)$

e $y = (x + 3)^2 - 2$

7   $y = x^2$ $(-3, -2)$

vertex is at $(-3, -2)$

f $y = (x - 3)^2 + 3$

$y = x^2$ 12 $(3, 3)$

vertex is at $(3, 3)$

EXERCISE 17B.3

1 a $y = (x + 1)^2 + 3$

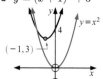

$y = x^2$ 4 $(-1, 3)$

b $y = (x - 3)^2 - 6$

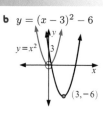

$y = x^2$ 3 $(3, -6)$

c $y = (x + 2)^2 - 5$

$y = x^2$ -1 $(-2, -5)$

d $y = (x - 1)^2 + 4$

$y = x^2$ 5 $(1, 4)$

e $y = (x - 1)^2 - 1$

$y = x^2$ $(1, -1)$

f $y = (x + \frac{5}{2})^2 - 6\frac{1}{4}$

$y = x^2$ $(-\frac{5}{2}, -6\frac{1}{4})$

g $y = (x + \frac{5}{2})^2 - 9\frac{1}{4}$

$y = x^2$ $(-\frac{5}{2}, -9\frac{1}{4})$

h $y = (x - \frac{3}{2})^2 + \frac{3}{4}$

$y = x^2$ $(\frac{3}{2}, \frac{3}{4})$

i $y = (x - \frac{5}{2})^2 - 4\frac{1}{4}$

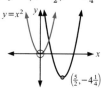

$y = x^2$ $(\frac{5}{2}, -4\frac{1}{4})$

3 a $y = (x - 1)^2 + 2$
b $y = (x - 3)^2 - 8$
c $y = (x + 2)^2 + 1$
d $y = (x + 1)^2 - 5$
e $y = (x - \frac{3}{2})^2 - \frac{5}{4}$
f $y = (x - \frac{9}{2})^2 - \frac{101}{4}$

EXERCISE 17B.4

1 a

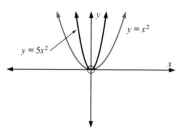

$y = x^2$ $y = 5x^2$

i $y = 5x^2$ is 'thinner' than $y = x^2$
ii graph opens upwards

b

$y = x^2$ $y = -5x^2$

i $y = -5x^2$ is 'thinner' than $y = x^2$
ii graph opens downwards

c

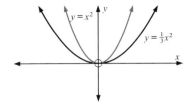

i $y = \frac{1}{3}x^2$ is 'wider' than $y = x^2$
ii graph opens upwards

d

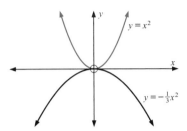

i $y = -\frac{1}{3}x^2$ is 'wider' than $y = x^2$
ii graphs opens downwards

e

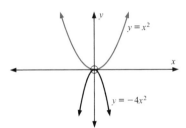

i $y = -4x^2$ is 'thinner' than $y = x^2$
ii graph opens downwards

f

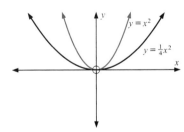

i $y = \frac{1}{4}x^2$ is 'wider' than $y = x^2$
ii graph opens upwards

3 a

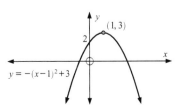

b

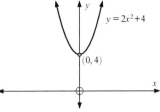

c

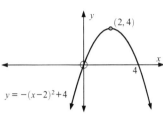

d

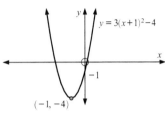

e

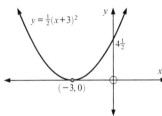

f

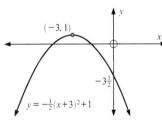

g

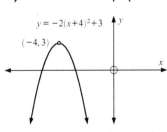

h

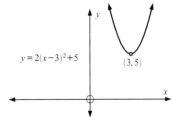

i

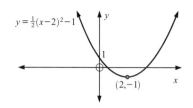

$y = \frac{1}{2}(x-2)^2 - 1$

$(2,-1)$

5 a $y = 2(x-1)^2 + 3$ **b** $y = -(x+2)^2 + 3$
  c $y = -2(x+1)^2 - 2$

6 a G **b** A **c** E **d** B **e** I **f** C
  g D **h** F **i** H

7 a i

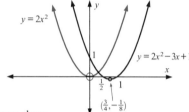

$y = 2x^2$

$y = 2x^2 - 3x + 1$

$\frac{1}{2}$ 1

$(\frac{3}{4}, -\frac{1}{8})$

  ii same shape

b i

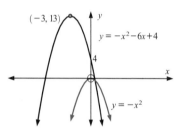

$(-3, 13)$

$y = -x^2 - 6x + 4$

4

$y = -x^2$

  ii same shape

c i

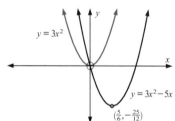

$y = 3x^2$

$y = 3x^2 - 5x$

$(\frac{5}{6}, -\frac{25}{12})$

  ii same shape

d i

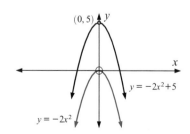

$(0, 5)$

$y = -2x^2 + 5$

$y = -2x^2$

  ii same shape

1 a 3 **b** 2 **c** -8 **d** 1 **e** 6 **f** 5
  g 6 **h** 8 **i** -2

2 a 3 and -1 **b** 2 and 4 **c** -3 and -2
  d 4 and 5 **e** -3 (touching) **f** 1 (touching)

3 a ± 3 **b** $\pm\sqrt{3}$ **c** -5 and -2 **d** 3 and -4
  e 0 and 4 **f** -4 and -2 **g** -1 (touching)
  h 3 (touching) **i** $2 \pm \sqrt{3}$ **j** $-2 \pm \sqrt{7}$ **k** $3 \pm \sqrt{11}$
  l $-4 \pm \sqrt{5}$

1 a

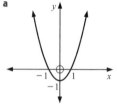

-1 1

-1

b

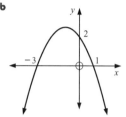

2

-3 1

c

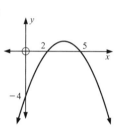

2 5

-4

d

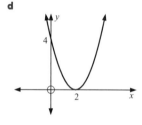

4

2

2 a i $a = 1$ **ii** 4 **iii** $x = 2$ (repeated)

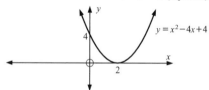

$y = x^2 - 4x + 4$

4

2

b i $a = 1$ **ii** -3 **iii** $x = -3$ or 1

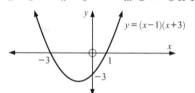

$y = (x-1)(x+3)$

-3 1

-3

c i $a = 2$ **ii** 8 **iii** $x = -2$ (repeated)

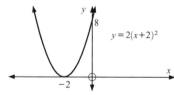

8

$y = 2(x+2)^2$

-2

d i $a = -1$ **ii** 2 **iii** $x = -1$ or 2

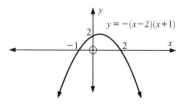

$y = -(x-2)(x+1)$

2

-1 2

e **i** $a = -3$ **ii** -3 **iii** $x = -1$ (repeated)

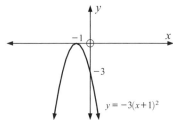

f **i** $a = -3$ **ii** -12 **iii** $x = 1$ or 4

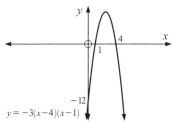

g **i** $a = 2$ **ii** 6 **iii** $x = -3$ or -1

h **i** $a = 2$ **ii** 2 **iii** no x-intercepts

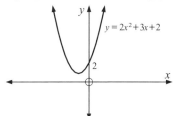

i **i** $a = -2$ **ii** 5 **iii** $x = -\frac{5}{2}$ or 1

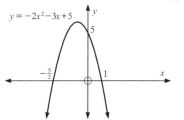

EXERCISE 17D

1 **a** $x = -2$ **b** $x = \frac{3}{2}$ **c** $x = -\frac{2}{3}$

  d $x = -2$ **e** $x = \frac{5}{4}$ **f** $x = 10$

  g $x = -6$ **h** $x = \frac{25}{2}$ **i** $x = 150$

2 **a** $(2, -2)$ **b** $(-1, -4)$ **c** $(0, 4)$

  d $(0, 1)$ **e** $(-2, -15)$ **f** $(-2, -5)$

  g $\left(-\frac{3}{2}, -\frac{11}{2}\right)$ **h** $\left(\frac{5}{2}, -\frac{19}{2}\right)$ **i** $\left(1, -\frac{9}{2}\right)$

3 **a** **i** x-intercepts $4, -2$, y-intercept -8

  ii axis of symmetry $x = 1$

  iii vertex $(1, -9)$

  iv $y = x^2 - 2x - 8$

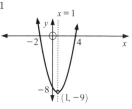

b **i** x-intercepts $0, -3$, y-intercept 0

  ii axis of symmetry $x = -\frac{3}{2}$

  iii vertex $\left(-\frac{3}{2}, -\frac{9}{4}\right)$

  iv $y = x^2 + 3x$

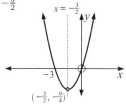

c **i** x-intercepts $0, 4$, y-intercept 0

  ii axis of symmetry $x = 2$

  iii vertex $(2, 4)$

  iv $y = 4x - x^2$

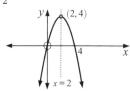

d **i** x-intercept -2, y-intercept 4

  ii axis of symmetry $x = -2$

  iii vertex $(-2, 0)$

  iv $y = x^2 + 4x + 4$

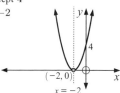

e **i** x-intercepts $-4, 1$, y-intercept -4

  ii axis of symmetry $x = -\frac{3}{2}$

  iii vertex $\left(-\frac{3}{2}, -\frac{25}{4}\right)$

  iv $y = x^2 + 3x - 4$

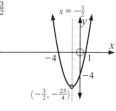

f **i** x-intercept 1, y-intercept -1

  ii axis of symmetry $x = 1$

  iii vertex $(1, 0)$

  iv $y = -x^2 + 2x - 1$

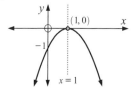

g **i** x-intercepts $-2, -4$, y-intercept -8
ii axis of symmetry $x = -3$
iii vertex $(-3, 1)$
iv $y = -x^2 - 6x - 8$

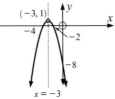

h **i** x-intercepts $1, 2$, y-intercept -2
ii axis of symmetry $x = \frac{3}{2}$
iii vertex $(\frac{3}{2}, \frac{1}{4})$
iv $y = -x^2 + 3x - 2$

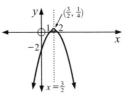

i **i** x-intercepts $\frac{1}{2}, -3$, y-intercept -3
ii axis of symmetry $x = -\frac{5}{4}$
iii vertex $(-\frac{5}{4}, -\frac{49}{8})$
iv $y = 2x^2 + 5x - 3$

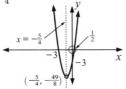

j **i** x-intercepts $-\frac{3}{2}, 4$, y-intercept -12
ii axis of symmetry $x = \frac{5}{4}$
iii vertex $(\frac{5}{4}, -\frac{121}{8})$
iv $y = 2x^2 - 5x - 12$

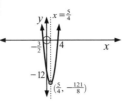

k **i** x-intercepts $\frac{2}{3}, -2$, y-intercept 4
ii axis of symmetry $x = -\frac{2}{3}$
iii vertex $(-\frac{2}{3}, \frac{16}{3})$
iv $y = -3x^2 - 4x + 4$

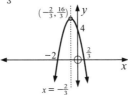

l **i** x-intercepts $0, 20$, y-intercept 0
ii axis of symmetry $x = 10$
iii vertex $(10, 25)$
iv $y = -\frac{1}{4}x^2 + 5x$

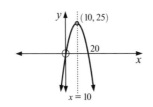

4 **a** $x = 2$ **b** $x = 1$ **c** $x = -4$

5 **a** **i**

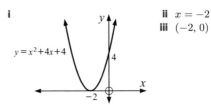

ii $x = -2$
iii $(-2, 0)$

b **i**

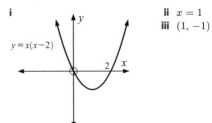

ii $x = 1$
iii $(1, -1)$

c **i**

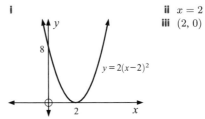

ii $x = 2$
iii $(2, 0)$

d **i**

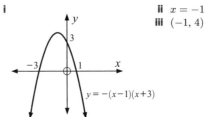

ii $x = -1$
iii $(-1, 4)$

e **i**

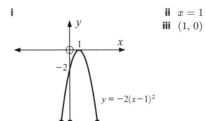

ii $x = 1$
iii $(1, 0)$

f **i**

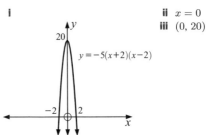

ii $x = 0$
iii $(0, 20)$

g i

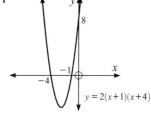

$y = 2(x+1)(x+4)$

ii $x = -2\frac{1}{2}$
iii $(-2\frac{1}{2}, -4\frac{1}{2})$

h i

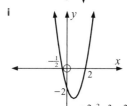

$y = 2x^2 - 3x - 2$

ii $x = \frac{3}{4}$
iii $(\frac{3}{4}, -\frac{25}{8})$

i i

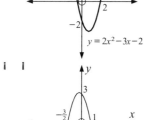

$y = -2x^2 - x + 3$

ii $x = -\frac{1}{4}$
iii $(-\frac{1}{4}, \frac{25}{8})$

6 a i

ii $x = \frac{1}{2}$

b i

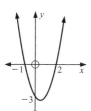

ii $x = 0$

c i

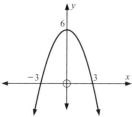

ii $x = -2$

d i

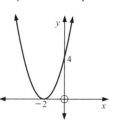

ii $x = 2$

7 a 1 and 3 **b** -1 and -2 **c** 2

EXERCISE 17E

1 a 4 sec **b** 80 m **c** 8 sec
2 a 25 bicycles **b** €425
  c €200. Due to fixed daily costs such as electricity and wages.
3 a 60 km h^{-1}
  b at $t = \frac{1}{2}$ and $1\frac{1}{2}$ sec
    The brakes are slow reacting, i.e., faulty.
  c at $t = 1$ sec **d** 66 km h^{-1}
4 a 30 taxis **b** $1600 **c** $200
5 a 25°C **b** 7.00 am (next day) **c** -11°C
6 b $x = 10$ **c** 200 m^2
7 1

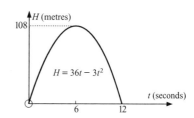

2 maximum height after 6 seconds
3 maximum height is 108 m **4** 12 seconds to leave the area
8 d $x = \frac{1}{2}$, $\frac{1}{2}$ cm^2

REVIEW SET 17A

1 a -15 **b** -17 **c** $x = 6$ or -3
2 a   **b**

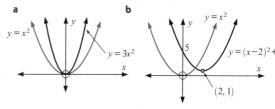

c

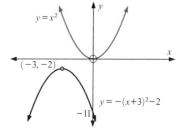

3 a i opens downwards **ii** 6 **iii** 1 and -3 **iv** $x = -1$
  b

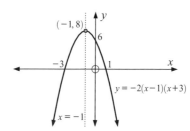

4 a **i** -15 **ii** 5 and -3 **iii** $x = 1$ **iv** $(1, -16)$

b

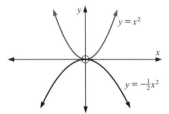

5 a 2 seconds **b** 80 m **c** 6 seconds

REVIEW SET 17B

1 a 1 **b** 13 **c** $x = -2$ or $\frac{3}{2}$

2 a

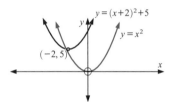

b

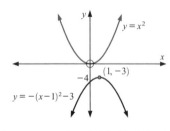

c

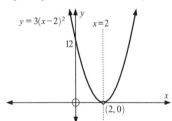

3 a **i** opens upwards **ii** 12 **iii** 2 (touching) **iv** $x = 2$

b

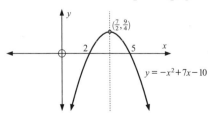

4 a **i** -10 **ii** 2 and 5 **iii** $x = \frac{7}{2}$ **iv** $\left(\frac{7}{2}, \frac{9}{4}\right)$

b

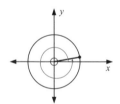

5 a 2 seconds **b** 25 m **c** 4.5 seconds

6 a $h = 2$ **b** $a = -\frac{3}{4}$, $k = 3\frac{1}{2}$

EXERCISE 18A

1 a $\frac{\pi}{3}$ **b** $\frac{2\pi}{3}$ **c** $\frac{\pi}{12}$ **d** $\frac{\pi}{18}$ **e** $\frac{2\pi}{9}$ **f** $\frac{7\pi}{6}$

2 a $\frac{\pi}{2}$ **b** $\frac{3\pi}{4}$ **c** $\frac{5\pi}{4}$ **d** $\frac{\pi}{8}$ **e** $\frac{\pi}{36}$ **f** $\frac{7\pi}{4}$

3 a 0.311^c **b** 1.04^c **c** 1.99^c **d** 3.80^c

4 a 36° **b** 72° **c** 10° **d** 50° **e** 18°
 f 126° **g** 20° **h** 100° **i** 9° **j** 63°
 k $22\frac{1}{2}^o$ **l** $67\frac{1}{2}^o$ **m** 420° **n** 330° **o** 675°

5 a 172° **b** 733° **c** 45.2^o **d** 123°

6 a

Deg	0	45	90	135	180	225	270	315	360
Rad	0	$\frac{\pi}{4}$	$\frac{\pi}{2}$	$\frac{3\pi}{4}$	π	$\frac{5\pi}{4}$	$\frac{3\pi}{2}$	$\frac{7\pi}{4}$	2π

b

Deg	0	30	60	90	120	150	180	210
Rad	0	$\frac{\pi}{6}$	$\frac{\pi}{3}$	$\frac{\pi}{2}$	$\frac{2\pi}{3}$	$\frac{5\pi}{6}$	π	$\frac{7\pi}{6}$

Deg	240	270	300	330	360
Rad	$\frac{4\pi}{3}$	$\frac{3\pi}{2}$	$\frac{5\pi}{3}$	$\frac{11\pi}{6}$	2π

7 b 30 cm, 150 cm^2 **c** 17.5 cm^2

EXERCISE 18B

1 a A$(\cos 67^o, \sin 67^o)$, B$(\cos 148^o, \sin 148^o)$,
 C$(\cos 281^o, \sin 281^o)$
 b A$(0.391, 0.921)$, B$(-0.848, 0.530)$, C$(0.191, -0.982)$

2 a

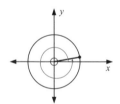

b

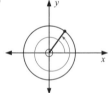

same point on unit
circle $\therefore$ same x-coord.
$(380^o = 360^o + 20^o)$

same point on unit
circle $\therefore$ same y-coord.
$(413^o = 360^o + 53^o)$

c

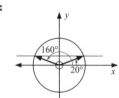

d

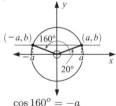

same y-coord.
on unit circle
$\therefore$ same sines

$\cos 160^o = -a$
$= -\cos 20^o$

3 a $\cos 0^o = 1$, $\sin 0^o = 0$ **b** $\cos 90^o = 0$, $\sin 90^o = 1$
 c $\cos 2\pi = 1$, $\sin 2\pi = 0$ **d** $\cos 450^o = 0$, $\sin 450^o = 1$
 e $\cos(-\frac{\pi}{2}) = 0$, $\sin(-\frac{\pi}{2}) = -1$
 f $\cos(\frac{7\pi}{2}) = 0$, $\sin(\frac{7\pi}{2}) = -1$
 g $\cos(-180^o) = -1$, $\sin(-180^o) = 0$
 h $\cos(-\frac{3\pi}{2}) = 0$, $\sin(-\frac{3\pi}{2}) = 1$

4 a $\pm\frac{4}{5}$ **b** $\pm\frac{\sqrt{15}}{4}$ **c** 0 **d** ± 1

5 a $\pm\frac{5}{13}$ **b** 0 **c** ± 1 **d** $\pm\frac{4}{5}$

6 a

Quad	Deg	Rad	$\cos\theta$	$\sin\theta$
1	$0 < \theta < 90$	$0 < \theta < \frac{\pi}{2}$	+ ve	+ ve
2	$90 < \theta < 180$	$\frac{\pi}{2} < \theta < \pi$	− ve	+ ve
3	$180 < \theta < 270$	$\pi < \theta < \frac{3\pi}{2}$	− ve	− ve
4	$270 < \theta < 360$	$\frac{3\pi}{2} < \theta < 2\pi$	+ ve	− ve

b **i** 3 and 4   **ii** 1 and 4   **iii** 3   **iv** 4

7 a $\frac{\sqrt{5}}{3}$ **b** $-\frac{3}{5}$ **c** $-\frac{2\sqrt{2}}{3}$ **d** $\frac{12}{13}$
e $\frac{4}{5}$ **f** $-\frac{\sqrt{15}}{4}$ **g** $\frac{\sqrt{7}}{4}$ **h** $-\frac{12}{13}$

EXERCISE 18C.1

1 a $\frac{1}{2}, \frac{\sqrt{3}}{2}, \frac{1}{\sqrt{3}}$ **b** $\frac{1}{\sqrt{2}}, \frac{1}{\sqrt{2}}, 1$ **c** $0, 1, 0$
d $\frac{1}{\sqrt{2}}, -\frac{1}{\sqrt{2}}, -1$ **e** $1, 0,$ undefined   **f** $\frac{\sqrt{3}}{2}, -\frac{1}{2}, -\sqrt{3}$
g $-1, 0,$ undefined   **h** $0, -1, 0$
i $-\frac{1}{2}, -\frac{\sqrt{3}}{2}, \frac{1}{\sqrt{3}}$ **j** $-\frac{\sqrt{3}}{2}, -\frac{1}{2}, \sqrt{3}$ **k** $\frac{1}{2}, -\frac{\sqrt{3}}{2}, -\frac{1}{\sqrt{3}}$
l $1, 0,$ undefined   **m** $-\frac{\sqrt{3}}{2}, \frac{1}{2}, -\sqrt{3}$ **n** $-\frac{1}{\sqrt{2}}, \frac{1}{\sqrt{2}}, -1$
o $-\frac{1}{2}, \frac{\sqrt{3}}{2}, -\frac{1}{\sqrt{3}}$ **p** $0, 1, 0$

2 a $\frac{1}{2}$ **b** $\frac{1}{4}$ **c** $\frac{1}{3}$ **d** $\frac{3\sqrt{3}}{8}$

3 a $30°, 150°$ **b** $30°, 330°$ **c** $45°, 135°$
d $210°, 330°$ **e** $225°, 315°$ **f** $150°, 210°$

4 a $60°, 120°, 420°, 480°$ **b** $120°, 240°, 480°, 600°$
c $180°, 540°$

5 a $\frac{\pi}{6}, \frac{5\pi}{6}$ **b** $\frac{\pi}{6}, \frac{11\pi}{6}$ **c** $\frac{3\pi}{2}$ **d** $0, 2\pi$ **e** $\frac{\pi}{4}, \frac{3\pi}{4}$
f $\frac{3\pi}{4}, \frac{5\pi}{4}$ **g** $0, \pi, 2\pi$ **h** $\frac{\pi}{4}, \frac{3\pi}{4}, \frac{5\pi}{4}, \frac{7\pi}{4}$ **i** $\frac{2\pi}{3}, \frac{4\pi}{3}$
j $0, \pi, 2\pi$ **k** $\frac{\pi}{3}, \frac{2\pi}{3}$ **l** cannot find θ

6 a $\theta = \frac{\pi}{4}$ or $\frac{5\pi}{4}$ **b** **i** $-\frac{3\pi}{4}, \frac{\pi}{4}$ **ii** $\frac{\pi}{4}, \frac{5\pi}{4}, \frac{9\pi}{4}, \frac{13\pi}{4}$

EXERCISE 18C.2

1 a

θ	0	$\frac{\pi}{6}$	$\frac{2\pi}{6}$	$\frac{3\pi}{6}$	$\frac{4\pi}{6}$	$\frac{5\pi}{6}$	π
$\cos\theta$	1	$\frac{\sqrt{3}}{2}$	$\frac{1}{2}$	0	$-\frac{1}{2}$	$-\frac{\sqrt{3}}{2}$	-1

θ	$\frac{7\pi}{6}$	$\frac{8\pi}{6}$	$\frac{9\pi}{6}$	$\frac{10\pi}{6}$	$\frac{11\pi}{6}$	2π
$\cos\theta$	$-\frac{\sqrt{3}}{2}$	$-\frac{1}{2}$	0	$\frac{1}{2}$	$\frac{\sqrt{3}}{2}$	1

b

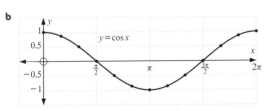

c 1, when $\theta = 0$ or 2π **d** -1, when $\theta = \pi$

2 a $0°, 180°, 360°, 540°, 720°$ **b** $30°, 150°, 390°, 510°$
c $60°, 120°, 420°, 480°$ **d** $270°, 630°$

3 a $0°, 360°, 720°$ **b** $120°, 240°, 480°, 600°$
c $135°, 225°, 495°, 585°$ **d** $90°, 270°, 450°, 630°$

EXERCISE 18D

1 a

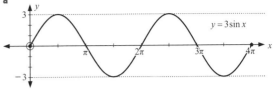

$y = 3\sin x$

b

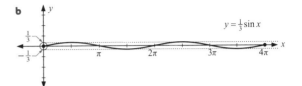

$y = \frac{1}{3}\sin x$

c

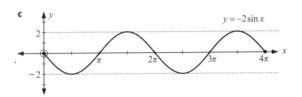

$y = -2\sin x$

d

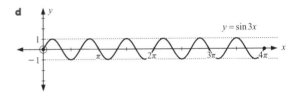

$y = \sin 3x$

e

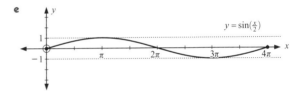

$y = \sin\left(\frac{x}{2}\right)$

f

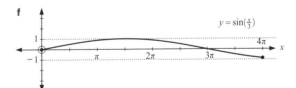

$y = \sin\left(\frac{x}{3}\right)$

2 a

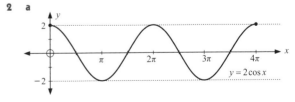

$y = 2\cos x$

b

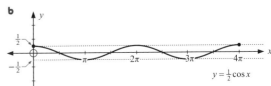

$y = \frac{1}{2}\cos x$

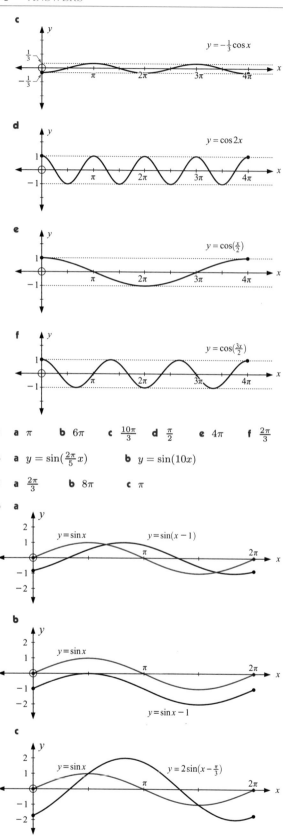

c

$y = -\frac{1}{3}\cos x$

d

$y = \cos 2x$

e

$y = \cos(\frac{x}{2})$

f

$y = \cos(\frac{3x}{2})$

3 **a** π **b** 6π **c** $\frac{10\pi}{3}$ **d** $\frac{\pi}{2}$ **e** 4π **f** $\frac{2\pi}{3}$

4 **a** $y = \sin(\frac{2\pi}{5}x)$ **b** $y = \sin(10x)$

5 **a** $\frac{2\pi}{3}$ **b** 8π **c** π

6 **a**

$y = \sin x$ $y = \sin(x-1)$

b

$y = \sin x$

$y = \sin x - 1$

c

$y = \sin x$ $y = 2\sin(x - \frac{\pi}{3})$

d

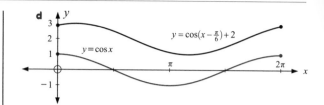

$y = \cos(x - \frac{\pi}{6}) + 2$

$y = \cos x$

e

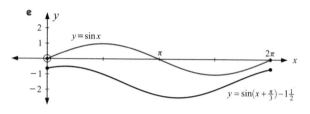

$y = \sin x$

$y = \sin(x + \frac{\pi}{3}) - 1\frac{1}{2}$

f

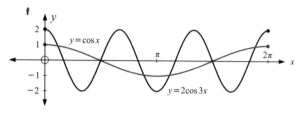

$y = \cos x$

$y = 2\cos 3x$

g

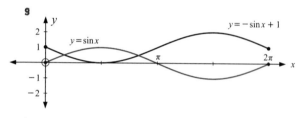

$y = -\sin x + 1$

$y = \sin x$

h

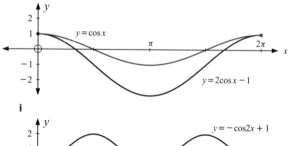

$y = \cos x$

$y = 2\cos x - 1$

i

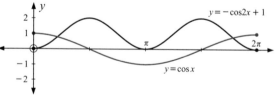

$y = -\cos 2x + 1$

$y = \cos x$

EXERCISE 18E

1 $T \approx 4.5 \sin \frac{\pi}{6}(t - 10.5) + 11.5\ ^\circ\text{C}$

2 $T \approx 5.5 \sin \frac{\pi}{6}(t - 10.7) + 22.5\ ^\circ\text{C}$

4 $H \approx 4 \sin 0.507(t - 9.3) + 6$ metres

5 Safe for about 65% to 66% of the time.

EXERCISE 18F

1 **a** $\theta \approx 0.730,\ 2.412$ **b** $\theta \approx 0.644,\ 2.498$
 c $\theta \approx 3.481,\ 5.943$ **d** $\theta \approx 0.896,\ 2.245$
 e $\theta \approx 3.560,\ 5.864$ **f** $\theta \approx 4.359,\ 5.066$

2 **a** $\theta \approx 0.723,\ 5.560$ **b** $\theta \approx 2.498,\ 3.785$
  c $\theta \approx 0.616,\ 5.667$ **d** $\theta \approx 1.849,\ 4.434$
  e $\theta \approx 2.443,\ 3.840$ **f** no solutions, impossible

3 **a** $\theta \approx 0.322,\ 3.463$ **b** $\theta \approx 1.190,\ 4.332$
  c $\theta \approx 2.111,\ 5.253$ **d** $\theta \approx 1.718,\ 4.860$
  e $\theta \approx 1.522,\ 4.664$ **f** $\theta \approx 2.773,\ 5.914$

4 **a** $\theta \approx 2.179,\ 4.104$ **b** $\theta \approx 4.069,\ 5.356$
  c $\theta \approx 1.869,\ 5.011$ **d** $\theta \approx 1.445,\ 4.587$
  e $\theta \approx 0.585,\ 5.698$ **f** no solutions, impossible
  g $\theta \approx 2.101,\ 4.182$ **h** $\theta \approx 0.661,\ 3.802$
  i $\theta \approx 3.273,\ 6.152$

5 **a** $\theta = \frac{\pi}{3},\ \frac{\pi}{2},\ \frac{3\pi}{2},\ \frac{5\pi}{3}$ **b** $\theta = 0,\ \frac{\pi}{2},\ \pi,\ 2\pi$
  c $\theta \approx 0.615,\ 2.526,\ 3.757,\ 5.668$
  d $\theta = 0,\ \pi,\ 2\pi$ or $\approx 0.927,\ 2.214$ **e** $\theta = 0,\ 2\pi$
  f $\theta = \frac{2\pi}{3},\ \pi,\ \frac{4\pi}{3}$ **g** $\theta = \frac{3\pi}{2}$
  h $\theta = 0,\ 2\pi$ or $\approx 1.772,\ 4.511$
  i $\theta = \frac{2\pi}{3},\ \frac{4\pi}{3}$ or $\approx 1.911,\ 4.373$

EXERCISE 18G

1 **a** $\sin\theta$ **b** $-4\sin\theta$ **c** $6\cos\theta$ **d** $11\sin\theta$
  e $\cos^2\alpha$ **f** $\sin^2\alpha$ **g** 1

3 **a** $2\cos\theta$ **b** $-3\cos\theta$ **c** $2\sin\theta$ **d** $-9\sin\theta$
  e $7\sin\theta$ **f** $7\cos\theta$

4 $\tan(90^o - \theta) \times \tan\theta = 1$

5 This proof is acceptable for θ being an acute angle only. Another method is required for a general proof.

EXERCISE 18H

1 **a** $\sin(B + C) = \sin B \cos C + \cos B \sin C$
  b $\cos(M - N) = \cos M \cos N + \sin M \sin N$
  c $\sin(P - Q) = \sin P \cos Q - \cos P \sin Q$
  d $\cos(\alpha + \theta) = \cos\alpha \cos\theta - \sin\alpha \sin\theta$
  e $\sin(\beta + \alpha) = \sin\beta \cos\alpha + \cos\beta \sin\alpha$
  f $\cos(\alpha - \beta) = \cos\alpha \cos\beta + \sin\alpha \sin\beta$

2 **a** $\cos\alpha$ **b** $\sin\beta$ **c** $\sin A$ **d** $-\sin\alpha$ **e** $-\sin\beta$
  f $-\sin\theta$ **g** $\frac{\sqrt{3}}{2}\sin\theta + \frac{1}{2}\cos\theta$ **h** $\frac{1}{2}\cos\alpha + \frac{\sqrt{3}}{2}\sin\alpha$
  i $\frac{1}{\sqrt{2}}(\sin\theta + \cos\theta)$ **j** $\frac{1}{\sqrt{2}}(\cos\phi - \sin\phi)$
  k $\frac{1}{\sqrt{2}}(\cos C - \sin C)$ **l** $\frac{\sqrt{3}}{2}\cos A + \frac{1}{2}\sin A$

3 **a** $\cos(A - B)$ **b** $\sin(\alpha - \beta)$ **c** $\cos(M + N)$
  d $\sin(C + D)$ **e** $2\sin(\alpha - \beta)$ **f** $-\cos(\alpha + \beta)$

4 **a** Use the expansions of $\sin(A + B)$ and $\cos(A + B)$ letting B be A.
  b **i** $-\frac{24}{25}$ **ii** $\frac{7}{25}$

6 **a** m **b** $\sqrt{1 + m^2}$ **c** $\dfrac{2m}{1 + m^2}$ **d** $\dfrac{1 - m^2}{1 + m^2}$

7 **a** $\overrightarrow{OP} = \begin{pmatrix} \cos B \\ \sin B \end{pmatrix}$, $\overrightarrow{OQ} = \begin{pmatrix} \cos A \\ \sin A \end{pmatrix}$ **b** Use $\overrightarrow{OP} \bullet \overrightarrow{OQ}$.

REVIEW SET 18A

1 **a** $\frac{5\pi}{12}$ **b** $\frac{\pi}{8}$ **2** **a** 18° **b** 140° **3** 159°

4 **a** $(\cos 237^o, \sin 237^o)$ **b** $\approx (-0.545, -0.839)$

5 **a** $-\frac{1}{\sqrt{2}}$ **b** $-\frac{\sqrt{3}}{2}$ **c** $\frac{1}{\sqrt{3}}$ **6** $\pm\frac{\sqrt{5}}{3}$ **7** $-\frac{1}{\sqrt{5}}$

8 **a** $-\frac{1}{\sqrt{2}}$ **b** $\theta = \frac{3\pi}{4},\ \frac{5\pi}{4}$

---

9 **a**
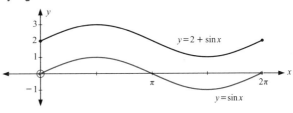

b
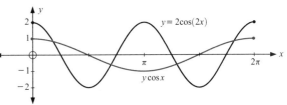

10 **a** $\theta \approx 0.848,\ 2.294$ **b** $\theta \approx 1.911,\ 4.373$
  c $\theta \approx 1.228,\ 4.369$

11 **a** $-\frac{1}{2}$ or 1 **b** $\theta = 0,\ \frac{2\pi}{3},\ \frac{4\pi}{3},\ 2\pi$

12 **a** $-\sin\theta$ **b** $\frac{\sqrt{3}}{2}\sin\theta - \frac{1}{2}\cos\theta$

13 $T \approx 12\sin\frac{\pi}{6}(t - 4) + 9$

14 **a** $1 + \sqrt{3}$ **c** **i** $\dfrac{\sqrt{2} + \sqrt{6}}{4}$ **ii** $2 + \sqrt{3}$

REVIEW SET 18B

1 **a** $\frac{7\pi}{12}$ **b** 70° **2** **a** $-\frac{1}{2}$ **b** $-\frac{1}{\sqrt{2}}$ **c** $-\frac{1}{\sqrt{3}}$

3 **a** $\pm\frac{4}{5}$ **b** $\pm\frac{3}{4}$ **4** $-\frac{2}{\sqrt{13}}$

5 **a** $\theta = \frac{2\pi}{3},\ \frac{4\pi}{3}$ **b** $\theta = \frac{\pi}{3},\ \frac{2\pi}{3}$

6 **a**
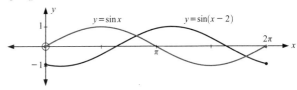

b
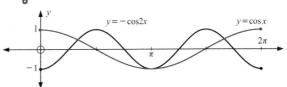

7 $\frac{2\pi}{3}$

8 **a** $\theta \approx 0.608,\ 5.676$ **b** no solution, impossible
  c $\theta \approx 2.093,\ 5.235$

9 **a** $\frac{1}{\sqrt{2}}(\sin\theta - \cos\theta)$ **b** $\frac{3}{2}\cos\phi - \frac{\sqrt{3}}{2}\sin\phi$

10 $\cos\alpha$ **11** $2\cos\theta$ **12** $\theta = \frac{\pi}{2},\ \frac{7\pi}{6},\ \frac{11\pi}{6}$

13 $T \approx 7.5\sin\frac{\pi}{6}(t - 4) + 14.5$

14 **a** Let $A = B = \theta$ in expansion formulae.
  b $\sin 3\theta = 3\sin\theta - 4\sin^3\theta$ **c** $\sin\theta = 0$ or $\pm\frac{\sqrt{3}}{2}$

EXERCISE 19A

1 a
$$\underset{3}{\quad - \quad | \quad + \quad} \; x$$

b
$$\underset{0 \qquad 1}{+ \quad | \quad - \quad | \quad +} \; x$$

c
$$\underset{-2 \qquad 5}{- \quad | \quad + \quad | \quad -} \; x$$

d
$$\underset{-2 \quad 0 \quad 2}{- \quad | \quad + \quad | \quad - \quad | \quad +} \; x$$

e
$$\underset{-3}{- \qquad | \qquad -} \; x$$

f
$$\underset{2}{+ \quad | \quad +} \; x$$

g
$$\underset{-2 \qquad 4}{+ \quad | \quad + \quad | \quad -} \; x$$

h
$$\underset{0}{- \quad \vdots \quad +} \; x$$

i
$$\underset{-5 \qquad 1}{+ \quad | \quad - \quad \vdots \quad +} \; x$$

2 a
$$\underset{-3 \qquad 1}{+ \quad | \quad - \quad | \quad +} \; x$$

b
$$\underset{0 \qquad 4}{+ \quad | \quad - \quad | \quad +} \; x$$

c
$$\underset{-5 \qquad 0}{+ \quad | \quad - \quad | \quad +} \; x$$

d
$$\underset{-2 \qquad 3}{- \quad | \quad + \quad | \quad -} \; x$$

e
$$\underset{-\frac{1}{3} \qquad 4}{- \quad | \quad + \quad | \quad -} \; x$$

f
$$\underset{\frac{1}{2} \qquad 3}{+ \quad | \quad - \quad | \quad +} \; x$$

g
$$\underset{-4 \qquad 4}{+ \quad | \quad - \quad | \quad +} \; x$$

h
$$\underset{-1 \qquad 1}{- \quad | \quad + \quad | \quad -} \; x$$

i
$$\underset{0 \qquad 2}{- \quad | \quad + \quad | \quad -} \; x$$

j
$$\underset{1 \qquad 3}{+ \quad | \quad - \quad | \quad +} \; x$$

k
$$\underset{-\frac{1}{3} \qquad \frac{1}{3}}{- \quad | \quad + \quad | \quad -} \; x$$

l
$$\underset{-\frac{2}{3} \qquad -\frac{1}{2}}{+ \quad | \quad - \quad | \quad +} \; x$$

m
$$\underset{-\frac{1}{3} \qquad 3}{- \quad | \quad + \quad | \quad -} \; x$$

n
$$\underset{-1 \qquad \frac{1}{2}}{- \quad | \quad + \quad | \quad -} \; x$$

o
$$\underset{-\frac{3}{5} \qquad \frac{3}{2}}{- \quad | \quad + \quad | \quad -} \; x$$

3 a
$$\underset{1}{+ \quad | \quad +} \; x$$

b
$$\underset{-4}{+ \quad | \quad +} \; x$$

c
$$\underset{-3}{- \qquad | \qquad -} \; x$$

d
$$\underset{2}{- \qquad | \qquad -} \; x$$

e
$$\underset{\frac{1}{3}}{+ \quad | \quad +} \; x$$

f
$$\underset{3}{+ \quad | \quad +} \; x$$

g
$$\underset{-2}{- \qquad | \qquad -} \; x$$

h
$$\underset{1}{- \qquad | \qquad -} \; x$$

i
$$\underset{-\frac{1}{2}}{- \qquad | \qquad -} \; x$$

4 a
$$\underset{-1 \qquad 2}{+ \quad | \quad - \quad \vdots \quad +} \; x$$

b
$$\underset{0 \qquad 1}{+ \quad \vdots \quad - \quad | \quad +} \; x$$

c
$$\underset{-\frac{5}{2} \qquad 2}{- \quad | \quad + \quad \vdots \quad -} \; x$$

d
$$\underset{\frac{1}{3} \qquad 4}{- \quad | \quad + \quad \vdots \quad -} \; x$$

e
$$\underset{-4 \qquad \frac{2}{3}}{+ \quad | \quad - \quad \vdots \quad +} \; x$$

f
$$\underset{0 \qquad 1}{- \quad | \quad + \quad \vdots \quad -} \; x$$

g
$$\underset{-1 \qquad 2}{- \quad \vdots \quad + \quad | \quad +} \; x$$

h
$$\underset{-3 \qquad 0}{- \quad \vdots \quad - \quad | \quad +} \; x$$

i
$$\underset{-2 \quad 0 \quad 4}{+ \quad | \quad - \quad | \quad + \quad | \quad -} \; x$$

j
$$\underset{-4 \quad 2 \quad 3}{+ \quad | \quad - \quad | \quad + \quad | \quad -} \; x$$

k
$$\underset{-1 \quad 2 \quad 5}{+ \quad \vdots \quad - \quad \vdots \quad + \quad | \quad -} \; x$$

l
$$\underset{-1 \quad 0 \quad 1}{+ \quad | \quad - \quad | \quad + \quad | \quad -} \; x$$

m
$$\underset{-3 \quad -1 \quad 1}{- \quad | \quad + \quad \vdots \quad - \quad | \quad +} \; x$$

n
$$\underset{1}{+ \quad \vdots \quad +} \; x$$

o
$$\underset{-1 \quad \frac{3}{2} \quad 3}{+ \quad \vdots \quad - \quad | \quad + \quad | \quad +} \; x$$

EXERCISE 19B

1 a
$$\underset{-2 \qquad 3}{\bullet\!\!-\!\!-\!\!-\!\!\bullet} \; x$$

b
$$\underset{0 \qquad 3}{\circ\!\!-\!\!-\!\!-\!\!\circ} \; x$$

c
$$\underset{1 \qquad 3}{\longleftarrow\!\!\circ \quad \circ\!\!\longrightarrow} \; x$$

d
$$\underset{2 \qquad 3}{\longleftarrow\!\!\bullet \quad \bullet\!\!\longrightarrow} \; x$$

e
$$\underset{-2 \qquad 1}{\longleftarrow\!\!\bullet \quad \circ\!\!\longrightarrow} \; x$$

f
$$\underset{-1 \qquad 4}{\circ\!\!-\!\!-\!\!-\!\!\bullet} \; x$$

g
$$\underset{-3 \qquad 0}{\bullet\!\!-\!\!-\!\!-\!\!\circ} \; x$$

h
$$\underset{0 \qquad 4}{\longleftarrow\!\!\circ \quad \bullet\!\!\longrightarrow} \; x$$

i
$$\underset{-1 \quad 0 \quad 3}{\bullet\!\!-\!\!-\!\!\bullet\!\!-\!\!-\!\!\bullet} \; x$$

j
$$\underset{-2 \quad 2 \quad 4}{\bullet \quad \bullet\!\!-\!\!-\!\!\bullet} \; x$$

k
$$\underset{-2 \quad 2 \quad 3}{\circ\!\!-\!\!-\!\!\circ \quad \circ\!\!\longrightarrow} \; x$$

l
$$\underset{-2 \quad -1 \quad 2}{\longleftarrow\!\!\circ \quad \circ\!\!-\!\!\bullet} \; x$$

2 a $\{x \mid -2 \leqslant x < 1\}$
  b $\{x \mid x \leqslant 0 \text{ or } x > 1\}$
  c $\{x \mid 2 \leqslant x \leqslant 4\}$
  d $\{x \mid -2 < x < 1\}$
  e $\{x \mid x < -1 \text{ or } x > 1\}$
  f $\{x \mid 0 < x \leqslant 4\}$
  g $\{x \mid x < 0 \text{ or } x \geqslant 3\}$
  h $\{x \mid x \leqslant -2 \text{ or } x \geqslant 2\}$
  i $\{x \mid x < -2 \text{ or } 1 < x \leqslant 4\}$
  j $\{x \mid -2 \leqslant x \leqslant 1 \text{ or } x > 3\}$

3 a i $\{x \mid -3 < x < 6\}$ **ii** $\{x \mid -3 \leqslant x \leqslant 6\}$
   iii $\{x \mid x < -3 \text{ or } x > 6\}$ **iv** $\{x \mid x \leqslant -3 \text{ or } x \geqslant 6\}$
  b i $\{x \mid x < -1 \text{ or } x > 2\}$ **ii** $\{x \mid x \leqslant -1 \text{ or } x > 2\}$
   iii $\{x \mid -1 < x < 2\}$ **iv** $\{x \mid -1 \leqslant x < 2\}$
  c i $\{x \mid -4 < x < 0 \text{ or } 0 < x < 5\}$
   ii $\{x \mid -4 < x \leqslant 5\}$ **iii** $\{x \mid x < -4 \text{ or } x > 5\}$
   iv $\{x \mid x < -4 \text{ or } x \geqslant 5 \text{ or } x = 0\}$

4 a $x \in [-1, 6]$ **b** $x \in \,]0, 5[$ **c** $x \in \,]-4, 7]$

d $x \in [4, 8[$ **e** $x \in \,] -\infty, 2] \cup [5, \infty[$
f $x \in \,] -\infty, -3[\, \cup \,]4, \infty[$ **g** $x \in \,] -1, 1] \cup [2, \infty[$
h $x \in \,] -\infty, -4[\, \cup \, [2, 7[$ **i** $x \in [3, 8[$ **j** $x \in [-2, 7]$
k $x \in \,] -\infty, -2] \cup \,]2, \infty[$ **l** $x \in \,] -\infty, -3[\, \cup \,]10, \infty[$
m $x \in \,] -\infty, 2] \cup \,]3, 5[$ **n** $x \in [-4, 1] \cup \,]4, \infty[$

EXERCISE 19C

1 **a** $x \geqslant 3$ **b** $x > -3$ **c** $x \leqslant \frac{1}{3}$ **d** $x > \frac{7}{2}$
e $x \leqslant -\frac{5}{3}$ **f** $x < -3$ or $x > 3$

2 **a** $1 \leqslant x \leqslant 3$ **b** $-\frac{3}{2} < x < 4$ **c** $x < -1$ or $x > 2$
d no solutions **e** $x \leqslant 0$ or $x \geqslant 2$ **f** $-\frac{1}{2} < x < 0$
g $-4 < x < 4$ **h** $-2 \leqslant x \leqslant 2$ **i** $x < -5$ or $x > 1$
j $-1 \leqslant x \leqslant 2$ **k** no solutions **l** $-2 < x < -\frac{3}{2}$
m $x \leqslant -\frac{4}{3}$ or $x \geqslant 2$ **n** $x \in \mathbb{R}, \, x \neq 1$ **o** $-1 \leqslant x \leqslant \frac{5}{2}$
p $x < -2$ or $x > \frac{2}{5}$ **q** $\frac{4}{3} < x < \frac{3}{2}$ **r** $x = \frac{2}{3}$

3 **a** $-2 < x < 3$ **b** $x < -3$ or $x > 2$
c $x \leqslant -4$ or $x > \frac{1}{2}$ **d** $0 < x \leqslant 3$
e $x < -3$ or $x \geqslant -1$ **f** $x < \frac{3}{2}$ or $x > 5$
g $0 < x < \frac{1}{3}$ **h** $x < -\frac{1}{3}$ or $x \geqslant -\frac{2}{7}$ **i** $-\frac{1}{2} < x < 1$
j $-2 \leqslant x < 0$ or $x \geqslant 2$ **k** $-3 < x < 0$ or $x > 4$
l $x < -1$ or $0 \leqslant x < 1$ **m** $-6 < x < -2$ or $x > 0$
n $x < -6$ or $-3 < x < 0$ or $x > 6$
o $x < -4$ or $x = -2$ or $x > 0$

4 **a** $x \geqslant 0$ **b** $x \geqslant 2$ **c** $x \leqslant \frac{3}{2}$ **d** $x > 0$ **e** $x > -2$
f $x > -\frac{5}{2}$ **g** $x \leqslant 0$ or $x \geqslant 2$ **h** $x \leqslant -1$ or $x \geqslant 3$
i $0 < x < 2$ **j** $x \leqslant -3$ or $x > 1$ **k** $x \leqslant 0$ or $x \geqslant 3$
l $1 \leqslant x \leqslant 5$

5 **a** $x < 0$ or $x > 1$ **b** $-1 < x < 0$ or $x > 1$
c $1 < x < 2$

EXERCISE 19D

1 6, when $a = b = 3$ **2** 4, when $a = b = 2$

3 **a** Hint: Let $a = x, \; b = \dfrac{9}{x}$

b

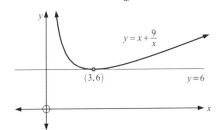

5 **a** $OR = \dfrac{a+b}{2}, \quad PQ = \sqrt{ab}$
b $OR \geqslant PQ$ with equality when O and P coincide, in which
case $a = b$.

6 25 m by 50 m, area $= 1250$ m^2 **8** $\frac{100}{3}$ m by 25 m

REVIEW SET 19A

1 **a**

b

c

2 **a**

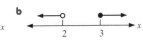

b

c

3 **a** $x \leqslant 0$ or $x \geqslant 4$ **b** $-\frac{3}{2} < x < 4$
c true for all $x \in \mathbb{R}$ **d** $2 < x \leqslant 3$
e $x < \frac{5}{9}$ or $x > 1$ **f** $-\sqrt{2} \leqslant x < 0$ or $x \geqslant \sqrt{2}$

4 **a** $x \leqslant 5$ **b** $x \leqslant 0$ or $x \geqslant 4$ **c** $0 \leqslant x \leqslant 5$

5 $0 < x < 1$ **6** $-\frac{1}{2} \leqslant ab \leqslant \frac{1}{2}$ **Note:** $\sqrt{a^2 b^2} = |ab|$

REVIEW SET 19B

1 **a**

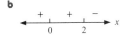

b

c

2 **a**

b

c

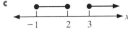

3 **a** $x < 0$ or $x > 1$ **b** $x > 1$
c $x \leqslant -\frac{1}{3}$ or $x \geqslant \frac{5}{2}$ **d** $\frac{1}{2} < x < 1$ **e** $1 < x \leqslant 6$
f $x < -\sqrt{10}$ or $0 < x < \sqrt{10}$

4 **a** $x \geqslant -\frac{1}{2}$ **b** $x < 0$ or $x > 4$ **c** $0 < x < 4$

5 $-\sqrt{2} \leqslant x < 0$ or $x \geqslant \sqrt{2}$

EXERCISE 20A

1 **a** 2×1 **b** 1×3 **c** 3×2 **d** 3×3

2 **a** 4 **b** 7 **c** -11

3 **a** $3 \neq -3$, for final elements
b Cannot be equal as they do not have the same shape.

4 **a** $a = 1, \; b = -5, \; c = 2, \; d = 3$
b $x = -2, \; a = 5, \; b = 10$ **c** $x = 4, \; y = 1, \; z = -2$
d $x = 3, \; y = 0, \; z = 0$ or 1

EXERCISE 20B.1

1 **a** $\begin{pmatrix} 3 & 7 & 7 \end{pmatrix}$ **b** $\begin{pmatrix} 2 \\ 6 \end{pmatrix}$ **c** cannot be done

d cannot be done **e** $\begin{pmatrix} 2 & 1 \\ 1 & 4 \\ -4 & 2 \end{pmatrix}$ **f** $\begin{pmatrix} 3 & -2 & -2 \\ -3 & 3 & 6 \\ -2 & -2 & 3 \end{pmatrix}$

g cannot be done **h** $\begin{pmatrix} 0 & 4 \\ 2 & -4 \end{pmatrix}$

2 **a** $\mathbf{B} = \begin{pmatrix} 0 & 0 \\ 0 & 0 \end{pmatrix}$ **b** $\begin{pmatrix} 0 & 0 & 0 \\ 0 & 0 & 0 \end{pmatrix}$

3 **a** **i** $\begin{pmatrix} 2 & 6 \\ 4 & 8 \end{pmatrix}$ **ii** $\begin{pmatrix} 3 & 9 \\ 6 & 12 \end{pmatrix}$

b To find 2A, we multiply every element of **A** by 2.
To find 3A, we multiply every element of **A** by 3.
c $k\mathbf{A}$ is obtained by multiplying every element of **A** by k.

4 $\begin{pmatrix} -4 & -2 \\ 1 & -3 \end{pmatrix}$

EXERCISE 20B.2

1 a $\begin{pmatrix} 1 & -2 \\ -2 & 3 \end{pmatrix}$ **b** $\begin{pmatrix} 16 & 4 \\ 8 & -12 \end{pmatrix}$ **c** $\begin{pmatrix} 0 & 2 \\ 1 & -1 \end{pmatrix}$

d $\begin{pmatrix} -3 & 0 \\ 3 & -6 \end{pmatrix}$ **e** $\begin{pmatrix} -3 & -1 \\ -3 & 5 \end{pmatrix}$ **f** $\begin{pmatrix} 6 & 1 \\ 0 & 1 \end{pmatrix}$

g $\begin{pmatrix} 12 & 7 \\ 8 & -11 \end{pmatrix}$ **h** $\begin{pmatrix} 5 & 3 \\ 2 & -2 \end{pmatrix}$ **i** $\begin{pmatrix} 0 & -2 \\ -1 & 1 \end{pmatrix}$

j $\begin{pmatrix} 2 & 0 \\ -2 & 4 \end{pmatrix}$

2 a A **b** B **c** 3A **d** 5B **e** O **f** -2C **g** $-$X
h B

EXERCISE 20B.3

2 a $X = B - A$ **b** $X = -A$ **c** $X = A - B$ **d** $X = \frac{1}{2}C$
e $X = \frac{1}{2}(A + C)$ **f** $X = \frac{1}{3}(B - A)$

EXERCISE 20C

1 a $\begin{pmatrix} 7 & -1 \\ 17 & -3 \end{pmatrix}$ **b** $\begin{pmatrix} 0 & 2 \\ 2 & 4 \end{pmatrix}$ **c** $\begin{pmatrix} -4 & 2 \\ -2 & 4 \end{pmatrix}$

d $\begin{pmatrix} 1 & 1 \\ 11 & -1 \end{pmatrix}$ **e** $\begin{pmatrix} 1 & 10 \\ 1 & 22 \end{pmatrix}$ **f** $\begin{pmatrix} 5 & 6 \\ 13 & 18 \end{pmatrix}$

g $\begin{pmatrix} 1 \\ 7 \end{pmatrix}$ **h** $\begin{pmatrix} 17 \\ 10 \end{pmatrix}$

2 a 31   **b** 28   **c** $a + b + c$

3 a $\begin{pmatrix} a & b & c & d \end{pmatrix} \begin{pmatrix} 1 \\ 1 \\ 1 \\ 1 \end{pmatrix}$ **b** $\frac{1}{4}\begin{pmatrix} a & b & c & d \end{pmatrix} \begin{pmatrix} 1 \\ 1 \\ 1 \\ 1 \end{pmatrix}$

4 A is 1×3, B is 2×3

i.e., the number of columns of **A** is not equal to the number of rows of **B**.
BA cannot be found for the same reason.

5 a $\begin{pmatrix} 14 & 8 & 3 \end{pmatrix}$ **b** $\begin{pmatrix} 12 \\ 6 \\ 12 \end{pmatrix}$ **c** $\begin{pmatrix} 3 & 5 \\ 3 & 5 \\ 1 & 2 \end{pmatrix}$

d $\begin{pmatrix} 9 & 5 & 7 \\ 7 & 3 & 10 \\ 9 & 5 & 7 \end{pmatrix}$

6 a i $AI = IA = \begin{pmatrix} 1 & 2 \\ 3 & 4 \end{pmatrix}$ **ii** $AI = IA = \begin{pmatrix} a & b \\ c & d \end{pmatrix}$
b $AI = IA = A$

7 a when $n = m$, **AB** is 3×4 **b** **BA** cannot be found

8 a e.g., if $A = \begin{pmatrix} 1 & 0 \\ 0 & 0 \end{pmatrix}$ and $B = \begin{pmatrix} 1 & 1 \\ 1 & 0 \end{pmatrix}$

then $AB = \begin{pmatrix} 1 & 1 \\ 0 & 0 \end{pmatrix}$ and $BA = \begin{pmatrix} 1 & 0 \\ 1 & 0 \end{pmatrix} \neq AB$

b If $A = \begin{pmatrix} 1 & 0 \\ 0 & 0 \end{pmatrix}$ and $B = \begin{pmatrix} 1 & 0 \\ 0 & 0 \end{pmatrix}$
then $AB = BA$ but $A \neq O$ and $B \neq O$.

9 a $\begin{pmatrix} 1 & 0 \\ 8 & 9 \end{pmatrix}$

b

a	b	c
2	1	4
2	-1	-4
2	2	2
2	-2	-2
2	4	1
2	-4	-1
0	0	0
4	0	0

c $\begin{pmatrix} 2 & 1 \\ 4 & 2 \end{pmatrix}, \begin{pmatrix} 2 & -1 \\ -4 & 2 \end{pmatrix},$
$\begin{pmatrix} 2 & 2 \\ 2 & 2 \end{pmatrix}, \begin{pmatrix} 2 & -2 \\ -2 & 2 \end{pmatrix},$
$\begin{pmatrix} 2 & 4 \\ 1 & 2 \end{pmatrix}, \begin{pmatrix} 2 & -4 \\ -1 & 2 \end{pmatrix},$
$\begin{pmatrix} 0 & 0 \\ 0 & 0 \end{pmatrix}, \begin{pmatrix} 4 & 0 \\ 0 & 4 \end{pmatrix}$

EXERCISE 20D

1 a -7 **b** 13 **c** 0 **d** -11 **e** 8 **2 a** 14 **b** 1
3 a $6\frac{1}{2}$ units^2 **b** $5\frac{1}{2}$ units^2 **c** $31\frac{1}{2}$ units^2 **d** $55\frac{1}{2}$ units^2
4 Points are collinear if $ad = bc$. **5** $x = -3\frac{1}{2}$ or $-11\frac{1}{2}$
6 25 units^2 **7 a** C is $(a + c, b + d)$ **b** $|ad - bc|$ units^2

EXERCISE 20E

1 a $\begin{pmatrix} \frac{4}{5} & -\frac{3}{5} \\ -\frac{1}{5} & \frac{2}{5} \end{pmatrix}$ **b** $\begin{pmatrix} 1 & 0 \\ \frac{2}{3} & -\frac{1}{3} \end{pmatrix}$ **c** does not exist

d $\begin{pmatrix} 0 & -1 \\ 1 & 0 \end{pmatrix}$ **e** $\begin{pmatrix} \frac{3}{7} & -\frac{1}{7} \\ \frac{1}{7} & \frac{2}{7} \end{pmatrix}$ **f** does not exist

2 a $A^{-1} = \begin{pmatrix} a & b \\ -b & a \end{pmatrix}$ **b** $B^{-1} = \begin{pmatrix} a & b \\ b & -a \end{pmatrix}$

3 a A **b** P **c** I **d** I **e** I **f** I **g** I **h** O
4 No

5 a $\begin{pmatrix} 3 & 0 \\ 1 & 5 \end{pmatrix}$ **b** $\begin{pmatrix} \frac{1}{3} & 0 \\ -\frac{1}{15} & \frac{1}{5} \end{pmatrix}$ **c** $\begin{pmatrix} \frac{4}{15} & -\frac{1}{15} \\ -\frac{1}{15} & \frac{4}{15} \end{pmatrix}$

d $\begin{pmatrix} \frac{1}{3} & 0 \\ -\frac{1}{15} & \frac{1}{5} \end{pmatrix}$

6 a $(AB)^{-1} = B^{-1}A^{-1}$
b Hint: Consider $(AB)(B^{-1}A^{-1})$ and $(B^{-1}A^{-1})(AB)$.

EXERCISE 20F.1

1 a $\begin{cases} 2x + 3y = 5 \\ x + 4y = 6 \end{cases}$ **b** $\begin{cases} 3x - y = -3 \\ -x + y = 11 \end{cases}$

c $\begin{cases} 4p + 7q = -5 \\ 11p - 2q = -7 \end{cases}$ **d** $\begin{cases} 3c - 4d = 5 \\ 7c - 2d = 17 \end{cases}$

2 a $\begin{pmatrix} 2 & -3 \\ 1 & 2 \end{pmatrix} \begin{pmatrix} x \\ y \end{pmatrix} = \begin{pmatrix} 8 \\ -5 \end{pmatrix}$

b $\begin{pmatrix} 7 & 2 \\ 4 & -5 \end{pmatrix} \begin{pmatrix} x \\ y \end{pmatrix} = \begin{pmatrix} -1 \\ 9 \end{pmatrix}$

c $\begin{pmatrix} 4 & 9 \\ 7 & 14 \end{pmatrix} \begin{pmatrix} c \\ d \end{pmatrix} = \begin{pmatrix} 8 \\ -11 \end{pmatrix}$

EXERCISE 20F.2

1 a $x = 3, y = 1$ **b** $x = -2, y = 3$ **c** $x = \frac{44}{19}, y = -\frac{4}{19}$
d $x = 4, y = -3$ **e** $x = -2, y = -3$
f $x = \frac{27}{28}, y = \frac{83}{28}$ **g** $x = -\frac{72}{13}, y = \frac{141}{13}$
h $x = -\frac{97}{4}, y = -\frac{67}{4}$ **i** $x = \frac{195}{53}, y = \frac{4}{53}$

2 a $x = \frac{3}{7}x' + \frac{1}{7}y'$ **b** $x = \frac{4}{10}x' + \frac{3}{10}y'$
$y = \frac{1}{7}x' - \frac{2}{7}y'$ $y = -\frac{2}{10}x' + \frac{1}{10}y'$
c $x = \frac{4}{29}x' + \frac{7}{29}y'$
$y = \frac{3}{29}x' - \frac{2}{29}y'$

3 $M^{-1} = \dfrac{1}{ad - bc}\begin{pmatrix} d & -b \\ -c & a \end{pmatrix}$, provided $ad - bc \neq 0$.

EXERCISE 20G.1

1 a O'(0, 0), A'(1, 3), B'(3, 2), C'(2, −1) **c** 7 units²
 d −7 **e** **i** sense is reversed, as det is < 0
  ii area is multiplied by 7

2 a O'(0, 0), A'(3, 1), B'(4, 5), C'(1, 4) **c** 11 units²
 d 11 **e** **i** sense is preserved, as det is > 0
  ii area is multiplied by 11

3 a O'(0, 0), A'(a, c), B'(a + b, c + d), C'(b, d)

4 a 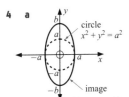 **b** $\dfrac{x^2}{a^2} + \dfrac{y^2}{b^2} = 1$

 c Area $= \left\| \begin{matrix} 1 & 0 \\ 0 & \frac{b}{a} \end{matrix} \right\| \times$ area of circle, etc.

EXERCISE 20G.2

1 a (−1, 3) **b** (3, −2) **c** $(1 + 2\sqrt{3}, -\sqrt{3} + 2)$
 d (0, 2) **e** $(-1 + \frac{1}{\sqrt{2}}, -1 - \frac{1}{\sqrt{2}})$ **f** $(\frac{5}{2}, -\frac{\sqrt{3}}{2})$

2 a $y^2 = x$ **b** $3x - 2y = -10$ **c** $xy = -4$
 d $[1 + \sqrt{3}]x + [\sqrt{3} - 1]y + 2 = 0$ **e** $y^2 - x^2 = 4$
 f $\sqrt{2}(y - x) = (x + y)^2$ **g** $[-5 - 2\sqrt{3}]x + [5\sqrt{3} - 2]y = 16$
 h $x(3\sqrt{3} - 1) - y(\sqrt{3} + 3) = 14$

EXERCISE 20G.3

1 a (5, 2) **b** (2, −3) **c** (−5, 0) **d** $(\frac{17}{5}, \frac{6}{5})$
 e $\left(\dfrac{-4 + 4\sqrt{2}}{3}, \dfrac{8\sqrt{2} + 2}{3} \right)$ **f** $\left(\dfrac{-1 - 3\sqrt{3}}{2}, \dfrac{-3 + \sqrt{3}}{2} \right)$

2 a $x = y^2 - 2y$ **b** $3x + 2y = -6$ **c** $2x + 5y = -10$
 d $-6x + 17y = 60$ **e** $-x + 7y = 40$
 f $2\sqrt{2}(y^2 - x^2) + 7xy = 36$

EXERCISE 20G.4

1 a rotation through $-\frac{\pi}{2}$ about O
 b reflection in the y-axis **c** reflection in the line $y = -x$
 d rotation through $\cos^{-1}(\frac{3}{5})$ about O ($\approx 0.927^c$)
 e reflection in the line $y = 2x$
 f reflection in the line $y = \frac{3}{5}x$
 g rotation through $\frac{\pi}{4}$ about O
 h reflection in the line $y = (1 - \sqrt{2})x$
 i rotation through -0.464^c about O

2 $x' = -\frac{4}{5}x - \frac{3}{5}y$ **3** $x' = \frac{1}{\sqrt{10}}x + \frac{3}{\sqrt{10}}y$
  $y' = \frac{3}{5}x - \frac{4}{5}y$ $y' = \frac{3}{\sqrt{10}}x - \frac{1}{\sqrt{10}}y$

EXERCISE 20G.5

1 a reflection in the y-axis **b** reflection in the line $y = x$
 c rotation about O through $-\cos^{-1}(\frac{8}{17}) \approx -1.08^c$
 d reflection in $y = -\frac{1}{3}x$
 e rotation about O through $\cos^{-1}(\frac{4}{5}) \approx 0.644^c$

2 a reflection **b** rotation

EXERCISE 20H

8 Note: From $\mathbf{AB} = \mathbf{A}$ you cannot deduce that $\mathbf{B} = \mathbf{I}$.

12 $\mathbf{A}^{-1} = \frac{1}{b}\mathbf{A} - \frac{a}{b}\mathbf{I}$

REVIEW SET 20A

1 a $\begin{pmatrix} 7 & -5 \\ -1 & 1 \end{pmatrix}$ **b** $\begin{pmatrix} -20 & 8 \\ -12 & 0 \end{pmatrix}$ **c** $\begin{pmatrix} \frac{7}{2} & -8 \\ -\frac{27}{2} & 3 \end{pmatrix}$

2 a $x = 3$, $y = 3$, $z = 2$ **b** $x = -1$, $y = 4$, $z = 6$

3 a $\begin{pmatrix} 15 & -21 \\ 9 & -10 \end{pmatrix}$ **b** $(-7 \quad -1)$ **c** $\begin{pmatrix} 8 \\ 12 \\ 10 \end{pmatrix}$

4 a $\begin{pmatrix} \frac{2}{7} & \frac{1}{14} \\ -\frac{3}{7} & \frac{1}{7} \end{pmatrix}$ **b** no inverse exists **c** $\begin{pmatrix} -\frac{4}{3} & -\frac{1}{3} \\ -\frac{1}{2} & 0 \end{pmatrix}$

5 $\begin{pmatrix} \frac{a}{2} & -\frac{b}{4} \\ b & \frac{a}{2} \end{pmatrix}$ **6** $5\frac{1}{2}$ units²

7 a $x = 2\frac{1}{2}$, $y = -4$ **b** $x = 2$, $y = -3$

8 a O'(0, 0), A'(2, 3), B'(1, 5), C'(−1, 2) **c** 7 units²

9 a $(\frac{3}{\sqrt{2}}, \frac{1}{\sqrt{2}})$ **b** $4x + y = \sqrt{2}$

10 a $(-\frac{1}{5}, \frac{18}{5})$ **b** $9x^2 - 24xy + 16y^2 + 20x + 15y = 0$

11 A clockwise rotation about O through $\theta \approx 0.983^c$.

12 A reflection in $y = -\frac{1}{3}x$.

13 a $\mathbf{X} = \frac{1}{3}\mathbf{A}$ **b** $\mathbf{X} = \frac{1}{2}(\mathbf{A} - \mathbf{B})$

REVIEW SET 20B

1 a $\begin{pmatrix} 4 & 2 \\ -2 & 3 \end{pmatrix}$ **b** $\begin{pmatrix} -5 & -4 \\ -2 & 6 \end{pmatrix}$ **c** $\begin{pmatrix} 7 & 6 \\ 4 & -11 \end{pmatrix}$
 d $\begin{pmatrix} -1 & 8 \\ 2 & -4 \end{pmatrix}$ **e** $\begin{pmatrix} 3 & 2 \\ -6 & -8 \end{pmatrix}$ **f** $\begin{pmatrix} \frac{1}{3} & \frac{2}{3} \\ 0 & -1 \end{pmatrix}$
 g $\begin{pmatrix} 9 & 4 \\ 0 & 1 \end{pmatrix}$ **h** $\begin{pmatrix} \frac{1}{3} & \frac{2}{3} \\ \frac{1}{6} & \frac{1}{12} \end{pmatrix}$

2 a $a = 0$, $b = 5$, $c = 1$, $d = -4$
 b $a = 2$, $b = -1$, $c = 3$, $d = 8$

3 a $\mathbf{A}$ **b** $2\mathbf{B}$ **c** $\mathbf{I}$ **4** $\begin{pmatrix} a & -\frac{b}{3} \\ -\frac{b}{2} & \frac{a}{6} \end{pmatrix}$

5 a $x = 0$, $y = -\frac{1}{2}$ **b** $x = \frac{12}{7}$, $y = \frac{13}{7}$

6 a $x = \frac{1}{3}x' + \frac{1}{3}y'$ **b** $x = \frac{d}{\triangle}x' - \frac{b}{\triangle}y'$
  $y = \frac{1}{3}x' - \frac{2}{3}y'$ $y = -\frac{c}{\triangle}x' + \frac{a}{\triangle}y'$
  where $\triangle = ad - bc$

7 $x = -1$ or -11

8 a A'(2, 1), B'(4, 2), C'(6, 8), D'(4, 7) **b** 2 units²
 c 10 units²

9 a $(-2\sqrt{2}, -2\sqrt{2})$ **b** $(-\frac{76}{17}, -\frac{2}{17})$

10 a $9x + y = 10\sqrt{2}$ **b** $53x + 9y = -68$

11 A rotation about O through $\theta \approx 0.927^c$.

EXERCISE 21A

1 a $x = 37$ **b** $x = 30$ **c** $x = 18$ **d** $x = 2.5$
 e $x = 2\sqrt{2}$ **f** $x = 2\sqrt{5}$

2 a $x = 3$ **b** $x = 2\sqrt{7}$ **c** $x = \sqrt{29}$

3 $2\sqrt{5}$ cm **4** $2\sqrt{21}$ cm

5 a CY = 5 cm **b** $x = 30$ **c** $a = 40$, $b = 50$
 d $a = 55$, $b = 55$ **e** XY = 12 cm **f** $a = 60$, $b = 40$

6 8 cm

7 **a** $x = 2\sqrt{3}$ {radius tangent theorem, Pythagoras}
 b $x = 3.9$ {radius tangent theorem, Pythagoras}
9 1 cm **10** 40 cm

EXERCISE 21B

1 **a** $x = 64$ **b** $x = 70$ **c** $x = 45$ **d** $x = 66$
 e $x = 94$ **f** $x = 25$
2 **a** $x = 46$ **b** $x = 30$, $y = 30$ **c** $a = 50$, $b = 40$
 d $a = 55$, $c = 70$ **e** $a = 80$, $b = 200$
 f $x = 75$, $y = 118$ **g** $x = 42$ **h** $x = 25$ **i** $x = 25$
3 **a** $x = 70$ **b** $x = 40$ **c** $x = 35$

EXERCISE 21C

1 **a** isosceles triangle
 b The line from the centre of a circle perpendicular to a chord
 • bisects the chord • bisects the angle at the centre
 subtended by the chord.
2 **c** The two tangents to a circle from an external point are equal
 in length.
3 **a** equal radii
 b **i** a^o **ii** b^o **iii** $2a^o$ **iv** $2b^o$ **v** $(a+b)^o$
 vi $(2a+2b)^o$
 c The angle at the centre of a circle is twice the angle at the
 circle subtended by the same arc.
4 **a** $2\alpha^o$ **b** α^o **c** $\widehat{ADB} = \widehat{ACB}$
5 **a** **i** 90° **ii** 90°
 b **i** $(90-\alpha)^o$ {radius tangent theorem}
 ii α^o {angle sum of triangle}
 iii α^o {angles on the same arc}
6 **a** **i** α^o **ii** $2\alpha^o$ **iii** $2\alpha^o$ **iv** $4\alpha^o$ **v** $3\alpha^o$
 b $\widehat{BOY} = 3\widehat{YOX}$
7 **a** $\widehat{BXA} = \widehat{BXC} = 90^o$ **b** collinear **c** yes
 d Yes, 4 semi-circles overlap such that whole area is covered.

EXERCISE 21D

1 **a** $\widehat{DOB} = 2a^o$, reflex $\widehat{DOB} = 2b^o$
 b $2a + 2b = 360$ ∴ $a + b = 180$
3 **a** $x = 107$ **b** $x = 60$ **c** $x = 70$ **d** $x = 90$
 e $x = 62$
4 **a** Yes, one pair of opposite angles are supplementary.
 b Yes, AD subtends equal angles at B and C. **c** No.
 d Yes, opposite angles are supplementary.
 e Yes, one pair of opposite angles are supplementary.
 f Yes, AD subtends equal angles at B and C.
5 No, opposite angles are not supplementary.

REVIEW SET 21A

1 **a** $a = 54$ **b** $a = 62$ **c** $a = 61$ **d** $a = 140$
 e $a = 104$ **f** $a = 2\sqrt{5}$ **g** $a = 80$ **h** $a = 63$
 i $a = 45$
2 $\alpha + \beta + \gamma = 180$ **3** $4\sqrt{10}$ cm **4** **a** $\widehat{DBO} = \alpha^o$

REVIEW SET 21B

1 **a** $x = 86$ **b** $x = \sqrt{34}$ **c** $x = 9$ **d** $x = 42$
 e $x = 55$ **f** $x = 55$
2 **a** $2\alpha^o$ **b** $2\beta^o$ **c** 180°
4 **a** **i** $2\alpha^o$ **ii** $2\alpha^o$ **iii** $2\alpha^o$ **iv** $2\alpha^o$ **c** 90°
 d [RS] is a diameter
5 **a** ...... the angle subtended by the chord in the alternate segment.
 b **i** $\widehat{PQB} = \alpha$, $\widehat{PQA} = \beta$ and $\widehat{AQB} = \alpha + \beta$

EXERCISE 22A

1 **a** -2 **b** -4 **c** -3
2 **a** -4 **b** -1 **c** -0.4
3 **a** 1.4 **b** 2.8 **c** 0.5
4 **a** 0.5 **b** 0.25 **c** 0.2

EXERCISE 22B

1 **a** 4 **b** 6 **2** **a** -2 **b** -4 **c** -6
3 **a** 3 **b** 2 **c** -4 **d** $-\frac{3}{2}$
4 $y = x^3$ is not a quadratic function.

EXERCISE 22C

1 **a** $(3+h)^2$ **b** $6+h$ **c** 6
2 **a** $(1+h)^3$ **b** $3 + 3h + h^2$ **c** 3
3 **a** $\dfrac{4}{1+h}$ **b** $-\dfrac{4}{1+h}$ **c** -4
4 **a** 8 **b** 12 **c** 4
5 **a** $2a$ **b** $3a^2$ **c** $4a^3$ **6** na^{n-1}

EXERCISE 22D.1

1 **a** $3x^2$ **b** $-\dfrac{1}{x^2}$ **c** $\dfrac{1}{2\sqrt{x}}$ **d** 0
2 **a**

$f(x)$	$f'(x)$
x^1	1
x^2	$2x$
x^3	$3x^2$
x^{-1}	$-x^{-2}$
$x^{\frac{1}{2}}$	$\frac{1}{2}x^{-\frac{1}{2}}$

 b $f'(x) = nx^{n-1}$
3 **a** 2 **b** $6x + 5$ **c** $6x^2 + 8x + 6$
4 **a** $f'(x) = a$ **b** $f'(x) = 2ax + b$
 c $f'(x) = 3ax^2 + 2bx + c$

EXERCISE 22D.2

1 **a** $15x^2$ **b** $5 - 2x$ **c** $3x^2 + 4$ **d** $2x^3$
 e $2x$ **f** $1 - \dfrac{1}{x^2}$ **g** $-\dfrac{1}{x^2}$ **h** $1 - \dfrac{5}{x^2}$
 i $-\dfrac{20}{x^3}$ **j** $\dfrac{3}{\sqrt{x}}$ **k** $2x - 1$ **l** $\dfrac{8}{x^3}$
 m $-\dfrac{2}{x\sqrt{x}}$ **n** $9x^2 - 2 + \dfrac{4}{x^3}$ **o** $-1 + \dfrac{1}{x\sqrt{x}}$
 p $3x^2 + 4x + 1$ **q** $8x - 4$ **r** $3x^2 + 12x + 12$
2 **a** $3x^2 + 4x - 3$ **b** 11, 17 **c** ...... at (2, 11) is 17.
3 **a** -6 **b** $-\frac{3}{2}$ **c** 5 **d** 3 **e** $\frac{3}{4}$ **f** $-\frac{1}{2}$
4 **a** $2x - y = 0$ **b** $x - 4y = -4$ **c** $3x + y = -5$
 d $x - 2y = -4$ **e** $3x + y = -8$
5 **a** $\left(-\frac{3}{2}, \frac{11}{4}\right)$ **b** $(1, 1)$ **c** $(-1, -1)$, $\left(\frac{1}{3}, -\frac{23}{27}\right)$
 d $(2, 3)$, $(-2, -1)$ **e** $\left(-\dfrac{b}{2a}, \dfrac{4ac - b^2}{4a}\right)$
6 **a** $a = 2$ **b** $a = -12$

EXERCISE 22E

1 a 26 employees **b** $100\,456$

2 250, when both numbers are 5 **3** 2, when the number is 1

4 Squares with sides about 3.92 cm.

5 a P is $(x, 9 - x^2)$ **b** $A = 18x - 2x^3$
 c $12\sqrt{3}$ units^2 when $x = \sqrt{3}$

6 a $x^2 + y^2 = 1$ **b** $S = x(1 - x^2) = x - x^3$
 c width 0.577 m, depth 0.816 m

7 a $x^2 + 4xy = 108$ **b** $y = \dfrac{27}{x} - \dfrac{x}{4}$
 c $C = 27x - \frac{1}{4}x^3$ **d** 6 cm by 6 cm

8 a $V = \frac{1}{3}\pi(144x - x^3)$ **b** $x = 4\sqrt{3}$

EXERCISE 22F

1 a

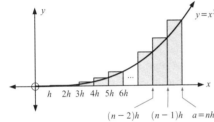

 b $S = \left(\dfrac{a}{n}\right)^4 \left(1^3 + 2^3 + 3^3 + 4^3 + \ldots\ldots + n^3\right)$
 d $\dfrac{a^4}{4}$ units^2

2 a $b - a$ units^2 **b** $\dfrac{b^2 - a^2}{2}$ units^2 **c** $\dfrac{b^3 - a^3}{3}$ units^2
 d $\dfrac{b^4 - a^4}{4}$ units^2

3 a $\dfrac{b^6 - a^6}{6}$ units^2 **b** $\dfrac{b^7 - a^7}{7}$ units^2

EXERCISE 22G.1

1 a **i** $\dfrac{x^2}{2} + c$ **ii** $\dfrac{x^3}{3} + c$ **iii** $\dfrac{x^7}{7} + c$ **iv** $-x^{-1} + c$
 b $\dfrac{x^{n+1}}{n + 1} + c$ **c** no as $\dfrac{x^0}{0}$ is undefined

2 a **i** $\frac{5}{3}x^3 + 2x^2 + c$ **ii** $\frac{5}{3}x^3 + 2x^2 + c$
 b Maybe $\int [f(x) + g(x)]\,dx = \int f(x)\,dx + \int g(x)\,dx$

3 $kx + c$

EXERCISE 22G.2

1 a $\dfrac{x^3}{3} + \dfrac{3x^2}{2} - 2x + c$ **b** $\dfrac{x^4}{4} - \dfrac{x^2}{2} + c$ **c** $\frac{10}{3}x^{\frac{3}{2}} + c$
 d $x^3 + c$ **e** $-x^{-1} + c$ **f** $\dfrac{x^3}{3} + 2\sqrt{x} + c$
 g $\dfrac{x^4}{2} + \dfrac{3x^2}{2} + \dfrac{4}{x} + c$ **h** $\dfrac{x^2}{2} + \dfrac{3}{x} - \dfrac{2}{x^2} + c$
 i $\frac{2}{5}x^2\sqrt{x} - 4\sqrt{x} + c$ **j** $\dfrac{x^3}{3} - 2x^2 + 4x + c$
 k $\frac{4}{3}x^3 + 2x^2 + x + c$ **l** $\dfrac{x^4}{4} + 2x^3 + 6x^2 + 8x + c$

EXERCISE 22H

1 a $10\frac{1}{2}$ **b** 16 **c** 12 **d** $-7\frac{1}{2}$ **e** $4\frac{2}{3}$ **f** 8

2 a $2\frac{2}{3}$ **b** $52\frac{2}{3}$ **c** 3 **d** 0 **e** $-30\frac{1}{2}$ **f** $43\frac{3}{4}$

3 a $8\frac{2}{3}$ units^2 **b** $4\frac{2}{3}$ units^2 **c** $10\frac{2}{3}$ units^2 **d** 96.8 units^2
 e 6 units^2 **f** $57\frac{1}{3}$ units^2 **g** $1\frac{3}{5}$ units^2 **h** 8 units^2

REVIEW SET 22A

1 -1 **2** $f'(x) = 2x - 2$

3 a $f'(x) = 21x^2$ **b** $f'(x) = 6x - 3x^2$
 c $f'(x) = 8x - 12$ **d** $f'(x) = 7 + 4x$

4 a $4x + y = 8$ **b** $(2\sqrt{2}, \sqrt{2})$ and $(-2\sqrt{2}, -\sqrt{2})$

5 6 cm high, 12 cm wide

6 a $P = 2r + \pi r + 2x$ m **b** $x = 100 - r - \dfrac{\pi r}{2}$
 d $r = 28.0$ m, rectangle has length 56.0 m, width 28.0 m

7 a $\frac{2}{3}x^{\frac{3}{2}} - \frac{2}{5}x^{\frac{5}{2}} + c$ **b** $\dfrac{x^5}{5} + \frac{10}{3}x^3 + 25x + c$
 c $\dfrac{1}{2x^2} + c$ **d** $\frac{2}{5}x^{\frac{5}{2}} - \frac{4}{3}x^{\frac{3}{2}} + 2x^{\frac{1}{2}} + c$

8 a $\dfrac{x^4}{4} + x^3 - x + c$ **b** $\frac{2}{5}x^{\frac{5}{2}} + c$ **c** $\dfrac{x^3}{3} - 2x - \dfrac{1}{x} + c$

9 a 6 **b** $\frac{7}{2} - 2\sqrt{2}$ **c** $\dfrac{94\sqrt{2} - 56}{15}$ units^2

10 $2\frac{2}{3}$ units^2 **11** $21\frac{1}{3}$ units^2

REVIEW SET 22B

1 a $f'(x) = \dfrac{1}{2\sqrt{x}}$ **b** $f'(x) = 24x^2 - 24x + 6$
 c $f'(x) = -\dfrac{1}{x^2} + \dfrac{8}{x^3}$ **d** $f'(x) = x^{-\frac{1}{2}} - \frac{1}{2}x^{-\frac{3}{2}}$

3 $9x - y = 11$ **4** $(\frac{1}{2}, 2\sqrt{2})$ **5** 6 cm squares

6 b $A = (x - 10)(y - 20)$ **d** $x = 70.7$ cm, $y = 141.4$ cm

7 a $\dfrac{x^3}{3} - x^2 + 4x + c$ **b** $-3x + c$ **c** $x^3 - \dfrac{4}{x} + c$
 d $x^2 - 2x^{\frac{1}{2}} + c$

8 a $\dfrac{x^4}{2} - \dfrac{x^3}{3} + c$ **b** $\frac{2}{5}x^{\frac{5}{2}} - \frac{8}{3}x^{\frac{3}{2}} + 8x^{\frac{1}{2}} + c$
 c $x - \frac{3}{2}x^2 + x^3 - \frac{1}{4}x^4 + c$

9 a $\frac{1}{3}$ **b** $\frac{2}{3}$ **c** $12\frac{2}{3}$

10 $20\frac{5}{6}$ units^2 **11** $k \approx 3.832$ (to 3 dec.pl.)

INDEX